NEWTON'S TELECOM DICTIONARY

by HARRY NEWTON

10TH EDITION

THE OFFICIAL DICTIONARY OF
TELECOMMUNICATIONS
COMPUTER TELEPHONY
DATA COMMUNICATIONS
VOICE PROCESSING
PC TELEPHONY
WINDOWS 95 & NT
COMMUNICATIONS
NETWORKING AND
THE INTERNET

A Flatiron Publishing, Inc. Book
Published by Flatiron Publishing, Inc.
NEWTON'S TELECOM DICTIONARY
copyright ©1996 Harry Newton

12 West 21 Street
New York, NY 10010
212-691-8215
1-800-999-0345
1-800-LIBRARY
Fax 212-691-1191
harrynewton@mcimail.com

ISBN # 0-936648-78-3

Manufactured in the United States of America

Tenth Edition, February 1996
Cover design by Mara Seinfeld
Printed at Bookcrafters, Chelsea, MI.

THE LoGIᴄ OF MY DICTIoNA Y

by Harry Newton

I wrote this book for those of us trying to keep up.

No other industry is changing as fast as telecommunications. There are seven driving forces:

1. The Technology. The main excitement centers on digital signal processors, fiber optics and new algorithms in speech recognition, compression, etc. And the continuing speedup in microprocessors (as reflected in Moore's Law) is making possible new telecom concepts like switches inside a PC, fast ATM, 100 meg Ethernet, etc. But the reality is that technology in telecom is improving in cost-performance far faster than it is in computing. Hence, the computer industry's new obsession with telecom, networking and voice.

2. New Standards. Barely 25 years ago, AT&T was the primary telecom standards setter in North America. It created the 1200 baud standard for modem. That was essentially its last. Since then the company has dropped out of standards-setting, leaving that task to a hodge-podge of volunteer bodies (from the ATM Forum to the ECTF, to the MVIP, to the SCSA, to the ITU-T, to ANSI, to the Internet Engineering Task Force) and to companies (from Hayes to Microsoft to Intel to Dialogic). There's been an explosion of new standards (and they're still coming) — defining everything from telecom operating systems, to buses that carry voice inside PCs, to high-speed lines, to new telecom "building block" software. Standards lead to growth. It is now early 1995. As I listen to my phone calls and hear the industry "buzz," I can feel the excitement in hundreds of engineering labs frenetically creating new telecom products and services. We're about to see telecom product out in the next few years based on these new standards that will positively blow your brains.

3. New Government Awareness That Competition Is Better Than Monopoly. The telecom industry has historically been closed — closed in architecture, closed to new suppliers, closed to new entrants. No longer. Europe, Japan, Australia, Russia, China — everywhere — governments are waking to one realization. Telecom is infrastructure. Companies and business go where infrastructure is strongest. You can't make modern infrastructure when you have one bloated, sluggish, government-run phone company. And you can't limit your entire country's telecom purchases to two or three hand-chosen suppliers (as each country in Europe has historically done). By the end of this century, European telecom should be as open as North America is today. That's another 300 million people hungry for decent, cheap communications. Everywhere, telecommunications is going from a totally-closed, government-controlled, highly-regulated, monopolistic, bureaucratic, anti-progress, anti-customer industry to an exploding free-for-all.

4. New Startups. The hottest place for venture capital is telecommunications. Smart engineers are leaving big, sluggish telecom manufacturers in droves and starting new companies. There are hundreds of "new telecom" millionaires already. There will be thousands by the end of the decade. Nothing can match the enthusiasm of an engineer obsessed with a great idea that he thinks he will make himself a millionaire. I'm enthusiastically behind each and every one of them. I publish three monthly telecom magazines — Call Center, Computer Telephony and TELECONNECT. I run one annual trade show — Computer Telephony Expo. I welcome these people and their products with open arms to my editorial pages and my speaking platforms.

5. New Uses. Telecommunications is becoming computer telephony. This is the name of the new industry which adds computer intelligence and computer power to the making and receiving of phone calls. As you add intelligence and power, you create brand new products — ones we can't even dream about today. An example: Who would have imagined the 1992-1995 phenomenon which produced the democratization and commercialization of the Internet? I believe that Internet happening is as important to the dissemination of knowledge as the invention of the Gutenberg Press was in 1453.

6. Telecom's Basically Incredible Economics. No industry in the world — neither software nor petroleum — can match the incredible

profitability of the zero-marginal cost telephone industry. If I call from New York to California, that call costs my supplier — AT&T, MCI, Sprint or whoever — essentially nothing. Nobody to this day knows how many conversations or how much information you can put down a single strand of fiber. They just keep putting more and more down it. It's truly amazing.

7. Demand for telecom is skyrocketing. Children want high-speed Internet access. Business people want "everywhere" computing. 40 million Americans want to work at home. They call it SOHO. It's brand-new, and one of telecom's fastest-growing markets. And all of us want the best quality and widest range of digital home telecom services — from movies to three-dimensional tele-gaming.

Writing telecom dictionary updates every six months is exhausting, exhilarating and very time-consuming. My children tell me, "Daddy, get a life!" I apologize to Claire and Michael for seeing so much of Daddy's back and the Daddy's monitor.

This is a dictionary to work every day with. Salespeople tell me they include the definitions in proposals to customers. Novices tell me they love it because it cuts through the clutter. Users explain telecom things to their boss with my definitions. Management uses it to understand telecom technicalities. Lawyers even use it in court. Often they call me as an "expert" witness. It probably pays better than being a juror. But it's probably as boring and as abusive. I always decline, though I'm always flattered.

You can give my dictionary to your users, to your customers, to your boss. You can even give it to your kids to let them understand what you do. They'll then understand why you, too, have no life.

Most technical dictionaries define terms tersely, often in other technical terms. As a result they leave you more confused. This dictionary is different, deliberately so. My definitions tell you what the term is, how it works, how you use it, what its benefits are, what its negatives are. I tell you how it fits into the greater scheme of things, and occasionally some warnings or checklists.

NEWTON'S TELECOM DICTIONARY

I don't claim my dictionary is comprehensive. But each edition gets bigger and better. I add new terms. I re-work and I update definitions. I'm always looking for new ones. That's an invitation. Send me your product names, your service descriptions, your in-house glossaries, your corrections.

The best way to get me is through harrynewton@mcimail.com

Blank Space	= ASCII 32	6	= ASCII 54
!	= ASCII 33	7	= ASCII 55
#	= ASCII 35	8	= ASCII 56
& (Ampersand)	= ASCII 38	9	= ASCII 57
-(Hyphen or dash)	= ASCII 45	: (colon)	= ASCII 58
. (Period)	= ASCII 46	; (semi colon)	= ASCII 59
/ (Forward slash)	= ASCII 47	A (capital A)	= ASCII 65
0 (zero)	= ASCII 48	Capital letters to ASCII 90	
1	= ASCII 49	\ (back slash)	= ASCII 92
2	= ASCII 50	Lower case letters	
3	= ASCII 51	start with a	= ASCII 97
4	= ASCII 52		
5	= ASCII 53		

HOW TO USE MY DICTIONARY

My definitions are in ASCII code order — NOT alphabetical order. ASCII is almost alphabetical order. In ASCII, capital letters come before lower case letters (who knows why). And ASCII gives some alleged order to hyphens, periods, forward slashes, etc. Here is the order of the more common characters you'll find in this dictionary:

ON SPELLING

My dictionary conforms to American spelling. To convert American spelling to British and Canadian spelling typically requires adding a second "L" in words like signaling and dialing (they're American) and changing "Z" in words like analyze to analyse. Center in American is Center. In Britain, Australia and Canada, it's Centre. This dictionary contains more British, Australian and European words than my previous editions — a result of several overseas lecture tours.

ON STYLE

All high-tech industries make up new words by joining words together. They typically start by putting two words next to each other. Later, they join them with a hyphen. Then, with age and familiarity, the hyphen tends to disappear. An example: Kinder garten. Kinder-garten. and now Kindergarten.

Sometimes it's just a matter of personal choice. Some people spell database as one word. Some as two, i.e. data base. I prefer it as one, since it has acquired its own logic by now. Sometimes it's a matter of how it looks. I prefer T1 (T-one) as T-1, simply because T-1 is easier to recognize on paper. I define co-location as co-location. Websters spells it collocation, with two Ls, one more than mine. I think mine is more logical.

Plurals give trouble. The plural of PBX is PBXs, not PBX's. The plural of PC is PCs, not PC's, despite what the New York Times says. The Wall Street Journal and all the major computer magazines agree with me. So there. In this dictionary, I spell out the numbers one through nine. Above nine, the numbers are written as arabic numerals, i.e. 10, 11, 12, etc.

In short, there are no rights or wrongs in the spelling business, except that my dictionary is now the correct way of spelling telecom words, because it's the biggest seller (by far) and because lawyers use it in court. (God help the justice system.)

THANK YOUs

A big "Thank You" to the dozens of people and dozens of companies who helped. I bet I left some of you out. If so, I apologize.

Among the manufacturers, special thanks to Amdahl, Anixter, Aspect Telecommunications, AT&T, Bellcore, Dialogic, Ecos Electronics, General Cable, Micom, MCI, NEC, Newbridge Networks, New York Telephone (now Nynex), Northern Telecom, Racal Data, Ricoh, Sigma Designs, Sharp and Teknekron. They'll recognize some of their words in this dictionary. Among the magazines I borrowed (or stole), the best were PC Magazine and our own TELECONNECT, Call Center and IMAGING Magazines. Special thank yous also to internetworking expert, Tad Witkowicz at CrossComm, Marlboro MA.; Ken Guy of Micom, Simi Valley (near LA); Michael Marcus, president of Able Communications, an excellent interconnect company based in Scarsdale NY, Frank Derfler of PC Magazine; Chris Gahan of 3Com; Jeff Deneen of the Norstar Division of Northern Telecom in Nashville; Stephen Doster of Telco Research in Nashville; bugging expert Jim Ross of Ross Engineering, Adamstown, MD; wiring experts John and Carl Siemon of The Siemon Company, Watertown CT; the fine folk at Novell, the local area network company in Provo, UT; to Jim Gordon and Parker Ladd at TCS Communications, Nashville, TN, the people who do workforce management software for automatic call distributors; to Judy Marterie and the electricity wiring, grounding and test experts at Ecos Electronics Corporation in Oak Park, Il; to Brian Newman of MCI, who understands wireless; to John Perri of SoftCom, NYC; to John Taylor of GammaLink, a Sunnyvale, CA company which produces beautiful fax products; to Charles Fitzgerald at Microsoft and Herman D'Hooge at Intel who jointly helped created Windows Telephony; to Charles Fitzgerald, again, who allowed me to steal all the words Microsoft makes up (you'd be surprised how many); to Bill Flanagan who's written fine books on T-1 and voice and data networking; to Jane Laino of Corporate Communications Consultants, NYC; to Henry Baird of Seattle consultants Baird & Associates; to Sharon O'Brien formerly of Hayes Microcomputer Products in Norcross (Atlanta); to Howard Bubb, Ed Margulies, John Landau, Jim Shinn and Nick Zwick at leading voice processing component manufacturer, Dialogic Corporation of Parsippany, NJ; to Al Wokas of voice processing company Rhetorex in San Jose, CA; to Alison Golan of networking company, Interphase Corporation in Dallas, which allowed me to steal some of the definitions from their excellent booklet, "A Hitchhiker's Guide to Internetworking Terms and Acronyms;" to Ian Angus at the Angus TeleManagement Group in Ajax, Ontario, who embarrassed me into expanding my Canadian coverage.

NEWTON'S TELECOM DICTIONARY

At Ziff Davis, which publishes this dictionary on CD-ROM discs (for your copy, call 800-827-7889 or 212-503-4400 or in England 44-344-714-441), I'm grateful to Denis Haskin. Their new CD-ROM division is called Information Access Corp, Medford, MA. In my own office, I'm very grateful to Muriel Fullam, Nick Morley, Christine Kern, Rose Bodin, Mara Seinfield and Jennifer Cooper-Farrow.

Without all these wonderful people, this dictionary wouldn't be as good as it's actually turning out. If I sound surprised, you're right. It's now the largest-selling telecommunications dictionary in the world.

If I've left any definitions out, or if some of my definitions are unclear, contact me on harrynewton@mcimail.com.

I wrote this dictionary on a series of ever-newer, ever-faster Toshiba laptops (very reliable machines) using The Semware Editor, a very beautiful text editor, which Sammy Mitchell of Marietta, GA wrote, and which I wholeheartedly recommend. The Toshiba laptop for this dictionary was the T4900CT. It's a 75 Mhz Pentium machine with 40 Meg of RAM and an 800 Meg hard disk. Jennifer and Christine Kern (ne. Fullam) typeset it on a Power PC Macintosh using QuarkXpress and Adobe Illustrator. Mara Seinfeld did the cover. It's gorgeous. Bookcrafters in Chelsea, Michigan printed it, as they've always done.

Harry Newton
12 West 21 Street
New York, NY 10010
212-691-8215 Fax 212-691-1191
HarryNewton@MCIMail.com
CompuServe 70600,2451

January, 1996

NUMBERS

" Double quotation marks. Typically used to signify something your computer should print (to screen, disk or paper), as in

PRINT "Thanks for being a good guy."

Some programs allow you to use single quotation marks interchangeable with double ones. Some programs don't. Try one or the other if in doubt.

The character on the bottom right of your touchtone keyboard, which is also typically above the 3 on your computer keyboard. It's commonly called the pound sign, but it's also called the number sign, the crosshatch sign, the tic-tack-toe sign, the enter key, the octothorpe (also spelled octathorp) and the hash. Musicians call the # sign a "sharp."

On some phones the # key represents an "Enter" key like the Enter key on a computer. On some phones it represents "NO." And on others it represents "YES." MCI, AT&T and some other long distance companies use it as the key for making another long distance credit card call without having to redial. Hold down the # key for at least two seconds before the person at the other end has hung up, you'll get a dial tone, punch in your phone number and you can make another long distance call — without having to punch in your credit card number again. (This service is often called Call Reorgination or just plain Next Call.)

The # key is used in the paging industry — national and local. When you dial a phone number which represents someone's beeper, you will typically hear a double beep. At that point you punch in your phone number, ending it with a #. At that point, the machine hangs up on you and sends out the numbers you punched in to the pager you just dialed.

Many digital phone pagers allow people to send actual text messages to pagers. Many use the # sign to signal the use of certain digits (c, f, i, l, o, s, v, y) as well as to signal the end of the transmittal.

& The "and" sign. Its real name is an "ampersand."

* The star sign. It's often used to represent a wild card or a joker. For example, the command

ERASE JOHN.*

will erase all the files on your disk beginning with JOHN, e.g. JOHN.TXT, JOHN.NEW, JOHN.OLD, JOHN.BAK, etc.

IEX in Richardson * key as a cancel character for its Call Valet application.

*57 The North American universal dialing code which you touchtone in imme-

1

diately after receiving a harrassing, obscence or annoying phone. By touchtoning that number in, you have alerted your central office to "tag" that phone call. Should a law enforcement agency get involved in investigating your annoying calls, they would be able to go into your records and find the phone number from which the annoying call was made. See TRAP and TRACE.

- The dash. The minus sign. Often we take two words and join them with a dash into a new word. As the word becomes more and more common, we remove the dash and the double word now becomes a fully-fledged single word.

/ The forward slash. Lotus made it famous.

@ The character typically above the 2 on your keyboard. It's called the "at sign." In English, its biggest use would be two apples @ 50 cents each equals $1 total." But in computerese, its big use is in electronic mail addressing. For example, Bill Gates's e-mail address is billg@Microsoft.com. Mine is harrynewton@mcimail.com. The @ is also used in spreadsheets and computer publishing.

**** The backslash. Used for designating directories on your MS-DOS machine. This dictionary is located in

C:\WORK\DICTIONA

That means it's in the "dictiona" subdirectory of the "work" directory.

^ The character typically above the 6 on your keyboard. It was originally a circumflex. In computer language it became the symbol that was written to represent the Control (Ctrl) key. It's also called the "hat."

~ This character is a tilde. It tells you how to pronounce the n in senor. According to William Safire, it's a Spanish word from the Latin term for a tiny diacritical mark used to change the phonetic value of a letter.

0345 NUMBERS A British Telecom LinkLine service in England where the caller is charged at the local rate irrespective of the distance of the call. The subscriber pays installation and rental charges in addition to a charge for each call.

0800 NUMBERS 1. A British Telecom LinkLine service in England where the caller is not charged for the call. Similar to the North American 800 IN-WATS service. 2. Ericsson has 0800-type service on cellular systems it's put in. Ericsson describes it as a "network-oriented service — based on time of day, day of week, or special day — which allows calls to be redirected to other numbers.

0891 AND 0898 NUMBERS A British Telecom Premium rate service in England where the caller is charged at a premium rate for the call. The calls are normally made to receive information or a service. The service provides revenue for the information provider who receives part of the call charge.

0839 AND 0881 NUMBERS Mercury's premium rate service numbers in England.

1+ Pronounced "One plus." In North America, dialing 1 as the first digit has come to signal to your local phone company that the phone number you are dialing is long distance, i.e. is designed to reach a long distance number in the United States, Canada, or several of the Caribbean islands, (including Bermuda,

Puerto Rico, the Virgin Islands, Barbados and the Dominican Republic). The number 1 will typically be followed by an area code and then seven digits. For example, to dial me from outside New York City, you would dial 1-212-691-8215. To reach other international countries, from the United States, you dial the international access code "011." This "1+" will work with your local phone company, signaling it that you want to reach another local area code. (In New York City, calling from Manhattan to Brooklyn means dialing 1+718+the seven digit Brooklyn number.) It also will work with the long distance company you have pre subscribed to, through the process known as equal access. To reach another long distance carrier and route calls over their network, you will need to dial 1-0XXX and then the area code and number.

1.544 MBPS The speed of a North American T-1 circuit. See T-1.

10-NET An original local area network invented by a company called Fox Research, Dayton, OH. 10-Net is a baseband, Ethernet CSMA/CD peer-to-peer LAN running on one twisted pair at one megabit per second. It is easy to install and has many advantages. It's also slow. Very slow. See ETHERNET.

10 BASE T See 10Base-T.

10 Base T See 100Base

100 TEST LINE A Northern Telecom switching term. The 100 test line, also known as a quiet or balanced termination, is used for noise and loss measurements. The S100 provides a quiet termination for noise measurements only. In this 100 family, there is the T100, S100 and N100 tests. The N100, a more recent version of the test, also includes a milliwatt test (i.e., a 102 test line) and therefore can be used for far-to-near loss measurements. The T100 is used when the equipment at the terminating office is unknown. When the T100 test line is performed, a two-second time-out is introduced to detect the presence or absence of a milliwatt tone. If the T100 test detects the milliwatt tone, it executes the N100 version of the test; otherwise, the S100 version is initiated. If the version of the distant office test line is known, then that version of the test line can be performed directly, and thus the two-second delay per trunk of the T100 test line test is eliminated.

The 101 test line is used to establish two-way communications between the test position and any trunk incoming to the system. The connection to the 101 test line is established through the switching network.

The 102 test line, also known as the milliwatt line, applies a 1004 Hz test tone towards the originating office to facilitate simple one-way or automatic transmission loss measurements. The test tone is applied for a timed duration of nine-seconds during which answer (off-hook) signal is provided. Then an on-hook signal followed by a quiet termination is transmitted to the originating end until the connection is released by the originating end.

The T103 is used for the overall testing of supervisory and signaling features on intertoll trunks. The test is performed to the far end to check overall supervisory and signaling features of the trunk. If the test fails or if a false tone signal is detected, the test is abandoned and the condition indicated.

The T104 test is used for two-way transmission loss measurements, far-to-near noise measurements and near-to-far noise checks. Normally used in testing toll trunks.

When a 105 test line at a far-end office is called and seized, timing functions are initiated and an off-hook supervisory signal and test progress tone are returned to the originating office. If the responder is idle, the test line is connected to the responder and test progress tone is removed. Transmission tests are then initiated.

The T108 test provides far-end loop-around terminations to which a near-end echo suppression measuring set is connected for the purpose of testing echo suppressors.

100BASE-FX 100-Mbps Ethernet implementation over fiber. The MAC layer is compatible with the 802.3 MAC layer. See 10Base-F.

100BASE-T A proposed standard for a 100 megabit-per-second local area network. The standard has the backing of the Fast Ethernet Alliance of 40 companies, including Intel, Synoptics, 3Com, Sun and Digital Equipment. The concept is that 100Base-T would be completely compatible with today's common 10Base-T 10 megabit-per-second, except that it would be ten times as fast. You could use 100Base-T LANs to connect 10Base-T LANs, for example, thus expanding the number of people on the LAN and increasing the overall speed. See 100VG-ANYLAN for the competing 100 megabit LAN standard.

100BASE-T4 100-Mbps Ethernet implementation using four-pair category 3,4, or 5 cabling. The MAC layer is compatible with the 802.3 MAC layer.

100BASE-TX 100-Mbps Ethernet implementation over Category 5 and Type 1 cabling. The MAC layer is compatible with the 802.3 MAC layer.

100VG-ANYLAN A proposed standard for a 100 megabit-per-second local area network. The 10VG-ANYLAN is a joint Hewlett Packard-AT&T proposal. It would use all four pairs using Category 5 cabling in the 10Base-T twisted pair wiring scheme to transmit or receive, rather than today's present system of using one pair to transmit and one pair to receive. The 5B6B coding used in 100VG splits the signal across the four wire pairs at 25 Mhz each. 100VG is based on quartet signaling and demand priority protocol. It retains 802.3 frame format and bridging with 10-Mbps CSMA/CD. See 100BASE-T for the competing 100 megabit LAN standard.

10BASE-2 IEEE 802.3 standard for baseband Ethernet at 10 Mbps in baseband form over coaxial cable to a maximum distance of 185 meters. Also known as THIN ETHERNET or THINWIRE ETHERNET.

10BASE-5 A transmission medium specified by IEEE 802.3 that carries information at 10 Mbps in baseband form using 50-ohm coaxial cable and accommodates 500-meter repeaterless runs. 10Base-5 was specified by the original Ethernet standards and is sometimes called ThickWire Ethernet.

10BASE-F Standard for Fiber optic Active and Passive Star based Ethernet segments. Described in IEEE 802.1j-1993 (not in an 802.3 supplement, as you might expect). 10Base-F includes the 10Base-FL standards.

10BASE-FB Part of the new IEEE 802.3 10BASE-F specification, "Synchronous Ethernet" which is a special-purpose link that links repeaters and allows the limit on segments and repeaters to be enlarged. It is not used to connect user stations. See 10Base-F.

10BASE-FL A part of the IEEE Base-F specification that covers Ethernet over fiber. It is interoperable with FOIRL. See 10Base-F.

10BASE-T An Ethernet local area network which works on twisted pair wiring that looks and feels remarkably like telephone cabling. In fact, 10Base-T was really invented to run on telephone cable. 10Base-T Ethernet local area networks work on home runs in which the wire from each workstation snakes directly to 10Base-T hub (like the wiring of a phone system). 10Base-T cards which fit inside PCs typically cost the same as those for Ethernet running on coaxial cable. The advantages are twofold — namely if one machine crashes, it doesn't bring down the whole network (coax Ethernet LANs are typically one long line, looping from one machine to another); and secondly, a 10Base-T Ethernet network is easier to manage because the 10Base-T hubs often come with sophisticated management software. Though 10Base-T is designed to work on "normal" telephone lines, there are multiple categories of wiring. See Category 1, 2, etc. If in doubt, pick a higher level. Sometimes old phone cabling will work. Mostly, it won't. Be safe. Put in new cabling. Put in decent new cabling. See 802.3 10Base-T.

10BROAD36 An IEEE 802.3 network specification employing a broadband transmission scheme using thick coax cable and running at 10 Mbits/sec.

10XXX CALLING An access code that is dialed, in addition to the telephone number, to connect with a long distance carrier. Each carrier has a unique three digit code represented here by XXX. 1-0-XXX calling allows customers to use long distance carriers other than one they subscribe to. AT&T's code is 1-0-288 (as in 1-0-ATT). MCI's is 1-0-222. Sprint's is 1-0-333. At some point in the future, that will change to 1-0-XXXX.

10XXXX CALLING See 10XXX.

110-TYPE CONNECTING BLOCK The part of a 110-type cross connect, developed by AT&T, that terminates twisted-pair wiring and can be used with either jumper wires or patch cords to establish circuit connections.

110-TYPE CROSS CONNECT A compact cross connect, developed by AT&T, that can be arranged for use with either jumper wires or patch cords. Jumper wires, used for more permanent circuits, must be cut down to make circuit connections. Patch cords allow ease of circuit administration for frequently rearranged circuits. The 110-type cross connect also provides straightforward labeling methods to identify circuits.

119 Japan's equivalent of the United States' emergency 911 number.

1394 An IEEE data transport bus that supports up to 63 nodes per bus, and up to 1023 buses. The bus can be tree, daisy chained or any combination. It supports both asynchronous and isochronous data.

144-LINE WEIGHTING In telephone systems, a noise weighting used in a noise measuring set to measure noise on a line that would be terminated by an instrument with a No 144-receiver, or a similar instrument.

1455 Johann Gutenberg, a goldsmith from Mainz, Germany, prints his Mazarin Bible, which is believed to be the first book printed with movable type, i.e. printed on his famous Gutenberg Press. It took Gutenberg two years to compose the type for his first bible. But once he had done that he could print multiple copies. Before Gutenberg, all books were copied by hand. Monks usually did the copying. They seldom managed to make more than one book a year. The Gutenberg press was a major advance. Before Gutenberg, there were only 30,000 books on the continent of Europe. By the year 1500, there were nine million. Some people (including me) have likened the invention of the Internet to the Gutenberg Press. Johann Gutenberg lived from 1397 to 1468.

16-BIT An adjective that describes systems and software that handle information in words that are 2 bytes (16 bits) wide.

16-BIT COMPUTER A computer that uses a central processing unit (CPU) with a 16-bit data bus and processes two bytes (16 bits) of information at a time. The IBM Personal Computer AT, introduced in 1984, was the first true 16-bit PC.

16450/8250A Found in most current PCs, these older UART chips use a 1-byte buffer that must be serviced immediately by the CPU. If not, interrupt overruns will result. See 16550 and UART.

16550 An enhanced version of the original National Semiconductor 16xxx series UART, which sits in and controls the flow of information into and out of virtually every PC serial port in the world. The older version contains only a one-byte buffer. This can slow down the transmission of high-speed data especially when you're using a multitasking program, like Windows. The "solution" is to get a serial card or port containing the 16550. This chip contains two 16-byte FIFO buffers, one each for incoming and outgoing data. Also new is the 16550's level-sensitive interrupt-triggering mechanism, which controls the amount of incoming data the buffer can store before generating on interrupt request. Together, these features help reduce your CPU's interrupt overhead and thus speed up your communications. See 16450/8250A and UART.

1791 April 27, Samuel Finley Breese Morse born.

1793 Semaphore invented.

1833 Analytical engine by Charles Babbage.

1836 Elisha Gray born. He invented the telephone at around the same time Alexander Graham Bell did. But Bell got his phone patented before Gray.

1837 Telegraphy by Samuel F. B. Morse.

1840 Samuel Morse patents the telegraph.

1843 1. First commercial test of Morse's telegraph. The US Government paid for a telegraph line between Baltimore and Washington, D.C. It worked. 2. First successful fax machine patented by Scottish inventor, Alexander Bain. His

"Recording Telegraph" worked over a telegraph line, using electromagnetically controlled pendulums for both a driving mechanism and timing. At the sending end, a style swept across a block of metal type, providing a voltage to be applied to a similar stylus at the receiving end, reproducing an arc of the image on a block holding a paper saturated with electrolytic solution which discolored when an electric current was applied through it. The blocks at both ends were lowered a fraction of an inch after each pendulum sweep until the image was completed. Bain's device transmitted strictly black and white images.

1844 Samuel Morse send sends first public telegraph message.

1845 First rotary printing press by Richard M. Hoe.

1865 First commercial fax service started by Giovanni Casselli, using his "Pantelegraph" machine, with a circuit between Paris and Lyon, which was later extended to other cities.

1866 First experimental wireless by Mahlon Loomis.

1867 Typewriter invented by Christopher L. Sholes.

1874 April 25, 1874, Guglielmo Marconi, born in Bologna, Italy.

1876 Braving a hostile ocean, the men of the Faraday, a steam-driven ship with three masts, laid the first transatlantic cable between Ireland and America. The cable was made by Siemens. It could carry 22 messages at one time. And it carried the world into a new era of communications.

1876 Telephone patent issued to Alexander Graham Bell; first long distance call transmitted by Bell.

1877 1. First telephone in a private home. First telephone in New York City. 2. Phonograph invented by Thomas Edison.

1880 Alexander Graham Bell develops the photophone which uses sunlight to carry messages. It was never commercially produced.

1881 First long distance line, Boston to Providence.

1887 AT&T (American Telephone & Telegraph Co.) starts business.

1889 1. A. B. Strowger invents the telephone switch, dial telephone. 2. Punch card tabulating machine by Herman Hollerith.

1891 Undersea telephone cable, England to France.

1895 Guglielmo Marconi of Italy invents wireless telegraph.

1899 Magnetic voice recorder by Vlademar Poulsen.

1906 Motion picture sound by Eugene Augustin Lauste.

1911 Multiplying and dividing calculating machine by Jay R. Monroe.

1915 First transcontinental phone call in USA.

1917 VHF Transatlantic radio by Guglielmo Marconi.

1920 First commercial AM radio broadcast in the U.S. KDKA, Pittsburgh.

1921 Facsimile technology (Wirephoto) from Western Union.

1922 First dial exchange in New York City — PE-6 from PEnnsylvania 6.

1924 1. Thomas J. Watson renames Computing-Tabulating-Recording (CTR) the International Business Machines Corporation. 2. The work of Herbert Ives at Bell Labs on the photoelectric effect leads to the first demonstraton of the transmission of pictures over telephone lines.

1925 IBM begins selling punch-card machinery in Japan. Frank B. Jewett becomes the first president of Bell Labs.

1926 1. AT&T Bell Labs invents sound motion pictures. 2. First public test of trans-atlantic radiotelephone service — between New York and London.

1927 1. April 7, 1929. First public demonstration of long distance TV transmission. Moving black and white pictures were sent over telephone wires between Secretary of Commerce Herbert Hoover in Washington DC and AT&T executives in New York. They went at 18 frames per second. Further development of this technology led to the creation of TV. 2. Harold S. Black's negative feedback amplifier custs distortion in long distance telephony. Black is at Bell Labs.

1929 1. Coaxial cable invented in Bell Telephone Laboratories; Herbert Hoover first president to have phone installed on his desk. 2. AT&T Bell Laboratories and Western Electric introduced the Sound Newsreel Camera. It used an AT&T "Light Valve" to record sound directly on the film as it passed through the camera. It was the first single system sound camera.

1933 FM radio invented by Edwin H. Armstrong.

1933 1. Karl G. Jansky at Bell Labs discovers radio waves from the Milky Way. His discovery leads to the science of radio astronomy. 2. Bell Labs transmits first stereo sound, a symphony concert, over phone lines from Philadelphia to Washington.

1936 First TV broadcast by the BBC in Great Britain.

193RD BIT The frame bit for a T-1 frame.

1938 Xerography invented by Chester Carlson.

1942 Harry Newton, born Sydney, Australia on June 10.

1944 Electronic Numerical Integrator and Computor (spelled with an O). Early computer, built in 1944.

1946 Dr. Robert N. Metcalfe, co-inventor of Ethernet, born Brooklyn, New York on April 7.

1947 Transistor invented at AT&T's Bell Labs in New Jersey. Inventors were John Bardeen, Walter Brattain and William Shockley. In 1956 they shared the Nobel Prize in Physics for creating the transistor.

1948 1. May 11: Birth of the International Communications Association, among the larger groups of telecommunications users in North America. 2. Claude E.

Shannon announces the discovery of information theory, the cornerstone of current understanding of the communcation process. Shannon is a Bell Labs.

1951 1. First direct distance calling. Phone users can dial long distance without an operator's assistance. 2. Sony unveils the first transistor radio.

1954 The solar cell invented by Gerald L. Pearson, Daryl M. Chapin and Calvin S. Fuller at Bell Labs. Also, the year William Shockley left Bell Labs to pursue the commercial opportunities offered by his invention of the transistor.

1955 Bill Gates, founder and chairman of Microsoft, born October 28, 1955.

1956 1. First transatlantic repeatered telephone cable. 2. First modem was invented by AT&T Bell Laboratories, according to AT&T. 3. Videotape recorder invented by Ampex.

1957 1. The U.S.S.R. launched Sputnik on October 4, 1957. It embarrassed the U.S. Government into a frenzy of space investments, culminating in the U.S. being the first country to have people walk on the moon. 2. Dr. Gordon E. Moore and Dr. Robert N. Noyce leave Fairchild Semiconductor and form Intel Corporation. Intel was founded with less than $5 million in startup monies using a two-page business plan written by legendary venture capitalist, Arthur Rock.

1958 Integrated circuit invented by Jack S. Kilby at Texas Instruments.

1960 1. First test of an electronic switch. 2. MITI creates the Japan Electronic Computer Corporation to promote its domestic computer industry. 3. Laser invented by Theodore Maiman of the U.S. Laser stands for Light Amplification by the Stimulated Emission of Radiation.

1962 1. LEDs — Light Emitting Diodes — invented. 2. First commercial communications satellite (Telstar). Owned by AT&T. 3. August 31, 1962 President Kennedy signed Communications Satellite Act. 4. Semiconductor laser invented. 5. Ross Perot forms EDS with a reputed $1,000. In 1984, he sold it to General Motors for $2.6 billion. In 1999, GM decided to spin it off in a deal worth $22.2 billion.

1963 1. Touch Tone service introduced. 2. Audio cassette tape introduced by Philips. 3. C. Kumar N. Patel at Bell Labs develops the carbon dioxide laser now used around the world as a cutting tool in surgery and industry.

1964 1. Prototype of the first video phone made by the Bell System shown at The World's Fair in Queens, New York City. Pictures were black and white and the technology was very expensive. It was called the Picturephone. 2. IBM showed the first word processor.

1965 1. PDP-8 minicomputer introduced by Digital Equipment Corporation. 2. First trial offers for reversing telephone charges.

1966 October, 1966 the Electronic Industries Association issues its first fax standard: the EIA Standard RS-328, Message Facsimile Equipment for Operation on Switched Voice Facilities Using Data Communications Equipment. The Group 1 standard, as it later became known, made possible the more generalized business use of fax. Transmission was analog and it took four to six minutes to send a page.

1967 1. First 800 call made in the United States. 2. Electronic handheld calculator introduced by Texas Instruments.

1968 Fiber optics for communications invented by Robert Maurer.

1969 1. Ken Thompson and Dennis Ritchie, computer scientists at AT&T Bell Laboratories, create the Unix software operating system. 2. ARPANET introduced by the Advanced Research Projects Agency of the U.S. Defense Department. 3. Traffic Service Position System replaces traditional cord switchboards. The system automates many operator functions for the first time.

1970 1. Optical fiber for long-range communications developed. 2. Relational database invented by Dr. E. F. "Ted" Codd at IBM. 3. Floppy disk invented by IBM. 4. Gilbert Chin creates a new type of magnetic alloy now used in most telephone handset speakers.

1971 Ted Hoff at Intel invents the microprocessor — a single chip that contained most of the logic elements used to make a computer. Intel's twin innovations with the device were to put most of the transistors that make up a computer's logic circuits on to a single chip and to make that chip programmable. Here, for the first time, according to Robert X. Cringely's book "Accidental Empires," was a programmable device to which a clever engineer could add a few memory chips and a support chip or two and turn it into a real computer you could hold in your hands. Intel's first microprocessor, the 4004, was released in November, 1971. See 4004. See also MICROPROCESSOR.

1972 First commercial video game (Pong) introduced by Nolan Bushnell at Atari.

1973 1. Computerized Axial Tomography (CAT Scan) invented by Allan Cormack and Godfrey N. Hounsfield. 2. Ethernet invented by Dr. Robert N. Metcalfe on May 22, 1973 at the Xerox Palo Alto Research Center (PARC). Dave Boggs (Dr. David R. Boggs) was the co-inventor. Metcalfe and Boggs (in that order) were the authors of THE Ethernet paper, published July 76 in CACM. CACM is the Communications of the ACM. ACM is the Association for Computing Machinery. 3. Vinton Cert, computer scientist, invents the basic design of the Internet - the intermediate level gateways (now called routers), the global address space and the concept of end/end acknowledgement. 4. Gerhard Sessler and James E. West of Bell Labs receive a patent for their unidirectional microphone that improves hands-free telephone conversations.

1974 1. AT&T introduces Picturephone, a two-way color videoconferencing service at 12 locations around the country. Businesses rented meeting rooms equipped with the technology. 2. Hewlett-Packard introduces the first programmable pocket calculator, the HP-65. 3. Structured Query Language (SQL) invented by Don Chamberlain and colleagues at IBM Research.

1975 1. MITS Altair 8800 personal computer kit from MITS. The Altair was the first commercially available personal computer kit. It was on the cover of the Popular Electronics January 1975 issue. 2. Live TV satellite feed. Ali-Frazier fight from HBO (Home Box Office). 3. Sony introduces Betamax, which didn't do as well as the Video Home System (VHS) introduced later by Matsushita/JVC.

1976 1. First digital electronic central office switch installed. 2. Apple Computer founded in a Cupertino, CA garage by Steve Jobs and Steve Wozniak.

1977 1. First lightwave system installed and begins operation. It's under the streets of Chicago. 2. Interactive cable system (Qube) installed by Warner Cable. 3. Commodore PET was among the hot PCs of 1977.

1978 Bell Labs invents cellular technology. CCITT comes out with Group 2 recommendation on fax. Intel introduces the 8086 chip, with 29,000 transistors and processing 16 bits of data at one time. A variation of this chip, the 8088, introduced in 1980, caught IBM's eye and IBM used it in its first PC.

1979 1. Chapter 11 Federal bankruptcy provision introduced. Chapter 11 is reorganization. Chapter 7 is liquidation. 2. CompuServe Information Service goes on-line. 3. Gordon Matthews invents corporate voice mail. See VMX.

1980 1. CCITT comes out with Group 3 recommendation on fax. Group 3 machines are much faster than Group 2 or 1. With Group 3 machines, after an initial 15-second handshake that is not repeated, they can send an average page of text in 30 seconds or less. 2. Supreme Court of the United States rules that patents for software can be issued.

1981 1. IBM PC debuts. 2. First portable computer, by Osborne. 3. National electronic phone directory (minitel) starts in France.

1982 January 8, 1982 the consent decree to break up AT&T into seven regional holding companies and what was left (long distance and manufacturing) is announced. The divestiture takes place two years later on January 1, 1984.

March 3, 1982, the FCC formally approved the startup of cellular phone services. The FCC indicated that it would accept applications for licenses in the top 30 markets 90 days after procedures were published and for smaller markets, 180 days after publication. The FCC subsequently gave one license in each market to the local phone company (the "wireline") and one for a competitor (the "non-wireline") carrier.

October 21, 1982, the FCC awards the first construction permit for a cellular radio license to AT&T's Ameritech subsidiary (this was prior to the AT&T breakup).

1983 1. Novell introduces its first network local area network software called NetWare. It was originally introduced to allow a handful of personal computers to share a single hard disk, which at that stage was a costly and scarce resource. As hard disks became more available, the product evolved to allow the sharing of printers and file servers. 2. Nintendo introduces Famicom, a computer turned video game. 3. Cellular radio in the United States gets its first subscriber. 4. Sony introduces the Camcorder. 5. October 13, 1983, Ameritech turns on its new cellular radio system in Chicago, the first in the nation. 6. IBM introduces the PC XT, the first IBM PC to contain a hard disk. 7. Bill Gates of Microsoft announces Windows at November's Comdex.

1984 January 2, 1984. The breakup of the Bell System. AT&T gave up its local operating phone companies, which got formed into seven, roughly equal holding companies. In turn, AT&T got the Justice Department off its back for an antitrust suit and got the right to get into industries other than telecommunications. Its chosen industry was the computer industry for which it felt it had unique skills.

January 24, 1984 Apple Computer Inc.'s Steve Jobs introduces the first Macintosh computer. It was the machine that changed the world of PC computing. Mr. Jobs often described the little machine as "insanely great."

March, 1984, Motorola introduced the DynaTAC 8000X, the first portable cellular phone. It listed for $3,995 and it weighed two pounds.

Ken Oshman sells Rolm to IBM for $1.26 billion. It was not one of IBM's better investments. Rolm is now part of Siemens, which understands telecommunications.

Prodigy Information Service, a service of IBM and Sears, starts.

1985 1. CD-ROM introduced by Philips and Sony. 2. Steve Jobs driven from Apple Computer by John Sculley.

1986 Novell's SFT NetWare, first fault tolerant local area network operating system.

1987 October, 1987, the one-millionth cellular subscriber signs up for service in America.

George Forrester Colony of Forrester Research is believed to have coined the term "client-server" computing. See CLIENT-SERVER.

1988 1. First transatlantic optical fiber cable. 2. Robert E. Allen takes over as CEO of AT&T.

1989 1. Fiber to the home field trial, Cerritos, CA. 2. Novell releases NetWare 3.0, the first 32-bit network operating system for Intel 80386/486-based servers. 3. 1989: Panasonic's household-size video phone with moving color images debuts in Tokyo.

1990 1. Demonstration of 2,000 kilometer link using optical amplifiers without repeaters. 2. MVIP formed and first product shipped.

1991 1. AT&T buys NCR for a gigantic $7.4 billion and soon renames it AT&T Global Information Solutions. Later AT&T took hundreds of millions of dollars in restructuring and other charges related to the fact that NCR lost pots of money after AT&T bought it. Part of the problem, according to analysts, was that AT&T bought NCR right at the time NR was making the transition from traditional mainframe computers to so-called massively parallel computers powered by collections of small, cheaper processors run in tandem. NCR also got hit by a decline in its traditional cash register business as low-margin PCs came in. The skinny around the industry at the time AT&T bought NCR was that AT&T bought NCR to disguise the fact that its own computer operations at that time were losing so much money. And the senior management of AT&T at that time wanted to retire with the glories of booming long distance revenues and not lousy computer results. 2. Motorola introduces the lightest cellular phone yet, the MicroTAC Lite for about $1,000 retail. 3. The Electronic Industries Association approves and publishes on July 9, 1991, the Commercial Building Telecommunications Wiring

Standard, the most important wiring standard ever published in the history of telecommunications. 4. Scott Hinton at Bell Labs heads a team that builds the first photonic switching fabric, bringing light-based switching technology in telecommunications networks closer to reality.

1992 1. AT&T introduces VideoPhone 2500 marketed as the first home-model color video phone which works on normal dial up analog phone lines. It meets cool reception because of poor image quality and its high price, namely $1,500. 2. Microsoft Windows 3.1 and IBM's OS/2 2.0 operating systems introduced. Windows NT (32-bit operating system) debuts in beta form. 3. Wang files for Chapter 11. 4. MCI introduces VideoPhone for normal dial-up analog phone lines. It retails for $750. It is not compatible with the AT&T phone. 5. The cellular industry signs its ten millionth subscriber on November 23, 1992. At least that's what the press releases said. Some carriers claimed that at year end, cellular subscribers in the United States had actually hit 11 million, way ahead of all predictions. 6. Apple, EO and others introduce the PDA, the Personal Digital Assistant.

1993 FCC announces its intention to auction off a chunk of spectrum larger than that used in 1993 for cellular radio. The new airwaves will be used for new types of wireless communications, including portable digital communications devices from phones to laptops, palmtops and PDAs equipped to receive and transmit data of all types, including faxes and video.

February 25, McCaw Cellular announces North America's first all-digital cellular service, in Orlando, Florida.

March 17. The Clinton administration urges Congress to eschew comparative hearings and institute a lottery for awarding new radio spectrum. See PCS.

December 31. Thomas J. Watson dies, age 79.

AT&T introduces the AT&T EO Personal Communicator 440, based on the Bell Labs-developed Hobbit microprocessor. This hand-held device combines the features of pen-based personal computers, telephones and fax machines. The device is later withdrawn from the market because of poor demand.

1994 1. GO-MVIP formed. Trade association for developers and manufacturers of MVIP computer telephony products. 2. AT&T pays $12.6 billion for McGaw Cellular Communications Inc. Robet E. Allen is CEO of AT&T.

1995 1. IBM buys Lotus for $3.5 billion, the main attraction being Lotus Notes. One of the key attractions of Lotus Notes is that it saves on phone bills. 2. August 24, Windows 95 finally ships. It contains heavy computer telephony features, including TAPI, VoiceView, fax on demand and binary file transfers using 3. September 20, 1995, AT&T announces it will split itself into three companies — long distance, equipment manufacturing and computers. Wall Street applauds the decision and in one day lifts the price of AT&T's stock by 10%, or about $6 1/2 billion. Meantime, AT&T announces that it will substantially reduce the size of its failed computer activities, which were called AT&T Global Information Solutions. See 1991. 4. December 8. Digital Versatile Disk (DVD) is announced. DVD is a specification announced by nine companies for a new type of digital videodisk, similar to CD-ROMs but able to store far more music, video or data in a common format. DVDs will be 5 inches in diameter and will be able to store 4.7 gigabytes on each side, equivalent to 133 minutes of motion picture and sound, or enough to hold most feature-length movies. The companies announcing DVD were Philips, Toshiba, Matsushita Electric Industrial, Sony, Time Warner, Pioneer Electronic, the JVC unit of Matsushita, Hitachi and Mitsubish Electric.

1A AT&T's first generation of standardized KEY TELEPHONE SYSTEM equipment based on a variety of interconnected phone-line-powered relays. Prior to 1A1, key systems were often patched together from a variety of non-standard parts, with varying wiring schemes, making repairs and upgrades very difficult.

1A1 AT&T's second generation of standardized KEY TELEPHONE SYSTEM equipment. Unlike the phone-line powered 1A1, it used commercial AC power for added features such as illuminated buttons to indicate line status.

1A2 AT&T's third generation of standardized KEY TELEPHONE SYSTEMS. It was distinctive for its use of plug-in circuit cards, making it much easier to add features or diagnose and cure problems.

1A3 A cute term for an historic TIE electronic key system that provided advanced features, but was priced competitively with 1A2 electromechanical key systems.

1BASE-5 A transmission medium specified by IEEE 802.3 that carries 1.0 Mbps in baseband form using twisted-pair conductors and accommodates 500 meter repeaterless runs.

1FB One Flat rate Business phone line. A phone line you pay a single monthly charge for and you may make as many local phone calls as you wish for free during that month. See also 1MB.

1MB One Message rate Business phone line. A phone line you pay a single monthly charge for. That charge typically allows you to make a small number of local calls for free. But that each additional local call will cost you. That cost may be by the minute, by the distance, or just by the call. See 1FB.

1PSS Packet Switching System. The AT&T Western Electric 1PSS is a high-capacity, X.25 packet switch.

2-WAY TRUNK A trunk that can be seized at either end.

2-WIRE FACILITY A 2-wire facility is characterized by supporting transmission in two directions simultaneously, where the only method of separating the two signals is by the propagation directions. Impedance mismatches cause signal energy passing in each direction to mix with the signal passing in the opposite direction. See 4-WIRE FACILITY.

23B+D An easy way of saying the ISDN Primary Rate Interface circuit. 23B+D has 23 64 Kbps (kilobits per second) paths for carrying voice, data, video or other information and one 64 Kbps channel for carrying out-of-band signaling information. ISDN PRI bears a remarkable similarity to today's T-1 line, except that T-1 can carry 24 voice channels. In ISDN, 23B+D the one D channel is out-of-band signaling. In T-1, signaling is handled in-band using robbed bit signaling. Increasingly, 23B+D is the preferred way of getting T-1 service since the out of band signaling is richer (delivers more information — like ANI and DNIS) and is more reliable than the in-band signaling on the older T-1. One good thing about PRI: You can now organize with your phone company to deliver the signaling for a bunch of ISDN PRI cards on one D channel. Thus your first line would have 23 voice channels, for example. Your second would have 24 voice channels, etc. Several of the more modern voice cards will accept the signaling for up to eight ISDN PRI channels on the D channel of the first one. See ISDN PRI, ROBBED BIT SIGNALING and T-1.

24-BIT MODE The standard addressing mode of Apple Macintosh's System 6 operating system, where only 24 bits are used to designate addresses. Limits address space to 16MB (2 to the 24th power), of which only 8MB is normally available for application memory. This mode is also used under System 7 (the Mac's more modern operating system) if 32-bit addressing is turned off. See 32-BIT.

24-BIT VIDEO ADAPTER A color video adapter that can display more than 16 million colors simultaneously. With a 24-bit video card and monitor, a PC can display photographic-quality images.

2500 SET The "normal" single-line touchtone desk telephone. It has replaced the rotary dial 500 set in most — but definitely not all — areas of the United States and Canada. No one seems to know why the addition of a "2" in front of a model number came to denote touchtone in the old Bell System.

2600 TONE Until the late 1960s, America's telephone network was run 100% by AT&T and used 100% in-band signaling. For in-band signaling to work there needs to be a way to figure when a channel is NOT being used. You can't have nothing on the line, because that "nothing" might be a pause in the conversation. So, in the old days, AT&T put a tone on its vacant long distance lines, those between its switching offices. That tone was 2600 Hertz. If its switching offices heard a 2600 Hz, it knew that that line was not being used. At one point in the 1960s, a breakfast cereal included a small promotion in its cereal boxes. It was a toy whistle. When you blew the whistle, it let out a precise 2,600 Hz tone. If you blew that whistle into the mouthpiece of a telephone after dialing any long distance number, it terminated the call as far as the AT&T long distance phone system knew, while still allowing the connection to remain open. If you dialed an 800 number, blew the whistle and then touchtoned in a series of tones (called MF — multi-frequency — tones) you could make long distance and international calls for free. The man who discovered the whistle was called John Draper and he picked up the handle of Cap'n Crunch in the nether world of the late 1960s phone phreaks. Since then, in-band signaling has been replaced by out-of-band signaling, the newest incarnation being called Signaling System 7. See 2600 CAPTAIN CRUNCH, MULTI-FREQUENCY SIGNALING and SIGNALING SYSTEM 7.

2780 A batch standard used to communicate with IBM mainframes or compatible systems.

2B+D A shortened way of saying ISDN's Basic Rate Interface interface, namely two bearer channels and one data channel. A single ISDN circuit divided into two 64 Kbps digital channels for voice or data and one 16Kbps channel for low speed data (up to 9,600 baud) and signaling. Either or both of the 64 Kbps channels may be used for voice or data. In ISDN 2B+D is known as the Basic Rate Interface. In ISDN, 2B+D is carried on one or two pairs of wires (depending on the interface) — the same wire pairs that today bring a single voice circuit into your home or office. See ISDN.

2B1Q Two Binary, One Quarternary. An ISDN line encoding technique which uses two bits to represent four variations in amplitude and polarity.

2W Two-Wire. See 2-WIRE FACILITY.

3:2 PULL-DOWN A method for overcoming the incompatibility of film and video frame rates when converting or transferring film (shot at 24 frames per second) to video (shot at 30 frames per second).

3172 IBM's network controller. It connects to the mainframe channel on one end and the LAN media (Ethernet, Token Ring, FDDI) on the other.

3174 IBM's cluster controller. It connects to terminals and other I/O devices on one end, and a mainframe channel on the other.

32-BIT An adjective that describes hardware or software that manages data, program code, and program address information in 32-bit-wide words. What is the significance of 32-bit? With 32-bit memory, each program can address up to 4 gigabytes (2 to the 32nd power) of memory. This is in contrast to Windows 3.x where programs are limited to 16 MB of memory. Possibly more significant than the amount of memory that is available to a 32-bit application is how that memory is accessed. Under Windows 3.x, memory is accessed by using two 16-bit values that are combined to form a 24-bit memory address. (24-bits is the size of the memory addressing path of the Intel 80286. The 80286 is the architecture that Windows 3.x was designed for.) The first 16-bit value (selector) is used to determine a base address. The second 16-bit value (offset) indicates the offset from the base address. One of the side effects of this architecture is that the maximum size of a single chunk of memory is 64 KB. Windows 95 and Windows NT are 32-bit operating systems. Windows 95 and Windows NT developers can address memory with a single 32-bit value. Such an addressing scheme allows developers to view memory as one flat, linear space with no artificial limits on the size of a single segment. No longer are programmers concerned about selectors and offsets and the 64 KB segment limit. Also, Windows 95 and Windows NT take full advantage of the protection features of the Intel 80386 microprocessor. 32-bit applications are given their own protected address space which tends to prevent applications from inadvertently overwriting each other.

32-BIT ADDRESSING See 32-BIT.

32-BIT COMPUTER A computer that uses a central processing unit (CPU) with a 32-bit data bus and central processing unit (CPU) which processes four bytes (32 bits) of information at a time. Personal computers advertised as 32-bit machines — such as Macintosh SE, and PCs based on the 80386X microprocessor — aren't true 32-bit computers. These computers use microprocessors (such as the Motorola 68000 and Intel 80386SX) that can process four bytes at a time internally, but the external data bus is only 16 bits wide. 32-bit microprocessors, such as the Intel 80386DX, the Pentium and the Motorola 68030, use a true 32-bit external data bus and can use 32-bit peripherals.

32-MEGABYTE BARRIER Versions of MS-DOS prior to 4.0 had a built-in limit on the size of a disk partition. Using the original design parameters of DOS, we can show how we got to the maximum size disk partition. One word, 16 bits, is defined for DOS to access sectors within its hard disk partition. A single 16-bit binary word can represent values from zero through 65,535. This limits the partition's total sector count to 65,536. Hard disk sectors are 512 bytes long. 512 bytes times 65,536 sectors = 33,554,432. Since there are 1,048,576 bytes in each megabyte, the maximum size partition calculates to 32 megabytes. MS-DOS 4.0 and 5.X can now create partitions of and read in one go a disk of up to 512 megabytes.

3270 IBM class of terminals (or printers) used in SNA networks.

3270 GATEWAY An electronic link which uses 3270 terminals to handle data communications between PCs and IBM mainframes.

3270SNA A specific variation of IBM's System Network Architecture for controlling communications between a 3270 terminal connected to an IBM mainframe.

3274 IBM series of Control Units or Cluster Controllers provide a control interface between host computers and clusters of 3270 compatible terminals.

327X Belonging to IBM's 3270 collection of data communications terminals.

3745 IBM's communications controllers, often called front-end processors. 3745 devices channel-attach to the mainframe and support connections to LANs and other FEPS.

3780 a batch protocol used to communicate with an IBM mainframe or compatible system.

386 See 80386.

386 ENHANCED MODE An operating mode of Microsoft Windows that takes full advantage of advanced technical capabilities such as multitasking, virtual memory, and protected mode. To use 386 Enhanced mode, your computer must have an 80386 or higher microprocessor and at least 2M of random-access memory (RAM).

386SLC The IBM 386SLC is IBM's improved version of Intel's 80386SX microprocessor chip. IBM designed it with Intel's help, so it's compatible with the Intel family of 8088, 80286, 80386, 80486 chips.

3DGF 3-D Geometry File. A platform independent format for exchanging 3-D geometry data among applications. Developed by Macromind.

4-WIRE FACILITY A 4-wire facility supports transmission in two directions, but isolates the signals by frequency division, time division, space division, or other techniques that enable reflections to occur without causing the signals to mix together. A facility is also called 4-wire if its interfaces to other equipment meet this 4-wire criteria (even if 2-wire facilities are used internally), as long as crosstalk between the two transmission directions, as measured at the interface, is negligible. See 2-WIRE FACILITY.

4.9% No regional Bell Operating Company is presently allowed to own more than 4.9% of the stock of a telecommunications manufacturing company. See DIVESTITURE.

4004 The world's first general-purpose microprocessor (computer on a chip). The 4004 was made by Intel, was 4-bit, was released on November 15, 1971 and contained 2,300 transistors. It executed 60,000 instructions per second. The tiny 4004 had as much computing power as the first electronic computer, ENIAC, which filled 3,000 cubic feet with 18,000 vacuum tubes when it was built in 1946. The 4004 found a home in desktop calculators, traffic lights and electronic scales. Despite its power, its 4-bit structure was too small to process all the bits of data at one time to handle all the letters of the alphabet. It was followed by the 8-bit 8008. See also 1971 and 1978.

41449 AT&T's specifications for its ISDN PRI (Primary Rate Interface). It is different to the ANSI standard T1.607.

419A A famous old Bell System tool which many installers found very convenient to hold a diminishing marijuana cigarette (called a 'roach') in the 1960s.

42A An early terminal block. The Model 42A is a plastic mounting base about two inches square with four screws and a cover. Before modular connections became widespread, the 42A was used to connect a phone's line cord to the wire inside a wall or running around the baseboard. Adapters, such as the No. 725A made by AT&T and Suttle Apparatus, can be used to convert a 42A into a 4-conductor modular jack. See also TERMINAL BLOCK.

46-49 In North America, most cordless phones operate within the band 46-49 MHz. That band contains only 10 channels and is horribly overcrowded. Recently, the FCC authorized a new frequency range — 905-928 MHz — for use by, amongst other things, cordless phones. The 900 Mhz contains 50 channels.

486 A shortened name for Intel's family of 80486 chips, the successor to and continuation of the line of chips that started with the 8088 and grew into the 8086, the 80286 and the 80386. The 80486 is a major step forward in speed, complexity and capability. In simple terms, the 486 is a combination microprocessor, floating point math coprocessor, memory cache controller and 8K of RAM cache, all in one chip. The 486 chip contains 1.2 million transistors and is capable of 41 MIPS operating at 50 MHz. See 80486.

486DX The full-powered 80486 from Intel. See 80486.

486SL A power-saving version of Intel's '486 chip, which it introduced in the fall of 1992 and targeted at manufacturers of laptops and notebooks. The chip runs at 3.3 volts, compared with 5.0 volts for its previous power-saving chip, the '386SL.

486SLC A name given to clones of 80486 chips. These clones are made by companies other than Intel, the manufacturer of the original chip. These clones are often not identical in power with the Intel chip. The Cyrix 486SLC, for example, is really a hybrid of the 386 and 486 chips. The Cyrix chip is intended to offer notebook manufacturers an easy way to upgrade machines originally designed to run on Intel 386SX processors. Cyrix built its 486SLC chip to fit the Intel 386SX sockets already in place in many popular notebook designs, thus requiring only minimal changes to the BIOS and motherboard. As with the Intel 386SX, the Cyrix processor has a 32-bit internal data path but communicates with the rest of the computer over a 16-bit data path. However, it uses the 486SX instruction set and boasts an on-board cache, although only 1K. The 486SLC's hardware multiplier, although not as fast as a true math coprocessor, can significantly speed some graphics calculations. Like Intel's 386SL chip, the Cyrix 486SLC operates at a low 3.3 volt. This is designed to extend battery life in portables. Despite its 486 name, though, it's probably more appropriate to compare the performance of 486SLC notebooks to machines powered by 386SX and 386SL chips, not those with Intel 486-class processors. Given their different design goals, it's not fair to expect the 486SLC to match the speed of the 486SX.

486SX The Intel 486SX processor is essentially a full-powered 486DX with its math coprocessor disconnected. Unlike the 386 line, in which the SX version used a 16-bit external path, Intel created the 486SX by simply disconnecting the 486DX's math coprocessor. The 486SX shares the DX's full 32-bit data path and 8K cache.

4A The last generation of "telco-quality" add-on speakerphones, with separately-housed microphone and speaker; made by both Western Electric (AT&T) and Precision Components, Inc.

4GL Fourth Generation Language.

500 SET The old rotary dial telephone deskset. The touchtone version was called a 2500 set.

5250 IBM class of terminals for midrange (System 3x and AS/400) environments.

5250 GATEWAY An electronic link which uses 5250 terminals to handle communications between PCs and IBM minicomputers.

56 KBPS A 64 Kbps digital circuit with 8 Kbps used for signaling. Sometimes called Switched 56, DDS or ADN. Each of the carriers have their own name for this service. The phone companies are obsoleting this service in favor of the more modern ISDN BRI, which has two 64 Kbps circuits and one 16 Kbps packet service.

5ESS A digital central office switching system made by AT&T. It is typically used as an "end-office," serving local subscribers.

5XB 5 X-Bar central office equipment

64 KBPS A 64 kbps circuit (DS0). "Clear Channel" is 64 kbps where entire bandwidth is used.

64 BIT ARCHITECTURE The wide data path over which instructions (words composed of bits) are moved to and from Intel's i860's internal registers and memory. Most conventional mainframes use a word length of 32 bits. Intel's i860

RISC-based microprocessor line, introduced in 1989, incorporates many firsts, including more than 1 million transistors on a single chip. The line currently comprises the i860 XR, with 1.2 million transistors, and the i860 XP, with 2.5 million transistors. See also 8-BIT, 16-BIT and 32-BIT.

64 KBPS 64,000 bits per second. The standard speed for V.35 interface, DDS service, and also the effective top speed of a robbed-bit 64 Kbps channel. See also ISDN.

66 BLOCK The most common type of connecting block used to terminate and cross-connect twisted-pair cables. It was invented by Western Electric eons ago and has stood the test of time. It's still being installed. Its main claims to fame: Simplicity, speed, economy of space. You don't need to strip your cable of its plastic insulation covering. You simply lay each single conductor down inside the 66 block's two metal teeth and punch the conductor down with a special tool, called a punch-down tool. As you punch it down, the cable descends between the two metal teeth, which remove its plastic insulation (it's called insulation displacement) and the cable is cut. The installation is then neat and secure.

66-TYPE CONNECTING BLOCK A type of connecting block used to terminate twisted-pair cables. All wires are manually cut down with a special tool to terminate or connect them. See 66 BLOCK.

66-TYPE CROSS CONNECT A cross connect made up of the 66-type connecting blocks and jumper wires for administering circuits. All wires, including jumper wires, must be cut down (or punched down) and seated with a special tool. See 66 BLOCK.

6611 IBM's multi protocol router, which supports APPN in addition to TCP/IP, DECnet, AppleTalk, IPX, NetBIOS, and other protocols.

6800 A Motorola microprocessor used in early Macintoshes, Mac Plus and SE, plus recent low cost units such as the Classic, Portable and PowerBook 100. The 6800 does not support virtual memory or 32-bit addressing.

68020 A Motorola microprocessor used in the Macintosh II and LC. On the Mac II there is a socket to hold a coprocessor called a PMMU which enables the Mac II to use virtual memory. There is no socket on the LC motherboard, so the processor must be upgraded in order to use virtual memory.

68030 A Motorola microprocessor used in the SE/30, PowerBook 140/145 and 170, and Modular Macs, except the LC, Mac II, and Quadras. It supports virtual memory without any additional hardware.

68040 A Motorola microprocessor used in Quadras. It supports virtual memory without any additional hardware. Has built-in floating point math capabilities (an optional coprocessor on the 68030).

7-BIT ASCII The standard code for text in which a byte (eight bits) holds the seven ASCII digits that define the character plus one bit for parity.

700 SERVICE An "area code" you dial, as in 1-700-XXX-XXXX. This "area code" has been reserved for the long distance companies to do so as they will. So dial 1-700- and then certain "office codes" (the next three digits), you'll get

AT&T and a service it calls Easyreach. It will give a service allowing your calls to follow you. Dial other 700 office codes, get MCI and you'll be able to make intralata "long distance" phone calls, such as those from Manhattan to Westchester County — for presumably cheaper than with the local phone company. 700 service is still evolving. Each carrier has the right to create whatever service it wants with its 700 numbers.

8.3 MINUTES The time it takes for light to travel from the Sun to the Earth.

8-BIT COMPUTER A computer that uses a central processing unit (CPU) with an 8-bit data bus and that processes one byte (8 bits) of information at a time. The first microprocessors used in personal computers, such as the MOS Technology 6502, Intel 8080, and Zilog Z-80, were installed in 8-bit computers such as the Apple II, the MSAI 8080, and the Commodore 64.

800 PORTABILITY 800 Portability refers to the fact that you can take your 800 number to any long distance carrier. A case example, we had 1-800-LIBRARY. For many years, that number was serviced by AT&T. When portability came along, we were able to change it from AT&T to MCI and still keep 1-800-LIBRARY. 800 Portability is provided by a series of complex databases the local phone companies, under FCC mandate, have built. 800 Portability started on May 1, 1993.

800 SERVICE Eight-hundred service. A generic and common (and not trademarked) term for AT&T's, MCI's, US Sprint's and the Bell operating companies' IN-WATS service. All these IN-WATS services have 800 and 888 as their area code. Dialing an 800-number is free to the person making the call. The call is billed to the person or company being called. The telephone company suppliers of 800 services use various ways to configure and bill their 800-services. One way: you can buy an 800 line which will ring on your normal phone line. You'll only pay per call, but you won't receive any incoming call if you're making an outgoing one. You can even terminate an 800 number on your cellular phone or your home number. You might pay a flat monthly rate plus "so-much" (i.e. timed usage) per call. That timed usage may include some calculation for the distance the incoming call traveled. 800-Service is now available for calls from Canada and many countries overseas Europe, though many of those companies pay a normal toll call to reach an American "toll-free" 800-number.

800 Service works like this: You're somewhere in North America. You dial 1-800 or 1-888 and seven digits. Your local central office sees the "1" and recognizes the call as long distance. It ships that call to a bigger central office (or perhaps processes the call itself). At that central office it's processed, a machine will recognize the 800 or 888 "area code" and examine the next six digits. Those six digits will tell which long distance carrier to ship the call to locally. That carrier then holds the call, while it sends a data communications query to a computer containing a big "translation" database. That computer will look up the 800 number and send back information on how the carrier should route the call. There are many ways the carrier can route the call. The simplest is to say "Dial the following number, i.e. 212-691-8215 and connect the call. Or it might say Connect it to your dedicated T-1 number 12345 in New York City.

As a real-life example, Telecom Library, publishers of this book, has an 800 number, namely 800-LIBRARY (or 800-542-7279). When you call that number, MCI routes that number to the first available circuit on the dedicated T-1 line which we have rented from MCI's POP (Point Of Presence) to our New York City office.

Because 800 long distance service is essentially a database lookup and translation telephone service, there are endless "800 services" you can create. You can change the routing instructions based on time of day, day of week, number calling etc. See EIGHT HUNDRED SERVICE for more, especially all the features you can now get on 800 service.

In May of 1993 the FCC has mandated that all 800 numbers will become "portable." That means that customers can take their 800 telephone number from one long distance company to another, and still keep the same number.

800 VALUFLEX SERVICE A New York and New England Telephone service which lets you make and receive regular phone calls and 800-number calls from local areas on your normal business phone lines. There are big advantages here. You don't have to rent additional phone lines. You don't have to expand your existing phone system — or buy a new one (if getting extra lines means you'd grow out). And you can combine your incoming 800 lines with features you can get on business lines — like call forwarding, conferencing, etc. Have your 800 calls come into your office during the day. Have them call forwarded at night to your home. 800 Valuflex is aimed at smaller business.

8008 Intel's 8-bit 8008 microprocessor was introduced in April 1972. It contained 2300 transistors. Its typical used was in dumb terminals, general calculators and bottling machines.

80186 The 80286 was Intel's second generation 8086 chip. But between the 8086 and the 80286, there was a chip called the 80186, which was used in the famous Tandy 2000, a powerful — but not fully IBM-compatible — PC, that was used as the in-store PC in all Radio Shacks for several years, and achieved a bit of a cult following. Michael Marcus has two of them in my closet, if someone would like to buy them.

802 IEEE committee on Local Area Networks (LANs) standards. See 802 STANDARDS.

802 STANDARDS The 802 Standards are a set of standards for LAN communications developed through the IEEE's Project 802. The 802 Standards segment the data link layer into two sublayers:

1. A Medium Access Control (MAC) layer that includes specific methods for gaining access to the LAN (Local Area Network). These methods — such as Ethernet's random access method and Token Ring's token procedure — are in the 802.3, 802.5 and 802.6 standards.

2. A Logical Link Control (LLC) Layer, described in 802.2 standard, that provides for connection establishment, data transfer, and connection termination services. LLC specifies three types of communications links:

* An Unacknowledged connectionless Link, where the sending and receiving

devices do not set up a connection before transmitting. Instead, messages are sent on a "best try" basis and there is no provision for error detection, error recovery, and message sequencing. This type of link is best suited for applications where the higher layer protocols can provide the error correction and functions, or where the loss of broadcast messages is not critical.

• A Connection-mode Link, where a connection between message source and destination is established prior to transmission. This type of link works best in applications, such as file transfer, where large amounts of data are being transmitted at one time.

• An Acknowledged-connectionless Link that, as its name indicates, provides for acknowledgement of messages without burdening the receiving devices with maintaining a connection. For this reason, it is most often used for applications where a central processor communicates with a large number of devices with limited processing capabilities.

802.1 IEEE standard for overall architecture of LANs and internetworking.

802.1B IEEE standard for network management.

802.1D IEEE standard for inter-LAN bridges (specifically between 802.3, 802.4, and 802.5 networks). Works at the MAC level.

802.2 IEEE data link layer standard used with the IEEE 802.3, 802.4 and 802.5 standards.

802.3 IEEE standard for carrier sense multiple access with collision detection (CSMA/CD). A physical layer standard specifying a LAN with a CSMA/CD access method on a bus topology. Ethernet and Starlan both follow the 802.3 standard. Typically they transmit at 10 megabits per second (Mbps). The theoretical limit of Ethernet, measured in 64 byte packets, is 14,800 packets per second (PPS). By comparison, Token Ring is 30,000 and FDDI is 170,000.

802.3 1Base5 IEEE standard for baseband Ethernet at 1 Mbps over twisted pair wire to a maximum distance of 500 meters. Also called Starlan.

802.3 10Base2 IEEE standard for baseband Ethernet at 10 Mbps over coaxial cable to a maximum distance of 185 meters. Also called "Cheapernet" or "Thin Ethernet."

802.3 10Base5 IEEE standard for baseband Ethernet at 10 Mbps over fax coaxial cable to a maximum distance of 500 meters.

802.3 10Broad36 IEEE standard for broadband Ethernet at 10 Mbps over broadband cable to a maximum distance of 3600 meters.

802.3 10Base-T 10Base-T is an IEEE standard for operating Ethernet local area networks (LANs) on twisted-pair cabling using the home run method of wiring (exactly the same as a phone system uses) and a wiring hub that contains electronics performing similar functions to a central telephone switch. The full name for the standard is IEEE 802.3 10Base-T. The 10Base-T standard, issued in the fall of 1990, defined the requirements for sending information at 10 million bits per second on ordinary unshielded twisted-pair cabling. The 10Base-T standard defines various aspects of running Ethernet on twisted-pair cabling such as:

• Connector types (typically eight-pin RJ-45),

• Pin connections (1 and 2 for transmit, 3 and 6 for receive),

• Voltage levels (2.2 volts to 2.8 volts peak), and

• Noise immunity requirements to filter outside interference from telephone lines or other electronic equipment.

Ethernet is the most popular LAN in the world. Ethernet running on loop coaxial cable — typically called thin Ethernet or thinnet — is the most popular way of running Ethernet local area networks. Loop networks suffer from the major problem that one cut in the cable can destroy the complete network. 10Base-T is a much more reliable — though more expensive — way of connecting LANs, since it requires electronics at the center of the home run. As I write this, the most common form of 10Base-T electronics is a small box joining about 12 workstations together. To get more on the LAN, you simply daisy chain the boxes together. The boxes are unbelievably reliably. They're easy to install and they often come with LAN management software, which gives you statistics on who's using the network, for how long, what the performance is, and what potential problems might crop up, etc. The cable 10Base-T networks use to connect between their central electronics and their attached workstations is typically standard twisted pair phone wiring, which is a lot easier to install than coaxial cable. 10Base-T networks are now becoming most popular and are being installed at faster rate than old-style loop coaxial wired LANs.

802.4 IEEE physical layer standard specifying a LAN with a token-passing access method on a bus topology. It is typically used with Manufacturing Automation Protocol (MAP) LANs. MAP was developed by General Motors. Typical transmission speed is 10 megabits per second.

802.5 IEEE physical layer standard specifying a LAN with a token-passing access method on a ring topology using unshielded twisted pair. Used by IBM's Token Ring hardware. Typical transmission speed is 4 or 16 megabits per second.

802.6 IEEE standard for MANs (Metropolitan Area Networks). Formerly known as QPSX (Queued Packet and Synchronous Exchange), now known as DQDB (Distributed Queue DOUBLE Bus.

802.7 IEEE technical advisory group on broadband LANs.

802.8 IEEE technical advisory group for fiber-optic LANs.

802.9 IEEE technical advisory on ISLAN, which stands for Integrated Services LAN. ISLAN is Isoethernet with switched or packetized voice on an Ethernet LAN, which is 10 megabits per seconds of Ethernet (used for data) plus six megabits per second of ISDN B channels, which gives you 96 B ISDN channels plus a D channel. You can used the B channels for voice.

802.X The Institute of Electrical and Electronics Engineers (IEEE) committee that developed a set of standards describing the cabling, electrical topology, physical topology, and access scheme of network products; in other words, the

802.X standards define the physical and data-link layers of LAN architectures. Or, in simple language, the set of IEEE standards for the definition of LAN protocols. IEEE 802.3 is the work of an 802 subcommittee that describes the cabling and signaling for a system nearly identical to classic Ethernet. IEEE 802.5 comes from another subcommittee and similarly describes IBM's Token-Ring architecture.

80286 In February, 1982 Intel unveiled its second generation (thus the 2) 8086 microprocessor chip — the 16-bit 80286. The 80286 featured 134,000 transistors. The 80286 (computer on a chip) drives the IBM AT. It is a true 16-bit processor. This chip will run at 6 MHz to 16 MHz. At 10 MHz it runs 1.5 mips. The 80286 has a 24-bit address bus and can address 16 MB of memory directly (which is two (2) raised to the 24th power). In late 1991 the chip cost $8.

80386DX Introduced in October, 1985, the 80386 is the third generation of the 8086 family (hence the 3). The Intel microprocessor (computer on a chip) which drives the IBM Model 80 and many others. It contains 275,000 transistors and is a 32-bit processor. It is typically clocked at 16 MHz, but there are now versions of it that will run at 33 MHz. Its 32-bit processor means is it can process data in 32-bit chunks, rather than the 16-bit chunks of the 80286 family. The 80386 DX comes in 20 MHz (4 MIPS), 25 MHz (6 MIPS) and 33 MHz (8 MIPS). The principal architectural advantage over its predecessors is the 386 CPU's superior memory management ability, which improves performance by enabling the CPU to work with memory segments larger than 64K and to have access to more than one megabyte of memory (both limitations of the 286). The 386 can address up to four gigabytes (billion bytes) of physical memory and 64 terabytes of virtual memory at a time. It can address the four million byte of memory because it has a 32-bit address bus which can address 2 to the 32 bytes or over 4 billion bytes! Virtual memory is an area of hard disk that is treated by the processor as part of main memory. The Intel 386 DX has a 32-bit external data bus. This 80386's 32-bit bus requires a larger bus — e.g. IBM's Micro Channel or EISA, the Extended Industry Standard Architecture. EISA is the independent computer industry's alternate to IBM's Micro Channel data bus architecture which IBM uses in its high end PS/2 line of desktop computers. EISA, like Micro Channel, is a 32-bit channel. But, unlike IBM's Micro Channel, plug-in boards which work inside the XT and AT-series of IBM and IBM clone desktop computers will work inside EISA machines. They won't work in the Micro Channel machines. There are now several versions of the 80386. The most important one is the 80386DX which is the "genuine" 386 and features 25 times the performance of the original IBM PC. Another important 386 is the 80386SX, also called the 80386sx. Intel calls its 386SX microprocessor "the entry level member of the Intel 386 family." It is a genuine 80386 chip, except that its external data bus is only 16 bits (i.e. the size of the normal AT bus), not 32 bits. It is capable of sustained execution of 2.5 to 3.5 million instructions per second. A third 386 chip is the 80386SL introduced in October 1990 designed specially for laptop and notebook portable personal computers. The 386SL contains a 386 CPU that has been re-engineered for low-power operation. Surrounding the CPU are a memory controller and a complete set of input/output (I/O) controllers like those used in most PCs. By combining these two components with a few external devices,

OEMs (Original Equipment Manufacturers) can build a complete, portable 386 PC with the same functionality as a 386 desktop with just five chips — nine, including memory. As a result, systems based on the 80386SL will consume one-third less board space and all components should fit easily on a 3" x 5" motherboard. PCs based on the 386SL SuperSet (Intel's name for its chip set) will also feature 50% longer battery life. The 386 SL will also let notebook users use "auto resume" which lets you shut your laptop off in the middle of a program, turn it on later and find yourself at exactly the place you were when you shut off, i.e. no rebooting is necessary. The 386SL contains 85,000 transistors — more than three times as many as the 386SX.

For history's sake: In 1984 the typical motherboard of a PC required about 170 components plus memory chips. By 1987 the number of components had dropped to 70 excluding memory. With Intel's 386SL, a design engineer can now implement a complete PC AT compatible in 10 components plus memory. By 1995 that number had dropped to under 5.

80386SL Intel introduced the 80386SL chip in October 1990. Intel designed the chip specially for laptop and notebook portable personal computers. The 386SL contains a 386 microprocessor-compatible CPU that has been re-engineered for low-power operation. Surrounding the CPU are a memory controller and a complete set of input/output (I/O) controllers like those used in most PCs. By combining these two components with a few external devices, OEMs (Original Equipment Manufacturers) can build a complete, portable 386 PC with the same functionality as a 386 desktop with just five chips — nine, including memory. As a result, systems based on the 80386SL will consume one-third less board space and all components should fit easily on a 3" x 5" motherboard. PCs based on the 386SL SuperSet (Intel's name for its chip set) will also feature 50% longer battery life. The 386SL will also let notebook users use "auto resume" which lets you shut your laptop off in the middle of a program, turn it on later and find yourself at exactly the place you were when you shut off, i.e. no rebooting is necessary. The 80386SL contains 855,000 transistors. In September 1991, Intel introduced a 25 MHz version of the 80386SL, which will run at 5.3 mips (million instructions per second). The 386SL contains 85,000 transistors — more than three times as many as the 386SX.

80386SX Intel calls its 80386SX microprocessor "the entry level member of the Intel 386 family." It is a genuine 80386 chip, except that its external data bus is only 16 bits (i.e. the size of the normal AT bus), not 32 bits. It is capable of sustained execution of 2.5 to 3.5 million instructions per second. The 80386SX contains 275,000 transistors. See also 80386DX.

80387 The Intel 80387 SX is a high performance floating point coprocessor designed to be used in 80385 SX microprocessor-based computers. It's basically a special purpose microprocessor designed to help the main "computer on a chip," the 80387 with mathematical calculations — like recalculating spreadsheets. You can install this chip in virtually all 80386SX based computers. But having the chip is only useful if you run software that can take advantage of it. Not all can.

80486DX Introduced on June 5, 1991, The Intel 80486DX microprocessor (computer on a chip) sports 1,185,000 transistors. It has a clock speed of 20 MHz to 50 MHz. It sports 50 times the performance of the original IBM PC. The Intel 486DX running at 50 MHz will process 41 million instructions per second (MIPS). As of early November, 1991, an 80486DX running at 50 MHz costs $644 in lots of a thousand. See also 486.

80486SX The Intel 80486 microprocessor without a math coprocessor. The 80486SX is a cheaper version of the 80486 chip.

80586 An Intel microprocessor containing more than three million transistors, introduced in April, 1993 and called the Pentium. It is 80% faster than the fastest 486. It is capable of executing 112 million instructions per second.

80686 An upcoming Intel microprocessor containing more than seven million transistors. It will be capable of executing 175 million instructions per second.

80786 An upcoming Intel microprocessor containing more than 20 million transistors. It will be capable of executing 250 million instructions per second.

8080 Intel brought out the 8-bit 8080 microprocessor in April, 1974. It contained 5,000 transistors and was 10-times more powerful than the 8008. The 8080 was, probably the "first" microprocessor. When it was invented, memory for computers was very expensive. The 8080 could directly address 64 thousand bytes of information. This limit of 64K was the direct result of the fact that the CPU chip had only 16 address lines. The address lines are a set of wires coming out of the CPU which allow the CPU to indicate what item of memory it wants to read or write. In most computers, the size of the "pieces" are bytes, or 8-bit characters. These 16 wires are called the Address Bus. The voltages on the 16 address lines are interpreted as a binary number (with the first pin representing the 1's place, the second pin representing the 2's place, the third pin representing the 4's place, etc. The resultant number is the Address addressable by the CPU (Central Processing Unit). The number of distinct patterns of 16 things, each of which can have two values, is 2 raised to the 16th power, or 65,536. This number is 64 times the quantity "1K" which is 1,024. See also 8086 which was the Intel chip which following the 8080.

8086 On June 8, 1978, Intel introduced the 8086, a 16-bit microprocessor with 29,000 transistors and ten times the performance of the 8080. The 8086, or more precisely its 16-bit counterpart, the 8088, became the brain of IBM's first personal computer. The 8086 chip is an upgraded version of the basic 8080 architecture. It is basically a doubling of a small portion of the internal workings of the 8086's address circuitry. Intel basically duplicated the address register (the transistors that hold the pattern of bits to place on the address bus), slid it left four bits, and added some simple circuitry to add it arithmetically to the "old" address register. This is called the Intel Segment Register. By making this simple kludge to the 8080, Intel created the 8086 and 8088 microprocessors which now effectively had twenty address lines and could therefore address two to the 20th locations, or a little over one million bytes. See also 8088 and 80286.

8088 Introduced in June 1979 by Intel, this is the 16-bit chip which drove the original IBM PC and the subsequent IBM XT. It is identical to the 8080 except that external bus width is 8-bit (the 8080 is 16). The 8088 has a clock speed of

4.77 MHz at 0.33 mips and 8 MHz at 0.75 mips. It had 29,000 transistors. It cost between $3 and $4 in late 1991. See also V20, which is a Japanese NEC version of the 8088. It's about 10% to 20% faster than the 8088. You can pull an 8088 out of your old PC (e.g. the AT&T 6300) and replace it with this chip. You'll get about a 20% (and noticeable) increase in speed. We have. It works fine. Some key systems use this chip.

8088-2 A speeded-up version of the 8088 microprocessor. It has a clock speed of 8 mhz. See also the V20-2 which is the Japanese version of the 8088-2. It's 10% to 20% faster than the 8088-2.

82596 The 82596 is an intelligent, 16-/32-bit local area network coprocessor from Intel. The 82596 implements the CSMA/CD access method and can be configured to support all existing 802.3 standards. Coupled with the 82503 Dual Serial Transceiver, the 82596 provides the optimal Ethernet connection to Intel1386 and Intel486 client PCs and servers. The board space required for an 82596/82503 motherboard implementation is less than six square inches. provides full Ethernet bandwidth performance while allowing the CPU to work independently. An on-board four-channel DMA controller along with an intelligent micro machine automatically manages memory structures and provide command chaining and autonomous block transfers while two large independent FIFOs accommodate long bus latencies and provide programmable thresholds.

888 SERVICE North America is running out of 800 numbers. So it is adopting a new prefix — 888. At the time of writing, it looked like the first 888 number would come in around April, 1996. That 888 prefix will have all the characteristics of today's 800 Service. See 800 SERVICE.

9-TRACK A standard for 1/2" magnetic tape designed for data storage. Its nine tracks hold a byte (eight bits) plus one parity bit in a row across the tape width-wise.

900 SERVICE A generic and common (and not trademarked) term for AT&T's, MCI's, Sprint's and other long distance companies' 900 services. All these services have "900" as their "area code." Dialing a 900-number is free to the company or person receiving the call, but costs money to the person making the call. Here's the story: 900 service was introduced as the industry's "information service" area code. You'd dial 1-900-WEATHER, for example, and punch in some touchtones in response to prompts and you could hear the weather in Sydney, Australia or Paris, France, wherever you might be planning your next vacation. For this service, you'd be charged perhaps 75 to 95 cents a minute. And you'd get the bill as part of your normal monthly phone bill. That was the original idea. Then some people got the idea that 900 would make a wonderful porn number and they started advertising "Call 900-666-3333 and speak with Diana. She really wants you." And they started charging $5 a minute. When huge 900-call bills started appearing on people's bills, there was an outcry from many subscribers who wouldn't pay the bills. Some children called on their parents' phones. Employees made calls from work and the company's accountants went nuts. So the industry retreated from 900 porn. Then someone thought — "Why not sell things through an 900 number?" We could sell a set of ginzu knives for just calling this 900 number. No messing with credit cards or checks. The bill goes straight on your phone bill. At about the same time someone thought that

900 numbers would be great for running sweepstakes. "Call up, register your name for a free trip with a racing car team to the Australian Indianapolis 500. Three lucky people will be chosen. The call will cost you only $2.75." So 900 services became a new type of gambling.

The long distance companies providing 900 services reacted predictably to some of the newer services. They clamped down on who they would sign up, which service and/or product you could, or could not sell. And, rather than charging "a piece of the action" as they did in the beginning, the long distance companies began to charge for them as if they were normal long distance calls: charge a set-up fee, a fee for carrying the call, a fee for collecting the money and a fee for the possibility of bad debts. There are variations on these themes.

The 900-service business is rife with stories of people who are alleged to have made millions overnight with innovative 900 numbers. Clearly enormous monies have been made — especially in the beginning when there was novelty to 900 calls. The prognosis is that the 900 number business will grow, that it will mature and that the North American public will wake up to its various scams and discover real value in many of its services. For example, one of the author's "genuine value" and favorite 900 services is fax-back. Dial a 900 number, punch in some touchtone digits, hang up and within seconds your fax machine begins to churn out useful information.

In the summer of 1991, AT&T issued guidelines for its EXPRESS900 service. Those guidelines included:

• The predominant purpose of the calls does not include Entertainment, Children's Programming, Credit/Loan Information, Fulfillment, Political Fundraising, Games of Chance, Postcard Sweepstakes, Job Lines and Personal Lines;

• Every program must have a Preamble and Caller Grace Period, with notification to callers of the opportunity to hang up before charging begins.

• Sponsors may not route calls to any telecommunications equipment or arrangements which allow charging to begin before the caller realizes any value on the call, e.g., Automatic Call Distribution (ACD) with call queuing, or Caller Hold.

9001 ISO 9001 is a rigorous international quality standard covering a company's design, development, production, installation and service procedures. Compliance with the standard is of increasing significance for vendors trading in international markets, in particular in Europe where ISO 9001 registration is widely recognized as an indication of the integrity of a supplier's quality processes. ISO is the International Standards Organization in Paris.

905-928 MHz A relatively new frequency range for use by, amongst other things, cordless phones. Most present cordless phones operate within the band 46-49 MHz. The 900 contains 50 channels for cordless telephone transmission. The 46-49 MHz band contains only 10.

911 SERVICE 911 is an emergency reporting system whereby a caller call dial a common number — 911 — for all emergency services. The caller will be answered at a common answering location which will figure the nature of the emergency and dispatch the proper response teams. The first 911 service came on line in 1968. Here are the reasons why 911 benefits a community: Only one number for all emergency services. It's an easy number to remember. It's an easy number to dial. It's great for travelers and new residents. Calls are received by trained personnel. See also E-911, which stands for Enhanced 911 service and typically includes ANI (Automatic Number Identification) and ALI (Automatic Location Information). 911 service is sometimes called B-911 which stands for basic 911 service. See also B-911 and E-911.

958 Dial 958 in New York City and a computer run by Nynex New York will read you the phone number you're calling from this. This is very useful. Imagine having a jack on your wall. You've lost track of which phone line it's connected to. Dial 958 and bingo you know. Other phone companies have similar services but they have different numbers.

9751 CBX A popular PBX from Rolm that ranges in size from 80 to 40,000 ports.

999 Great Britain's equivalent of the United States emergency number 911.

**** Filenames or other resource names that begin with the string \\ mean that they exist on a remote computer. They are called UNC (as in Universal Naming Convention) Names.

A 1. Abbreviation for AMP or AMPERE, a unit of electric current. See AMPERE. 2. The local wireline cellular carrier. In one of its less intelligent decisions, the FCC decided to issue two cellular franchises in each city of the United States. They gave one to the local phone company and one to a competitor. This duopoly has naturally meant little real competition. And one day, the FCC will issue other licenses and the price of cellular phone calls will drop dramatically. Meantime, the "A" carrier on your cellular phone is the local wireline carrier, i.e. the local phone company (or that was the company who had the license originally). And "B" is the other one.

A & A1 Control leads that come from 1A2 key telephone sets to operate features like flashing of lights to indicate on hold, line ringing, etc.

A & B BITS Bits used in digital environments to convey signaling information. A bit value of one generally corresponds to loop current flowing in an analog environment. A bit zero corresponds to no loop current, i.e. to no connection. Other signals are made by changing bit values; for example a flash-hook is set by briefly setting the A bit to zero.

A & B LEADS Additional leads used typically with a channel bank two-wire E&M interface to certain types of PBXs (also used to return talk battery to the PBX).

A & B SIGNALING Procedure used in most T-1 transmission links where one bit, robbed from each of the 24 subchannels in every sixth frame, is used for carrying dialing and controlling information. A type of in-band signaling used in T-1 transmission. A and B signaling reduces the available user bandwidth from 1.544 Mbps to 1.536 Mbps.

A BATTERY Another term for TALK BATTERY.

A LAW The PCM coding and companding standard used in Europe. See A LAW ENCODING.

A LAW ENCODING The method of encoding sampled audio waveforms used in the 2048K bit(s) 30 channel PCM primary system, widely used outside North America.

A LINK Access Link. A CCS/SS7 signaling link used to connect a Signaling End Point (SEP) and its home pair of STPs (Signal Transfer Points).

A PORT Refers to the port in an FDDI topology which connects the incoming primary ring and the outgoing secondary ring of the FDDI dual ring. This port is part of the dual attachment station or a dual attachment concentrator.

A-B ROLLS A technique by which audio/video information is played back from two videotape machines rolled sequentially, often for the purpose of dubbing the sequential inforamtion onto a third tape, usually a composite master.

A-B TEST Direct comparison of the sound/picture quality of two pieces of audio/TV equipment by playing one, then the other.

A/B SWITCH 1. A switch that allows manual or remote switching between one input and two outputs. See A/B SWITCH BOX. 2. A feature found on all new cellular telephones permitting the user to select either the "A" (non-wireline) carrier or the "B" (wireline) carrier when roaming away from home.

A/B SWITCH BOX A device used to switch one input between two devices, such as printers, modems, plotters, mice, phone lines, etc. An example of how you use such a box: You plug one phone line into the "C" (for Common) jack. You plug a fax machine into the "A" jack. You plug a modem into the "B" jack. By turning the switch, you can use one phone line for either a modem or a fax. A/B switch boxes comes in many many flavors, including also serial and parallel port versions. There are also A/B/C switches that switch among three devices, e.g. a fax, a modem and a phone. There is also a Crossover Switch that connect two inputs and two outputs. In one position the switch might connect input A with output D and input B with output C. In the other position, it might connect input A with output C and input B with output D.

A/D Analog to Digital conversion.

A/D CONVERTER Analog to Digital converter, or digitizer. It is a device which converts analog signals (such as sound or voice from microphone), to digital data so that the signal can be processed by digital circuit such as a digital signal processor.

A/UX An alternate operating system for the Macintosh based on UNIX. A/UX has its own 32-bit addressing mode.

A20 LINE A control line on the Intel 80386 microprocessor that allows MS-DOS and an extended memory manager to create the High Memory Area, or HMA. Only one program can claim control over the A20 at a time.

AA Automated Attendant. A device which answers callers with a digital recording, and allows callers to route themselves to an extension.

AABS A new software feature being introduced in the telephone industry. It allows collect and third-number billed calls to be placed by the caller using voice synthesis of an operator's voice plus a digital recording of the caller's voice without using a human operator. It is automated in much the same way as calling card services have been automated.

AAC-1 ATM Access Concentrator for T-1/E-1 networks from ADC Kentrox uses cell multiplexing to concentrate multiple protocols onto a single T-1 or E-1 access facility to the ATM or SMDS network, including SMDS, DXI, ATM DXI, SRI and Frame Relay.

AAC-3 ATM Access Concentrator for T-3/E-3 networks from ADC Kentrox uses cell multiplexing to concentrate multiple protocols onto a T-3 or E-3 access facility to the ATM or SMDS network (including SMDS, DXI, ATM DXI, SRI and Frame Relay).

AAL ATM Adaptation Layer. ATM Adaptation Layer that sits above ATM and converts non-ATM bit streams — end user data — into ATM cells. The AAL is the protocol used on top of ATM to support higher-layer service requirements. For data communications services,the AAL defines a segmentation/reassembly protocol for mapping large data packets into the 48-octet payload field of an ATM cell.

AAP Administrative and Accounting Package. The name of a feature on an InteCom PBX which provides call accounting reports relating to usage and cost.

AAR Automatic Alternate Routing.

AARP AppleTalk Address Resolution Protocol.

ABAM A designation for 22 gauge, 110 ohm, plastic insulated, twisted pair Western Electric cable normally used in central offices.

ABANDONED CALL The nontechnical explanation is: A call that is answered, but disconnected before any conversation happens. The technical explanation is: A call which has been offered into a communications network or telephone system, but which is terminated by the person originating the call before it is answered by the person being called. Follow this sequence for an explanation: You call an airline. You hear ringing. Their phone rings. A machine, called an automatic call distributor, answers the call, plays you some dumb message, "Please don't hang up. A real human will answer eventually." You, the caller, are put on Eternity Hold. You get bored waiting and hang up before a live operator answers. You have just abandoned your phone call. Thus the term, Abandoned Call. Information about abandoned calls is useful for planning how many people (also called operators, agents or telephone attendants) an airline should employ on what days and during what times of the day. Thus you can organize to get the right percentage of incoming calls answered within the "right" amount of time and give your callers (i.e. your customers) the service they deserve (or the service you think they deserve, or, the service they think they deserve).

ABANDONED CALL COST The amount of revenue lost because of abandoned calls. This is calculated based on the number of calls, your estimate of the percentage abandoning, and your estimate of the revenue per call. It's an impossible number to calculate since many callers do, in fact, call back and place their orders on another later call.

ABBREVIATED ADDRESS CALLING A calling method that allows the user to employ an address having fewer characters. The destination's assigned device addresses these characters when initiating a connection. May also be called abbreviated dialing when specifically used in connection with telephone systems.

ABBREVIATED DIALING A feature of phone systems which allows users to place calls by dialing typically one or two digits. The system translates the abbreviated number into the destination number. See also SPEED DIALING and PREDICTIVE DIALING.

ABC Automatic Bill Calling — a method of billing for payphone calls. Changed in 1982 to Calling Card service.

ABCD SIGNALING BITS These are bits robbed from bytes in each DS-0 or T-1 channel in particular subframes and used to carry in band all status information such as E&M signaling states.

ABDN Attendant Blocking of Directory Number.

ABEND ABnormal END. When Novell's NetWare local area operating system detects a serious problem, such as a hardware or software failure, the system issues an abend (abnormal end) message. The abend stops the file server. And you're dead in the water. Abend is also called ABortive END. Also called system crash. Almost always bad news. Usually caused by input or data presented to a computer which is beyond its ability to cope. If an abend happens in a single-task program (like MS-DOS), the machine will cease to take input ("lock up") and must be restarted ("re-booted"). Multitasking operating systems (like UNIX) allow other programs to continue running while only stopping the one causing trouble.

ABLATION Optical memory data writing techniques in which a laser burns holes (or pits) into thin metal film.

ABM 1. Asynchronous Balanced Mode. A service of the data link level (Logical Link Control) in IBM's token-passing ring. ABM operates at the Systems Network Architecture data link control level and allows devices to send data link commands at any time. 2. Anyone But Microsoft

ABN ABNormal alarm status.

ABORT To stop doing something. Often to get out of a software program. Also, to discontinue sending or receiving a message.

ABORT SEQUENCE A series of 12 to 18 1-bits appearing at the end of an AppleTalk LLAP frame. The sequence delineates the end of the frame.

ABOVE 890 DECISION The 1959 FCC decision which allowed companies to build their own private microwave communications systems. The decision resulted from AT&T Long Lines' reluctance to provide companies with long distance service to remote places, such as oil wells, gas pipelines, power stations and paper plants. The decision got its name because the FCC allowed privately-owned microwave systems using radio frequencies "above 890" megahertz — which are naturally called "microwave." See also MICROWAVE and ENTELEC.

ABOVE THE LINE Expenses incurred by telephone company that are charged to the ratepayer by being allowed in the company's rate-base.

ABR 1. Available Bit Rate. Traffic defined by the ATM Forum. 2. AutoBaud Rate detect. A process by which a receiving data device determines the speed, code level, and stop bits of incoming data by examining the first character — usually a preselected sign-on character (often a carriage return). ABR allows the receiving device to accept data from a variety of transmitting devices operating at different speeds without needing to establish data rates in advance.

ABRASION RESISTANCE Ability of material or cable to resist surface wear.

ABRUPT CLOSE Close of a connection on a network without any attempt to prevent any loss of data.

ABS Alternate Billing Services. These are IN (Intelligent Network) services that allow subscribers to charge a call to a number or telephone other than the one they are using. For example, by using a charge card, credit card or personal identification number.

ABSENT-SUBSCRIBER SERVICE A service offered by local telephone companies to subscribers who will be away. A live operator or a machine intercepts the calls and delivers a message. When you come back, you get your old number. But in the meantime, while you're away, you pay less money per month than you would for normal phone service.

ABSOLUTE DELAY The time interval or phase difference between transmission and reception of a signal.

ABSOLUTE GAIN 1. The ratio, usually expressed in decibels, between the signal level at the output of a device and its input under specified operating conditions; e.g., no-load gain, full-load gain, small signal gain. 2. Of an antenna, for a given direction: the ratio, usually expressed in decibels, of the power that would be required at the input of an ideal isotropic radiator to the power actually supplied to the given antenna so that the radiation intensity in the far-field region in the given direction would be the same. If no direction is quoted, that corresponding to maximum radiation is assumed.

ABSOLUTE ZERO A temperature about 460 degrees below zero in Fahrenheit.

ABSORPTION Attenuation caused by dissipation of energy. See ABSORPTION LOSS.

ABSORPTION LOSS The attenuation of an optical signal within a fiber optic transmission system and specified in terms of dB/km.

ABT Advanced Broadcast Television.

AC Alternating Current. Typically refers to the 120 volt electricity delivered by your local power utility to the three-pin power outlet in your wall. Called "alternating current" because the polarity of the current alternates between plus and minus, 60 times a second. The other form of electricity is DC, or direct current, in which the polarity of the current stays constant. Direct current, for example, is what comes from batteries. Outside North America, electricity typically alternates at 50 times a second — which is neither better nor worse, just different. In North America, standard 120 volt AC may be also be referred to as 110 volts, 115 volts, 117 volts or 125 volts. Con Edison, the electricity supplier to New York City, told me that they are only obliged to deliver voltage to 120 volts plus or minus 10%. This means your outlet may deliver anywhere from 118 volts to 132 volts before your power company will get concerned. But you probably should. Telephone and computer are sensitive to voltage fluctuations — some more to high voltages; some more to low voltages. My suggestion: If your stuff is valuable, protect it with a voltage regulator. Or better, power it with stable DC current, which you've converted from fluctuating AC power

Your AC electrical circuit consists of two supply conductors — hot and neutral. There is also a "load." That is the term for the device you're running. The hot, energized or live conductor is ungrounded and delivers energy to the load. The hot conductor is connected to the fuse or circuit breaker at the main service entrance. The neutral or common conductor is grounded and completes the circuit from the load back to the utility transformer. The load is any electric or electronic appliance or gadget plugged into the AC electrical outlet. It completes the circuit from the transformer through the hot conductor, to the load, through the neutral conductor and back to the utility transformer. Standard 120 volt circuits also include an equipment ground conductor. This equipment grounding conductor provides an intended path for fault current and is never intended to be a part of the load circuit. The equipment ground serves three very important purposes.

1. It maintains metal appliance cases at zero volts, thus protecting people who touch the cases from receiving an electrical shock. 2. It provides an intentional

fault path of low impedance path for current flow when the hot conductor contacts equipment cases (ground fault). This current causes the fuse or circuit breaker to open the circuit to protect people from electric shock. 3. Any electronic equipment (not electrical) uses the equipment ground as a zero volt reference for logic circuits to provide proper equipment performance.

See AC POWER, GROUNDING, BATTERY and SURGE ARRESTOR.

ACO Alarm Cut Off

ACONET A research network in Austria.

AC POWER Phone systems typically run on AC, Alternating Current. Except for small systems, phone systems typically need their own dedicated AC power line. This line should be "cleaned" with a power conditioner, voltage regulator. It also should be protected with a surge arrestor. If possible, the phone system should also be backed by a battery-based power pack, called UPS for Uninterruptible Power Supply. The most reliable battery backup is lead acid, the same technology as used in your car. Phone systems consume more power as they process more phone calls. For example, a PBX brochure says that at minimum capacity, it needs less power than eight 100-watt light bulbs. But that at its maximum duplex capacity, it needs the same power as 26 100-watt light bulbs — or 2600 watts. See AC, GROUND and GROUNDING.

AC TO DC CONVERTER An electronic device which converts alternating current (AC) to direct current (DC). Most phone systems, computers and consumer electronic devices (from answering machines to TVs) run on DC. Most phone systems have an AC to DC converter in them. Hint: it's probably buried in the power supply.

AC-DC RINGING A type of telephone signaling that uses both AC and DC components — alternating current to operate a ringer and direct current to aid the relay action that stops the ringing when the called telephone is answered.

ACA Automatic Circuit Assurance.

ACADEMMET A network within Russia which connects universities.

ACADEMIC COMPUTING RESEARCH FACILITY NETWORK ACRFNET. A network connecting various research units such as colleges and research and development laboratories in the U.S.

ACAT Additional Cooperative Acceptance Testing. A method of testing switched access service that provides a telephone company technician at the central office and a carrier's technician at its location, with suitable test equipment to perform the required tests. ACAT may, for example, consist of the following tests:

Impulse Noise Phase Jitter Signal-to-C-Notched Noise Ratio Intermodulation (Nonlinear) Distortion Frequency Shift (Offset) Envelope Delay Distortion Dial Pulse Percent Break

ACB 1. A Northern Telecom term for Architecture Control Board. 2. Annoyance Call Bureau.

ACC Automatic Callback Calling.

ACCELERATED AGING A test performed on material or cable meant to duplicate long term environmental conditions in a short period of time.

ACCELERATED DEPRECIATION A method which allows greater depreciation charges in the early years of an asset's life and progressively smaller ones later on. The total amount of depreciation charged is still equal to 100% of the asset's value. By taking the charges early on in the asset's life, you get the time value of money, i.e. depreciation charged today (and tax saved today) is worth more than the same amount of depreciation charged (or tax saved) tomorrow.

ACCELERATOR 1. A chemical additive which hastens a chemical reaction under specific conditions. A term used in the telecommunications cable industry. 2. In a Windows program, an accelerator is a keystroke that dispatches a message to a program, invoking one of its functions. For example, Alt-F4 tells the current Windows application of Windows itself to quit.

ACCELERATOR BOARD A board added onto a personal computer's main board and designed to increase the PC's performance in writing to screen or disk, etc. See also ACCELERATOR CARD.

ACCELERATOR CARD An Apple term. An accelerator card is an add-on product that upgrades the CPU of a Macintosh to a higher speed or more powerful generation of processor. An accelerator card is usually a "daughter board" that clips onto the original CPU or is inserted into the socket that held the original CPU. You need an accelerator card to use virtual memory or enhanced 24-bit addressing on LC, Mac Plus, SE and Classic. See ACCELERATOR BOARD.

ACCEPTABLE USE POLICY AUP. Many transit networks have policies which restrict the use to which the network may be put. A well known example is NSFNET's (National Science Foundation Network) AUP which does not allow commercial use. Enforcement of AUP which does not allow commercial use. Enforcement of AUPs varies with the network.

ACCEPTANCE Acceptance refers to the amount of time within which a buyer has to decide whether an item is acceptable. Different from a warranty, it applies more to the equipment's appearance and to whether or not it is what the buyer ordered. Acceptance periods usually range from two to four weeks, but are determined on a case-by-case basis. It's commonly used in the secondary telecom equipment marketplace. See ACCEPTANCE TEST.

ACCEPTANCE ANGLE The angle over which the core of an optical fiber accepts incoming light. It's usually measured from the fiber axis.

ACCEPTANCE TEST The final test of a new telephone system. If the system passes the test — i.e. it meets all specifications laid down in the sales contract — and is working well, then, and only then, will the customer finish paying for it. See also ACCEPTANCE.

ACCESS As a verb, to dial into a feature, a circuit or a piece of equipment. As a noun, the point at which you enter a circuit or other communications facility. In data processing, access means to retrieve information from, or store data in memory or mass storage.

ACCESS BUS Access Bus is correctly spelled Access.bus. It is a 100KBps bus currently being implemented as part of the Video Electronics Standards Association's Display Data Channel for controlling PC monitors. Access Bus has four pins per connector. See also USB and FIREWIRE.

ACCESS CHARGE After the FCC deregulated the long distance phone business, it declared that all users having access to United States public switched long distance networks would pay an Access Charge. The charge will differ for residential and business users and may also differ between Centrex and PBX users. It varies from $1 to $6 per month. The charge is theoretically, to make up for the "subsidies" once paid by AT&T Long Lines (now called AT&T) to the local operating telephone companies — Bell and independent. A more formal definition is — A surcharge levied per the Code of Federal Regulations. Title 47, part 69, on each line or circuit that has the ability to access or be accessed by a public exchange network. The fee is paid by landline and cellular subscribers, as is a federal telephone excise tax.

ACCESS CODE A series of digits or characters which must be dialed, typed or entered in some way to get use of something. That "something" might be the programming of a telephone system, a long distance company, an electronic mail service, a private corporate network, a mainframe computer, a local area network. Once the user dials the main number for the service he must then enter his assigned Access Code to get permission use the system. An Access Code becomes an Account Code when it is used for identifying the caller and doing the billing. Access Code may also mean the digit, or digits, a user must dial to be connected to an outgoing trunk. For example, the user picks up his phone and dials "9" for a local line, dials "8" for long distance, dials "76" for the tie line to Chicago, etc. In programming a phone system such as Northern Telecom's Norstar, there are Access Codes to begin Startup, Configuration programming, and Administration programming.

ACCESS CONTROL A technique used to define or restrict the rights of individuals or application programs to obtain data from, or place data into, a storage device.

ACCESS CONTROL LIST ACL. Most network security systems operate by allowing selective use of services. An Access Control List is the usual means by which access to, and denial of, services is controlled. It is simply a list of the services available, each with a list of the computers permitted to use the service.

ACCESS CONTROL METHOD Sets of rules distinguishing different local area network technologies. It regulates each workstation's physical access to the transmission medium (normally cable), directs traffic around the network and determines the order in which nodes gain access so that each user gets service. Examples are token passing, used by Token Ring, ARCent, FDDI and Ethernet's CSMA/CD.

ACCESS CONTROL SYSTEM A system designed to provide secure access to services, resources, or data; for computers, telephone switches or LANs.

ACCESS CONTROLS An electronic messaging term. Controls that enable a system to restrict access to a directory entry or mailbox either inclusively or exclusively.

ACCESS COORDINATION An MCI definition. The process of ordering, installing, and maintaining the local access channel for MCI customers.

ACCESS COUPLER A device placed between two fiber optic ends to allow signals to be withdrawn from or entered into one of the fibers.

ACCESS CUSTOMER NAME ABBREVIATION ACNA. A three-character abbreviation assigned to each IntereXchange Carrier (IXC) and listed in the Local Exchange Routing Guide (LERG).

ACCESS EVENT Information with a logical content that the functional user and the Network Access FE (Functional Entity) exchange. Definition from Bellcore.

ACCESS GROUP All terminals or phones have identical rights to make use of the computer, the network or the data PBX.

ACCESS LEVEL Used interchangeably with ACCESS CODE. "Level" in dialing tends to mean a number.

ACCESS LINE A telephone line reaching from the telephone company central office to a point usually on your premises. Beyond this point the wire is considered inside wiring.

ACCESS LINK The local access connection between a customer's premises and a carrier's POP (Point Of Presence). The POP is the carrier's switching central office. That carrier might be a local or long disance carrier.

ACCESS METHOD The technique or the program code in a computer operating system that provides input/output services. By concentrating the control instruction sequences in a common sub-routine, the programmer's task of producing a program is simplified. The access method typically carries with it an implied data and/or file structure with logically similar devices sharing access methods. The term was coined, along with data set, by IBM in the 1964 introduction of the System/360 family. It provides a logical, rather than physical, set of references. Early communications access methods were primitive; recently they have gained enough sophistication to be very useful to programmers. Communications access methods have always required large amounts of main memory. In a medium size system supporting a few dozen terminals of dissimilar types, 80K to 100K bytes of storage is not an unusual requirement. The IEEE's 802 standards 802.3 through 802.9 specify access methods for LANs and MANs. See ACCESS METHODS.

ACCESS METHODS Techniques and rules for figuring which of several communications devices — e.g. computers — will be the next to use a shared transmission medium. This term relates especially to Local Area Networks (LANs). Access method is one of the main methods used to distinguish between LAN hardware. How a LAN governs users' physical (electrical) access to the cable significantly affects its features and performance. Examples of access methods are token passing (Arcnet and Token Ring) and Carrier Sense Multiple Access with Collision Detection (CSMA/CD) (Ethernet). See ACCESS METHOD.

ACCESS PROTECTION Refers to the process of protecting a local loop from network outages and failures.

Access protection can take many forms, such as purchasing two geographically diverse local facilities, adding protection switches to the ends of geographically diverse local loops, or buying service from a local access provider which offers a survivable ring-based architecture to automatically route around network failures.

ACCESS SERVICE REQUEST ASR. The ASR is used by the Carrier to request the ICSC to provide Special Access or Switched Access as specified in the various Access Services Tariffs.

ACCESS SIGNALING A term which Northern Telecom's Norstar telephones use to indicate their ability to access a remote system (such as a Centrex or a

PBX), or dial a number on an alternate carrier by means of Access Signaling (also referred to as "End-to-End" Signaling).

ACCESS SWITCH Feeder node to Enterprise Network Switches that perform multiprotocol bridge/routing and support a wide range of serial-link (e.g., SDLC BSC, asynchronous) attached devices.

ACCESS TANDEM A Local Exchange Carrier switching system that provides a concentration and distribution function for originating or terminating traffic between end offices and a Carrier's location. In short, a type of local phone company central office specifically designed to provide equal access for all long distance carriers in that area. The access tandem provides the interexchange carrier with access to more than one end office within the LATA. More than one access tandem may be needed to provide access to all end offices within LATA.

ACCESS TIME There are many definitions of access time: 1. In a telecommunications system, the elapsed time between the start of an access attempt and successful access. Note: Access time values are measured only on access attempts that result in successful access. 2. In a computer, the time interval between the instant at which an instruction control unit initiates a call for data and the instant at which delivery of the data is completed. 3. The time interval between the instant at which storage of data is requested and the instant at which storage is started. 4. In magnetic disk devices, the time for the access arm to reach the desired track and for the rotation of the disk to bring the required sector under the read-write mechanism. 5. The amount of time that lapses between a request for information from memory and the delivery of the information; usually stated in nanoseconds (ns). When accessing data from a disk, access time includes only the time the disk heads take to settle down reaching the correct track (seek time); the time the heads take to settle down after reaching the correct track (seek time); and the time required for the correct sector to move under the head (latency). Disk access times range between 9ms (fast) and 100 ms (slow).

ACCESS TOOLKIT Northern Telecom makes a telephone system for up to 100 users called Norstar. The phone system is "open," meaning you can program it. To be able to program it, you need the Norstar Access Toolkit, which you may or may not have to pay for. The Norstar Access Toolkit is a basically set of C Language routines which allows programmers to build applications on an industry standard MS-DOS Personal Computer which is joined to the Norstar with a Norstar interface card. The Toolkit provides access to the D channel messages broadcast to each device on the Norstar. The PC interfaces with the D channel via a PC Interface Card which is inserted into a standard PC-AT slot (the standard ISA bus).

Through the use of the interface card and a set of TSR (Terminate and Stay Resident) drivers, PC applications can insert messages in the D channel and read messages from it which can be received by any other device on the system. Applications on the PC can also be accessed by other devices on the system. In other words, a telephone set can use a feature code which addresses an application on the PC and have access to special information on the PC. Conversely, the application on the PC can monitor a telephone on the system and control how it functions under certain sets of predefined situations.

The basic relationship established between the Norstar telephone sets and the

PC is one of server and terminals. Each telephone (terminal) has access to information on the PC (server) and vice versa. No longer are users limited to the set of features and functions which have been defined by Northern Telecom, they can have a phone system which meets their needs. This means you can program a Norstar to act like an automatic call distributor or a predictive dialer or a contact management phone system, or whatever your heart desires. So long as you can program it, or buy the program from someone else who's already done it. As I wrote this in the winter of 1992, shrink-wrapped software packages for Norstar were beginning to appear, as they have appeared for over 10-years for PCs.

ACCESS UNIT 1. AU. An electronic messaging term, used for implementing value-added services such as fax, Telex, and Physical Delivery via X.400. 2. In the token ring LAN community, an access unit is a wiring concentrator.

ACCOLC Access Overload Class. A term used in the cellular phone business to allow the cellular system some way of choosing which calls to complete based on some sort of priority. Originally, when the Federal government began designing cellular systems, the government intended to give certain emergency vehicles (such as police, ambulances, and fire departments) codes in their cellular phones that would allow them priority over other subscribers to communicate during emergencies. There is no standard in use within the United States at this time.

ACCOUNT CODE (VOLUNTARY OR ENFORCED) A code assigned to a customer, a project, a department, a division — whatever. Typically, a person dialing a long distance phone call must enter that code so the computer can bill the cost of that call at the end of the month or designated time period. Many service companies, such as law offices, engineering firms, advertising agencies, etc. use account codes to bill their clients. Some account codes are very complicated. They include the client's number and the number of the particular project. The Account Code then includes Client and Matter number. These long codes can tax many call accounting systems, even some very sophisticated ones.

ACCOUNT-A-CALL Pioneers in providing call accounting services since 1972. Account-A-Call works with telecommunications management to assist in cost allocation and analysis of telephone expenses by offering a series of reports and consulting services. One of the country's biggest service bureaus. Based in Pasadena, CA.

ACCOUNTANT Someone who figures your numbers, then numbers your figures and then sends you a bill. See also ECONOMIST.

ACCOUNTING RATE A price used between long distance companies to "balance up" what they owe each other. For example, if AT&T sends France Telecom one million minutes of calls, but France sends only 500,000 minutes back to AT&T, then AT&T will have to pay France Telecom for the imbalance. If the accounting rate between France and the United States is $1 per minute, then AT&T will pay France Telecom $250,000 for its work in completing the 500,000 extra calls. AT&T pays France Telecom only half the cost because AT&T does half the work itself.

ACCOUNTING SERVERS A local area network costs money to set up and run. Thus it makes sense to charge for usage on it. In Novell's NetWare LANs, the network supervisor sets up accounting through a program called SYSCON. When this happens, the current file server automatically begins to charge for services. The supervisor can authorize other network services (print servers, database servers, or gateways) to charge for services, or can revoke a server's right to charge.

ACCS Automatic Calling Card Service.

ACCUCALL A PBX integration utility for voice processing from Rhetorex, Campbell, CA.

ACCUNET A family of digital long distance transmission services from AT&T. Services are leased, switched or high speed. One, called Accunet Packet Service, is a packet switching digital network. Another one is called Accunet Reserved 1.5 Service, which AT&T describes as a general purpose, common user, modal-based digital service using dual 1.544 Mbps terrestrial and satellite facilities. Accunet Spectrum of Digital Services (ASDS) is AT&T's leased line (also called private line) digital service at 56 Kbps. MCI and Sprint have similar services. It is available in N x 56/64 Kbps, for N = 1, 2, 4, 6, 8, 12.

ACCURACY Absence of error. The extent to which a transmission or mathematical computation is error-free. There are obvious ways of measuring accuracy, such as the percentage of accurate information received compared to the total transmitted.

AC/DC RINGING A common way of signaling a telephone. An alternating current (AC) rings the phone bell and a direct current (DC) is used to work a relay to stop ringing when the called person answers.

ACD See the next seven definitions, AUTOMATIC CALL DISTRIBUTOR and ACIS.

ACD APPLICATION BRIDGE Refers to the link between an ACD and a database of information resident on a user's data system. It allows the ACD to communicate with a data system and gain access to a database of call processing information such as Data Directed Call Routing.

ACD APPLICATION-BASED CALL ROUTING In addition to the traditional methods of routing and tracking calls by trunk and agent group, the latest ACDs route and track calls by application. An application is a type of call, e.g. sales vs. service. Tracking calls in this manner allows accurately reported calls especially when they are overflowed to different agent groups.

ACD CALL BACK MESSAGING This ACD capability allows callers to leave messages for agents rather than wait for a live agent. It helps to balance agent workloads between peak and off-peak hours. In specific applications, it offers callers the option of waiting on hold. A good example is someone who only wishes to receive a catalog. Rather than wait while people place extensive orders, they leave their name and address as a message for later follow-up by an agent. This makes things simpler for them and speeds up service to those wanting to place orders.

ACD CALLER DIRECTED CALL ROUTING Sometimes referred to as an auto attendant capability within the industry, this ACD capability allows callers to direct themselves to the appropriate agent group without the an operator. The caller responds to prompts (Press 1 for sales, Press 2 for service) and is automatically routed to the designated agent group.

ACD CONDITIONAL ROUTING The ability of an ACD to monitor various parameters within the system and call center and to intelligently route calls based on that information. Parameters include volume levels of calls in queue, the number of agents available in designated overflow agent groups, or the length of the longest call. Calls are routed on a conditional basis. "If the number of calls in queue for agent group #1 exceeds 25 and there are at least 4 agents available in agent group #2, then route the call to agent group #2."

ACD DATA DIRECTED CALL ROUTING A capability whereby an ACD can automatically process calls based on data provided by a database of information resident in a separate data system. For example, a caller inputs an account number via touch tone phone. The number is sent to a data system holding a database of information on customers. The number is identified, validated and the call is distributed automatically based on the specific account type (VIP vs. regular business subscriber, as an example).

ACD INTELLIGENT CALL PROCESSING The ability of the latest ACDs to intelligently route calls based on information provided by the caller, a database on callers and system parameters within the ACD such as call volumes within agent groups and number of agents available.

ACD-DN A Northern Telecom term for an Automatic Call Distribution-Directory Number (ACD-DN), which refers to the queue where incoming calls wait until they are answered. Calls are answered in order in which they entered the queue.

ACF Advanced Communication Function. A family of software products used by IBM allowing its computers to communicate.

ACF/NCP Advanced Communication Function/ Network Control Program. In host-based IBM SNA networks, ACF/NCP is the control software running on a communications controller that supports the operation of the SNA backbone network.

ACF/VTAM Advanced Communication Function/Virtual Terminal Access Method. In host-based IBM SNA networks the ACF/VTAM is the control software running on a host computer that allows the host to communicate with terminals on an SNA network.

ACFG Short for AutoConFiGuration. The Plug and Play BIOS extensions, now turning up on PCs, are also known as the ACFG BIOS extensions.

ACIS Automatic Customer/Caller Identification. This is a feature of many sophisticated ACD systems. ACIS allows the capture of incoming network identification digits such as DID or DNIS and interprets them to identify the call type or caller. With greater information, such as ANI, this data can identify a calling subscriber number. This is also possible by employing a voice response device to request an inbound caller to identify themselves with a unique code. This could be a phone number, a subscriber number or some other identifying factor. This data can be used to route the call, inform the agent of the call type and even pre-stage the first data screen associated with this call type automatically. See ANI.

ACK In data communications, ACK is a character transmitted by the receiver of data to ACKnowledge a signal, information or packet received from the sender. See also ACKNOWLEDGMENT.

ACK AHEAD A variation of the XMODEM protocol that speeds up file transmission across error-free links. See XMODEM.

ACK1 Bisync acknowledgment for odd-numbered message.

ACKNOWLEDGMENT In data communications, the transmission of acknowledgment (ACK) characters from the receiving device to the sending device indicates the data sent has been received correctly.

ACL 1. Access Control List. A roster of users and groups of users, along with their rights. 2. Applications Connectivity Link. Siemens' protocol for linking its PBX to an external computer and having that computer control the movement of calls within a Siemens PBX. See also OPEN APPLICATION INTERFACE.

ACM 1. Address Complete Message. One of the ISUP call set-up messages. A message sent in the backward direction indicating that all the address signals required for routing the call to the called party have been received. See ISUP. 2. Association for Computing Machinery. www.acm.org 3. Automatic Call Manager. The integration of both inbound call distribution and automated outbound call placement from a list of phone contacts to be made from a database. Telemarketing and collections applications are targets for this type of system.

ACO Alarm Cut Off

ACOUSTIC COUPLER An acoustic modem. A modem designed to transfer data to the telephone network acoustically (i.e by sound), rather than electronically. An acoustic coupler looks like the reverse of a telephone handset and is typically made of rubber. The data communications link is achieved through acoustic (sound) signals rather than through direct electrical connection. It is attached to the computer or data terminal through an RS-232-C connector. To work the acoustic coupler, start the computer's communications program, dial the distant computer on a single line telephone with a normal (e.g. old-fashioned) handset. When the distant computer answers with a higher pitched "carrier tone," you place the telephone handset in the acoustic coupler and transmit data. Since the data is transmitted by sound between the handset and the acoustic coupler (and vice versa), the quality isn't always reliable. You can usually transmit up to 300 baud. People use acoustic couplers when they're short of time or cannot physically connect their modem electrically, e.g. they're using a payphone without an RJ-11 jack. (There are precious few.)

ACOUSTIC MODEL In automatic speech recognition, an acoustic model models acoustic behavior of words by gluing together models of smaller units, such as phonemes. (Sorry for the definition of the word model with the word model. But it's actually the best way of defining this term. HN)

ACOUSTIC (OR AIR) SUSPENSION A loudspeaker system that uses an airtight sealed enclosure.

ACOUSTICS That branch of science pertaining to the transmission of sound. The qualities of an enclosed space describing how sound is transmitted, e.g. its clarity.

ACOUSTO-OPTIC The interactions between acoustic waves and light in a solid medium. Acoustic waves can be made to modulate, deflect, and focus light waves by causing a variation in the refractive index of the medium. See also FIBER OPTICS.

ACQUISITION 1. In satellite communications, the process of locking tracking equipment on a signal from a communications satellite. 2. The process of achieving synchronization. 3. In servo systems, the process of entering the boundary conditions that will allow the loop to capture the signal and achieve lock-on. See also phase-locked loop.

ACQUISITION TIME 1. In a communication system, the amount of time required to attain synchronization. 2. In satellite control communications, the time required for locking tracking equipment on a signal from a communications satellite. See also satellite.

ACP Activity Concentration Point.

ACRFNET Academic Computing Research Facility Network. A network connecting various research units such as colleges and research and development laboratories in the U.S.

ACROBAT A standardized way of viewing a file without needing the associated software. For example, you run Word 6.0 or QuarkXpress, make a pretty desktop published document, replete with diagrams, photos and drawings. Now you want to send the file to someone to view it in all its glory. Simple. Convert the file to an Acrobat file (which has a .PDF extension) and modem it or send it on disk. The receiving person will run an Acrobat viewer program and see your beautiful work. They won't be able to change your work. But they will be able to see it. Acrobat is from Adobe, the Los Altos, CA company which produces PostScript. Acrobat has three benefits: The Acrobat viewing program is very cheap. You can use Acrobat to view any virtually any Windows software created file. Third, an Acrobat file can be up to 75% smaller than the original file in its native form, i.e. the original Word or QuarkXpress file.

ACRONYM A pronounceable artificial word formed from the first (or first few) letters of each word or group of words. For example, BASIC, the Beginner's All-purpose Symbolic Instruction Code, or COBOL, the computer language, which comes from COmmon Business Oriented Language.

ACS 1. Automatic Call Sequencer. A rudimentary automatic call distributor. See AUTOMATIC CALL SEQUENCER. 2. Advanced Communication System. An old name for AT&T's data communications/data processing service, later called Net 1000. In late 1986, after 10 years in birth, AT&T finally buried ACS because it offered too little in the face of what — by then — had become cheap, powerful desktop microcomputers and under $200 1200 baud modems.

ACSE Association Control Service Element. An application-level protocol. The method used in OSI for establishing a connection between two applications.

ACT Applied Computer Telephony is Hewlett Packard's program that is a strategy and set of open architecture commands and interfaces for integrating voice and database technologies. The idea is that with ACT a call will arrive at the telephone simultaneously with the database record of the caller. And such call and database record can be transferred simultaneously to an expert, a supervisor, etc. ACT works on both HP 3000 and HP 9000 computers. ACT essentially controls the telephone call movement within PBXs it connects to. See also OPEN APPLICATION INTERFACE.

ACTA America's Carriers Telecommunications Association, a Casselberry, FL organization founded in 1985 by 15 small long distance companies wishing to create an association in which the members controlled the direction of the organization. (That's their words.) "The focus established was to provide national representation before legislative and regulatory bodies, while continuing to improve industry business relations." There are now more than 130 members.

ACTAS Alliance of Computer-Based Telephony Application Suppliers — a part of the North American Telecommunications Association (NATA), which has now changed its name to MMTA. ACTAS's mission, according to ACTAS, is to deliver the benefits of computer-based telephone applications to the broadest possible range of customers. The high costs of customization and marketing currently relegate computer-based telephony applications to Fortune 100-level companies. ACTAS will work to lower the threshold for delivering the benefits of these applications, which include integrated voice and database processing systems automation and customer service, to the general business market. See MMTA.

ACTGA Attendant Control of Trunk Group Access. A complicated term for a simple concept, namely that your operator completes long distance calls. A primitive form of toll control.

ACTIUS Association of Computer Telephone Integration Users and Suppliers. A British organization based in Orpington, Kent. 011-44-689-873-333.

ACTIVATED RETURN CAPACITY A cable TV term. The capability of transmitting signals from a subscriber or user premises to the cable headend.

ACTIVATION A one time initial connection fee to get cellular phone service. As competition has intensified, so more and more carriers are dropping or severely reducing their activation fees. They do this in order to attract more new subscribers.

ACTS Association of Competitive Telecommunications Suppliers. Trade association of telephone equipment dealers in Canada.

ACTION MEDIA BOARD Intel i750 based PC board set that performs real-time compression and full-screen playback.

ACTIONMEDIA An imaging term. DVI Technology's product family, introduced in 1990 and consisting of single-board delivery and single board capture capability for AT or Micro Channel architecture buses (introduced with IBM), e.g. ActionMedia 750 ADP, etc.

ACTIVATION FEE Fee for the initial connection to the cellular system.

ACTIVE CALL An term which Hayes defines in its Hayes ISDN System adapter manual. An active call is a voice call to which you are connected that is not on hold.

ACTIVE CIRCUITS An MCI definition. MCI circuits for which are there is a completed "install order" and a "completed date."

ACTIVE CONTRACT One you must sign. See CONTRACT.

ACTIVE COUPLER A fiber optic coupler that includes a receiver and one or more transmitters. It regenerates (thus "active") input signals and sends them through output fibers, instead of passively dividing input light.

ACTIVE HUB A device used to amplify transmission signals in certain local area network topologies. You can use an active hub to add workstations to a network or to lengthen the cable distance between workstations and the file saver.

ACTIVE LINE A voice or data communications channel currently in use.

ACTIVE MATRIX LIQUID CRYSTAL DISPLAY A technique of making liquid crystal displays for computers in which each of the screen's pixels — the tiny elements that make up a picture — is controlled by its own transistor. Active matrix LCD display technique uses a transistor for each monochrome or each red, green and blue pixel. It provides sharp contrast, speedier screen refresh and doesn't lose your cursor when you move it fast (also knowing as submarining). Some active matrix CD screens are as fast as normal glass CRTs.

ACTIVE MEDIUM The material in fiber optic transmission, such as crystal, gas, glass, liquid or semiconductor, which actually "lases." It's also called laser medium, lasing medium, or active material.

ACTIVE OPEN Used in TCP to request connection with another node.

ACTIVE PIXEL REGION On a computer display, the area of the screen used for actual display of pixel information.

ACTIVE (RECURRING) CUSTOMER An MCI definition. An MCI customer who was installed and not canceled as of the first day of the month. The system determines the customer to be recurring if the install date does not equal the current billing month.

ACTIVE SPLICING Aligning the ends of two optical fibers with the aim of minimizing the splice loss.

ACTIVE VIDEO LINES All video lines not occurring in the horizontal and vertical blanking intervals. In other words, the lines conveying the video and audio signals.

ACTIVE VOCABULARY A phrase used in voice recognition to mean a group of words which a recognizer has been trained to understand and is attempting to understand at a given time. It is a subset of the total vocabulary of the recognizer.

ACTIVE WINDOW A Windows term. The active windows is the window in which the user is currently working. An active window is typically at the top of the window order and is distinguished by the color of its title bar, typically dark blue.

ACTIVE/PASSIVE DEVICE On a local area network, a device that supplies current for the loop is considered active. Such a device is s Token Ring MAU (Multistation Access Unit). A device which does not supply current is considered passive.

ACTIVITY CONCENTRATION POINT ACP. A location on a telecommunications network where there is high communications traffic, including voice, data, document distribution and teleconferencing. Generally, there will be some switching equipment present at the ACP.

ACTIVITY FACTOR A decimal fraction which represents the percentage of speech on a voice channel versus those periods of (non-talking) silence on that channel. Most voice channels carry actual speech 30% to 40% of the total available time. This represents an activity factor of 0.3 to 0.4.

ACTIVITY REPORT A report printed by a facsimile machine which lists all transmissions and receptions — their time, date, and number of documents; the remote unit type, diagnostic codes; and machine identification.

ACTS Automatic Coin Telephone Service includes a telephone company central office that can complete all types of payphone calls automatically without an operator. Recorded announcements are used to convey instructions to the customer.

ACU Automatic Calling Unit. Also an 801 ACU. A telephone company-provided device instructed by a computer to place a call on behalf of the computer. The call is then connected to a telephone company-provided Data Set. Anyone other than an IBM shop would simply buy a Hayes or Hayes-compatible modem, and not bother with the trouble and expense of an ACU.

ADA 1. Average Delay to Abandon. Average time a caller is held in queue before they get frustrated and decide to hang up. 2. A high level computer language which the Department of Defense has been trying to foist on its suppliers and thus, make a standard. ADA is named for British mathematician Ada Lovelace, known at the time as Lady Lovelace. She was the girlfriend of Charles Babbage, the inventor of the computer.

ADAD Automatic Dialing and Announcing Device. Device which automatically places calls and connects them to a recording or agent. A Canadian term for an automatic dialer.

ADAPTER A device used to connect a terminal to some circuit or channel so it will be compatible with the system to which it is attached. An adapter converts one type of jack or plug to another, for example, from old 4-prong telephone jacks to new modular. An adapter may also combine various items, such as putting three plugs in one jack.

ADAPTER CARD A printed circuit card installed inside of a computer. It takes data from memory and transmits it over cable to connected devices such as a modem, or printer.

ADAPTER SEGMENT A name sometimes used for the upper memory area of a PC, at hexadecimal addresses A000 through EFFF (640K to 1024K).

ADAPTIVE ANTENNA ARRAY An antenna array in which the received signal is continually monitored in respect of interference (usually adjacent or co-channel). Its directional characteristics are then automatically adjusted to null out the interference. Such a concept often employs computer control of a planar type antenna.

ADAPTIVE CHANNEL ALLOCATION A method of multiplexing wherein the information-handling capacities of channels are not predetermined but are assigned on demand.

ADAPTIVE COMMUNICATION Any communication system, or portion thereof, that automatically uses feedback information obtained from the system itself or from the signals carried by the system to modify dynamically one or more of the system operational parameters to improve system performance or to resist degradation.

ADAPTIVE COMPRESSION Data compression software that continuously analyzes and compensates its algorithm (technique), depending on the type and content of the data and the storage medium.

ADAPTIVE EQUALIZATION An electronic technique that allows a modem to continuously analyze and compensate for variations in the quality of a telephone line.

ADAPTIVE INTERFRAME TRANSFORM CODING A class of compression algorithms commonly used in video codecs to reduce the data transmission rate.

ADAPTIVE LOGICALLY PROVIDED SERVICES An AT&T term for services that adapt to an end customer's needs, on demand, in any combination of voice, data or image by the dynamic allocation of network resources (bandwidth, switching, bridging, feature processing, etc.) under sophisticated software logic control.

ADAPTIVE DIFFERENTIAL PULSE CODE MODULATION See ADPCM.

ADAPTIVE PULSE CODE MODULATION A way of encoding analog voice signals into digital signals by adaptively predicting future encodings by looking at the immediate past. The adaptive part reduces the number of bits per second that another rival and more common method called PCM (Pulse Code Modulation) requires to encode voice. Adaptive PCM is not common because, even though it reduces the number of bits required to encode voice, the electronics to do it are expensive. See PULSE CODE MODULATION.

ADAPTIVE ROUTING A method of routing packets of data or data messages in which the system's intelligence selects the best path. This path might change with altered traffic patterns or link failures.

ADAS Automated Directory Assistance Service. A service from Northern Telecom which automates the greeting and inquiry portion of the directory assistance call. With ADAS, directory assistance callers are greeted by the automated system and asked to state the name of the city and the listing they are seeking. They are then connected with an operator. The ADAS service knocks a few seconds off each directory assistance call.

ADC Analog-to-Digital Converter.

ADCCP Advanced Data Communications Control Procedures, A bit-oriented ANSI-standard communications protocol. It is a link-layer protocol. ADCCP is ANSI's version of SDLC/HDLC.

ADCU Association of Data Communications Users.

ADD-IN CARD An expansion board that fits into the computer's slots and is used to expand the system's memory or extend the operation of another device.

ADD-ON 1. A telephone system feature which allows connecting a third telephone to an existing conversation. This "add-on" feature is initiated by the originator of the call. The feature is also known as "Three-Way Calling." 2. Hardware, often referred to as peripheral equipment, that is added to a system to improve its performance, add memory or increase its capabilities. Voice mail, Automated Attendant and Call Detail Recording Equipment are examples of PBX add-on devices. AT&T and some other manufacturers call them APPLICATIONS PROCESSORS.

ADD-ON CONFERENCE A PBX feature. Almost always used in conjunction with another feature called consultation hold, this feature allows an extension user to add a third person to an existing two-person conversation. The user places an existing central office call or internal call on Hold, and obtains system dial tone. The user can then call another internal extension or an outside party. After speaking with the "consulted" party, the originating phone reactivates the initiating command (typically a button push) and creates a three-party conference with the call previously placed on Hold.

ADD-ON CONFERENCE — INTERCOM ONLY Allows a telephone user to add someone else to an existing intercom (within-the-same office) conversation.

ADD-ON DATA MODULE Plug-in circuit cards which allow a PBX to send and receive analog (voice) and digital (data) signals.

ADDED BIT A bit delivered to the intended destination user in addition to intended user information bits and delivered overhead bit. An added bit might be used to round out the number of bits to some error checking scheme, for example.

ADDITIONAL COOPERATIVE ACCEPTANCE TESTING ACAT. A method of testing switched access service that provides a telephone company technician at the central office and a carrier's technician at its location, with suitable test equipment to perform the required tests. ACAT may, for example, consist of the following tests:

Impulse Noise Phase Jitter Signal-to-C-Notched Noise Ratio Intermodulation (Nonlinear) Distortion Frequency Shift (Offset) Envelope Delay Distortion Dial Pulse Percent Break

ADDITIONAL PERIOD Billing periods charged after initial, first or minimum period on a call. Usually, long distance toll/DDD has a one-minute initial period at premium rate; subsequent "additional" minutes (period) are billed at a lower rate. Additional period billing increments vary by long distance company.

ADDITIVE PRIMARIES By definition, three primary colors result when light is viewed directly as opposed to being reflected: red, green and blue (RGB). According to the tri-stimulus theory of color perception, all other colors can be adequately approximated by blending some mixture of these three lights together. This theory is harnessed in color television and video communications. It doesn't work so well in color printing where special colors are often printed separately.

ADDMD Administrative Directory Management Domain. A X.500 directory management domain run by a PTT (Posts, Telegraph, and Telephone administration) or other public network provider.

ADDRESS Characters identifying the recipient or originator of transmitted data. An address is the destination of a message sent through a communications system. A telephone number is considered the address of the called person. In computer terms, an address is a set of numbers that uniquely identifies something — a workstation on a LAN, a location in computer memory, a packet of data traveling through a network. IEEE 802.3 and 802.5 recommend having a unique address for each device worldwide. An address may also denote the position of data in computer memory or the data packet itself while in transit through a network.

ADDRESS COMPLETE MESSAGE ACM. A CCS/SS7 signaling message that contains call-status information. This message is sent prior to the called customer going off-hook.

ADDRESS FIELD In data transmission, the sequence of bits immediately following the opening flag of a frame identifying the secondary station sending, or designated to receive, the frame.

ADDRESS FILTERING A way of deciding which data packets are allowed through a device. The decision is based on the source and destination MAC (Media Access Control, the lower part of ISO layer two) addresses of the data packet.

ADDRESS MASK An electronic messaging term. A bit mask used to select bits from a network address (e.g. Internet) for sub-net addressing. The mask is 32 bits long and selects the network portion of the address and one or more bits of the local portion. Sometimes called sub-net mask.

ADDRESS RESOLUTION An internetworking term. A discovery process used when, as in LAN protocols such as TCP/IP and IBM NetBIOS, only the Network Layer address is known and the MAC address is needed to enable delivery to the correct device. The originating end station sends broadcast packets with the device's NLA to all nodes on the LAN; the end station with the specified NLA address responds with a unicast packet, addressed to the originating end station, and containing the MAC address. See ADDRESS RESOLUTION PROTOCOL.

ADDRESS RESOLUTION PROTOCOL The Internet protocol used to map dynamic Internet addresses to physical (hardware) addresses on local area networks. Limited to networks that support hardware broadcasts.

ADDRESS SIGNALING Signals either the end user's telephone or the central office switching equipment that a call is coming in.

ADDRESS SIGNALS Address signals provide information concerning the desired destination of the call. This is usually the dialed digits of the called telephone number or access codes. Typical types of address signals are DP (Dial Pulse), DTMF, and MF.

ADDRESS SPACE The amount of memory a PC can use directly is called its address space. MS-DOS can directly access 1024K of memory (one megabyte). A protected mode control program like Microsoft Windows 3.x or OS/2 can directly address up to 16 megabytes of memory. Here is a definition of address space, as supplied by the Personal Computer Memory Card International Association (PCMCIA) as address space applies to PCMCIA cards: "An address space is a collection of registers and storage locations contained on a PC Card which are distinguished from each other by the value of the Address Lines applied to the Card. There are three, separate, address spaces possible for a card. These are the Common Memory space, the Attribute Memory space and the I/O space."

ADDRESSABLE PROGRAMMING A cable TV (CATV) industry term. A subscriber orders a movie or sports event. He does that calling a phone number (generally an 800 number). A computer answers, grabs the calling number, confirms the request, then hangs up. The computer passes the request onto the cable company's computer, which checks the calling phone number against its accounting records. If the subscriber has good credit, the cable company sends a coded message down its cable network to the caller's set-top cable box/converter. The message temporarily enables that particular converter to descramble the channel offering the desired program.

ADDRESSABILITY 1. In computer graphics, the number of addressable points on a display surface or in storage. 2. In micrographics, the number of addressable points, within a specified film frame, written as follows: the number of addressable horizontal points by the number of addressable vertical points, for example, 3000 by 4000. 3. A cable TV term. The capability of controlling the operation of cable subscriber set-top converters by sending commands from a central computer. Such addressability is absolutely require for a cable system to offer pay-per-view services.

ADDRESSABLE POINT In computer graphics, any point of a device that can be addressed. See ADDRESSABILITY.

ADDRESSEE The intended recipient of a message.

ADDRESSING Refers to the way that the operating system knows where to find a specific piece of information or software in the application memory. Every memory location has an address.

ADF Automatic Document Feeder

ADH Average Delay to Handle. Average time a caller to an automatic call distributor waits before being connected to an agent.

ADHERENCE A term used in telephone call centers to connote whether the people working in the center are doing what they're meant to be doing. Are they at work? Are they on break? Are they answering the phone? Are they at lunch? All these activities are scheduled by workforce management software. If they're in line, the workers is "in adherence." If not, they're "out of adherence." See ADHERENCE MONITORING.

ADHERENCE MONITORING Adherencing monitoring means comparing real-time data coming out an ACD with forecast call volumes, forecast service levels and forecast workforce employment levels. The idea is to see if the people, the calls and the system are working as forecast. This a measure of how well your forecasting work. You need to know how well it works since it's your forecasting on which you base your employment. See ADHERENCE.

ADJACENT CHANNEL INTERFERENCE When two or more carrier channels are placed too close together, they interfere with each other and mess up each other's conversations.

ADJACENT MTA An MTA (Message Transfer Agent) that directly connects to another MTA. A Message Transfer Agent operated by a public service provider or PTT (Post, Telegraph, and Telephone administration), or a client MTA.

ADJACENT SIGNALING POINTS Two CCS/SS7 signaling points that are directly interconnected by signaling links.

ADJUNCT 1. Network system in the Advanced Intelligent Network Release 1 architecture that contains SLEE (Service Logic Execution Environment) functionality, and that communicates with an Advanced Intelligent Network Release 1 Switching System in processing AIN Release 1 calls. Definition from Bellcore. See also ADJUNCT PROCESSOR. 2. An auxiliary device connected to the ISDN set, such as a speakerphone, headset adapter, or an analog interface.

ADJUNCT KEY SYSTEM A system installed behind a PBX or a Centrex. Such key system provides the users with several more features than the PBX or Centrex. Not a common term today.

ADJUNCT PROCESSOR A computer outside a telephone switching system that "talks" to the switch and gives it switching commands. An adjunct processor might include a database of customers and their recent buying activities. If the database shows that a customer lives in Indiana, the call from the customer might be switched to the group of agents handling Indiana customers. Adjunct processors might be concerned with energy management, building security etc.

ADJUNCT SYSTEM APPLICATION INTERFACE See ASAI.

ADJUSTED RING LENGTH When a segment of Token Ring (in practice a dual ring) trunk cable fails, a function known as the Wrap connects the main path to the backup path. In the worse case — the longest path — would occur if the shortest trunk cable segment failed, so ARL is calculated during network design to ensure the network will always work.

ADK Application Definable Keys

ADM An AT&T term for an Add/Drop Multiplexer. A network element that can add and drop standard DSn or SONET signals from a line signal.

ADMD Administration Management Domain. An X.400 Message Handling System public carrier. Examples include MCImail and ATTmail in the U.S., British Telecom's Gold400mail in the U.K. The ADMDs in all countries worldwide together provide the X.400 backbone.

ADMINISPHERE The rarefied organizational layers beginning just above the rank and file. Decisions that fall from the adminisphere are often profoundly inappropriate or irrelevant to the problems they were designed to solve. This definition from Wired Magazine.

ADMINISTRABLE SERVICE PROVIDER An SCSA definition. A service provider which supports administrable services (for example, SCSA Call Router).

ADMINISTRATION A term used by the telephone industry to program features into a phone system. On a Northern Telecom Norstar system, administration includes making settings on 1. System speed dial; 2. Names on phones; 3. Time and date; 4. Restrictions; 5. Overrides; 6. Permissions; 7. Night Service and 8. Passwords.

ADMINISTRATION BY TELEPHONE The capability for the system administrator to perform most routine system administrative functions remotely from any Touch Tone pad. Such functions include mailbox maintenance (e.g. create, delete, set password, set class of service, etc.) and disk maintenance.

ADMINISTRATIVE ALERTS A Window NT term. Administrative alerts relate to server and resource use; they warn about problems in areas such as security and access, user sessions, server shutdown because of power loss (when UPS is available), directory replication, and printing. When a computer generates an administrative alert, a message is sent to a predefined list of users and computers.

ADMINISTRATION DIRECTORY MANAGEMENT DOMAIN Administrative Directory Management Domain. A X.500 directory management domain run by a PTT (Posts, Telegraph, and Telephone administration) or other public network provider.

ADMINISTRATIVE DOMAIN AD. A group of hosts and networks operated and managed by a single organization. An Internet term.

ADMINISTRATIVE MANAGEMENT DOMAIN An X.400 electronic mail term: A network domain maintained by a telecommunications carrier.

ADMINISTRIVIA A silly term for administrative tasks, most often related to the maintenance of mailing lists, digests, news gateways, etc. An Internet term.

ADMINISTRATION SUB-SYSTEM Part of AT&T's premises distribution system that distributes hardware components for the addition or rearrangement of circuits.

ADMINISTRATIVE POINT A location at which communication circuits are administered, i.e. rearranged or rerouted, by means of cross connections, interconnections, or information outlets.

ADMINISTRATIVE SERVICE LOGIC PROGRAM ASLP. The SLP responsible for managing the feature interactions between Advanced Intelligent Network AIN Release 1 features resident on a single SLEE (Service Logic Execution Environment).

ADMINISTRATIVE SUBSYSTEM That part of a premises distribution system where circuits can be rearranged or rerouted. It includes cross connect hardware, and jacks used as information outlets.

ADMINISTRATOR The individual responsible for managing the local area network (LAN). This person configures the network, maintains the network's shared resources and security, assigns passwords and privileges, and helps users.

ADN Advanced Digital Network. ADN is Pacific Bell of California's low-cost leased 56-Kbps digital service. ADN is available for intraLATA calls.

ADOBE SYSTEMS The name of the company which produces PostScript. See POSTSCRIPT and OUTLINE FONT. Adobe Systems got its name from the creek than ran past its founder's home in Los Altos, California. See ACROBAT.

ADP 1. Apple Desktop Bus. A synchronous serial bus allowing connection of the Mac keyboard, mouse and other items to the CPU. A Mac keyboard or mouse is called an ADB device. Contrast with peripherals, which attach through the SCSI interface. 2. Automatic Data Processing. The same as DP, data processing. 3. The name of a company which processes my pay check.

ADPCM Adaptive Differential Pulse Code Modulation. A speech coding method which calculates the difference between two consecutive speech samples in standard PCM coded telecom voice signals. This calculation is encoded using an adaptive filter and therefore, is transmitted at a lower rate than the standard 64 Kbps technique. Typically, ADPCM allows an analog voice conversation to be carried within a 32Kbit digital channel; 3 or 4 bits are used to describe each sample, which represents the difference between two adjacent samples. Sampling is done 8,000 times a second. In short, ADPCM, which many voice processing makers use, allows encoding of voice signals in half the space PCM allows.

ADRMP (pron. add-rump) AutoDialing Recorded Message Player. A device that calls a bunch of telephone numbers and upon connection will play a message to the answering person. ADRMPs are used for lead solicitation and message delivery. They are often unpopular due to their indiscriminate dialing pattern and random message playing.

ADSI Analog Display Services Interface. ADSI is a Bellcore standard defining a protocol on the flow of information between something (a switch, a server, a voice mail system, a service bureau) and a subscriber's telephone, PC, data terminal or other communicating device with a screen. The simple idea of ADSI is to add words to, and therefore a modicum of simplicity of use to a system that usually uses only touchtones. Imagine a normal voice mail system. You call it. It answers with a voice menu. Push 1 to listen to your messages, 2 to erase them, 3 to store them, 4 to forward them, etc. It's confusing. You have to remember which is which. ADSI is designed to solve that. It's designed to send to your phone's screen the choices in words that you're hearing. You then have the choice of responding to what you hear or what you see. Your response is the same — a touchtone button. ADSI's signaling is DTMF and standard Bell 202 modem signals from the service

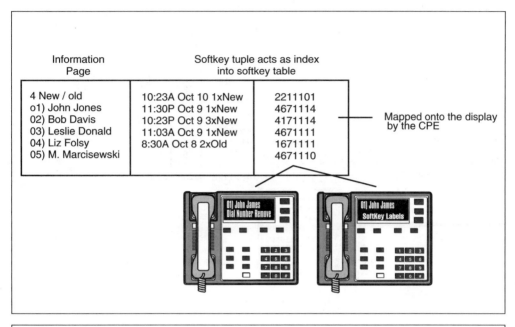

Information Page	Softkey tuple acts as index into softkey table	
4 New / old o1) John Jones 02) Bob Davis 03) Leslie Donald 04) Liz Folsy 05) M. Marcisewski	10:23A Oct 10 1xNew 11:30P Oct 9 1xNew 10:23P Oct 9 3xNew 11:03A Oct 9 1xNew 8:30A Oct 8 2xOld	2211101 4671114 4171114 4671111 1671111 4671110

Mapped onto the display by the CPE

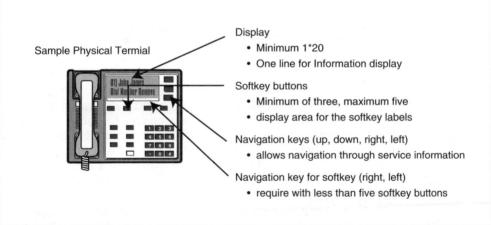

Sample Physical Termial

Display
• Minimum 1*20
• One line for Information display

Softkey buttons
• Minimum of three, maximum five
• display area for the softkey labels

Navigation keys (up, down, right, left)
• allows navigation through service information

Navigation key for softkey (right, left)
• require with less than five softkey buttons

to your 202-modem equipped phone. From the phone to the service it's only touchtone. With ADSI, you don't hear the modem signaling because every time the service gets ready to send you information, it first sends a "mute" tone. ADSI works on every phone line in the world.

For ADSI to work visually, you'll need a special ADSI-equipped phone or a piece of ADSI software in your PC. The nice feature of ADSI is that the standard is so flexible, it can work on cheap phones with a small display and more expensive phones with a bigger display and on a PC with a real big display. These three diagrams show a little of the basic concepts behind ADSI — Information Page Mapping and Softkey Mapping.

		Softkey definer	Label text	Return String
		1		No Return
Information Page	Softkey tuple acts as index into softkey table	2	ERA	DTMF 2
		3	EXIT	Hang-up
4 New / old	10:23A Oct 10 1xNew	2211101	4	DIAL	Line No.
o1) John Jones	11:30P Oct 9 1xNew	4671114	5	UND	Line No.
02) Bob Davis	10:23P Oct 9 3xNew	4171114	6	NUM	Line No.
03) Leslie Donald	11:03A Oct 9 1xNew	4671111	7	REM	Line No.
04) Liz Folsy	8:30A Oct 8 2xOld	1671111	8		Goto Line
05) M. Marcisewski		4671110	9		Goto Line

Softkey information is taken from the softkey table to define the softkeys and scroll keys

ADSL Asymmetrical Digital Subscriber Line. Bellcore's term for one-way T-1 to the home over the plain old, single twisted pair wiring already going to homes. ADSL is designed to carry video to the home. ADSL is one-way video with control signals returning from the home at 16 Kbps. ADSL, like ISDN, uses adaptive digital filtering, which is a way of adjusting itself to overcome noise and other problems on the line.

According to Northern Telecom, initial ADSL field trails and business cases have focused on ADSL's potential for Video on Demand service, in competition with cable pay-per-view and neighborhood video rental stores. But ADSL offers a wide range of other applications, including education and healthcare. Once telephone companies are able to deliver megabits to the home, Northern Telecom expects an explosion in potential applications including work-at-home access to corporate LANs, interactive services such as home shopping and home banking and even multi-party video gaming, interactive travelogues, and remote medical diagnosis. Multimedia retrieval will also become possible, enabling the home user to browse through libraries of text, audio, and image data — or simply subscribe to CD-qual ity music services. In the field of education, ADSL could make it possible to provide a low-cost "scholar's workstation" — little more than a keyboard, mouse, and screen — to every student, providing access to unlimited computer processing resources from their home. For a more modern version of ADSL, see DMT, which stands for Discrete Multi-Tone. See also ADSL Forum.

ADSL FORUM The ADSL Forum is an industry association formed to promote the ADSL concept and to facilitate the development of ADSL system architectures and protocols for major ADSL applications. www.sbexpos.com/sbexpos/associations/adsl/home.mtml

ADSTAR Automated Document STorage And Retrieval.

ADT Abstract Data Type.

ADU Asynchronous Data Unit.

ADVANCE REPLACEMENT WARRANTY A warranty service whereby the dealer sends the customer a replacement component before the customer returns the defective product. This not only accelerates the replacement time, but also helps the buyer if the component is vital. When you buy vital telecom gear, it's good to check that your equipment has an Advance Replacement Warranty or Guarantee.

ADVANCED BRANCH EXCHANGE ABX. An uncommon term meaning a private branch exchange (PBX) with advanced features normally including the ability to handle both voice and data in some sort of integrated way.

ADVANCED COMMUNICATION SYSTEM ACS. The old name for a proposed packet switched network from AT&T. The service was called Net 1000. AT&T finally killed the service in late 1986. For a bigger explanation, see ACS.

ADVANCED DIGITAL NETWORK ADN is Pacific Bell of California's low-cost leased 56-Kbps digital service. ADN is available for intraLATA calls.

ADVANCED INTERACTIVE EXECUTIVE AIX. An IBM version of UNIX. AIX runs on PS/2 computers, IBM workstations, minicomputers, and mainframes.

ADVANCED INTERACTIVE VIDEO AIV. Interactive videodisc format and system using LV-ROM, a method of storing analog video, digital audio, and digital data on a single videodisc. The system was developed by Philips UK, the British Broadcasting Corporation, Acorn Computer, and Logica Ltd. Most prominent application was the BBC's Domesday Project.

ADVANCED INTELLIGENT NETWORK AIN. The local Bell telephone companies' architecture for the 1990s and beyond. See AIN for a much fuller explanation.

ADVANCED 800 SERVICES AT&T's name for a family of 800 In-WATS services that include time of day and area code routing, single number 800 service (for both interstate and intrastate), automatic number identification, etc. See also 800 SERVICE and ENHANCED 800 SERVICES.

ADVANCED PRIVATE LINE TERMINATION An AT&T term which means the PBX user gets access to all the services of an Enhanced Private Switched Communications Services (EPCS) network. It also works when it is associated with AT&T's Common Control Switching Arrangement (CCSA) network.

ADVANCENET An Ethernet-based local area network from Hewlett Packard, Palo Alto, CA. See ETHERNET.

ADVANTIS A partnership between IBM and Sears Roebuck to provide advanced voice and data network services to users worldwide. As of writing, it's not exactly clear what this new company will do.

ADVISORY TONES Signals such as dial tone, busy, ringing, fast-busy, call-waiting, camp-on and all the other tones your telephone system uses to tell you that something is happening or about to happen.

ADVOCACY A General Magic term. Advocacy is the process for getting developers and information providers to commit to developing for Magic Cap devices and Telescript.

AEB Analog Expansion Bus. The analog voice processing bus designed by

Dialogic which allows multiple cards to route audio signals within a PC. It is used to interface DTI/124 and D/4x voice response component boards which fit in an AT-expansion slot of a PC. See also PEB and SCSA which are more modern digital expansion buses.

AECS PLAN Aeronautical Emergency Communications System Plan. The AECS Plan provides for the operation of aeronautical communications stations on a voluntary, organized basis to provide the President and the Federal Government, as well as heads of state and local governments, or their designated representatives, and the aeronautical industry, with a means of communicating during an emergency.

AEMIS Automatic Electronic Management Information System. This was the first computerized UCD/ACD reporting system introduced by AT&T for CO UCD (Uniform Call Distribution). This package was updated to become the PRO 150/500 system for UCD management on the Dimension PBX/UCD. AEMIS was the successor to the FADS or Force Administration Data System. It was an electro-mechanical system of peg counters and different colored busy lamp fields used to note trunk and position status.

AERIAL CABLE Cables strung outside and overhead. They're called aerial even though they only hang from poles or buildings. Some aerial cable hangs by its own strength. Some is supported by steel wire above it. Stringing aerial cable is cheaper than burying it, though buried cable lasts longer.

AERIAL DISTRIBUTION METHOD A method of running cables through the air, typically pole-to-pole. The old fashioned way. Some phone companies say aerial cable is more reliable than underground. Certainly, it's cheaper to fix or add to. It just looks less appetizing.

AERONAUTICAL RADIO INC. ARINC. The organization that coordinates the design and management of telecommunications systems for the airline industry. It's one of the largest buyers of telecommunications services and equipment in the world.

AEROSPACE Air force publicists coined the term "aerospace" to convince everyone that space was the business of those who fly in the air. According to the Economist Magazine, the "aerospace industry" was quickly accepted into the language, perhaps because President Eisenhower's alternative, the "military industrial complex," sounded rather more sinister. After the Apollo program, which ended in 1972, the "space" in aerospace often seemed like a syllable tacked on to make building airplanes sound grander. But the growth in satellite use in the 1980s made space a respectable business in its own right. In America as of writing in the fall of 1991, the annual sales of space hardware are now bigger than those of civilian aircraft.

AET Application Entity Title. The authoritative name of an OSI application entity, usually a Distinguished Name from the Directory.

AFACTS Automatic FACilities Test System. AFACTS is a Rolm CBX feature. An automatic testing system for identifying faulty tie and central office trunks. AFACTS can pinpoint faulty trunks and generate exception and summary reports.

AFAIK As Far As I Know.

AFCEA Armed Forces Communications and Electronics Association. An organization of military communications personnel and suppliers who fulfill the specialized needs of government and military communications. They run an big convention each year in Washington in May-June. 703-631-4693.

AFE See ANALOG FRONT END.

AFFILIATED SALES AGENCY ASA. A term for a company which resells the service of a phone company. Typically, the phone company pays the ASA a commission. Sometimes the commission is so large that it blurs the thinking of the ASA into recommending to its customers telecom products and services they would be better without.

AFIPS American Federation of Information Processing Societies. A national, highly-respected organization formed by data processing societies to keep abreast of advances in the field. AFIPS organizes one of the biggest trade shows in the data processing industry — the NCC (National Computer Conference).

AFNOR Acronym for Association Francais Normal. France's national standards-setting organization.

AFP AppleTalk File Protocol. Apple's network protocol, used to provide access between file servers and clients in an AppleShare network. AFP is also used by Novell's products for the Macintosh.

AFT Automatic Fine Tuning; SEE AFC.

AFTER-CALL WRAP-UP The time an employee spends completing a transaction after the call has been disconnected. Sometimes it's a few seconds. Sometimes it can be minutes. Depends on what the caller wants.

AGC Automatic Gain Control. There are two electronic ways you can control the recording of something — Manual or Automatic Gain Control (AGC). AGC is an electronic circuit in tape recorders, speakerphones, and other voice devices which is used to maintain volume. AGC is not always a brilliant idea since it will attempt to produce a constant volume level, that is, it will try to equalize all sounds — the volume of your voice, and, when you stop talking, the circuit static and/or general room noise which you do not want amplified. Never record a seminar or speech using AGC. The recording will be decidedly amateurish. Manual Gain Control means there is record volume control and is thus, preferred in professional applications.

AGCOMNET US Department of Agriculture's voice and data communications network.

AGED PACKET A data packet which has exceeded its maximum predefined node visit count or time in the network.

AGENT 1. This term comes from the huge telephone call-in reservation centers which the airlines, hotels and car rental services run. An agent is the person who answers your call, takes your order or answers your question. Agents are also called Telephone Sales Representatives or Communicators. The term "agent" was first used in the airline business. It came from gate or counter ticket agent. 2. An "Agent" is the person or persons you have legally authorized to order your telephone service and equipment from telephone companies. 3. In the computer programming sense of the word, an agent acts on behalf of another person or thing, with delegated authority. The agent's goals are those of the entity that created it. An agent is an active object with a mission, but agents are abstractions that can be implemented in any way, whereas an object has a formal definition. Business Week in its February 14,1994 issue wrote, "It's what computer scientists call an 'agent' — a kind of software program that's powerful and autonomous enough to do what all goods robots should: help the harried humans by carrying out tedious, time-consuming, and complex tasks. Software agents just now emerging from the research labs can scan data banks by the dozen, schedule meetings, tidy up electronic in-boxes, and handle a growing list of clerical jobs." 4. Windows 95 Resource Kit defined agent slightly differently. It said that an agent was software that runs on a client computer for use by administrative software running on a server. Agents are typically used to support administrative actions, such as detecting system information or running services.

AGENT LOGON/LOGOFF A call center term. The agent begins their day by punching some buttons on their phone. This indicates to the automatic call distributor that they are now ready to take calls. Later in the day, they punch some other buttons and indicate to the ACD that they are now ready to stop working. This is called logoff.

AGENT SIGN ON/SIGN OFF A feature which allows any ACD agent to occupy any position in the ACD without losing his or her personal identity. Statistics are collected and consolidated about this agent and calls are routed to this agent no matter where he sits or how many positions he may occupy at one time.

AGGREGATE BANDWIDTH The total bandwidth of channel carrying a multiplexed bit stream.

AGGREGATE RATE The sum of the channel data rates for a given application.

AGGREGATOR A new breed of long distance reseller. An aggregator is essentially a sales agent for a long distance company. Here's how it works: The aggregator goes to a long distance company and says "May I sell your long distance service at a discount?" The long distance company says Yes! The aggregator hits the street and sells cut-rate long distance service to any and everyone. The long distance provider installs the service and bills it. The aggregator makes his profit by charging a fixed monthly service fee, a percentage of savings or some other arrangement. The key to it: The end user saves some money because his calls are "aggregated" with those of ALL the customers of the aggregator and the long distance company extends a bulk savings to the aggregator. Here's what TELECONNECT Magazine wrote about aggregators under the headline, "Aggregator Warning."

"Aggregators are companies which buy long distance wholesale and sell it retail. Aggregators exist because AT&T decided it wanted to win back long distance business it had lost. AT&T sliced its rates, liberalized its bulk billing rules and encouraged those consultants who had recommended their clients switch to MCI and US Sprint to become aggregators. These consultant-turned aggregators simply solicit anyone's long distance business and add it to their collection. AT&T sends their end-user a bill and the consultant-turned-aggregator a commission check.

"Should you — as an end-user — consider buying your long distance from an aggregator? The simple answer is YES? AT&T's discounts are so deep it's not uncommon for a company using AT&T today directly to switch to billing through an aggregator and save 20% to 25% — with nothing of substance happening. They still get their bills from AT&T and they still place and receive calls on AT&T as they had been doing. No wires are touched. No routing is changed.

"What about the pitfalls? There are some: First, don't buy long distance that isn't billed directly by the long distance carrier providing the service. If the aggregator does the billing, there's too much opportunity for "mischief," says Dick Kuehn, Cleveland consultant. "There's opportunity for doing things like increasing each of your calls by 30 seconds. And because a user has no answer supervision on his call detail records, it's very hard for the user to figure his exact timing." The problem, says Dick, is there's no way for a user to verify his own bill. Dick says "Carriers are honest. Resellers (aggregators that bill) are open to question."

"TELECONNECT also believes you probably shouldn't deal with an aggregator who bills you a percentage of "savings." This is also open to abuse. There are so many rates, so many changes monthly, so many options that it's virtually impossible for the user to figure out what he would have paid had he not gone with the aggregator. The calculation is too open to abuse. TELECONNECT's feeling: pay a flat service fee.

"P.S. Imagine buying an automobile tire. The local garage carries two options: a Bridgestone for $30 and a Pirelli for $100. You opt for the Bridgestone at $30. You've thus saved $70. The garage proprietor splits your "savings" with you and charges you $35.

By late 1992, the panapoly of companies in the long distance business — not only aggregators — had expanded dramatically. And confusion between companies and what they did became rife. All, of course, purport to save you money on your long distance bills. And many do. Here's a simple explanation of the major categories:

CARRIER. Owns most of its circuits. Has own sales force and possibly independent sales agents. Best examples: AT&T, MCI, Allnet and Sprint.

TRADITIONAL RESELLER. Rents/leases most circuits or buys bulk time from carrier. Resells under own brand name, has published prices, sends own bills. Appears to be (and for all practical purposes is) same as the carriers.

AGGREGATOR. "Sponsor" who buys carrier's (typically AT&T) multi-location 800 or outbound service; enrolls other businesses as sites; volume discounts for all based on total calling at all sites. End user is still the carrier's, not the aggregator's. The carrier typically does the billing.

REBILLER: (Also called "Switchless Reseller"). Buys service as multi-location customer from carrier. Signs up individual sites (just like aggregator). Generates own end-user bills. No switch or network, but does sales, customer service, billing for long distance calls. Sometimes the rebiller's bills are more detailed than the bills you get directly from the carrier.

SALES AGENTS: Businesses or groups who are not direct employees of carrier, but who receive sales commissions from carrier. Customers belong to carrier and carrier does billing.

OTHER THIRD-PARTY MARKETERS. Buying co-ops, user groups, long distance brokers, pyramid (legal) marketing systems, shared tenant providers, Centrex aggregators, affinity groups (like college alumni and church congregation groups).

AGGREGATION An AMA (Automatic Message Accounting) function that accumulates AMA data, resulting in a less than detailed AMA record. Definition from Bellcore.

AGGREGATION DEVICE A specialized ISDN terminal adapter that can aggregate, or bond, the two B channels "on the fly" into a single higher-speed connection. some aggregation devices also include an Ethernet bridge, i.e. a connection to a local area network.

AGING The change in properties of a material with time under specific conditions.

AGTK Application Generator ToolKit. A set of tools that are used to implement and modify a voice-processing application. It includes software to create the script and packages for the creation and editing of prompts. See APPLICATION GENERATOR.

AHD Audio High Density. System of digital audio recording on grooveless discs, employing an electronically-guided capacitance pickup.

AHOY See HELLO.

AHR Abbreviation for ampere hour, measurement of battery power: how much current may be drawn for an hour. Important specification for portable computers, cellular phones, etc.

AHT Average Handle time. The amount of time an employee is occupied with an incoming call. This is the sum of talk time and after-call-work time.

AHT DISTRIBUTION Average Handle Time Distribution. A set of factors (either 48 or 96) for each day of the week that defines the typical distribution of average handle times throughout the day. Each factor measure how far AHT in the half or quarter hour deviates from the AHT for day as a whole.

AI Artificial Intelligence. Perhaps the next phase of computing. The present forms of AI in computer software are called Expert or Knowledge Based systems.

AIA An SCSA term. Application Interface Adapter. A software module that converts the function calls issued by a client application, via the API, into standard SCSA messages. See SCSA MESSAGE PROTOCOL.

AICC Automatic Incoming Call Connection. A Rolm term for connecting an incoming call to the person's phone, without requiring them to press any keys.

AIDS A Trojan Horse software program (a virus) which caused extensive damage in December 1989.

AIIM Association for Information and Image Management.

AIM Amplitude intensity modulation.

AIMS An Acronym for Auto Indexing Mass Storage. Indicates the AIMS Specification which is a standard card interface for storing large data such as image and multimedia files.

AIN Advanced Intelligent Network. A term promoted by Bellcore (Bell Communications Research Inc.), adopted by Bellcore's owners, the regional Bell holding companies, and by AT&T and virtually every other phone company to indicate the architecture of their networks for the 1990s and beyond. While every phone company has a different interpretation of what their AIN is, there seems to be two consistent threads. First, the network can affect (i.e. change) the routing of calls within it from moment to moment based on some criteria other than the normal, old-time criteria of simply finding a path through the network for the call. Second, the originator or the ultimate receiver of the call can somehow inject intelligence into the network and affect the flow of his call (either outbound or inbound). The concept of AIN is simple. Before calls are sent to their final destination, the network queries a database. "What should I do at this very moment with this phone call?" Depending on the response, depends the disposition of the call. That database may belong to the phone company. Or it may belong to the customer. It makes no difference, so long as they're connected. And various carriers (phone companies) have proposed and implemented various ways of joining these databases. Initial AIN services tend to be focused on inbound 800 toll-free calls. Although no two phone companies seem to have the same idea as to what an Advanced Intelligent Network is, (some call it just an Intelligent Network), it generally includes three basic elements:

1. Signal Control Points. SCPs. Computers that hold databases in which customer-specific information used by the network to route calls is stored.

2. Signal Switching Points. SSPs. Digital telephone switches, which can talk to SCPs and ask them for customer-specific instructions as to how the call should be completed.

3. Signal Transfer Points. STPs. Packet switches that shuttle messages between SSPs and SCPs.

All three communicate via out of band signaling, typically using Signaling System 7 (SS7) protocol. The AIN has increased in complexity, as carriers have added voice response equipment that can prompt callers to enter further instructions as to how they'd like their call handled. Despite the differences between AIN networks, all work fundamentally the same, according to Mark Langner of TeleChoice, Verona, NJ: The SS7 identifies that a call requires intelligent network processing. The SSP creates a query to find out how this call should be handled. The query is passed via out-of-band signaling through STPs to an SCP. That interprets the query based on the criteria in its database and information provided by the SSP. Once the SSP has determined how the calls is to be handled, it returns a message through STPs to the SSP. This message instructs the SSP how the call should be handled in the network. According to Langner, the number of actions that could take place at the SCP are truly infinite. The call could be translated into a different number for completion. It could be routed to a user's private network for on-net handling. It could be sent to a voice response unit in the carrier network, where a message is played to the caller. Or it could even be blocked, preventing completion of the call.

Ericsson has done focus groups on Mobile Intelligent Network Services. Among the new IN (Intelligent Network) services, Ericsson identified: * Enhanced number translation services functions * Enhanced screening services, i.e. selective call diversion * Selective forwarding of calls * Location-dependent call forwarding * Improvements to voice announcements * Services to support fixed and mobile integration, i.e. personal communications services, PCS and universal personal telecommunications, UPT, and * Enhanced billing.

See IN, NCD, SCP, SiteRP, SS7, SSP, STP and the AIN definitions below.

AIN RELEASE O Advanced Intelligent Network Release defined by individual Bell Operating Companies for initial deployment in 1991, or so. See AIN.

AIN REL O.1 Advanced Intelligent Network Release provides for some additional functionality and more extensions to Rel 0.0. Contains 5 trigger detection points. Promised deployment by NT and AT&T by mid 1994. See AIN.

AIN RELEASE 0.0 Advanced Intelligent Network Release based on Ameritech specifications with input from Bellcore and some vendors. Contains three trigger detection points. Deployed in 1992 (US) and end of 1993 (Canada). First service for this architecture was "Switch Redirect" for Bell Atlantic (for switch or line failure.) See AIN.

AIN REL 1.0 Advanced Intelligent Network Release target architecture for AIN. Researched by US West 1991. Contains 32 trigger detection points. Too difficult/complicated for switch vendors to implement right now. (Hence Rel 0.0 & 0.1). See AIN.

AIN RELEASE 1 LOGICAL RESOURCES For Bell Operating Companies, the logical network resources configured and updated to provide Advanced Intelligent Network Release 1 subscriber services (e.g., SLP and trigger data). Definition from Bellcore. See AIN.

AIN RELEASE 1 SWITCHING SYSTEM An access tandem, local tandem or end office that contains an ASC (Advanced Intelligent Network Release 1 Switch Capabilities) functional group. Definition from Bellcore. See AIN.

AIN RELEASE 2 An Advanced Intelligent Network Release for initial deployment in 1995, involving from AIN Release 1 and supporting an expanded range of information networking services from the Bell operating telephone companies. Definition from Bellcore. See AIN.

AIN SWITCH CAPABILITIES ASC. A functional group residing in an Advanced Intelligent Network Release 1 Switching System that contains the Network Access, Service Switching, Information Management, Service Assistance and Operations FEs (Functional Entities). Definition from Bellcore. See AIN.

AINTCC Automated INTercept Call Completion. A new feature of Northern Telecom's central offices. The AINTCC feature provides options for

- connecting a caller automatically to an intercepted number after hearing an announcement, or

- connecting a caller to an intercepted number without an announcement.

Not using an announcement makes the number change transparent to the caller. The called (intercepted) party then has the option of informing the caller of the number change.

AIOD Automatic Identification of Outward Dialing is the ability of the telephone system to know the specific extension placing a call. It's used as part of the process of recording the detail of each telephone call for billback and cost control purposes. See AIOD LEADS and CALL ACCOUNTING SYSTEM.

AIOD LEADS Terminal equipment leads used solely to transmit automatic identified outward dialing (AIOD) data from a PBX to the public switched telephone network or to switched service networks (e.g., EPSDS), so that a vendor can provide a detailed monthly bill identifying long-distance usage by individual PBX extensions, tie-trunks, or the attendant.

AIR CONDITIONING In the Department of Defense, air conditioning is a synonym for the term "environmental control," which is the process of simultaneously controlling the temperature, relative humidity, air cleanliness, and air motion in a space to meet the requirements of the occupants, a process, or equipment.

AIR SPACE COAXIAL CABLE One in which air is the essential dielectric material. A spirally wound synthetic filament of spacer may be used to center the conductor.

AIRBRUSH A computer imaging term. A fine-mist paint tool used to create halos, fog, clouds, and similar effects. Most paint programs let you control the size and shape of the application area. Some packages provide a transparency adjustment that determines the density of the applied color.

AIRCRAFT EARTH STATION A mobile Earth station in the aeronautical mobile-satellite service located on board an aircraft.

AIRLINE MILEAGE The monthly charge for many leased circuits is billed on the basis of "airline mileage" between the two points. Though it sounds as if it's the distance a crow would fly directly between the two points, when in reality, it is the distance in mileage between two Rate Centers whose position is laid down according to industry standards, originally created by AT&T. The entire U.S. is divided by a vertical and horizontal grid. The coordinates — vertical and horizontal — of each rate center are defined and applied to a square root formula which yields the distance between the two points. Think back to school. There's a right-angled triangle. At the top is one Rate Center. At the side is the other Rate Center. The horizontal is the horizontal coordinate. The vertical is the vertical coordinate. The formula is simple: Square the vertical distance. Square the horizontal distance. Add the two together. Then take their square root. That will give you the distance across the hypotenuse — the side opposite the right angle in the triangle. Thus, your "airline" mileage. For sample V and H city coordinates and the formula on how to calculate airline mileage, see V & H under the letter V.

AIRLINE MILES See AIRLINE MILEAGE.

AIRTIME Actual time spent talking on a cellular telephone. Most cellular carriers bill their customers based on how many minutes of airtime they use each month. Whether the calls are incoming or outgoing makes no difference, the customer is still billed. Whether the calls are going to a toll-number or a toll-free 800 number also makes no difference. The customer racks up airtime and he pays. The more minutes of time spent talking on the phone, the higher the bill. Airtime charges during peak periods of the day in North America vary from 25 to 80 cents per minute. Most carriers offer a discount on these rates for off-peak usage. Some carriers offer a discount on these rates if the customer pays a higher minimum usage charge each month.

AIS Alarm Indication Signal. Formerly called a "Blue Alarm" or "Blue Signal." A signal that replaces the normal traffic signal when a maintenance alarm indication has been activated. An AIS is a signal transmitted downstream informing that an upstream failure has been detected.

AIX Advanced Interactive eXecutive: IBM's implementation of UNIX. The Open Software Foundation (OSF) based its first operating system (OSF-1) on AIX. The next revision of the OSF operation system (OSF-2) will also be based on AIX with a Mach kernel (Mach was developed by Carnegie Mellon University).

AIW Application Implementer's Workshop. A group of vendors working with IBM to develop software and hardware consistent IBM's Advanced Peer-to-Peer Networking protocol.

AKO Bisync acknowledgment for even-numbered message.

ALAP AppleTalk Link Access Protocol. In an AppleTalk network, this link access-layer (or data link-layer) protocol governs packet transmission on LocalTalk.

ALARM DISPLAY Attendant console indicators show the status (i.e. what's happening) in the telephone system. There are usually two types of displays — minor and major. Minor displays may be something as "minor" as a "hung" trunk, i.e. one that didn't hang up when the person speaking on it hung up. They can often be remedied by turning the PBX off, counting to ten, and then turning it on. (Before you do, check it will load itself.) Major problems — such as a blown line card in the PBX, one console out or half the trunks out — often require a service call and are often covered under the Emergency Conditions section of telephone service contracts.

ALARM INDICATION SIGNAL AIS. A signal that replaces the normal traffic signal when a maintenance alarm indication has been activated.

ALBO Automatic Line BuildOut. ALBO is a means of automatic cable equalization used in T-1 span-line interface equipment.

ALC 1. Automatic Level Control. 2. See AUTOMATIC LIGHT CONTROL.

ALE 1. Approvals Liaison Engineer. This engineer acts on your behalf to asses design and component changes to your BABT approved products. BABT is the British Approvals Board for Telecommunications. 2. See AUTOMATIC LINK ESTABLISHMENT

ALERTER In an AT&T ISDN phone, the alerter takes the place of a mechanical ringer. The alerter has eight ringing signals, eight personalized ringing patterns, and the ability to play music.

ALERTER SERVICE A Window NT term. Notifies selected users and computers of administrative alerts that occur on a computer. Used by the Server and other services. Requires the Messenger service.

ALERTING A signal sent to a customer, PBX or switching system to indicate an incoming call. A common form is the signal that rings a bell in the telephone set. Others signals can trigger such devices as whistles, gongs and chimes.

ALERTING SIGNAL A ringing signal put on subscriber access lines to indicate an incoming call. Bellcore defines an alerting signals more broadly; thus: "Alerting signals (for example, ringing, receiver off-hook) are transmitted over the loop to notify the customer of some activity on the line."

ALEX Software which provides Internet users with a transparent read capability of remote files at anonymous FTP sites.

ALIAS A nickname for a domain or host computer on the Internet.

ALGORITHM A prescribed finite set of well defined rules or processes for the solution of a problem in a finite number of steps. In normal English, it is the mathematical formula for an operation, such as computing the check digits on packets of data that travel via packet switched networks.

ALI Automatic Location Information. ALI is a feature of E-911 (Enhanced 911) systems. ALI is provided to agents answering E-911 calls. It may include information such as name, phone number, address, nearest cross street and special pre-existing conditions (i.e. hazardous materials). On some systems it may also provide the appropriate emergency service address for the particular address. ALI is retrieved from a computer database. The database may be held on site or at a remote location and may be maintained by the local phone company (or its parent) or another agency.

ALIAS 1. A feature of the Apple Macintosh System 7 allowing the user to create a file that points to the original file. When you click on an alias, the original application is launched. Aliases can work across a network; so you can access a program residing on a file server or a Mac that runs System 7 file sharing. 2. An assumed name under which users of an electronic bulletin board may post messages. For example, Jane Smith may post as "Marketing Group." The system usually provides a list of aliases and the names of the users to which they belong. Some BBS packages allow anonymous message posting. 3. Unwanted signals generated during the A-to-D (Analog to Digital) conversion process. This is typically caused by a sampling rate that is too low to faithfully represent the original analog signal in digital form. Typically, a rate that is less than half the highest frequency to be sampled.

ALIASING Distortion in a video signal. It shows up in different ways depending on the type of aliasing in question. When the sampling rate interferes with the frequency of program material the aliasing takes the form of artifact frequencies that are known as sidebands. Spectral aliasing is caused by interference between two frequencies such the luminance and chrominance signals. It appears as herringbone patterns, wavy lines where straight lines should be and lack of color fidelity. Temporal aliasing is caused when information is lost between line or field scans. It appears when a video camera is focused on a CRT and the lack of scanning synchronization produces a very annoying flickering on the screen of the receiving device.

ALIGNED BUNDLE A bundle of optical fibers in which the relative spatial coordinates of each fiber are the same at the two ends of the bundle. Also called "Coherent Bundle."

ALIT Automatic Line Insulation Testing.

ALJ An administrative law judge appointed by a State Commission to review a Commission docket, such as a rate case or incentive regulation proposal, and to make recommendations to the Commissioners.

ALL CALL PAGING With this feature, a user can broadcast an announcement — a page — to someone through the speakers of all the telephones on the system and, possibly, any external loudspeakers. If you want instant fame, ask your secretary to call all the airports in the country and page you. Mike Todd, the movie mogul, used to have this secretary perform this wonderful task. Mr. Todd gave gigantic egos a whole new meaning.

ALL CHANNEL TUNING Ability of a television set to receive all assigned channels. VHF and UHF, channels 2 through 83.

ALL DIELECTRIC CABLE Cable made entirely of dielectric (insulating) materials without any metal conductors.

ALL NUMBER CALLING Once upon a time, the first two digits of telephone exchanges sort of corresponded to their location. For example, MU-8 meant Murray Hill 8 in Murray Hill, Manhattan, New York City. Then the phone company started running out of letters, so it went to All Number Calling. The All Number Calling provides a theoretical maximum of 792 central office exchange (NNX) codes per area code (NPA). This is derived on the basis of 800 NXX code combinations (8x10x10) leaving out eight special service combinations, including 411, 611, 911.

ALL TRUNKS BUSY When a user tries to make an outside call through a telephone system and receives a "fast" busy signal (twice as many signals as a normal busy in the same amount of time), he is usually experiencing the joy of All Trunks Busy. No trunks are available to handle that call. The trunks are all being used at that time for other calls or are out of service. These days, many long distance companies are replacing a "fast" busy signal with a recording that might say something like, "I'm sorry. All circuits are busy. Please try your call later."

ALLEN, ROBERT Chairman of the board of AT&T since 1988. In 1980, he headed a task force to look into AT&T's future. The recommendation of the task force: keep equipment manufacturing at all costs.

ALLIANCE TELECONFERENCING SERVICE A direct-dial AT&T service which allows you to teleconference as few as three and as many as 59 telephones around the world. You can dial the numbers to call or you can schedule a meeting, called "Meet-Me Service." If you want to set the conference up, you dial 0-700-456-1000, then punch in the number of locations, then put in the numbers, ending each with a #. End your dialing with another # — to add yourself to the teleconference.

ALLOY A combination of two or more metals that forms a new or different metal with specific or desirable qualities.

ALM 1. AppWare Loadable Module. A visual computer telephony applications generator that works on Novell's NetWare. An ALM works by tying into Novell NetWare's NLMs. See APPWARE. 2. Automated Loan Machine. Like an ATM (Automated Teller Machine), an ALM sits in the wall of a building or inside a building on a wall. However, instead of giving money you own, an ALM dispenses money in the form of an instant loan. One of the leading ALM manufacturing companies is Affinity Technologies of Columbia, South Carolina. Alan Fishman of Columbia Financial Partners contributed this definition. Mr. Fishman is a leading New York City venture capitalist, who helped Affinity get started. Mr. Fishman's company is Columbia Financial Partners. 3. Airline Miles. The method used to calculate the distance (for pricing purposes) of the point-to-point long distance lines in long distance telephone networks. See AIRLINE MILEAGE.

ALOHA A method of data transmission in which the device transmits whenever it wants to. If it gets an acknowledgement from the device it's trying to reach, it continues to transmit. If not (as in the case of a collision with someone else trying to transmit simultaneously), it starts all over again. The ALOHA method get its name from a dying satellite that was donated to university researchers in the Pacific. It was used to transmit data by satellites among South Sea islands, especially Hawaii. The ALOHA "method" — called "transmit at will" — was invented because the users were short of funds to develop more sophisticated data transmission protocols, and they had a free satellite, which typically had more bandwidth than they had stuff to send. See ALOHANET.

ALOHANET An experimental form of frequency modulation radio network developed by the University of Hawaii. Alohanet is implemented by creating transmission frames containing data, control information, and source and destination addresses which are broadcast for reception by the destination receiver and ignored by all others. Actually, Alohanet is an early version of Ethernet, the local area network technique. See ALOHA.

ALPETH Aluminum-polyethylene primary covering known as the sheath for aerial cable.

ALPHA 1. Only alphabetic characters. 2. A family of microprocessors from Digital Equipment Corporation first introduced in February 1992. The first chip introduced was the 21064, described by DEC as a .75 micron CMOS-based super-scalar, super-pipelined processor using dual instruction issue and a 150 MHz cycle time. By relying on its 64-bit RISC architecture, the Alpha can deliver 400 million instructions per second. 3. The first version of software. It typically has so many bugs you only let your employees play with it. A beta is the next version. It's a pre-release version and selected customers (and the press) become your guinea pigs.

ALPHA CHANNEL The upper 8 bits of the 32-bit data path in some 24-bit graphics adapters. The alpha channel is used by some software for controlling the color information in the lower 24 bits.

ALPHA GEEK The most knowledgeable, technically proficient person in an office or work group. "Ask Harry, he's the alpha geek around here."

ALPHA TEST Testing of product prototypes performed by the vendor. When testing is done by potential users, it's called a beta test.

ALPHABETIC Only alphabetic characters. See also ALPHANUMERIC.

ALPHANUMERIC A set of characters that contains both letters and numbers — either individually or in combination. Numeric is 12345. Alphabetic is ABCDEF: Alphanumeric is 1A4F6HH8. American and Australian zip codes are numeric. Canadian and English postal codes are alphanumeric. No one knows why.

ALPHANUMERIC DISPLAY A display on a phone or console showing calling phone number, called number, trunk number, type of call, class of service and perhaps, some other characteristics of the call. It may also contain instructions as to how to move the call around, set up a conference call, etc. The display may be liquid crystal or light emitting diode. Typically, it's liquid crystal.

ALPHANUMERIC MEMORY A cellular radio feature that allows you to store names with auto-dial phone numbers.

ALTAIR ETHERNET Motorola's name for its wireless local area network, which transmits at the very high frequency of 18 to 18 megahertz. Altair users need to fill out a small, one-page FCC application in order to use the system.

ALTEL Association of Long distance TELephone companies. A trade association composed of alternative (to AT&T) long distance carriers and resellers of long distance services.

ALTERNATE ANSWERING POSITION Usually refers to a second receptionist's desk which has a telephone switchboard or console functioning like the main one. Also refers to when the main receptionist is away from his/her desk, or is very busy taking calls, the telephone system automatically sends the calls to another console or to a phone that will be answered.

ALTERNATE BUFFER In a data communications device, the section of memory set aside for the transmission or receipt of data after the primary buffer is full. This helps the device control the flow of data so transmission is not interrupted due to lack of space for the incoming or outgoing data.

ALTERNATE LOCK CODE A three-digit lock code to be used with the partial lock feature in some cellular phones.

ALTERNATE RECIPIENT An electronic messaging term. In X.400 terms, a user or distribution list that a recipient MTA (Message Transfer Agent) delivers a message to (if allowed) when the message cannot be sent to the preferred recipient.

ALTERNATE ROUTE A second or subsequent choice path between two exchanges, usually consisting of two or more circuit groups in tandem. Sometimes called "alternative route" or "second-choice route."

ALTERNATE ROUTING A feature used with long distance calls that permits the telephone system (typically a PBX) to send calls over different (alternate) phone lines. It might do this because of congestion of the primary phone lines the calls would normally be sent over. Alternate routing is often confused with LEAST COST ROUTING, in which the telephone system chooses the least expensive way (available at that time) to route that call. Least Cost Routing typically works with so-called "look-up" tables in the memory of the PBX. These tables are put into the PBX by the user. The PBX does not automatically know how to route each call. It must be told by the user. That "telling" might be as simple as saying "all 312 area codes will go via the AT&T FX line." Or it might be as complex as actually listing which exchanges in the 312 area code go by which method. LEAST COST ROUTING tells the calls to go over the lines which are perceived by the user to be the least cost way of getting the call from point A to point B. Alternate routing happens when the least cost routes get congested and alternate routes (typically more expensive) are found from the look-up tables in the PBX's memory.

ALTERNATE USE The ability to switch communications facilities from one type of service to another, i.e., voice to data, etc.

ALTERNATE VOICE DATA AVD. An older service which is a single transmission facility which can be used for either voice or data (up to 9600 bps). Arrangement includes a manually operated switch (on each end) to allow customers to alternately connect the line to their modem or PBX.

ALTERNATING CURRENT See AC.

ALTERNATIVE NON-TRAFFIC SENSITIVE COST-RECOVERY PLANS New charges proposed by the regional Bell holding companies to supplement subscriber line charges. In short, another charge on the subscriber with an interesting, though dubious, justification. They have not been fully implemented.

ALTERNATIVE REGULATORY FRAMEWORK ARF.

ALTERNATOR A machine which generates electricity which is alternating current. See AC.

ALTS Alternative Access Providers to the local telephone network i.e., Teleport.

ALU Arithmetic Logic Unit. The part of the CPU (Central Processing Unit) that performs the arithmetic and logical operations. See MICROPROCESSOR.

ALVYN Aluminum-polyethylene, the sheath used for riser cable where a flame retardant sheath is required.

AM See Amplitude Modulation.

AMA Automatic Message Accounting. AMA is the phone company's name for Call Detail Recording or Station Message Detail Recording (SMDR). See AMA TAPE.

AMA TAPE A telephone company machine-readable magnetic tape which contains the customer's long distance calling and billing data for a given month.

AMA TELEPROCESSING SYSTEM AMATPS. The primary method for delivery of AMA data from the network to billing systems. The current AMATPS architecture consists of an AMA Transmitter (AMAT) and a collector. Definition from Bellcore.

AMATPS AMA TeleProcessing System.

AMBIENT LIGHTING The general level of illumination throughout a room or area.

AMD Air Moving Device. IBM-speak for a fan.

AMBIENT NOISE The level of noise present all the time. There is always noise, unless you're in an anechoic chamber. When measured with a sound level meter, it is usually measured in decibels above a reference pressure level of 0.00002 pascal in SI units, or 0.00002 dyne per square centimeter in cgs units.

AMERICA ONLINE An on-line computer service you call with your PC or Macintosh which provides e-mail, forums, software downloads, news, weather, sports, financial information, conferences, on-line gaming, an encyclopedia, and other features, to its subscribers.

AMERICAN BELL, INC. The old name for the unregulated telephone equipment supply subsidiary of American Telephone & Telegraph. American Bell Inc. had its name changed to AT&T Information Systems. At that point it was no longer separately incorporated. It became a division of AT&T. It has been reorganized many times. When it was American Bell, it was only selling telecommunications products and services to end users. When it become AT&T Information Systems, it sold AT&T phone systems and AT&T computer systems. It then merged with AT&T Long Lines, which was then called AT&T Communications and is now called simply AT&T. By the time you read this, it will probably be called something else. Sadly, old gadgetry, knick-knacks and momentos bearing the name American Bell, Inc. have no marketable value as antiques or examples of American folk art.

AMERICAN NATIONAL STANDARDS INSTITUTE See ANSI.

AMERICAN STANDARD CODE FOR INFORMATION INTERCHANGE ASCII. The standard 7-bit code for transferring information asynchronously on local and long distance telecommunications lines. The ASCII code enables you to represent 128 separate numbers, letters, and control characters. By using an eighth bit — as in extended ASCII or IBM's EBCDIC — you can represent 256 different characters. ASCII often uses an eighth bit as a parity check or a way of encoding word processing symbols, not as a way of broadening the number of characters and symbols which it can represent. See also ASCII.

AMERICAN WIRE GAUGE AWG. Standard measuring gauge for non-ferrous conductors (i.e. non-iron and non-steel). AWG covers copper, aluminum, and other conductors. Gauge is a measure of the diameter of the conductor. See AWG for a bigger explanation.

AMERITECH Ameritech Corp is one of the Regional Bell operating companies formed as a result of the AT&T Divestiture. Ameritech covers five states and includes the operating telephone companies: Illinois Bell, Indiana Bell, Michigan Bell, Ohio Bell, and Wisconsin Bell. It also includes some other subsidiaries, which fit into two classifications — administrative (centralized buying, real estate, etc.) or entrepreneurial (cellular mobile radio, venture capital, etc.).

AMI Alternate Mark Inversion. The line-coding format in T-1 transmission systems whereby successive ones (marks) are alternately inverted (sent with polarity opposite that of the preceding mark). Here's AT&T definition: A line code that employs a ternary signal to convey binary digits, in which successive binary ones are represented by signal elements that are normally of alternating, positive and negative polarity but equal in amplitude, and in which binary zeros are represented by signal elements that have zero amplitude. This is an AT&T definition.

AMIS See AUDIO MESSAGING INTERCHANGE SPECIFICATION. A standard for networking voice mail systems.

AML Anolog Microwave Link

AMPACITY The maximum current an insulated wire or cable can safely carry without excluding either the insulation or jacket materials limitations.

AMPERAGE RATING The amperage which may be safely applied to a circuit, service or equipment. See also AMPERE.

AMPERE The unit of measurement of electric current or the flow of electrons. One volt of potential across a one ohm impedance causes a current flow of one ampere. AMP is the abbreviation for ampere. It is mathematically equal to watts divided by volts. Note that in the electrical context, WATTS is spelled with two "Ts." In telecommunications, WATS, meaning Wide Area Telecommunications Service, is spelled with only one "T."

AMPERE-HOUR UNIT Measurement of battery capacity, determined by multiplying the current delivered by the time it is delivered for. See AMPERE.

AMPHENOL CONNECTOR Amphenol is a manufacturer of electrical and electronic connectors. They make many different models, many of which are compatible with products made by other companies. Their most famous connector is probably the 25-pair connector used on 1A2 key telephones and for connecting cables to many electronic key systems and PBXs. The telephone companies call the 25-pair Amphenol connector used as a demarcation point the RJ-21X. The RJ-21X connector is made by other companies including 3M, AMP and TRW. People in the phone business often call non-amphenol 25-pair connectors, amphenol connectors.

AMPLIFIED HANDSET An amplified handset is the best phone gadget you can buy. You use it to crank up the volume of incoming calls (and in some cases the volume of outgoing calls) and save yourself enormous amounts of money on callbacks. "We have a bad line. I'll call you back." There are three types of amplified handsets:

1. The handset with a built-in amplifier. These devices suck their power from the phone line and since the phone line doesn't have much power, you won't have much amplification. I'm not overly impressed with amplified handsets. 2. The handset with amplifying circuits built into the phone. Ditto for our comments about power. 3. The handset with the little external box amplifier which is powered by either AC or by several batteries, typically AA alkalines. Such an external amplifier will produce much greater amplification. This is the type we prefer at TELECONNECT Magazine.

AMPLIFIER When telephone conversations travel through a medium, such as a copper wire, they encounter resistance and thus become weaker and more difficult to hear. An amplifier is an electrical device which strengthens the signal. Unfortunately, amplifiers in analog circuits also strengthen noise and other extraneous garbage on the line. Amplifiers are used in all telephone systems, analog and digital. But in digital systems, signals are regenerated and then amplified. As a result, noise is much less prevalent and less likely to be amplified in digital systems.

AMPLITUDE The distance between high or low points of a waveform or signal. Also referred to as the wave "height." See AMPLITUDE MODULATION.

AMPLITUDE DISTORTION The difference between the output wave shape and the input wave shape.

AMPLITUDE EQUALIZER A corrective network that is designed to modify the amplitude characteristics of a circuit or system over a desired frequency range. Such devices may be fixed, manually adjustable, or automatic.

AMPLITUDE MODULATION Also called AM, it's a method of adding information to an electronic signal in which the signal is varied by its height to impose information on it. "Modulation" is the term given to imposing information on an electrical signal. The information being carried causes the amplitude (height of the sine wave) to vary. In the case of LANs, the change in the signal is registered by the receiving device as a 1 or a 0. A combination of these conveys different information, such as words, numbers or punctuation marks. The principal forms of Amplitude Modulation are QDM: Double-band Amplitude Modulation QAM: Quadrature Amplitude Modulation SSB: Single-sideband Modulation VSB: Vestigial Sideband Modulation

AMPS Advanced Mobile Phone Service. It's another word for analog cellular radio. Advanced Mobile Phone Service is the term used by AT&T's Bell Laboratories (prior to the break-up in 1984) to refer to its cellular technology. The AMPS standard has been the foundation for the industry in the United States, although it has been slightly modified in recent years. "AMPS-compatible" means equipment designed to work with most analog cellular telephones. Digital cellular is called D-AMPS.

AMS 1. Account Management System. 2. Attendant Management System. An NEC term. With the NEAX2400 IMS, the AMS is an on-screen, dynamic Open Applications Interface (OAI) computer application that emulates and enhances attendant console capabilities. A typical AMS workstation combines the NEC HDAC console and headset with a color display and standard keyboard. The computer is equipped with the UNIX System V operating system, the NEC Applications Manager support platform, and a comprehensive package of software components. Communication between the HDAC and the AMS computer software is made possible by the OAI connection between the computer and the NEAX2400 IMS (ICS).

ANA Assigned Night Answer.

ANALOG Comes from the word "analogous," which means "similar to." In telephone transmission, the signal being transmitted — voice, video, or image — is "analogous" to the original signal. In other words, if you speak into a microphone and see your voice on an oscilloscope and you take the same voice as it is transmitted on the phone line and ran that signal into the oscilloscope, the two signals would look essentially the same. The only difference is that the electrically transmitted signal (the one over the phone line) is at a higher frequency. In correct English usage, "analog" is meaningless as a word by itself. But in telecommunications, analog means telephone transmission and/or switching which is not digital. Outside the telecom industry, analog is often called linear and covers the physical world of time, temperature, pressure, sound, which are represented by time-variant electrical characteristics, such as frequency and voltage. See ANALOG TRANSMISSION.

ANALOG BRIDGE A circuit which allows a normal two-person voice conversation to be extended to include a third person without degrading the quality of the call.

ANALOG CELLULAR The current standard for cellular communications.

ANALOG CHANNEL A channel which transmits in analog waveforms. See ANALOG.

ANALOG COMPUTER A computer that performs its tasks by measuring continuous physical variables — pressure, voltage, flow — and manipulating these variables to produce a solution, which is then converted into a numerical equivalent. Analog computers are largely used as special purpose machines in scientific or technical applications. The earliest analog computers were purely mechanical devices with levers, cogs, cams, etc., representing the data or operator values. Modern analog computers typically employ electrical parameters such as voltage, resistance, or current to represent the quantities being manipulated.

ANALOG DIGITAL CONVERTER An A/D Converter. Pronounced: "A to D Converter." A device which converts an analog signal to a digital signal.

ANALOG FACSIMILE Facsimile which can transmit and receive grey shadings — not just black and white. It is called analog because of its ability to transmit what appear to be continuous shades of grey. "Analog" facsimile is usually transmitted digitally.

ANALOG FRONT END The part of the fax machine that converts between the digitally modulated signal and the analog signal used on the telephone line.

ANALOG LOOP-BACK A method of testing modems and data terminals by disconnecting the device from the telephone line and looping a signal out through the device's transmit side and in through its receive side. The test tells if the trouble is with the telephone line or with the modem.

ANALOG MONITOR A computer screen that uses an analog signal, a smoothly varying value of current or voltage that varies continuously. VGA, SVGA and Macintosh models are examples of analog monitors. Most computer screens are analog. Most analog monitors are designed to accept input signals at a precise frequency. Higher frequencies are needed to carry higher-resolution images to the monitor. For this reason, multiscanning monitors have been developed that automatically adjust themselves to the incoming frequency. See also ANALOG and DIGITAL MONITOR.

ANALOG RECORDING System of recording in which music is converted into electrical impulses that form "patterns" in the grooves of phonograph record masters or in the oxide particles of master tapes representing (or analogous to) musical waveforms.

ANALOG SWITCH Telephone switching equipment that switches signals without changing the analog form. The major form of analog switching is circuit switching.

ANALOG SYNCHRONIZATION A synchronization control system in which the relationship between the actual phase error between clocks and the error signal device is a continuous function over a given range.

ANALOG TERMINAL ADAPTER ATA. A Northern Telecom telephone device permits analog devices (for example, faxs, answering machines, and single line telephones) to connect to the Northern Telecom Norstar telephone system.

ANALOG TRANSMISSION A way of sending signals — voice, video, data — in which the transmitted signal is analogous to the original signal. In other words, if you spoke into a microphone and saw your voice on an oscilloscope and you took the same voice as it was transmitted on the phone line and threw that signal onto the oscilloscope, the two signals would look essentially the same. The only difference would be that the electrically transmitted signal would be at a higher frequency.

ANALOG VIDEO Signals represented by an infinite number of smooth transitions between video levels. TV signals are analog. By contrast, a digital video signal assigns a finite set of levels. Because computer signals are digital, analog video must be converted into a digital form before it can be shown on a computer screen.

ANALOG WIRELESS The dominant radio transmission standard in the United States; also called AMPS.

ANALOGUE An English/European way of spelling ANALOG, which is the correct North American spelling. See ANALOG.

ANAMORPHIC Unequally scaled in vertical and horizontal dimensions.

ANC All Number Calling.

AND Automatic Network Dialing.

ANECHOIC CHAMBER A perfectly quiet room. A room in which sound or radio waves do not reflect off the walls. An anechoic chamber is the only place in which a speakerphone will work perfectly. The more a room resembles an anechoic chamber — i.e. lots of drapes, plush carpet, etc. — the better a speakerphone will work.

ANGLE MODULATION Modulation in which phase angle or frequency of a sine wave carrier is varied.

ANGLE OF DEVIATION In fiber optics, the net angular deflection experienced by a light ray after one or more refractions or reflections. The term is generally used in reference to prisms, assuming air interfaces. The angle of deviation is then the angle between the incident ray and the emergent ray.

ANGLE OF INCIDENCE The angle between an incident ray and the normal to a reflecting or refracting surface.

ANGLED END An optical fiber whose end is deliberately polished at an angle to reduce reflections.

ANGSTROM A unit of length in optical measurement.

ANGULAR MISALIGNMENT LOSS The optical power loss caused by angular deviation from the optimum alignment of source to optical fiber — fiber-to-fiber, or fiber-to-detector.

ANI Automatic Number Identification. A phone call arrives at your home or office. Somewhere in that phone call is a series of digits which tell you the phone number of the phone calling you. These digits may arrive in analog or digital form. They may arrive as touchtone digits inside the phone call or in a digital form on the same circuit or on a separate circuit. You will need some equipment to decipher the digits AND to do "something" with them. That "something" might be throwing them into a database and bringing your customer's record up on a screen in front of your telephone agent as he answers the call. "Good morning, Mr. Smith." Some large users say they could save as much as 30 seconds on the average IN-WATS call if they knew the phone number of the person calling them. They would avoid asking regular customers for routine identification information since it would all be there in the database. ANI is touted as one of ISDN's most compelling advantages — but it is really an advantage of Signaling System 7 (and therefore distinct from ISDN) and you don't need ISDN to get ANI. In the US, there are various types of "ANI." There's the ANI you get from a long distance phone company, which may arrive over the D channel of an ISDN PRI circuit or on a dedicated single line before the first ring. In contrast, the signaling for Caller ID, as delivered by a local phone company, is delivered between the first and second rings. In Canada, caller ID for both local and long distance is delivered in the same technical way — between the first and second rings. In the US, there are no accepted standards, as yet. In November of 1995, local phone companies in the US are scheduled to deliver both local and long distance ANI exactly as they do today in Canada — between the first and second rings. Thus normal dial-up users, who subscribe to caller ID (and usually pay a few extra dollars a month for the privilege) will be able to figure who's calling before, or as they pick up the incoming call. At one stage, ANI was not available in many states. But those restrictions are disappearing. There are some people who believe ANI is long distance and delivered by long distance phone companies; and Caller ID is local and delivered by local phone companies. And these same people believe the technologies of delivery are different. In reality, ANI and Caller ID are rapidly becoming synonymous. See CALLER ID, CLASS, COMMON CHANNEL SIGNALING, DNIS, ISDN and ISUP.

ANIMA Someone who communicates with you telepathically.

ANIMATION The process of displaying a sequential series of still images to achive a motion effect.

ANISOCHRONOUS Pertaining to transmission in which the time interval separating any two significant instants in sequential signals is not necessarily related to the time interval separating any other two significant instants. Isochronous and anisochronous are characteristics, while synchronous and asynchronous are relationships.

ANISOTROPIC Pertaining to a material whose electrical or optical properties vary with the direction of propagation or with different polarizations of a traveling wave.

ANM ANswer Message. The fourth of the ISUP call set-up messages. A message sent in the backward direction indicating that the call has been answered. See ISUP and COMMON CHANNEL SIGNALING.

ANNEAL The act of using heat to soften a metal such as copper, making it less brittle.

ANNEX A The first of the frame relay standard extensions, Annex A outlines provisions for a Local Management Interface (LMI) between customer premises equipment and the frame relay network for the purpose of querying network status information

ANNEX D The second frame relay standard extension dealing with the communication and signaling between customer premises equipment and frame relay network equipment for the purpose of querying network status information.

ANNOUNCEMENT SERVICE Allows a phone user to hear a recording when he dials a certain phone number or extension. These days, announcement services are provided increasingly by totally solid-state digital announcers. These gadgets are more reliable, deliver a clearer message and last much longer than analog tape-based machines (like answering machines), which use recording tape.

ANNOUNCEMENT SYSTEM A arrangement for providing information by means of recorded announcements.

ANNOYANCE CALL BUREAU The department in your local phone company which you call when you need help with annoying or harassing phone calls you are receiving. The Bureau will recommend you file a report with your local phone company. And then it may apply TRAP and TRACE equipment and techniques to try to locate the source of your annoying phone calls. The Annoyance Call Bureau is the stepchild of the phone industry, which means it is typically underfunded. See TRAP and TRACE.

ANNUAL PERCENTAGE RATE APR. A percentage calculation of the finance charge portion of financing contact.

ANNULAR RING An indicator (or ring) around the circumference of the coaxial cable every so many feet — often 2.5 meters (8.2 feet) — to indicate a point where transceivers are to be connected. Same as transceiver attachment mark.

ANNUNCIATOR Original name for the indicator on magnetic switchboards which indicates the particular line that is calling the exchange. Now it is simply a light, a bell or a device that tells you something. That something might be the ringing of a phone or it might be a problem that you're having with some piece of remote equipment. A communicating annunciator is a sophisticated device that is connected to a phone line and gets on that line (dial-up or leased) to let you know that something is broken.

ANONYMOUS CALL REJECTION ACR. A service some local phone companies are providing their subscribers. It allows subscribers to automatically stop certain calls from ringing their phone. The calls stopped are "restricted," namely they would be displayed as "P" or "Private" on a subscriber's Caller ID device, meaning that the calling person did not send you his calling number. The person who makes such a call would hear, "We're sorry. The party you have reached is not accepting private calls. To make your call, hang up, dial *82 or 1182 on a rotary phone and re-dial." The caller will be able to reach you only by re-dialing without restricting display of his or her number.

ANONYMOUS FTP A way of logging in anonymously to distant hosts on the Internet and often freeware (free software) from the Internet. With an implementation of the FTP protocol, users can get public domain software from Internet sites, using the word "anonymous" for a login ID, and their userid@hostname.domain as the password. A database called Archie contains a list of what is available from anonymous FTP sites, and can be reached at "archie.mcgill.ca" and at "archie.sura.net." See FTP.

ANONYMOUS TELEPHONE NUMBER A telephone number that should not be displayed or voiced back to the called party. Such a designation is stored in switch memory and is included in signaling information sent to the terminating switch for interSPCS calls.

ANS Answer. (What else?)

ANSI American National Standards Institute. A standards-setting, non-government organization, which develops and publishes standards for "voluntary" use in the United States. The British have their own equivalent of ANSI. It's called the BSI, British Standards Institute. Standards set by national organizations are accepted by vendors in that country. ANSI is located at 1430 Broadway, New York NY 10018 212-642-4900. They put out a biweekly newsletter called "ANSI Standards in Action." See also CCITT, ECMA, IEEE, and ISO. See ANSI CHARACTER SET. www.ansi.org

In a press release, ANSI described itself as "a private non-profit membership organization that coordinates the U.S. voluntary standards system, bringing together interests from the private and public sectors to develop voluntary standards for a wide array of U.S. industries. ANSI is the official U.S. member body to the world's leading standards bodies — the International Organization for Standardization and the International Electronic Commission via the U.S. National Committee. The Institute's membership includes approximately 1,300 national and international companies, 30 government agencies, 20 institutions and 250 professional, technical, trade, labor and consumer organizations."

ANSI TIX9.4 ANSI's Sonet standard.

ANSI T1.110-1987 Signaling system number 7 (SS7) - General Information.

ANSI T1.111-1988 Signaling system number 7 (SS7) - Message Transfer Part (MTP)

ANSI T1.112-1988 Signaling System number 7 (SS7) - Signaling Connection Control Part (SCCP)

ANSI T1.113-1988 Signaling System 7 (SS7) - Integrated Services Digital Network (ISDN) user part.

ANSI T1.114-1988 Signaling System 7 (SS7) - Transaction Capability Application Part (TCAP)

ANSI T1.206 Digital Exchanges and PBXs - Digital circuit loopback test lines.

ANSI T1.301 ANSI ADPCM standard.

ANSI T1.401-1988 Interface between carriers and customer installations - Analog voice grade switched access lines using loop-start and ground-start signaling.

ANSI T1.501-1988 Network performance - Tandem encoding limits for 32 Kbit/s Adaptive Differential Pulse-Code Modulation (ADPCM).

ANSI T1.601-1988 Integrated Services Digital Network (ISDN) - Basic access interface for use on metallic loops for application on the network side of the NT (Layer 1 specification).

ANSI T1.605-1989 Integrated Services Digital Network (ISDN) - Basic access interface for S and T reference points (Layer 1 specification).

ANSI T1.Q1 ANSI's standard for telecommunications network performance standards, switched exchange access network transmission performance standard exchange carrier-to-interexchange carrier standards.

ANSI X3T9.5 TPDDI Twisted-Pair Distributed Data Interface (TPDDI) is a new technology that allows users to run the FDDI standard 100 Mbps transmission speed over twisted-pair wiring. Unshielded twisted-pair has been tested for distances over 50 meters (164 ft.). TPDDI is designed to help users make an earlier transition to 100 Mbps at the workstation.

ANSI CHARACTER SET The American National Standards Institute 8-bit character set. It contains 256 characters.

ANSI.SYS A device driver is used by MS-DOS to control output to the screen. Some (very few) MS-DOS programs require you to have the statement DEVICE=ANSI.SYS in your CONFIG.SYS file. It provides the "buttons" that these programs then push to make certain things happen on the screen. The "buttons" are pushed by ANSI.SYS commands. The commands begin with Escape (character 27 in ASCII) followed by a left bracket. You can simply type these commands to make the screen change color, blink, etc., if you have the DEVICE=ANSI.SYS statement in your CONFIG.SYS file when you boot your PC. If you put the following line in your AUTOEXEC.BAT you will enjoy an attractive C: prompt.

Prompt $e[37;44;1m $_ DATE $d TIME $t $_$P$g

But note, loading ANSI.SYS will take an extra 7,000 bytes of so of RAM. and most programs — even those that use color, including Windows — don't use ANSI.SYS. They have color commands built in. My advice is simple: Don't load ANSI.SYS unless your program specifically demands it via an error message. Save yourself the RAM memory.

ANSI.SYS TERMINAL EMULATION ANSI.SYS is a popular terminal emulation used on many bulletin board systems. ANSI X3.64 control sequences are recognized to provide visual attributes including color display and full support of the IBM PC graphics character set. Some editors, chiefly those in communications packages such as Smartcom, are configured especially to create ANSI.SYS documents.

ANSWER BACK A signal or tone sent by a receiving equipment or data set to the sending station to indicate that it is ready to accept transmission. Or a signal or tone sent to acknowledge receipt of a transmission. See ANSWER SUPERVISION.

ANSWER BACK SUPERVISION Another word for answer supervision. See ANSWER SUPERVISION.

ANSWER CALL The name of a Bell Atlantic service. Here are Bell Atlantic's words. Answer Call is an answering machine without the machine. This automated messaging service answers your calls right through your touch-tone phone — 24 hours a day — even when you're on the phone. And since it's on Bell Atlantic network, there's no equipment to buy...nothing to turn to...no wires to connect... and no maintenance. By simply dialing a private passcode, you can listen to your messages, replay them or even change your greeting. What's more, Answer Call gives you the option of providing your employees (who share one line) with up to eight private "mailboxes" to receive and retrieve their own messages.

ANSWER DETECT The use of a digital signal processing technique to determine the presence of voice energy on a telephone line. It is used with call (answer) supervision, to identify an answered line. It's beginning to be used with computerized dialing equipment as it eliminates the need for a telephone representative to constantly monitor call set-up progress on each telephone line in the event a call is answered. See ANSWER SUPERVISION and ANSWER SIGNAL.

ANSWER MESSAGE ANM. A CCS/SS7 signaling message that informs the signaling points involved in a telephone call that the call has been answered and that call charging should start.

ANSWER MODE When a modem is set by the user to receive data, it is in Answer Mode. In any conversation involving two computers, two terminals or one computer and one terminal, one side of the conversation must always be in Answer Mode. Putting a modem/computer in answer mode is sometimes done through software and sometimes through hardware, i.e. a switch on the side of the machine. You cannot run a data communications "conversation" if both sending and receiving equipment are in "Answer Mode." Computers — mainframe and mini — which receive a lot of phone calls are typically put in "Answer Mode." The terminals or computers calling them are typically in transmit mode.

ANSWER SIGNAL A supervisory signal, usually in the form of a closed loop, returned from the called telephone to the originating switch when the called party answers. This signal stops the ringback signal from being returned to the caller.

ANSWER SUPERVISION Follow this scenario: I call you long distance. My central office must know when you answer your phone so my central office can start billing me for the call. It works like this: when you, the called party, answer your phone, your central office sends a signal back to my central office (the originating CO). This tells my central office to start billing me for the call. This signal is called Answer Supervision. Before the Divestiture of the Bell System in early 1984, most of the nation's long distance companies — with the exception of AT&T Communications — did not receive Answer Supervision. They did not know precisely when the called party answered. So they started their billing cycle after some time — 20 or 30 seconds after the caller completed dialing. These long distance companies presumed that after this time, some one will have answered and the call will be in progress and can then be timed and billed. Without Answer Supervision, their billing of calls is inaccurate. They may bill for calls which didn't occur. And you may pay more for calls which did occur.

With the Divestiture of the Bell System, and the introduction of Equal Access, the local phone companies have been told by the FCC that they must provide accurate answer supervision to all long distance phone. And with that answer supervision, the pricing of your long distance calls should be accurate. Not all long distance companies, however, choose to buy answer supervision (it costs a little more). And thus your long distance calls may still be billed inaccurately.

Check. If you are "accessing" your preferred long distance carrier by dialing a seven digit local number, then dialing your number and your account code, your carrier is probably not receiving Answer Supervision and the timing and billing of your long distance calls may be inaccurate. Check this out. Remember: just because your town has equal access doesn't mean your preferred long distance phone company has opted for it because it is expensive or for some other reason.

Virtually no hotels have answer supervision. So they start billing you arbitrarily. Some start billing you after three rings. Some after four. When you check out, carefully check your phone bill. You will, in most instances, find you have been billed for many uncompleted calls. Tell your family to pick up the phone quickly when you're out of town and may be calling them. Don't let the phone ring too many times as you're likely to be billed for the dubious pleasure of listening to ringing signals.

"Answer supervision" is getting better, however, as the electronics of "listening" to sounds on phone lines get better. Electronics are now available to do — to a 95% accuracy — what we as humans do — to a 100% accuracy — namely distinguish between a normal ringing sound, a fast busy sound and a person or fax machine answering the phone and saying "Hello." These electronics are getting better and less expensive, by the month. See ANSWER SUPERVISION-LINE SIDE.

ANSWER SUPERVISION-LINE SIDE Answer Supervision-Line Side is a service I first read about in a US West publication, which describes it as "providing an electrical signal that is passed back to the originating end of a switched connection. This signal indicates that the called line has gone off-hook. This service offering has applicability for record start and end, announcement start and end, dialtone reorigination prevention, call progress sequence indications, and other uses. This service offering may be used by terminal equipment (PBX, pay telephone, call diverter, etc). connected to the calling line to determine that the call has been answered."

ANSWERBACK In data communications, answerback is a response programmed into a data terminal to identify itself when polled by a remote computer or terminal. This response is usually in reply to a Control-E (ASCII Character 5, Inquiry), which is known on the Telex and TWX networks as a "Who Are You?" character, or "WRU." The Answerback allows a remote computer to verify it has dialed correctly (usually on the Telex or TWX networks) by matching the Answerback received with the Answerback expected.

ANSWERING TONE The tone an asynchronous modem will transmit when it answers the phone. The tone indicates that it is willing to accept data.

ANTC Advanced Networking Test Center. An FDDI interoperability testing center established in 1990.

ANTEDILUVIAN Before the flood. Very old fashioned.

ANTENNA A device for transmitting, receiving or transmitting and receiving signals. Antennas come in all shapes and sizes. Their shape depends on the frequency signal they're receiving. Electrical signals with frequencies higher on the spectrum, for example, are shorter and more directional. As they get higher on the spectrum, they look more like light. These must be focused and thus, require antennas which are shaped like the mirror reflector of a focusing flashlight. This parabolic shape focuses the broad beam (of the bulb or the electrical signal) into a narrow, focused beam. The weaker the received signal, the bigger the antenna must be. Antennas come in many varieties and have cute names, like parabola, caresgrain, helix, lens and horn.

ANTENNA GAIN The ratio, usually expressed in decibels, of the power required at the input of a loss-free reference antenna to the power supplied to the input of the given antenna to produce, in a given direction, the same field strength, or the same irradiance, at the same distance. When not specified otherwise, the gain refers to the direction of maximum radiation. The gain may be considered for a specified polarization.

ANTENNA LOBE A picture showing an antenna's radiation pattern. A more technical explanation: A three-dimensional radiation pattern of a directional antenna bounded by one or more cones of nulls (regions of diminished intensity).

ANTENNA MATCHING The process of adjusting impedance so that the input impedance of an antenna equals or approximates the characteristic impedance of its transmission line over a specified range of frequencies. The impedance of either the transmission line, or the antenna, or both, may be adjusted to effect the match.

ANTHROPOMORPHISM The process of giving human qualities to inanimate objects. For example, getting a file cabinet to talk about what's inside it, or getting a modem to explain how to do communications.

ANTI ALIASING A computer imaging term. A blending effect that smooths sharp contrasts between two regions of different colors. Properly done, this eliminates the jagged edges of text or colored objects. Used in voice processing, anti-aliasing usually refers to the process of removing spurious frequencies from waveforms produced by converting digital signals back to analog.

ANTI CURL A feature marketed by manufacturers of slimy paper fax machines (i.e. thermal paper). As the paper emerges from the fax machine, "anti-curl" simply sends the paper through a path which causes it to bend slightly in the opposite direction to which it was rolled over the roll. This bending purports to make the paper less curly when it emerges. It works to an extent. Virtually all slimy fax machines now have the "feature," though most don't advertise it.

ANTI REFLECTION COATING A thin, dielectric or metallic film (or several such films) applied to an optical surface to reduce its reflectance and thereby increase the transmittance of the optical fiber. The ideal value of the refractive index of a single layer film is the square root of the product of the refractive indices on either side of the film, the ideal optical thickness being one quarter of a wavelength.

ANTI STATIC A material, such as packing material, that is treated to prevent the build-up of static electricity. The static charges gradually dissipate instead of building up a sudden discharge.

ANTI STUFFING A mechanical flap in a coin phone which prevents the blocking by paper or other material of coin chutes. An anti-stuffing flap is meant to assure that you, the user, get your money back after you've tried to make a call but didn't get through.

ANTI TINKLING DEVICE Leahtta Welch of Tampa Florida

ANTI VIRAL PROGRAMS Programs which scan disks looking for the tell-tale signatures of computer viruses.

ANTIALIASING See ANTI ALIASING.

ANTICIPOINTMENT Raising people's levels of anticipation and then disappointing them. A definition contributed by Gerald Taylor, president, of MCI.

ANTISTATIC A material, such as packing material, that is treated to prevent the build-up of static electricity. The static charges gradually dissipate instead of building up a sudden discharge.

ANYLAN A proposed high speed local area network which Hewlett-Packard Co. and International Business Machines Corp. have created the specifications for. According to HP, AnyLAN will allow work groups operating token ring and ethernet lans to swap many more data-intensive applications at much greater speeds than at present. AnyLAN, which was announced in the early fall of 1993, is proposed to increase the speed and capacity of LANs sixfold to tenfold. HP and IBM announced they would give the technology of AnyLAN to any competitor free of charge, in order to establish it as a standard and expand the size of the total market.

ANYNET/MVS IBM product name for the ACF/VTAM feature that implements IBM's "Networking Blueprint" technology on hosts and OS/2 workstations and permits SNA LU 6.2 applications to work over TCP/IP or TCP/IP-oriented sockets applications to run over SNA.

ANYWHERE The name of an ISDN service from Bell Atlantic and BellSouth. New York Telephone thought up the name, but delayed so long implementing the service that either Northern Telecom or AT&T (one of the two ISDN equipment vendors to New York Telephone) took the idea to Bell Atlantic. And Bell Atlantic announced the service very quickly. This irritated New York Telephone's senior executives, especially its EVP at the time, Arnie Eckelman, who delayed introducing New York Telephone's own ISDN Anywhere for reasons that were unclear to both Northern and AT&T.

ANYWHERE FIX The ability of a Global Positioning System (GPS) receiver to start position calculations without being given an approximate location and approximate time. See GPS.

AoC Advice of Charge. A wireless telecommunications term. A supplementary service provided to a customer under GSM, Global System for Mobile Communications.

AOL A Windows-based on-line computer service you call with your PC which provides e-mail, forums, software downloads, news, weather, sports, financial information, conferences, on-line gaming, an encyclopedia, and other features, to its subscribers. Competitors include CompuServe and the Microsoft Network.

AOS Alternate Operator Services. Today there are many Operator Services Providers not owned by the Bell Telephone Companies or AT&T. The AOS industry is dropping the descriptive term "alternate" and communicating that they be known as OSPs. AOS was coined by AT&T. See AOSP and OPERATOR SERVICE PROVIDERS.

AOSP Alternate Operator Service Provider. A new breed of long distance phone company. It handles operator-assisted calls, in particular Credit Card, Collect, Third Party Billed and Person to Person. Phone calls provided by OSP companies are typically fare more expensive than phone calls provided by "normal" long distance companies, i.e. those which have their own long distance networks and which you see advertised on TV. You normally encounter an OSP only when you're making a phone call from a hotel or hospital phone, or a privately-owned payphone. It's a good idea to ask the operator the cost of your call before you make it.

AOSSVR Auxiliary Operator Services System Voice Response.

AOW Asia and Oceania Workshop. One of the three regional OSI Implementors' Workshops.

AP See ADD-ON or APPLICATIONS PROCESSOR. AP is an AT&T word for a piece of equipment which hangs off the side of their PBX and makes it do more things, like voice mail.

APA All Points Addressable (APA) method of host graphics implementation which uses vertical and horizontal pixel coordinates to create a more graphic image. An SNA definition.

APAD Asynchronous Packet Assembler/Disassembler.

APC Adaptive predictive coding. A narrowband analog-to-digital conversion technique employing a one-level or multilevel sampling system in which the value of the signal at each sample time is adaptively predicted to be a linear function of the past values of the quantized signals. APC is related to linear predictive coding (LPC) in that both use adaptive predictors. However, APC uses fewer prediction coefficients, thus requiring a higher bit rate than LPC.

APCC The American Public Communications Council, which is part of the North American Telecommunications Association (NATA).

APD Avalanche PhotoDiode. A diode that, when hit by light, increases its electrical conductivity by a multiplication effect. APDs are used in lightwave receivers because the APDs have great sensitivity to weakened light signals (i.e. those which have traveled long distances over fiber). APDs are designed to take advantage of avalanche multiplication of photocurrent.

APERIODIC ANTENNA An antenna designed to have an approximately constant input impedance over a wide range of frequencies; e.g., terminated rhombic antennas and wave antennas.

APERTURE For a parabolic reflector or a horn antenna, aperture is the dimension of the open mouth and represents a surface over which it is possible to calculate the radiation pattern. For a series of n stacked transmitting elements such as dipoles or slots, the vertical aperture is usually defined as n times the element spacing in wavelengths.

APERTURE DISTORTION In facsimile, the distortions in resolution, density, and shape of the recorded image caused by the shape and finite size of the scanning and recording apertures or spots.

APERTURE GRILLE A type of monitor screen made up of thin vertical wires. Said to be less susceptible to doming than iron shadow mask.

API An Application Programming Interface is software that an application program uses to request and carry out lower-level services performed by the computer's or a telephone system's operating system. For Windows, the API also helps applications manage windows, menus, icons, and other GUI elements. In short, an API is a "hook" into software. An API is a set of standard software interrupts, calls, and data formats that application programs use to initiate contact with network services, mainframe communications programs, telephone equipment or program-to-program communications. For example, applications use APIs to call services that transport data across a network. Standardization of APIs at various layers of a communications protocol stack provides a uniform way to write applications. NetBIOS is an early example of a network API. Applications use APIs to call services that transport data across a network.

APL Automatic Program Load in telecom. In data processing, it's a popular programming language.

APLT Advanced Private Line Termination. Provides the PBX user with access to all the services of an associated enhanced private switched communications services (EPSCS) network. it also functions when associated with a common control switching arrangement (CCSA) network. See Advanced Private Line Termination.

APM 1. Average Positions Manned, the average number of ACD positions manned during the reporting period for a particular group.

2. Advanced Power Management. A specification sponsored by Intel and Microsoft to extend the life of batteries in battery-powered computers. The idea of the specification if for the application programs, the system BIOS and the hardware to work together to reduce power consumption. An APM-compliant BIOS provides built-in power management services to the operating system. The operating system passes calls and information between the BIOS and the application programs. It also arbitrates power management calls in a multi-tasking environment (such as Windows) and identifies power-saving opportunities not apparent to applications. The application software communicates power-saving data via predefined APM interfaces. Only a very few programs presently conform to APM.

APOCALYPSE, FOUR HORSEMEN OF The four horsemen of the Apocalypse were War, Plague, Famine and Death.

APOGEE The point on a satellite orbit that is most distant from the center of the gravitational field of the Earth.

APOLOGIZE To lay the foundation for a future offense.

APPC Advanced Program-To-Program Communications. In SNA, the architectural component that allows sessions between peer-level application transaction programs. The LUs (Logical Units) that communicate during these sessions are known as LU type 6.2. APPC is an IBM protocol analogous to the OSI model's session layer: it sets up the necessary conditions that enable application programs to send data to each other through the network.

APPC/PC An IBM product that implements APPC on a PC.

APPEARANCE Usually refers to a private branch exchange line or extension which is on (i.e. "appears") on a multi-button key telephone. For example, extension 445 appears on three key systems.

APPEARANCE TEST POINT The point at which a circuit may be measured by test equipment.

APPEND To add the contents of a list, or file, to those of another.

APPGEN A shortened form of the words APPlications GENerator.

APPLE COMPUTER, INC., Cupertino, CA. Manufacturer of personal computers. Heavy penetration in the graphics/desktop publishing business. Apple was formed on April Fool's Day, 1976, by Steve Wozniak and Steve Jobs, aided greatly by Mike Markkula.

APPLE DESKTOP BUS The interface on a Mac where non-peripheral devices, such as the keyboard, attaches. A Mac keyboard or mouse is called an ADB device. Contrast with peripherals, which attach through the SCSI interface.

APPLE DESKTOP INTERFACE ADI. A set of user-interface guidelines, developed by Apple Computer and published by Addison-Wesley, intended to ensure that the appearance and operation of all Macintosh applications are similar.

APPLE MENU The Apple icon in the upper left hand corner of the Apple Macintosh screen. The Apple menu contains aliases, control panels, the chooser and other desk accessories.

APPLE PIE Both an American icon, and the name chosen for Apple Computer's Personal Interactive Electronics (PIE) division, chartered with extending the company into new growth areas such as Personal Digital Assistants (PDAs), e.g. the Apple Newton. The PIE division includes Apple Online Services, Newton and Telecommunications group, publishing activities, and ScriptX-based multimedia PDA development.

APPLE URP Apple Update Routing Protocol. The network routing protocol developed by Apple for use with Appletalk.

APPLESHARE Apple Computer's local area network. It uses AppleTalk protocols. AppleShare is Apple system software that allows sharing of files and network services via a file server in the Apple Macintosh environment. See APPLETALK.

APPLET A small application that performs a specific task, such as the Cardfile and Calculator in Microsoft Windows. See also JAVA.

APPLETALK Apple Computer's proprietary networking protocol for linking Macintosh computers and peripherals, especially printers. This protocol is independent of what network it is layered on. Current implementations exist for LocalTalk (230.4 Kbps) and EtherTalk (10Mbps).

APPLICATION A software program that carries out some useful task. Database managers, spreadsheets, communications packages, graphics programs and word processors are all applications.

APPLICATION BINARY INTERFACE ABI. The rules by which software code is written to operate specific computer hardware. Application software, written to conform to an ABI, is able to be run on a wide variety of system platforms that use the computer hardware for which the ABI is designed.

APPLICATION BRIDGE Aspect Telecommunications' ACD to host computer link. Originally it ran only over R2-232 serial connections, but it now runs over Ethernet, using the TCP/IP link protocol. See also OPEN APPLICATION INTERFACE.

APPLICATION CLASS An SCSA term. A group of client applications that perform similar services, such as voice messaging or fax-back services.

APPLICATION EQUIPMENT MODULE AEM. A Northern Term telcom for a device within the Meridian 1 Universal Equipment Module that supports Meridian Link Modules. The Meridian Link Module (MLM) is an Application Module, specially configured to support the Meridian Link interface to host computers.

APPLICATION FOR SERVICE A standard telephone company order form that includes pertinent billing, technical and other descriptive information which enables the company to provide communications network service to the customer and its authorized users.

APPLICATION FRAMEWORK This usually means a class library with a fundamental base class for defining a complete program. The framework provides at least some of the facilities through which a program interfaces with the user, such as menus and windows, in a style that is internally consistent and abstracted from the specific environment for which it has been developed.

This is an explanation I received from Borland. I don't quite understand it, yet. An application framework is an object-oriented class library that integrates user-interface building blocks, fundamental data structures, and support for object-oriented input and output. It defines an application's standard user interface and behavior so that the programmer can concentrate on implementing the specifics of the application. An application framework allows developers to reuse the abstract design of an entire application by modeling each major component of an applications as an abstract class.

APPLICATION GENERATOR AG. A program to generate actual programming code. An applications generator will let you produce software quickly, but it will not allow you the flexibility had you programmed it from scratch. Voice processing "applications generators," despite the name, often do not generate programming code. Instead they are self-contained environments which allow a user to define and execute applications. They are more commonly called applications generator, since one generator can define and execute many applications. See APPLICATIONS GENERATOR for a longer explanation.

APPLICATION PROFILE As SCSA term. A description of the kinds of resources and services required by a client application (or an application class). An application profile is defined once for an instance of an application; then system services such as the SCR will be able to fulfill the needs of the application without the application having to state its needs explicitly.

APPLICATION MODULE A Northern Telecom term for a computer that can be attached to a Northern Telecom phone system and add intelligence and programmability to the phone system. Often, the AM will be a computer conforming to open standards, such as DOS or Windows, or it may be VME-based.

APLICATION MODULE LINK AML. A Northern Telecom internal and proprietary link that connects the Meridian 1 (via EDSI or MSDL port) to the Meridian Link Module.

APPLICATION PROGRAM A computer software program designed for a specific job, such as word processing, accounting, spreadsheet, etc.

APPLICATION PROGRAM INTERFACE API. A set of formalized software calls and routines that can be referenced by an application program to access underlying network services.

APPLICATION PROGRAMMING INTERFACE API. A set of functions and values used by one program to communicate with another program or with an operating system. See API for a better explanation.

APPLICATION SERVICE ELEMENT ASE. A messaging term. A module or portion of a protocol in the application layer 7 of the OSI (Open Systems Interconnection) protocol stack. Several ASEs are usually combined to form a complete protocol, e.g., the X.400 P1 protocol which consists of the MTSE (Message Transfer Service Element), and the RTSE (Reliable Transfer Service Element).

APPLICATION SOFTWARE INTERFACE ASI. The Application Software Interface is a product of the Application Software Interface Expert Working Group of the ISDN Implementor's Workshop. The Interface focuses on the definition of a common application interface for accessing and administering ISDN services provided by hardware commonly referred to in the vendor community as Network Adapters (NAs) and responds to the applications requirements generated by the ISDN Users Workshop (IUW). The characteristics of this Application Interface shall be

• Portable across the broadest range of system architectures;

• Extensible (their words, not mine)

• Abstracted beyond ISDN to facilitate interworking;

• Defined in terms of services and facilities consistent with OSI layer interface standards.

According to Application Software Interface Group, the primary goal of the ASI is to provide a consistent set of application software interface services and application software interface implementation agreement(s) in order that an ISDN application may operate across a broad range of ISDN vendor products and platforms. The application software interface implementation agreements will be referenced by (and tested against) the IUW (ISDN Users Workshop) generated applications. It is anticipated that the vendor companies involved in the development of these implementation agreements will build products for the ISDN user marketplace which conform to them. ASI Implementation Agreements are likely to become a US Government Federal Information Processing Standard (FIPS).

APPLICATIONS ENGINEERING Applications engineering is the process of analyzing your telephone network to find products and services that will reduce your monthly bill without sacrificing network quality. It can be as simple as calling the telephone company to convert a particular service to a Rate Stabilization Plan (RSP). In many instances, the use of applications engineering concepts will increase the quality of your network. For example, putting DIDs onto a T1 will save you money and provide your network with a digital backbone. Unfortunately, most applications engineering is done by the telephone company or by their sales agents. Their main goal is not to save you money, but rather to sell telephone company products. Therefore, they are unlikely to advise you of all the hidden costs of converting to a particular service. A true application engineer will provide you with a complete cost analysis that includes all the conversion costs, and provides you with the "break-even date." The break-even date is the date that your monthly saving offsets the initial conversion cost of the service. It is often used synonymously with the term break-even point.

APPLICATIONS GENERATOR An Application generator (AG) is a software tool that, in response to your input, writes code a computer can understand. In simple terms, it is software that writes software. Applications generators have three major benefits: 1. They save time. You can write software faster. 2. They are perfect for quickly demonstrating an application. 3. They can often be used by non-programmers. Applications generators have two disadvantages. 1. The code they produce is often not as efficient as the code produced by a good programmer. 2. They are often limited in what they can produce. Applications generators tend to be either general purpose tools or very specific tools, providing support for specific applications, such as connecting voice response units to mainframe databases, voice messaging system development, audiotex system development, etc. There are simple AGs. There are complex AGs. There are general purpose AGs. There are specialized AGs. There are character-based AGs. There are GUI-based AGS. In researching AGs to write computer telephony and interactive voice response applications, I found three different levels of AG packages. First, there are the sort of non-generator generators. They don't really create new software, but they allow you to tweak existing application blocks. There's no compiling and they're pretty simple to use (though they often lack database and host connectivity). Then there are the pretty GUI forms-based app gens. They usually entail building a call-flow picture, using either pretty icons or easy to understand templates. When you're done filling in all the blanks, you compile it and actually "generate" new software. They're very cute. Finally, there's the script level language of a company like Parity Software, San Francisco. Real programmers dig this. They often feel it gives them a lot more power and flexibility. For very complex apps (with T-1/ISDN, ANI, host connection, speech recognition, multimedia capabilities, etc.) you'll probably need the power and flexibility of a script language. Most of the better GUI application generators let you drop down to a script-level language (and C too).

APPLICATIONS LAYER The seventh and highest layer of the Open Systems Interconnection (OSI) data communications model of the International Standards Organization (ISO). It supplies functions to applications or nodes allowing them to communicate with other applications or nodes. File transfer and electronic mail work at this layer. See OSI MODEL.

APPLICATIONS PARTNER An Applications Partner is AT&T's new name for an outside company which will write software to work on AT&T phone systems, such as the Merlin, Legend and the Definitely. AT&T is setting up an Applications Partner Program to work with companies to help them develop programs and distribute their products. See also DESKTOP CONNECTION.

APPLICATIONS PROCESSOR A special purpose computer which attaches to a telephone system and allows it (and the people using it) to perform different "applications," such as voice mail, electronic mail or packet switching. We think AT&T invented the term. See also ADD-ON.

APPLIQUE Circuit components added to an existing system to provide additional or alternate functions. Some carrier telephone equipment designed for ringdown manual operation can be modified with applique to allow for use between points having dial equipment.

APPN Advanced Peer-to-Peer Networking (APPN) is, according to its creator IBM, a leading-edge distributed networking feature IBM has added to its Systems Network Architecture (SNA). It provides optimized routing of communications between devices. In addition to simplifying the addition of workstations and systems to a network and enabling users to send data and messages to each other faster, APPN is designed to support efficient and transparent sharing of applications in a distributed computing environment. Because APPN permits direct communication between users anywhere on a network, it facilitates the development of client/server computing, in which workstation users anywhere on a network can share processing power, applications and data without regard to where the information is located. Workstations on an APPN network are dynamically defined so they can be relocated easily on the network without extensive re-programming. APPN also allows remote workstations to communicate with each other, without intervention by a central computer. Also, IBM's Advanced Peer-to-Peer Networking software.

APPN END NODE An APPN end node is the final destination of user data and cannot function as an intermediate node in an APPN network and cannot perform routing functions. See APPN.

APPROVED GROUND Grounds that meet the requirements of the NEC (National Electrical Code), such as building steel, concrete-encased electrodes, ground rings, and other devices. See AC and GROUNDING.

APPSERVER A SCSA term. AppServer defines the software environment that enables voice processing applications to run on any computing platform. AppServer sits on a PC equipped with call processing hardware and allows a remotely hosted application to control the call processing hardware.

APR Annual Percentage Rate. A percentage calculation of the finance charge portion of financing contact.

APS Automatic Protection Switching. A switching device which automatically initiates the switching from a primary circuit to a secondary (usually geographically diverse) circuit when the error rate on the primary line exceeds a set threshold.

ARA Appletalk Remote Access. Provides an asynchronous AppleTalk connection to another Macintosh and its network services through a modem. A remote user using ARA can log on to a remote server and mount the volume on his desktop as if he were connected locally.

ARAM Audio grade DRAM. DRAMS are low cost integrated circuits that are widely use in consumer electronic's products to store digital data.

ARBITRATED LOOP A Fiber Channel topology where nodes are linked together in a closed loop. An arbitrated loop can connect to fabric via an FL_Port.

ARCHIE An Internet term. Located on several computers around the country, Archie is a kind of superdirectory to the files on the internet. If you're looking for a file or even a particular topic, Archie provides its specific location. Veronica, Jughead and WAIS (Wide Area Information Servers) are other tools for searching the huge libraries of information on the Internet. Some companies, such as Hayes, make Archie software which give you a menu driven interface that lets you browse through the various Archie servers on the Internet as though browsing through card catalogs of remote libraries.

ARCHIVAL Readable (and sometimes writeable) media. Archival media have defined minimum life-spans over which the information will remain stable (i.e, accurate without degradation).

ARCHIVE BIT A Window NT term. Backup programs use the archive bit to mark files after backing them up, using the normal or incremental backup types.

ARCHIVE SERVER An email-based file transfer facility offered by some computers on Internet.

ARCHITECT One who drafts a plan of your office and then plans a draft of your money.

ARCHITECTURAL FREEDOM An AT&T term for flexibility in locating functions, such as control, storage or processing of information, at any site in or around a network, such as customer premises, central offices or regional service bureaus. Architectural freedom also means the ability to distribute functions among combinations of locations and have them interrelate through a high-throughput, low-delay, transparent network. See also ARCHITECTURE.

ARCHITECTURE The architecture of a system refers to how it is designed and how the components of the system are connected to, and operate with, each other. It covers voice, video, data and text. Architecture also includes the ability of the system to carry narrow, medium and broadband signals. It also includes the ability of the system to grow "seamlessly" (i.e. without too many large jumps in price).

ARCHITECTURE POLICE An individual or group within a company that makes sure software and hardware development follows established corporate guidelines. The architecture police tend to rein in creative development efforts.

ARCHIVE A backup of a file. An archived file may contain backup copies of programs and files in use or data and materials no longer in use, but perhaps needed for historical or tax purposes. Archive files are kept on paper, on microfilm, on disk, on floppies, etc. They may be kept in compressed or uncompressed form. See ARCHIVER.

ARCHIVER A software program for compressing files. If you compress files, you will save on communications charges, since you will be able to transmit those files faster as they're now smaller. My favorite MS-DOS archiver, also called file compression utility is Phil Katz's PKZIP.EXE and PKUNZIP.EXE. You can cut a database by as much as 90% and a word processed file by maybe 30% by using PKZIP. How much you can cut is determined by how much fluff is in the file. PKZIP is the most widely-used archive and compression utility today. You can recognized "zipped" files because their extension is always ZIP. There are other compression programs out there which you will recognize by these extensions, ARC, AR7, ARJ, LZH, PAK and ZOO.

ARCHIVING FILES This is a process where the information contained in an active computer file is made ready for storing in a non-active file, perhaps in off-line or near-line storage. Typically when files are archived, they are compressed to reduce their size. To restore the file to its original size requires a process known as unarchiving. See also ARCHIVER.

ARCNET Attached Resource Computer NETwork. One of the earliest and most popular local area networks. A 2.5M-bits-per-second LAN that uses a modified token-passing protocol. Developed by Datapoint, San Antonio, TX, Arcnet interface cards are now manufactured by many vendors, including Standard Microsystems and Pure Data, Ltd. Arcnet has lost popularity in recent years to Ethernet (IEEE 802.3) and Token Ring (IEEE 802.5).

ARDIS A public data communications wireless network that allows people carrying handheld devices to send and receive short data messages. Such messages might be from sheriff standing in the street searching his department's data base for unpaid parking tickets. ARDIS is jointly owned by Motorola and IBM. It is an outgrowth of a network originally created for IBM service technicians. A competitor to Ardis is RAM Mobile Data.

AREA CODE A three-digit code designating a "toll" center in the United States, Canada and Mexico. Until January, 1995 the first digit of an area code was any number from 2 through 9. The second digit was always a "1" or "0." In January 1995, North America (i.e. the US and Canada) adopted the North American Numbering Plan (NANP) and second digits could be any number. This dramatically increased the number of possible area codes — from 152 to 792 and the number of phone numbers to more than six billion. For a full explanation, see NORTH AMERICAN NUMBERING PLAN. For a full listing of area codes, see NORTH AMERICAN AREA CODES.

AREA CODE EXPANSION The new North American Numbering Plan (NANP) allowed basically any three numbers to become an area code. This exploded the number of area codes now possible. Some manufacturers of phone equipment, e.g. Rockwell, choose to call this happening "Area Code Expansion." They claimed that their switch would accommodate to all future permutations and combinations of area codes.

AREA CODE RESTRICTION The ability of the telephone equipment (or its ancillary devices) to selectively deny calls to specific (but not all) area codes. Area code restriction is often confused with "0/1" (zero/one) restriction which denies calls to all area codes by sampling the first and second dialed digits (is it a 0 or 1?) and thus, identifying and blocking an attempt at making a toll call. For a full listing of area codes, see NORTH AMERICAN AREA CODES.

ARENA A term from a ISV called Integrated North Coast. Here's their explanation: North Coast's Arena Applications allow one computer to work with a NEAX

PBX more efficiently than several computers. The Arena is a common platform which allows for the sharing of information among programs. This allows several functions; such as voice mail, call accounting, and IVR to sit on one computer and operate on one common platform. It is easiest to understand the Arena when described in theatrical terms. The Arena platform itself is a "stage" shared by a number of programs (Arena Actors). When information is received by one actor, it is "spoken" into the Arena. This information is then shared by all other actors. Information such as SMDR or CDR, even credit card numbers (literally hundreds of types of information), can be acted upon. This creates the ability to: cost calls, file CDR, call a bank and act as an ATM, open or close a relay, etc. Actors can be added or removed to change the functionally of the Arena.

ARENIX Arena for UNIX. A platform developed by North Coast Logic. This UNIX-based application takes advantage of UNIX multi-tasking and, using a centralized location for sharing data, allows a variety of telecommunications solutions to operate on the same computer. The platform allows programs to offer a true single point of entry — ensuring that information such as names and extension numbers only need to be entered once. Arenix Applications (Call Accounting, Voice Messaging, Fax, Facilities Management), which share the Arenix Platform, are used to provide additional functionality to the NEC NEAX 2400 IMS/ICS and NEAX 2000 IVS.

ARF Alternative Regulatory Framework.

ARGUMENT SEPARATOR In spreadsheet programs and programming languages, a comma or other punctuation mark that sets off one argument from another in a command or statement. The argument separator is essential in commands that require more than one argument. Without the separator, the program can't tell one argument from another.

ARINC Aeronautical Radio INC. The collective organization that coordinates the design and management of telecommunications systems for the airline industry. It's one of the largest buyers of telecommunications services and equipment in the world.

ARITHMETIC LOGIC UNIT ALU. The part of the CPU (Central Processing Unit) that performs the arithmetic and logical operations. See MICROPROCESSOR.

ARITHMETIC OPERATION The process that results in a mathematically correct solution during the execution of an arithmetic statement or the evaluation of an arithmetic expression.

ARITHMETIC REGISTER A register (i.e. short-term storage location) that holds the operands or the results of operations such as arithmetic operations, logic operations, and shifts.

ARITHMETIC UNIT The part of a computing system which contains the circuits that perform the arithmetic operations. See also ALU.

ARAB Attendant Release Loop. A feature of the PBX console. See RELEASE.

ARM Asynchronous Response Mode. A communication mode involving one primary station and at least one secondary station, where either the primary or one of the secondaries can initiate transmission.

ARMAGEDDON The fabled battlefield where God's heavenly forces are to defeat the demon-led forces of evil. The final battle.

ARMOR Mechanical protection usually accomplished by a metallic layer of tape, braid or served wires or by a combination of jute, steel tapes or wires applied over a cable sheath for additional protection. It is normally found only over the outer sheath. Armor is used mostly on cables lying on lake or river bottoms or on the shore ends of oceans. See ARMORED CABLE.

ARMORED CABLE A stainless steel handset cord which is meant to resist vandalism. Typically used on a coin phone, most stainless steel handset cords are too short. This is said to be because they were first ordered for use in prisons, where guards wanted to be certain they would not be used by the prisoners as hanging devices. Thus, they requested Western Electric to make them too short for such a use. Whether there is any validity to this story is dubious, however, it is part of telephone industry folk history and therefore, worth preserving.

ARP Address Resolution Protocol. A protocol within the Transmission Control Protocol/Internet Protocol (TCP/IP) suite that "maps" IP addresses to Ethernet addresses. TCP/IP requires ARP for use with Ethernet.

ARPA Advanced Research Projects Agency of the U.S. Department of Defense. (The whole DOD annual telecommunications bill exceeds $1 billion.) Much of the country's early work on packet switching was done at ARPA. At one stage it was called DARPA, which stands for Defense Advanced Research Projects Agency. ARPA was the US government agency that funded research and experimentation with the ARPANET and later the Internet. The group within DARPA responsible for the ARPANET is ISTO (Information Systems Techniques Office), formerly IPTO (Information Processing Techniques Office). See also DARPA INTERNET. DARPA has changed its name to ARPA and back again. It's hard to keep up.

ARPANET Advanced Research Projects Agency NETwork. A Department of Defense data network, developed by ARPA, which ties together many users and computers in universities, government and businesses. ARPANET has been the forerunner of many developments in commercial data communications, including packet switching, which was first tested on a large scale on this network. ARPANet is a predecessor of the Internet. It was started in 1969 with funds from the Defense Department's Advanced Projects Research Agency.

ARQ Automatic Retransmission reQuest. The standard method of checking transmitted data, used on virtually all high-speed data communications systems. The sender encodes an error-detection field based on the contents of the message. The receiver recalculates the check field and compares it with that received. If they match, an "ACK" (acknowledgment) is transmitted to the sender. If they don't match, a "NAK" (negative acknowledgment) is returned, and the sender retransmits the message. Note: this method of error correction assumes the sender temporarily or permanently stores the data it has sent. Otherwise, it couldn't possibly retransmit the data. No error detection scheme in data transmission is foolproof. This one is no exception.

ARRAY 1. The description of a location of points by coordinates. A 2-D array is described with x,y coordinates. A 3-D array is described with x,y,z coordinates. 2. A named, ordered collection of data elements that have identical attributes; or an ordered collection of identical structures.

ARRAY ANTENNA Take a bunch of directional antennas. Aim them at the same transmitting source. Join them together. Presto, you now have a very powerful giant antenna. Array antennas are used for picking up weak signals. They are often used in astronomical and defense communications systems.

ARRAY CONNECTOR A connector for use with ribbon fiber cable that joins 12 fibers simultaneously. A fan-out array design can be used to connect ribbon fiber cables to non-ribbon cables.

ARRAY PROCESSOR A processor capable of executing instructions in which the operands may be arrays rather than data elements.

ARRESTOR A device used to protect telephone equipment from lightning, electrical storms, etc. An arrestor is typically gas filled so when lightning strikes, the gas ionizes and, bingo, a low resistance to the ground that drains the damaging high voltage elements of the lightning away.

ARS Automatic Route Selection, also called Least Cost Routing. A way that your phone system automatically chooses the least expensive way of making the call that it is presented with. That least expensive way may be a tie line or a WATS line, etc. It may even be dial-up. See LEAST COST ROUTING and ALTERNATE ROUTING.

ARTICLE An Internet term. An article is a USENET conversation element. It is a computer file that contains a question or piece of information made available to the USENET community by posting to a newsgroup.

ARTIFACTS Distortions in a video signal. Unintended, unwanted visual aberrations in a video image.

ARTIFICIAL INTELLIGENCE In 1950, Alan Turing, a British mathematician, challenged scientists to create a machine that could trick people into thinking it was one of them. And this for long was THE classic definition of artificial intelligence. One way to trick people is to have the computer make typing mistakes, like real humans do. The real challenge these days with artificial intelligence, now more commonly called "expert systems," is not to recreate people but to recognize the uniqueness of machine intelligence and learn to work with it in intelligent, useful ways.

ARTIFICIAL LINE INTERFACE In T-1 transmission, refers to the ability of a piece of transmission equipment to attenuate its output level to meet the required loop loss of 15-22.5 dB normally switch selectable between 0,7.5, and dB.

ARTS A Rockwell ACD term. Audio Real Time Status. From any touchtone phone, you can call into a Rockwell Spectrum ACD, enter a password, and obtain real time statistics...e.g. average speed of answer, # call in queue, activity by agent group. Neat feature.

ARU Audio Response Unit.

AS Autonomous Systems. Part of the internet layer that routers use to relate to network connectivity and packet addressing. The router checks the network address and only routes on the host address if the source and destination are on the same network.

AS IS A term used in the secondary telecom equipment business. "As is" is equipment that is bought or sold with no stated or implied warranties. You should expect any condition from good to bad, from complete to incomplete. Buy As Is equipment at your own risk.

AS IS TESTED or AS IS WORKING A term used in the secondary telecom equipment business. One step up from "as is" condition. The product has been tested. It works and is complete, unless otherwise specified. Buyer should test upon receipt. There is no warranty beyond receipt. Seller is guaranteeing the product will work upon arrival. After that, the buyer is responsible for any problems.

AS&C Alarm Surveillance and Control

AS/400 IBM's mid-range mini-computer. AS/400 stands for Application System/400. IBM has a product called CallPath/400 which allows AS/400 computers to link to PBXs from the leading manufacturers.

ASA 1. Average Speed of Answer. How long the average caller has to wait before they speak to an agent. The time can vary, even over the course of one day, due to call volumes and staff levels. An important measure of service quality.

2. Affiliated Sales Agency. A term for a company which resells the service of a phone company. Typically, the phone company pays the ASA a commission. Sometimes the commission is so large that it blurs the thinking of the ASA into recommending to its customers telecom products and services they would be better without.

ASAI AT&T's Adjunct Switch Application Interface. A long detailed set of technical specifications for having an outside computer control an AT&T PBX. See also APPLICATIONS PARTNER, OPEN APPLICATION INTERFACE, PSAI and SCAI.

ASC AIN Switch Capabilities. See AIN.

ASCII Pronounced: as'-kee. American Standard Code for Information Interchange. It's the most popular coding method used by small computers for converting letters, numbers, punctuation and control codes into digital form. (Computers can only understands zeros or ones.) Once defined, ASCII characters can be recognized and understood by other computers and by communications devices. ASCII represents characters, numbers, punctuation marks or signals in seven on-off bits. A capital "C", for example, is 1000011, while a "3" is 0110011. As a seven-bit code, and since each bit can only be a "one" or a "zero," ASCII can represent 128 "things," i.e. 2 x 2 x 2 x 2 x 2 x 2 x 2 which equals 128. ASCII is the code virtually every personal computer in the world encodes "things," including IBM, Apple and Radio Shack/Tandy. This compatible encoding (it was developed by ANSI — the American National Standards Institute) allows virtually all personal computers to talk to each other, if they use a compatible modem, or null modem cable and transmit and receive at the same speed. There are variations of ASCII. (Nothing is totally standard anymore.) The most important variation — one originally from IBM — is called Extended ASCII. It codes characters into eight bits (or one byte) and uses those ASCII characters above 127 to represent foreign language letters, and other useful symbols, such as those to draw boxes. But at 127 and below, extended 8-bit ASCII is identical to standard 7-bit ASCII. The CCITT (now called the ITU-T) calls ASCII International Telegraph Alphabet 5.

The other major method of encoding is IBM's EBCDIC (pronounced ebb'-si-dick). It's largely used on IBM and IBM-compatible mainframe computers (but not their PCs, which use ASCII and extended ASCII.) EBCDIC is an eight-bit encoding scheme, thus allowing up to 256 "things" to be encoded, i.e. 2 x 2 x 2 x 2 x 2 x 2 x

2 x 2 = 256. EBCDIC codes letters, characters and punctuation marks in a totally different way than ASCII. For ASCII files to be read by an IBM mainframe (one that reads EBCDIC), those ASCII files must be translated into EBCDIC by one of the many translation programs available. See also ASCII EDITOR, BAUDOT, EBCDIC, EXTENDED GRAPHICS CHARACTER SET, MORSE CODE and UNICODE.

ASCII EDITOR An ASCII editor (also called a "text," "DOS" or "non-document mode" editor) does NOT use extended ASCII and printer [ESCAPE] codes, which are used by word processor to create advanced features such as bold, italic, underlining, and super/subscript printing effects; and fancy formatting such as automatic paragraph reformat, pagination, hyphenation, footers, headers, and margins. I initially wrote this dictionary using an ASCII editor called ZEdit, which is a customized version of QEdit, undoubtedly the best editor ever written. Then, the author QEdit, produced a new and more powerful editor, called The Semware Editor. And I'm now using it to write this edition. Since an ASCII editor can't do so much, why would anyone use one? Well, its strength is in the lack of those very things a word processor has, which clutter it and slow it down! Here are my benefits:

1. It's lightning fast. No word processor can match an ASCII editor's speed at loading itself, loading files, finding things in files, etc.

2. A file produced by an ASCII editor can be read and edited by any word processor (absolutely any). Thus it's the universal word processing file. A WordPerfect file typically can't be read by WordStar and vice versa. The reason is that every word processor uses different high-level codes for the same features (underlining, bolding, etc.) There is no consistency among word processors as to how they encode their text so they can tell printers to do bolding, etc.

3. An ASCII editor is better to type programming languages, such as EDLIN (for batch files), BASIC, FORTRAN, PASCAL, etc. If QEDIT used extended ASCII and printer codes, it could not be used by these programs...for each program interprets these "high level" codes differently from another program. An ASCII editor types straight, "vanilla" text...nothing fancy about it.

ASCII file An ASCII file consists solely of ASCII 127 and below ASCII characters that are visible. You create an ASCII file using a simple editor, also called an ASCII editor. An ASCII file is also called a text file. See ASCII.

ASCII-TO-FAX CONVERSION Allows the transfer of a word-processed file directly to your fax board so it can be faxed without being scanned from a hard copy print-out. Documents faxed with ASCII-TO-FAX conversion come out much cleaner at the other end, since the scanning process always degrades the image.

ASDS Accunet Spectrum of Digital Services. AT&T's leased line (also called private line) digital service at 56 Kbps. MCI and Sprint have similar services. It is available in N x 56/64 Kbps, for N = 1, 2, 4, 6, 8, 12. The 56/64 Kbps POP-POP service (between long distance carrier central offices) costs the same as an analog line.

ASE A messaging term. Application Service Element. A module or portion of a protocol in the application layer 7 of the OSI (Open Systems Interconnection) protocol stack. Several ASEs are usually combined to form a complete protocol, e.g., the X.400 P1 protocol which consists of the MTSE (Message Transfer Service Element), and the RTSE (Reliable Transfer Service Element).

ASH Ardire-Stratigakis-Hayduk, a synchronous compression algorithm that is said to offer four times throughput on a typical synchronous channel. It can be used in bridges, routers, ISDN and modems. Transcend of Cleveland, OH said at one point that it was the exclusive licensor of ASH.

ASI 1. Advanced Services Implementation. 2. Application Software Interface. An important ISDN term. See APPLICATION SOFTWARE INTERFACE.

3. Adapter Support Interface. The driver specification developed by IBM for networking over IEEE 802.5 Token-Rings.

ASIC Application Specific Integrated Circuit. This is a chip that has been built for a specific application. Manufacturers use it to consolidate many chips into a single package, reducing system board size and power consumption. Many video boards and modems use ASICs. ASICs span programmable array logic (PAL) devices, electrically programmable logic devices (EPLDs), field programmable logic devices (FPGAs), gate arrays, standard cell-based devices, and full custom, designed from scratch ICs. See also ASSP.

ASIC CHIP Application Specific Integrated Circuit Chip. A fancy name for microprocessor chips which do specific tasks. For example, an ASIC chip might be responsible for a graphics display.

ASL Adaptive Speed Leveling. A US Robotics term for adjusting the transmission speed of a modem up or down, depending on the conditions on the line. US Robotics says it can adjust speed in 2 or 3 seconds after detecting changed line conditions. It requires like modems on either end of the transmission.

ASN Abstract Syntax Notation.

ASN.1 Abstract Syntax Notation One. LAN "grammar," with rules and symbols, that is used to describe and define protocols and programming languages. ASN.1 is the OSI standard language to describe data types.

ASP 1. A Northern Telecom term for Attached Support Processor. 2. Adjunct Service Point. An intelligent-network feature that resides at the intelligent peripheral equipment and responds to service logic interpreter requests for service processing. See also AIN.. 3. Administrable Service Provider. A SCSA term. 3. Abstract Service Primitive

ASPECT RATIO The ratio of the width of a rectangular image to its height. The aspect ratio of NTSC and PAL TV is four units of width to every three units of height. This is expressed as 4 x 3 aspect ratio. A 35mm frame measures 24 x 36 mm, which means it has three units of width to two units of height. It is different in size from a TV screen. This is why the side parts of movies are chopped off on TV. For VGA and Indeo video technology, the aspect ratio is 4:3 yielding 160X120, 320X240 and 640X480 sizes.

ASPECT TELECOMMUNICATIONS The name of a very successful automatic call distributor manufacturer based in San Jose. Allegedly, the name of the company came from a conglomeration of the words Applications Specific Telecommunications.

ASPI ASPI stands for Advanced SCSI Programming Interface set, which is software primitives and data structures which allow software using the ASPI interface to be SCSI host adapter-independent. SCSI stands for Small Computer System

Interface. (Pronounced Scuzzie.) ASPI is software that acts as a liaison between SCSI device drivers (the software that drives the SCSI devices) and the interface card (also known as the host adapter). Whenever a new device is added to a computer system, a software program called a "driver" must tell the computer how to talk to the new device. Instead of forcing vendors to write drivers for every host adapter, ASPI lets them write a driver to ASPI standards, supposedly guaranteeing that the device the driver controls will work with all ASPI-compatible host adapters.

The idea behind ASPI is to create a "black box" software interface - one which allows programmers to create software without having to know anything about the details of the SCSI interface hardware used in your computer. With ASPI, it's possible to write programs that can be used with any SCSI-based device used on a computer system that supports ASPI. While things are not always 100% perfect in all cases, ASPI greatly reduces potential compatibility problems for you, the user.

How does ASPI work? Essentially, there are two parts to an ASPI implementation. First, there's the ASPI "manager" which is a device driver supplied by the hardware manufacturer, and the ASPI software application. It's important to note that without an ASPI manager, ASPI compatibility is not possible. It's the manager that creates the standard ASPI-compatibility layer between the SCSI host adapter hardware and the ASPI-compatibility application. The manager is very hardware-specific, and is almost always supplied by the manufacturer of your SCSI host adapter.

ASR 1. Automatic Speech Recognition. See INTERACTIVE VOICE RESPONSE. 2. Automatic Send-Receive teletype or telex machine. Such a machine, if left on and loaded with paper, will receive incoming messages and print them, even when nobody is present. See also AUTOMATIC SEND RECEIVE.

ASSEMBLER A program which translates an assembly programming language into the code of ones and zeros used by computers. See also ASSEMBLY LANGUAGE.

ASSEMBLY Pertaining to the translation of a program from symbolic language into machine code. See ASSEMBLY LANGUAGE.

ASSEMBLY LANGUAGE A computer language for writing software. It is a language which is converted by programs called compilers or interpreters into machine language programs which consist of only 1s and 0s and which a computer can understand. Even though an assembly language consists of recognizable nemonics and meaningful words, it's not easy to program in. It is referred to as a "low-level language". Assembly language programs run faster than high-level language programs, such as BASIC, COBOL or FORTRAN, which are much easier to learn and program in. Choosing a programming language is typically a tradeoff of ease for speed.

ASSERTED A signal is asserted when it is in the state which is indicated by the name of the signal. Opposite of Negated.

ASSIGNATION A secret romantic rendezvous. The invitation to an assignation doesn't work if she doesn't know the meaning of the word. Are you listening Jane Laino?

ASSIGNED FREQUENCY The center of the assigned frequency band assigned to a station.

ASSIGNED FREQUENCY BAND The frequency band within which the emission of a station is authorized; the width of the band equals the necessary bandwidth plus twice the absolute value of the frequency tolerance. Where space stations are concerned, the assigned frequency band includes twice the maximum Doppler shift that may occur in relation to any point of the Earth's surface.

ASSIGNED NIGHT ANSWER ANA. After business hours or when you place your phone system on "Night Answer," this feature sends calls from specified trunks to designated extensions or departments. You may use this feature to send calls directly to modems, or to emergency numbers, or even to outside home numbers.

ASSIGNED PLANT CONCEPT A pair is dedicated from the central office to the subscriber home and maintained at that address, even when idle. See REASSIGNMENT.

ASSIGNMENT A call center term. The process of assigning individual employees to specific schedules in a Master File or Daily Workfile. Master File assignment can be done either manually or automatically (based on employee schedule preference and seniority).

ASSOCIATE A verb used in Windows by File Manager. You associate a three character extension with an application. This tells File Manager that, when you click twice on the file, File Manager will know which application to launch. For example, you may tell Windows that the .QXD extension is associated with QuarkXpress. When you click on a QXD file, File Manager will launch Quark and load that particular file.

ASSOCIATED COMMON-CHANNEL SIGNALING A form of common-channel signaling in which the signaling channel is associated with a specific trunk group and terminates at the same pair of switches as the trunk group. The signal channel is usually transmitted by the same facilities as the trunk group.

ASSOCIATED VOICE PORT AVP. A Northern Telecom term. A voice port is used to pass signaling and supervision information to establish a connection for the data port. The term is also used in reference to the configuration of modems and voice grade switched circuits connected to the voice-port-data-port pair.

ASSOCIATION A relationship between two connection segments that share a common Leg O (i.e., a common subscriber is in control of connection segments). Definition from Bellcore.

ASSOCIATION CONTROL SERVICE ELEMENT ACSE. The International Standards Organization's Open Systems Interconnect (OSI) application layer services used, for example, in Manufacturing Automation Protocol V3.0 (MAP).

ASSP Application Specific Standard Product is an integrated circuit that performs functions for a single application (e.g., keyboard controller). ASSP is a more precise term for a device often referred to as an ASIC.

AST Automatic Scheduled Testing. A method of testing switched access service (Feature Groups B, C, and D) where the customer provides remote office test lines and 105 test lines with associated responders or their functions' equivalent; consists of monthly loss and C-message noise tests and annual balance test.

ASTM American Society for Testing and Materials, a non-profit industry-wide organization which publishes standards, methods of test, recommended practices, definitions and other related material.

ASYMMETRIC Faster in one direction than the other. The faster direction is called the main channel and the slower is the back channel.

ASYMMETRICAL COMPRESSION Techniques where the decompression process is not the reverse of the compression process. Asymmetrical compression is more computer-intensive on the compression side so that the decompression of video images can be easily performed at the desktop or in applications where sophisticated codecs are not cost effective. In short, any compression technique that requires a lot of processing on the compression end, but little processing to decompress the image. Used in CD-ROM creation, where time and costs can be incurred on the production end, but playback must be inexpensive and easy. See ASYN.

ASYMMETRICAL MODULATION A duplex transmission technique which splits the communications channel into one high speed channel and one slower channel. During a call under asymmetrical modulation, the modem with the greatest amount of data to transmit is allocated the high speed channel. The modem with less data is allocated the slow, or back channel. The modems dynamically reverse the channels during a call if the volume of data transfer changes.

ASYMMETRICAL MODEM A type of modem which uses most of the available bandwidth for transmission and only a small part for reception.

ASYMMETRICAL MULTIPROCESSING A relatively simple implementation of multiprocessing in which the operating system kernel runs on one dedicated CPU and assigns tasks as they come in to other "slave processors." It is also known as "master/slave" processing.

ASYMMETRICAL PVC This terms refers to a PVC (Private Virtual Circuit) which supports simplex, or asymmetrical, assignments of committed information rate in each direction of transmission. A PVC transmission path is duplex, meaning that there must be a communications path in each direction between the two points being connected. However with an asymmetrical PVC, the network capacity in each direction does not necessarily have to be equal.

ASYN Greek prefix meaning "not."

ASYNCHRONOUS See ASYNCHRONOUS TRANSMISSION.

ASYNCHRONOUS BALANCED MODE ABM. Used in the IBM Token Ring's Logical Link Control (LLC), ABM operates at the SNA data link control and allows devices on a Token Ring to send data link commands at any time and to initiate responses independently.

ASYNCHRONOUS GATEWAY A routing device used for dial-up services such as modem communications.

ASYNCHRONOUS REQUEST An SCSA term. A request where the client does not wait for completion of the request, but does intend to accept results later. Contrast with synchronous request.

ASYNCHRONOUS TERMINAL A terminal which uses asynchronous transmissions. See ASYNCHRONOUS TRANSMISSION.

ASYNCHRONOUS TRANSFER MODE ATM is the technology selected by the Consultative Committee on International Telephone & Telegraph (CCITT) International standards organization in 1988 (now called the ITU-T) to realize a Broadband Integrated Services Digital Network (B-ISDN). It is a fast, cell-switched technology based on a fixed-length 53-byte cell. All broadband transmissions (whether audio, data, imaging or video) are divided into a series of cells and routed across an ATM network consisting of links connected by ATM switches. Each ATM link comprises a constant stream of ATM cell slots into which transmissions are placed or left idle, if unused. The most significant benefit of ATM is its uniform handling of services, allowing one network to meet the needs of many broadband services. ATM accomplishes this because its cell-switching technology combines the best advantages of both circuit-switching (for constant bit rate services such as voice and image) and packet-switching (for variable bit rate services such as data and full motion video) technologies. The result is the bandwidth guarantee of circuit switching combined with the high efficiency of packet switching. For a longer explanation, see ATM.

ASYNCHRONOUS TRANSMISSION Literally, not synchronous. A method of data transmission which allows characters to be sent at irregular intervals by preceding each character with a start bit, and following it with a stop bit. It is the method most small computers (especially PCs) use to communicate with each other and with mainframes today. In every form of data transmission, every letter, number or punctuation mark is transmitted digitally as "ons" or "offs." These characters are also represented as "zeros" and "ones" (See ASCII). The problem in data transmission is to define when the letter, the number or the punctuation mark begins. Without knowing when it begins, the receiving computer or terminal won't be able to figure out what the transmission means.

One way to do this is by using some form of clocking signal. At a precise time, the transmission starts, etc. This is called SYNCHRONOUS TRANSMISSION. In ASYNCHRONOUS transmission there's no clocking signal. The receiving terminal or computer knows what's what because each letter, number or punctuation mark begins with a start bit and ends with a stop bit. Transmission of data is called SYNCHRONOUS if the exact sending or receiving of each bit is determined before it is transmitted or received. It is called ASYNCHRONOUS if the timing of the transmission is not determined by the timing of a previous character.

ASYNCHRONOUS is used in lower speed transmission and by less expensive computer transmission systems. Large systems and computer networks typically use more sophisticated methods of transmission, such as SYNCHRONOUS or BISYNCHRONOUS, because of the large overhead penalty of 20% in ASYNCHRONOUS transmission. This is caused by adding one start bit and one stop bit to an eight bit word — thus 2 bits out of ten.

The second problem with large transfers is error checking. The user sitting in front of his own screen checks his ASYNCHRONOUS transmission by looking at the screen and re-typing his mistakes. This is impractical for transferring long files at high speed if there is not a person in attendance.

In SYNCHRONOUS transmission start and stop bits are not used. According to the book Understanding Data Communications, characters are sent in groups called blocks with special synchronization characters placed at the beginning of the block and within it to ensure that enough 0 to 1 or 1 to 0 transitions occur for the receiver clock to remain accurate. Error checking is done automatically on the entire block. If any errors occur, then the entire block is retransmitted. This technique also carries an overhead penalty (nothing is free), but the overhead is far less than 20% for blocks or more than a few dozen characters.

AT 1. Access Tandem. 2. Advanced Technology. Refers to a 16 bit Personal Computer architecture using the 80X86 processor family which formed the basis for the ISA Bus as found in the first IBM PC. 3. AudioTex. See AUDIOTEX.

AT BUS The electrical channel used by the IBM AT and compatible computers to connect the computer's motherboard and peripheral devices, such as memory boards, video controllers, PC card modems, bus mouse boards, hard and floppy disk controllers and serial/parallel input/output devices. The AT bus supports 16 bits of data in one slug, whereas the original IBM PC supported only 8 bits (and was called the ISA bus for Industry Standard Architecture). These days there are much faster "buses," including the EISA, MCA (MicroChannel Architecture), Local Bus, PCI, VESA, etc.

AT COMMAND SET Also known as the Hayes Standard AT Command Set. A language that enables PC communications software to get an asynchronous and "Hayes-compatible modem" to do what you want it to do. So called "AT" because all the commands begin with "AT," which is short for ATtention. The most common commands include ATDT (touchtone a number), ATA (manually answer the phone), ATZ (reset modem — it will answer OK), ATSO=O (disable auto-answer), and ATH (hang up the phone).

To avoid having yourself knocked off your data call by the beep that comes in on the phone company's call waiting, put the following line in your modem setup: ATS10=20. That will increase your S10 register to two seconds. This register sets the time between loss of carrier (caused by the 1.5 second call waiting signal) and internal modem disconnect. Factory default on most modems is 1.4 seconds — just perfect to be cut off by the wall waiting tone! (Dumb.)

If you have to dial through several phone systems, waiting for dial tone on the way and/or going through fax/modem switches, you may consider a dial stream that looks like ATDT 1-800-433-9800 [W]212-989-4675 [W]22, where [W] means (in some software programs) "Wait for any key. When you get it, touchtone out the next digits." In other software programs — pure Hayes command — W means wait for second dialtone.

If [W] doesn't work for you, then change X3 in your setup line to X1; change your computer's dialed number to 9; and dial your distant computer with your phone. When you hear the modem at the other end answer, tell your computer's software to dial 9. It will dial 9, hear the modem tone at the other end and connect as though it had dialed it all by itself. X1 tells your modem to dial (or touchtone) immediately — without waiting for dial tone.

You can use several AT commands on one line. You only need AT before the first one. Some modems require commands typed in capital letters. When your dialing fails and you can't figure why, get out of your communications software program and start again. Or in total desperation, turn your computer and modem completely off and start again. The word "Hayes" comes from the manufacturer of modems called Hayes Microcomputer, Norcross, GA, the creator of the command set. Not all Hayes compatible modems are. See also HAYES COMMAND SET.

AT LOCAL MODE One of the command modes available on the ISDN set. It is used for compatibility with existing communications packages for analog modems or for data-only application programs. See AT COMMAND SET.

AT WORK Pronounced "At Work." Microsoft's office equipment architecture announced on June 9, 1993. Microsoft's idea is to put a set of software building blocks into both office machines and PC products, including:

* Desktop and network-connected printers. * Digital monochrome and color copiers. * Telephones and voice messaging systems. * Fax machines and PC fax products. * Handheld systems. * Hybrid combinations of the above.

According to Microsoft, the Microsoft At Work architecture focuses on creating digital connections between machines (i.e. the ones above) to allow information to flow freely throughout the workplace. The Microsoft At Work software architecture consists of several technology components that serve as building blocks to enable these connections. Only one of the components, desktop software, will reside on PCs. The rest will be incorporated into other types of office devices (the ones above), making these products easier to use, compatible with one another and compatible with Microsoft Windows-based PCs. The components, according to Microsoft, are:

• Microsoft At Work operating system. A real-time, pre-emotive, multitasking operating system that is designed to specifically address the requirements of the office automation and communication industries. The new operating system supports Windows-compatible application programming interfaces (APIs) where appropriate for the device.

• Microsoft At Work communications. Will provide the connectivity between Microsoft At Work-based devices and PCs. It will support the secure transmission of original digital documents, and it is compatible with the Windows Messaging API and the Windows Telephony API of the Windows Open Services Architecture (WOSA).

• Microsoft At Work rendering. Will make the transmission of digital documents, with formatting and fonts intact, very fast and, consequently, cost-effective; will ensure that a document sent to any of these devices will produce high-quality output, referred to as "What You Print Is What You Fax Is What You Copy Is What You See."

• Microsoft At Work graphical user interface. Will make all devices very easy to use and will make sophisticated features accessible; will provide useful feedback to users. Leveraging Microsoft's experience in the Windows user interface, Microsoft At Work-based products will use very simple graphical user interfaces designed for people who are not computer users.

• Microsoft At Work desktop software for Windows-based PCs. Will provide Windows-based PC applications the ability to control, access and exchange information with any product based on Microsoft At Work. Desktop software is the one piece of the Microsoft At Work architecture that will reside on PCs.

See also FAX AT WORK, VOICE SERVER, WINDOWS, WINDOWS TELEPHONY and WOSA.

AT&T American Telephone and Telegraph Company. Not much telegraph, plenty of telephone and some computing. AT&T, once the largest company in the world, is now 75% smaller as a result of the Divestiture of its operating telephone companies on December 31, 1983. At one stage, it had two main divisions, AT&T Communications (the long distance phone company) and AT&T Technologies (equipment). These were merged to form one AT&T with several divisions. Then we rewrote this definition. Then they reorganized. We rewrote this definition so many times we finally gave up. Suffice, AT&T is American Telephone and Telegraph Company. It provides long distance phone service, makes and sells phones and phone switches (from small to very large), is in the cellular phone business (through its acquisition of McCaw Cellular) and makes and sells computers (in 1991, it bought NCR). It has also increasingly widespread investments in entrepreneurial "information age" startups. See also AT&T BELL LABS.

AT&T ALLIANCE A direct-dial AT&T service which allows you to teleconference as few as three and as many as 59 telephones around the world. You can dial the numbers to call or you can schedule a meeting, called "Meet-Me Service." If you want to set the conference up, you dial 0-700-456-1000, then punch in the number of locations, then put in the numbers, ending each with a #. End your dialing with another # — to add yourself to the teleconference.

AT&T APPLICATIONS PARTNER A software developer who develops applications for AT&T hardware and software. See also DESKTOP CONNECTION.

AT&T BELL LABS The research and development arm of AT&T. It used to be known simply as Bell Laboratories. It is one of the most important research laboratory in the United States. Bell Labs is credited with inventing many electronics things including the transistor.

AT&T COMMUNICATIONS AT&T-Comm or AT&T-C. The part of AT&T that was at one stage responsible for long distance services. It used to be called AT&T Long Lines, which we liked better. AT&T Communications is now the largest part of AT&T.

AT&T CREDIT CORPORATION AT&T's financing arm, which provides customized leases for telephone equipment including the MERLIN II, MERLIN Plus, Legend, SPIRIT and Definity Systems, as well as for other equipment, such as AT&T FAX Machines and computers.

AT&T FAX ATTENDANT SYSTEM A voice mail-like product providing fax store-and-forward broadcast, personal fax mailboxes for confidential reception, remote retrieval and plain paper fax. The FAX Attendant also adds Fax-on-Demand through a automated attendant/fax response. The AT&T FAX Attendant System can be integrated with AT&T's AUDIX Voice Power Voice Mail system to provide a single interface for retrieving messages and combined notification.

AT&T GBCS AT&T Global Business Communications Systems. The new name for the merger of two divisions into one division now responsible for all the business telephone system sales of AT&T worldwide. The two divisions that were merged into GBCS were called General Business Systems (office systems 80 lines and smaller) and Business Communications Systems (systems bigger than 80 lines). The merger happened during the summer of 1992.

AT&T GLOBAL INFORMATION SOLUTIONS A new name for NCR (originally National Cash Register). AT&T bought NCR in 1991. The new name was announced in January 1994.

AT&T INFORMATION SYSTEMS AT&T-IS used to be one of AT&T's sales arms. It used to be responsible for (or used to be responsible for) sales of certain equipment, including telephone systems and computers, to both end-users and some selected distributors. AT&T-IS used to be responsible for selling a service called Net 1000, which was an end-to-end data communications/data processing service, whose exact service is hard to define and has now been killed.

AT&T INTEREXCHANGE COMPANY ATTIX, a suggested name for the long distance part of AT&T, which, at the time was called AT&T Long Lines. It was then called AT&T Communications. The reason the name ATTIX was rejected is that it reminded someone at AT&T of the word "drug addicts." No one has explained logically why AT&T ever needed to change the name "Long Lines," which most people in the industry related to very warmly. Including us.

AT&T LONG LINES The long distance part of AT&T. It was called that for over 100 years. Then they changed the name to just AT&T. Long Lines remains a favorite for old timers.

AT&T MAIL A way of sending electronic ASCII messages, binary files and faxes over phone lines and paper mail (through the US Postal Service) from your PC instantly to other people who have AT&T Mail Mailboxes, to anyone on an electronic mail system connected to AT&T Mail (like Internet, MCI Mail, CompuServe, etc.) to anyone who has a fax machine anywhere in the world or to anyone who receives US Mail (i.e. all of us).

AT&T NETWORK SERVICES This is an AT&T Technologies division which sells equipment primarily to Bell Operating companies, independent phone companies, overseas phone companies and large, Fortune 500-type users. It's doing very well.

AT&T TECHNOLOGIES Formerly called Western Electric, it is the equipment manufacturing arm of AT&T. No one knows why this company changed its name, since Western Electric had a wonderful reputation and is remembered with great fondness. It has an excellent reputation for high quality products and is still used as a brand name on some AT&T Technologies' products.

AT&T WORLDWORX AT&T WorldWorx Solutions is a family of AT&T products and services that provide simultaneous, real-time interactive voice, video and data communications among two or more people. According to AT&T, WorldWorx allows teams of people at locations all over the world to work together and see each other on their desktop computers, while sharing files and data.

ATA 1. American Telemarketing Association. 2. Analog Terminal Adapter. A device for a Northern Telecom Norstar phone system that lets it use analog devices, for example FAX, answering machines, modems and single line phones, behind the Norstar's central telephone unit (its KSU). Before you buy the analog terminal adapter, check that its speed is fast enough for you. In mid-1995, it was constrained to 9,600 bps, or 14,400 bps if the phone line was clear. 3. AT Attachment. Refers to the interface and protocol used to access a hard disk on AT compatible computers. Disk drives adhering to the ATA protocol are commonly referred to as IDE interfaced drives for PC compatible computers. The ATA specification is fully backward compatible with the ST-506 standard it superseded.

IDE drives are sometimes referred to as ATA drives or AT bus drives. The newer

ATA-2 specification defines the EIDE interface, which improves upon the IDE standard. See ATA2, IDE and ENHANCED IDE.

ATA2 The second generation AT attachment specification for IDE devices that defines faster transfer speeds and LBA (Logical Block Address) sector-locating method. See ATA, IDE and ENHANCED IDE.

ATA DOCUMENT The latest draft of the ANSI X3.T9 subcommittee AT Attachment document.

ATA REGISTERS These registers are accessed by a host to implement the ATA protocol for transferring data, control and status information to and from the PC Card. They are defined in the ATA Document. These registers include the Cylinder High, Cylinder Low, Sector Number, Sector Count, DriveHead, Drive Address, Device Control, Error, Feature, Status and Data registers. The I/O and memory address decoding options for these registers are defined within this specification.

ATAPI Attachment Packet Interface specification does for CD-ROM and tape drives why ATA-2 does for hard drives. It defines device-side characteristics for an IDE-connected peripheral. The benefits of having a single interface for the most common non-disk storage device in the desktop world, the CD-ROM are obvious. For the manufacturer, there is no need to add a separate controller card for the CD-ROM. For the end-user it means no more fussing with interrupts, cards and proprietary driver software. ATAPI essentially adapts the established SCSI command set to the IDE interface.

ATB ALL TRUNKS BUSY. One measure which your phone company or phone systems might give you of telephone traffic in and out of your office. See ALL TRUNKS BUSY.

ATD 1. Asynchronous Time Division. 2. ATention Dial the phone. The first three letters in the most frequently-used command in the Hayes command set for asynchronous modems — typically those used with microcomputers.

ATIS Alliance for Telecommunications Industry Solutions, a trade group based in Washington, D.C. It was originally called The Exchange Carriers Standards Association.

ATM 1. Automated Teller Machine. The street corner banking machine which is usually hooked up to a central computer through leased local lines and a multiplexed data network. 2. Asynchronous Transfer Mode. Very high speed transmission technology. ATM is a high bandwidth, low-delay, packet-like switching and multiplexing technique. Usable capacity is segmented into 53-byte fixed-size cells, consisting of header and information fields, allocated to services on demand. The ITU has selected ATM as the basis for the future broadband network in view of its flexibility and suitability for both transmission and switching. Each ATM cell contains a 48 octet payload field and a 5-octet Header which identifies the cells virtual circuit. The fixed length cells require lower processing overhead and allow higher transmission speeds than traditional packet switching methods. ATM allocates bandwidth on demand, making it suitable for high-speed connection of voice, data, and video services. ATM services will be available at access speeds up to 622 Mbps.

Here's a full explanation: Conventional networks carry data in a synchronous manner. Because empty slots are circulating even when the link is not needed, network capacity is wasted. The ATM concept which has been developed for use in broadband metropolitan area networks (MAN) and optical fiber based systems is supported by both CCITT (now called the ITU-T) and ANSI standards, can also be interfaced to SONET (Synchronous Optical Network). ATM automatically adjusts the network capacity to meet the system needs and can handle data, voice, video and television signals. These are transferred in a sequence of fixed length data units called cells. Common standards definitions are provided for both private and public networks so that ATM systems can be interfaced to either or both. ATM is therefore a wideband, low delay, packet-like switching and multiplexing concept that allows flexible use of the transmission bandwidth and capable of working at data rates as high as 622.08 Mbit/s. Each data packet consists of five bytes of header field plus 48 bytes for user data. The header contains data that identifies with related cell, a logical address that identifies the routing, forward error correction (FEC) bits, plus bit for priority handling and network management functions. FEC applies only to the header as it is assumed that the network medium will not degrade the error rate below an acceptable level. All the cells of a virtual connection (VC) follow the same path through the network that was determined during call set-up. There are no fixed time slots in the system so that any user can access the transmission medium whenever an empty cell is available. ATM is capable of operating at bit rates of 155.52 and 622.08 million bits per second and the cell stream is continuous and without gaps. The position of the cells associated with a particular VC is random and depends upon the activity of the network. Cells produced by different streams to the ATM multiplex are stored in queues awaiting cell assignment. Since a call is only accepted when the necessary bandwidth is available, there is a probability of queue overflow. Cell loss due to this forms one ATM impairment. However, this can be minimized through the use of statistical multiplexers. Bit errors in the header which are beyond the FEC capability can lead to misrouting. See ATM FORUM and ATM FORM UNI V3.0.

ATM FORUM An industry organization with some 450 members, co-founded by N.E.T. and three other leading networking companies, focused on speeding the development, standardization and deployment of ATM products. It has been remarkably successful. See ATM. www.atmforum.com/atmforum/home.html

ATM FORUM UNI V3.0 The ATM Forum UNI V3.0 implementation agreement is based on a subset of the ITU-TS broadband access signaling protocol standards. Additions to this subset have been made where necessary to support early deployment and interoperability of ATM equipment. The procedures and protocol defined in the agreement apply to both public and private UNIs. Moreover, since the protocol is symmetrical, it also applies in the configuration ATM-end-point to ATM-end-point. See ATM and ATM FORUM.

ATMARP ATM Address Resolution Protocol.

ATSC Advanced Television System Committee. www.atsc.org

ATT Automatic Toll Ticketing. A system which telephone companies use to automatically keep call detail records including calling number, number called, time of day and length of call. The phone company uses this information, together with the cost of phone calls, to generate an invoice to its customers.

ATTACH A command that assigns a connection number to a workstation and attaches the workstation to the LOGIN directory on the default (or specified) file server. As many as 100 workstations can be attached to a file server running NetWare v2.2. When loaded the NetWare shell (workstation file NETx.COM) automatically attaches your workstation to the nearest file server. You can also specify in SHELL.CFG which server you prefer to attach to.

ATTACH TERMINAL To assign a terminal for exclusive use by the application program. Contrast with Detach Terminal.

Attachment The process of attaching a file to an electronic message.

ATTACK TIME The time interval between the instant that a signal at the input of a device or circuit exceeds the activation threshold of the device or circuit, and the instant that the device or circuit reacts in a specified manner, or to a specified degree, to the input. The term often implies a protective action such as the provided by a clipper (peak limiter) or compressor, but may be used to describe the action of a device such as a vox (Voice Operated circuit), where the action is not protective.

ATTEMPT Trying to make a telephone call. Also defined as a call offered to a telecommunications system, regardless of whether it is completed.

ATTENDANT The "operator" of a phone system console. Typically, the first person to answer an incoming call. That person usually directs incoming calls to the proper person or department. That person may also assign outgoing lines or trunks to people requesting them. Few companies spend any time training their attendants. They should. There are two types of things attendants should be trained for: 1. Manners, including the correct way to keep people waiting and to screen incoming calls, and 2. The structure of the company. If a caller asks for some help, the attendant should know which department or person might be responsible for providing that help. Increasingly in North America, company phone systems are answered by devices called "automated attendants." They allow a caller to punch in the extension he wants or the department he wants. See AUTOMATED ATTENDANT.

ATTENDANT BUSY LAMP FIELD Lamps, lights or LEDs that show whether a PBX or key system extension is busy or not. These days, many attendant busy lamp fields are being incorporated into CRT displays. We hope more will do this as many lamp-based attendant busy lamp fields are difficult to read.

ATTENDANT CALL WAITING INDICATION An unusual feature on a PBX console. The call waiting button on the attendant console lights to indicate a predetermined number of calls in queue. The light flashes when a second (programmable) threshold is reached.

ATTENDANT CAMP-ON If the extension is busy, the attendant or operator can place the call in a queue behind the call already in progress. When the call is over, the "camped-on" call will automatically ring the extension.

ATTENDANT CONFERENCE PBX feature that allows the attendant (or operator) to establish a conference connection between central office trunks and internal phones.

ATTENDANT CONSOLE An attendant console is the larger, specialized telephone set used by the operator or attendant to answer incoming calls and send those calls to the proper extension. Consoles are becoming more sophisticated these days in several ways. Operators need to punch fewer buttons to move calls around, while the information they present to the attendant is more useful for keeping tabs on calls and letting people know what's happening. Many consoles are acquiring TV screens that report the status of each extension, who's speaking, where the call is going, and whether there are problems, such as broken lines or trunks, etc. anywhere on the system. Some of the more modern screens will allow the operator to send messages around the company that can alert someone as to who's calling before he/she picks up the phone. You can also easily program switches through consoles with CRT (also called TV) screens. In the old days you needed to punch in complex codes. Now you can respond to "Yes/No" decisions on a screen with lots of explanatory words and help menus.

ATTENDANT CONTROL OF TRUNK GROUP ACCESS The telephone operator or attendant controls the users' access to trunks for making local and/or long distance calls. This may reduce long distance call abuse.

ATTENDANT DIRECT STATION SELECT This feature gives an operator the ability to reach an extension by simply pushing one button. In direct station select, every extension has its own button. Direct Station Select usually comes with some form of Attendant Busy Lamp Field which shows whether the extensions are busy. Some attendants like direct station select. Others don't, preferring to simply punch in 345, instead of hunting for the button which corresponds to extension 345. The best consoles these days are using some form of easy-to-read screen prompts.

ATTENDANT EXCLUSION A PBX feature which stops the attendant from listening in on a phone call once she or he has passed the call to the correct extension.

ATTENDANT FORCED RELEASE An attendant-activated (pushbutton) facility that will automatically "disconnect" all parties on a given circuit when that circuit is "entered" by the attendant.

ATTENDANT INCOMING CALL CONTROL A PBX feature which diverts incoming trunk calls automatically to a predetermined phone after a predesignated period of time or number of rings.

ATTENDANT KEY PAD Allows the attendant to perform all functions using a standard touch tone key pad on the console or adjacent to it.

ATTENDANT LOCKED LOOP OPERATION PBX feature which allows the attendant at a console to retain supervision or recall capability of any particular call which has been processed.

ATTENDANT LOCKOUT This feature denies an attendant the ability to re-enter a phone call unless specifically recalled by that PBX extension.

ATTENDANT LOOP TRANSFER Allows the attendant to transfer any call to another attendant.

ATTENDANT MONITOR A special attendant circuit which allows "listening in" on all circuits with the console handset/headset transmitter deactivated.

ATTENDANT OVERRIDE A feature that allows an attendant to enter a busy trunk connection and key the trunk number within the PBX. A warning tone will be heard by the connected parties, after which they connected parties and the attendant will be in a three-way connection.

ATTENDANT POSITION Where a telephone operator sits to answer calls and send them on to the people in the company. This is usually in front of a telephone system with buttons, toggle switches, etc. that facilitate this process.

ATTENDANT RECALL When a phone call has been transferred to a telephone extension and not answered, this telephone system feature sends the call back to the attendant. Sometimes the call will return to a special part of the attendant console which will indicate to the attendant that it is a "returned" call. It's a good idea to pay attention to the speed of recall back to the operator. People hate to be extended into endless ringing. Think of calling a hotel and how aggravating it is to wait until the call comes back to an operator after she/he extended it to the room...and it rings and rings.

ATTENDANT RECALL ON TRUNK HOLD The system will recall the attendant if a trunk placed on hold is not re-entered within a predetermined time.

ATTENDANT TRANSFER OF INCOMING CALLS A PBX and Centrex feature. A telephone extension is talking on a line but that person wants to transfer the call to someone else. The person hits their hookswitch a couple of times. (The hookswitch is the toggle switch the handset depresses when you replace it.) This flashing of the hookswitch signals the attendant to join the call. The person asks the attendant "to please transfer this call." The attendant then transfers the call to the new extension. This feature is totally inefficient as it's hard to reach the attendant, who's always busy, etc. etc. All newer phones can transfer both incoming and outgoing calls automatically by just flashing the hookswitch, dialing the extension number and hanging up.

ATTENDED A telephone system having an attendant or receptionist whose primary job is to answer all incoming calls. Many smaller systems, such as key systems, are not centrally "attended." The phone is simply answered by whoever is near. A non-attended phone system should be set up so anyone can answer an incoming call. Some systems, such as most key systems, come this way from the factory. Others, such as PBXs, have to be specially set up. Some systems can be set up so an attendant will get first shot at answering the incoming call, but then, after a couple of rings, anyone else can answer the call (perhaps a loud "night" bell will ring). This is the system we use at TELECONNECT Magazine.

ATTENDED MODE Imagine a communications situation where your computer is connected over a phone line to another user on another computer and you are uploading and downloading files. Attended mode refers to a situation where both users manually enter the commands required to send or receive a file concurrently, usually while conversing over the phone. Compare this to UNATTENDED MODE.

ATTENTION KEY A key or combination of keys on a computer or terminal which signals the main computer to stop its present task and wait for a new command. The ESCape key is often the Attention Key. In Crosstalk, it's Control A.

ATTENUATE To decrease electrical current, voltage or power in communicating channel. Refers to audio, radio or carrier frequencies. See ATTENUATION.

ATTENUATION The decrease in power of a signal, light beam, or lightwave, either absolutely or as a fraction of a reference value. The decrease usually occurs as a result of absorption, reflection, diffusion, scattering, deflection or dispersion from an original level and usually not as a result of geometric spreading, i.e., the inverse square of the distance effect. Optical fibers have been classified as high-loss (over 100 dB/km), medium- loss (20 to 100 dB/km), and low-loss (less than 20 dB/km). In other words, attenuation is the loss of volume during transmission. The received signal is lower in volume than the transmitted signal due to losses in the transmission medium (such as that caused by resistance in the cable). Attenuation is measured in decibels. It is the opposite of Gain. Some electrical components are listed as "with attenuation" which means they will compensate for irregular electrical supply (e.g. surges). See GAIN.

ATTENUATION COEFFICIENT The rate at which average power decreases with distance.

ATTENUATION EQUALIZER Any device inserted in a transmission line or amplifier circuit to improve the shape of its frequency response.

ATTENUATOR A device to reduce signal amplitude by a known amount without introducing distortion.

ATTIX See AT&T INTEREXCHANGE COMPANY.

ATTND Attendant. (What else?)

ATTO Atto means one quintillion, which is 10 to the power of 18. See also FEMTO, which is 10 to the power 15.

ATTRIBUTE The form of information items provided by the X.500 Directory Service. The directory information base consists of entries, each containing one or more attributes. Each attribute consists of a type identifier together with one or more values. See ATTRIBUTES.

ATTRIBUTES Information about a MS-DOS file that indicates whether the file is read-only, hidden, or system, and whether it has been changed since it was last backed up. You can assign attributes to a file using the ATTRIB command. You can identify a file as read-only (meaning others can't change it, but can read it) and/or as a file you want to archive when using the BACKUP, RESTORE, and XCOPY commands. The command to make a file read only is typically

ATTRIB +R filename

By using the ATTRIB command to make a file "read only," you also make it impossible to erase the file from your disk. If you want to remove the "read only" protection, i.e. make the file "read and write, the command is

ATTRIB -R filename

ATUG Australian Telecommunications Users Group, based in Milsons Point, Sydney, Australia.

ATV Advanced TV. Refers to any system of distributing television programming that generally results in better video and audio quality than that offered by the NTSC 525-line standard. This group of techniques is based on digital signal processing and transmission. HDTV (High Definition TV) can be considered one type of ATV. Although ATV systems are collectively considered to offer better quality than the NTSC signal, they can carry multiple pictures of lower-quality and can also support the cancellation of artifacts in ordinary NTSC signals.

ATX Audiotex. Interactive voice response systems that deliver information or entertainment to general telephone callers, i.e. anyone with a phone. Audiotex services are typically widely advertised. They include everything from sex to the weather. See also AUDIOTEX.

AUC Authentication Center. A functional piece of the HLR (Home Location Register) used to authenticate the user of mobile station equipment. The AUC performs secret, mathematical computations to verify the authenticity of the mobile station to complete the call.

AUDIBLE INDICATION CONTROL Three fancy words for the ability to turn up or down the bell or beeper on your PBX attendant console.

AUDIBLE RING A sound sent from the called party's switch to inform the calling party that the called line is being rung. A long explanation for a bell or buzzer that tells you it's for you.

AUDIBLE RINGING TONE The information tone sent back to the calling telephone subscriber as an indication that the called line is being rung.

AUDIBLE TONES Audible tones are the sounds provided by the network or an attached switch to inform callers of the status of the line or of an event. Audible tones most frequently encountered in computer telephony applications include: ringing, busy tones (called party busy and network busy), SIT tones (Special Information Tones), and special tones used by computer telephony systems such as the "record at the beep" (which is usually a 1,000 HZ tone).

AUDIO Sound you hear which may be converted to electrical signals for transmission. A human being who hasn't had his ears blown by listening to a Sony Walkman or a ghetto blaster can hear sounds from about 15 to 20,000 hertz.

AUDIO FREQUENCY The band of frequencies (approximately 30 hertz to 20,000 hertz) that can be heard by the healthy human ear.

AUDIO FREQUENCIES Those frequencies which the human ear can detect (usually in the range of 20 to 20,000 hertz). Only those from 300 to 3,000 hertz are transmitted through the phone, which is why the phone doesn't sound "Hi-Fi."

AUDIO MENU Options spoken by a voice processing system. The user can choose what he wants done by simply choosing a menu option by hitting a touchtone on his phone or speaking a word or two. Computer or voice processing software can be organized in two basic ways — menu-driven and non-menu driven. Menu-driven programs are easier for users to use, but they can only present as many options as can be reasonably spoken in a few seconds. Audio menus are typically played to callers in automated attendant/voice messaging, voice response and transaction processing applications. See also MENU and PROMPTS.

AUDIO MESSAGING INTERCHANGE SPECIFICATION AMIS. Issued in February 1990, AMIS is a series of standards aimed at addressing the problem of how voice messaging systems produced by different vendors can network or inter-network. Before AMIS, systems from different vendors could not exchange voice messages. AMIS deals only with the interaction between two systems for the purpose of exchange voice messages. It does not describe the user interface to a voice messaging system, specify how to implement AMIS in a particular systems or limit the features a vendor may implement.

AMIS is really two specifications. One, called AMIS-Digital, is based on completely digital interaction between two voice messaging systems. All the control information and the voice message itself, is conveyed between systems in digital form. By contrast, the AMIS-Analog specification calls for the use of DTMF tones to convey control information and transmission of the message itself is in analog form. AMIS was discussed in detail in the October 1990 issue of Business Communications Review, a monthly magazine out of Hinsdale, IL. AMIS specifications are available from Alison Caughman 4040-355-7785.

AUDIO RESPONSE UNIT A device which translates computer output into spoken voice. Let's say you dial a computer and it said "If you want the weather in Chicago, push 123, then it would give you the weather. But that weather would be "spoken" by an audio response unit. Here's a slightly more technical explanation: An audio response unit is a device that provides synthesized voice responses to dual-tone multi-frequency signaling input. These devices process calls based on the caller's input, information received from a host data base, and information carried with the incoming call (e.g., time of day). ARUs are used to increase the number of information calls handled and to provide consistent quality in information retrieval. See also AUDIOTEX and INTERACTIVE VOICE RESPONSE.

AUDIO TRACK The section of a videodisc or tape which contains the sound signal that accompanies the video signal. Systems with two seperate audio tracks (most videodiscs) can offer either stereo sound or two independent soundtracks.

AUDIOGRAPHICS The technology which allows sound and visual images to be transmitted simultaneously. According to AT&T, audiographics generally refers to single frame or slow frame visual images as opposed to continuous frame image transmission (e.g. television). Audiographic transmission is often used to teach or train people in remote locations from an educational institution or business training center, saving travel and housing expense.

AUDIOTEX A generic term for interactive voice response equipment and services. Audiotex is to voice what on-line data processing is to data terminals. The idea is you call a phone number. A machine answers, presenting you with several options, "Push 1 for information on Plays, Push 2 for information on movies, Push 3 for information on Museums." If you push 2, the machine may come back, "Push 1 for movies on the south side of town, Push 2 for movies on the north side of town, etc." See also INFORMATION CENTER MAILBOX.

AUDIOTEXT A different, and less preferred, spelling of AUDIOTEX. See AUDIOTEX.

AUDIO/VISUAL MULTIMEDIA SERVICES AMS is an ATM term. It specifies service requirements and defines application requirements and application program interfaces (APIs) for broadcast video, videoconferencing, and multimedia traffic. AMS is being developed by the ATM Forum's Service Aspects and Applications (SAA) working group. An important debate in the SAA concerns how MPEG-2 applications will travel over ATM (asynchronous transfer mode). Early developers chose to carry MPEG-2 over ATM adapation layer 1 (AAL 1); others found AAL 5 a more workable solution. Recently, some have suggested coming up with a new video-only AAL using the still-undefined AAL 2.

AUDITORY PATTERN RECOGNITION Auditory pattern recognition is the ability to recognize spoken words.

AUDIT To conduct an independent review and examination of system records and activities in order to test the adequacy and effectiveness of data security and data integrity procedures, to ensure compliance with established policy and operational procedures, and to recommend any necessary changes.

AUDIT FILE On some systems, each time a billing file is generated, an audit file is created to record the details of the generation process.

AUDIT TRAIL A record of all the events that occur when users request and use specific resources. An audit trail gives you the ability to trace who did what and who was responsible for what. An audit trail is a chronological record of system activities that is sufficient to enable the reconstruction, review, and examination of the sequence of environments and activities surrounding or leading to an operation, a procedure or an event in a transaction from its inception to final results. Audit trail may apply to information in an automated information system, to the routing of messages in a communications system, or to material exchange transactions, such as in financial audit trails.

AUDITING 1. An AT&T ISDN term for the monitoring of the status of either the network or the ISDN set.

2. Tracking activities of users by recordand selected types of events in the security log of a server or a workstation.

AUDIX VOICE POWER A voice processing application, part of Integrated Solution III (IS-III), that provides Automated Attendant, call answering, voicemail, message drop, and information services for use with the AT&T Merlin telephone system.

AUGER A type of drill bit typically used to make large, deep holes for passing wire or cable through wood.

AUI Autonomous Unit Interface or Attachment Unit Interface. Most commonly used in reference to the 15 pin D type connector and cables used to connect single and multiple channel equipment to an Ethernet transceiver.

AUP Acceptable Use Policy. The term used to refer to the restrictions placed on use of a network; usually refers to restrictions on use for commercial purposes.

AURAL Relating to the sense of hearing.

AUSTPAC A packet-switched network implemented in Australia.

AUTHENTICATE To establish, usually by challenge and response, that a transmission attempt is authorized and valid. To verify the identity of a user, device, or other entity in a computer system, or to verify the integrity of data that have been stored, transmitted, or otherwise exposed to possible unauthorized modification. A challenge given by voice or electrical means to attest to the authenticity of a message or transmission.

AUTHENTICATION The process whereby a user or information source proves they are who they claim to be. In other words, the process of determining the identiy of a user attempting to access a system.

AUTHENTICATION TOKEN A portable device used for authenticating a user. Authentication tokens operate by challenge/response, time-based code sequences, or other techniques. An example is Security Dynamics Technologies Inc.'s SecurID card.

AUTOCHANGER A jukebox-style optical media system that permits the storage and playback multiple discs. Autochangers are available for both 5-,8, and 12-inch optical discs.

AUTHORING Authoring is the process of using multimedia applications to create multimedia materials for others to view. Multimedia authoring uses many tools, from the more familiar text editor or desktop publishing application, to tools for capturing and manipulating video images or editing audio files. Authors might include specialized creators of training, sales, or corporate applications such as insurance claims processing. Or, they might be creators of everyday business communications like voice-annotated email. Over time, everyone involved in business communications will probably have some level of multimedia authoring capability.

AUTHORING SYSTEM Software which helps developers design interactive courseware easily, without heavy computer programming. A specialized, high-level, plain-English computer language which permits non-programmers to perform the programming function of courseware development. The program logic and program content are combined. See AUTHORING.

AUTHORIZED AGENT Also called Authorized Sales Agent. A term chosen by some of the Bell operating companies and many of the cellular phone companies to refer to companies which sell their network services on commission. Some of these companies have specific industry knowledge and have written specialized software. The idea is to work with businesses to arm them with the absolute best package of telecommunications hardware, software and services.

AUTHORIZED BANDWIDTH The necessary bandwidth required for transmission and reception of intelligence. This definition does not include allowance for transmitter drift or Doppler shift.

AUTHORIZED DEALER See DEALER.

AUTHORIZED FREQUENCY A frequency that is allocated and assigned by an authority to a specific user for a specific purpose.

AUTHORIZATION Think of charging things on your MasterCard, Visa, or American Express card. If the store cannot authorize the amount of your purchase, your Visa card will not allow you to make the purchase. Authorization is needed for many long distance calls, especially those made using credit cards, telephone company calling card, etc. Authorization is done by the operator's computer checking with the remote validation database service. See BVA, BVS and VALIDATION.

AUTHORIZATION CODE A code in numbers and/or letters employed by a user to gain access to a system or service. If you are making a call out on a restricted line, the PBX will ask you for an authorization code. If you have one, your call will go through. If not, your call will be denied (i.e. not go through). Authorization codes come in various flavors. Some can be used for making long distance calls. Some can be used also for international calls, etc. See AUTHORIZED USER.

AUTHORIZED USER A person, firm, corporation or any other legal entity authorized by the provider of the service to use the service being provided.

AUTO ADJUST An AT&T ISDN term. The automatic setting of the baud rate. The baud rate is automatically set through the use of the AT portion of the command line. The speed of the computer is determined from the A and the parity is determined from the combination of the A and T. For this reason, it is not necessary to set speed and parity parameters for the ISDN set.

AUTO ATTENDANT A shortened name for an automated attendant, a device which answers a company's phones, encourages you to touchtone in the extension you want, and rings that extension. If that extension doesn't answer, it may send the call to voice mail or back to the attendant. It may also allow you to punch in digits and hear information, e.g. the company's hours of business, addresses of local branches, etc. See also AUTOMATED ATTENDANT.

AUTO ANSWER The capability of a phone, a terminal, a video phone, a modem or a computer to answer an incoming call and to set up a connection without anyone actually doing anything to physically answer the call. I have auto answer on my video phone. When it rings, my phone answers and I see who's calling. It's nice.

AUTO BAUD Automatic speed recognition. The ability of a device to adapt to the data rate of a companion device at the other end of the link.

AUTO BAUD DETECT See AUTO BAUD.

AUTO BUSY REDIAL A feature of a phone or phone system where the phone has the ability to keep trying a busy number until answered. The circuit actually recognizes the busy tone, hangs up, and dials again. One of the greatest time-savers ever invented.

AUTO CALL Automatic Calling; a machine feature that allows a transmission control unit or a station to automatically initiate access to (i.e. dial) a remote system over a switched line.

AUTO DIAL A feature of phone systems and modems which allows them to dial a long phone number (usually long distance) by punching fewer buttons than there are numbers to dial. One button auto dial on electronic phones is very common these days. Most communications software programs will allow you to auto dial a string of 35 to 40 digits, which you may need if you're dialing through a complex network.

AUTO DIAL AUTO ANSWER A modem feature. Auto Dial lets you dial a phone number through your modem, using your personal computer or data terminal keyboard. Auto Answer permits the modem to automatically answer the incoming call without anybody having to be there.

AUTO DIALER See AUTOMATIC DIALER.

AUTO FAX TONE Also called CNG, or Calling Tone. This tone is the sound produced by virtually all Group 3 fax machines when they dial another fax machine. CNG is a medium pitch tone (1100 Hz) that lasts 1/2 second and repeats every 3 1/2 seconds. A FAX machine will produce CNG for about 45 seconds after its dials. See also CNG.

AUTO LINE FEED An instruction in a communications program which causes the program to perform a Line Fee (LF) when you hit a carriage return or the "Enter" key.

AUTO PARTITION A feature of 10BaseT. When 32 consecutive collisions are sensed by a port in a hub or concentrator from its attached workstation or network segment, or when a packet that far exceeds the maximum allowable length is received, the port stops forwarding packets. The port continues to monitor traffic and will automatically begin normal packet forwarding when the first correct packet is received.

AUTO RECOGNITION A term used in file conversion in which your conversion software figures out by itself in what form the original file was — WordPerfect 5.0, Word 6.0, Wordstar 5.5 etc. See also AUTO STYLING.

AUTO SELECTION TOOL An imaging term. A tool that selects an entire area within a specified range of color values around a selected pixel.

AUTO SENSING See AUTO STYLING.

AUTO START A standby electrical power system that starts up when the normal supply of commercial power fails.

AUTO STREAM An AT&T ISDN term. The method of data flow in which both channels between the ISDN set and the application are in use simultaneously.

AUTO STYLING Auto styling is a term we found in a database conversion software program. What it means is that the program looks at the data in a field and determines from that data if the field is a numeric, character or memo, etc. The problem with auto styling is that it's frequently wrong. For example, it might check one field, find all numbers and decide it's a numeric field. Such a field might be a zip code, which actually is normally a character field. One reason why you might want you zip code to be a character field is that character fields are set left. Numeric fields are set right. (They line up at the decimal point.) Another name for auto styling is auto sensing.

AUTOANSWER A feature of a telephone which automatically answers incoming calls without the user of the phone lifting a handset or otherwise answering the call. Modems and fax machines also autoanswer. In North America, it's spelled AUTO ANSWER. In Britain, it's spelled AUTOANSWER.

AUTOATTENDANT See AUTOMATED ATTENDANT.

AUTOBAUDING The process by which the terminal software determines the line speed on a dial-up line.

AUTODIAL BUTTON An Autodial button on a phone provides one-touch dialing of outside numbers, intercom numbers, or feature codes.

AUTODIN The worldwide data communications network of the U.S. Department of Defense. Acronym for "AUTOmatic DIgital Network."

AUTOEXEC.BAT The first file executed after a PC is started (i.e. cold or warm booted). AUTOmatic EXECute BATch file contains a list of MS-DOS commands which are executed by your PC once your machine is turned on. Essentially, once you've started your MS-DOS computer, your asks "OK, you're got me started now. What would you like me to do?" Your AUTOEXEC.BAT contains these answers. Your AUTOEXEC.BAT file allows you to tailor the MS-DOS operating system to your needs, for example, setting the PATH command. The AUTOEXEC.BAT file must be installed in the root directory of your boot disk — either hard or floppy disk (the place your computer looks for the initial MS-DOS commands).

AUTOMATED ATTENDANT A device which is connected to a PBX. When a call comes in, this device answers it and says something like, "Thanks for calling the ABC Company. If you know the extension number you'd like, pushbutton that extension now and you'll be transferred. If you don't know your extension, pushbutton "0" (zero) and the live operator will come on. Or, wait a few seconds and the operator will come on anyway." Sometimes the automated attendant might give you other options, such as, "dial 3" for a directory of last names and dial 4 for a directory of first names. Automated attendants are also connected also to voice mail systems ("I'm not here. Leave a message for me."). Some people react well to automated attendants. Others don't. A good rule to remember is before you spring an automated attendant on your people/customers/subscribers, etc., let them know. Train them a little. Ease them into it. They'll probably react more favorably than if it comes as a complete surprise. The first impression is rarely forgotten, so try to make it a good experience for the caller. See also DIAL BY NAME.

AUTOMATED COIN TOLL SERVICE ACTS. In the old days, operators handled routine toll calls by counting the sound of coins hitting the box, checking prices, putting calls through, figuring and collecting overtime charges, etc. ACTS does all this automatically. It figures charges, tells those charges by digitized computerized voice to the customer, counts the coins as they are deposited and then sets up the call.

AUTOMATED INTERCEPT CALL COMPLETION AINTCC. A new feature of Northern Telecom's central offices. The AINTCC feature provides options for

• connecting a caller automatically to an intercepted number after hearing an announcement, or

• connecting a caller to an intercepted number without an announcement.

Not using an announcement makes the number change transparent to the caller. The called (intercepted) party then has the option of informing the caller of the number change.

AUTOMATED MARITIME TELECOMMUNICATIONS SYSTEM An automatic, integrated and interconnected maritime communications system serving ship stations on specified inland and coastal waters of the United States.

AUTOMATED RADIO A radio with the capability for automatically controlled operation by electronic devices that requires little or no operator intervention.

AUTOMATED VOICE RESPONSE SYSTEMS AVRS. Devices which automatically answer calls. They may simply inform the caller that the call is in a queue and will be answered soon; alternatively they can prompt the caller to use voice commands, or touchtones to seek more information.

AUTOMATED TACTICAL COMMAND AND CONTROL SYSTEM A command and control system or part thereof which manipulates the movement of information from source to user without intervention. Automated execution of a decision without human intervention is not mandatory.

AUTOMATIC ADDRESS DISCOVERY This refers to the process by which a network device can poll other network devices to discover the network addresses which each device supports. Automatic address discovery makes the set up and on-going maintenance of complex internetworks much simpler than if all address updates were performed manually.

AUTOMATIC BUTTON RESTORATION When the telephone handset of a multi-line instrument (typically a 1A2 multi-line key set) is placed back in its cradle, the line button being used automatically "pops" back up. Conversely, when a user picks up the handset, he must always push down a line button to make a call. Most phones with this feature can be disabled, so the buttons stay down when the handset sits on the cradle. A twist of a single screw inside the instrument will usually solve the aggravation of the automatic button restoration. Some people like automatic button restoration because it saves a user from accidentally barging into someone else's call. This was a much greater problem with 1A2 key systems. It no longer is a problem with most electronic key systems since they usually extend the user automatic privacy once they get on a call so no one else can barge in, even if they want to.

AUTOMATIC CALL DISTRIBUTOR ACD. A specialized phone system designed originally for handling many incoming calls, now increasingly used by companies also making outgoing calls. You receive and make lots of phone calls typically to customers. You need an ACD. Once used only by airlines, rent-a-car companies, mail order companies, hotels, etc., it is now used by any company that has many incoming calls (e.g. order taking, dispatching of service technicians, taxis, railroads, help desks answering technical questions, etc.). There are very few large companies today that don't have at least one ACD. Many smaller companies, like the company that publishes this dictionary, also has one.

An ACD performs four functions. 1. It will recognize and answer an incoming call. 2. It will look in its database for instructions on what to do with that call. 3. Based on these instructions, it will send the call to a recording that "somebody will be with you soon, please don't hang up!" or to a voice response unit (VRU). 4. It will send the call to an agent as soon as that operator has completed his/her previous call, and/or the caller has heard the canned message.

The term Automatic Call Distributor comes from distributing the incoming calls in some logical pattern to a group of operators. That pattern might be Uniform (to distribute the work uniformly) or it may be Top-down (the same agents in the same order get the calls and are kept busy. The ones on the top are kept busier than the ones on the bottom). Or it may be Specialty Routing, where the calls are routed to answerers who are most likely to be able to help the caller the most. Distributing calls logically is the function most people associate with an ACD, though it's not the most important.

The management information which the ACD produces is much more valuable. This information is of three sorts: 1. The arrival of incoming calls (when, how many, which lines, from where, etc.) 2. How many callers were put on hold, asked to wait and didn't. This is called information on ABANDONED CALLS. This information is very important for staffing, buying lines from the phone company, figuring what level of service to provide to the customer and what different levels of service (how long for people to answer the phone) might cost. And 3. Information on the origination of the call. That information will typically include ANI (Automatic Number Identification — picking up the calling number and DNIS (Direct Number Identification Service) picking up the called number. Knowing the ANI allows the ACD and its associated computer to look up the caller's record and thus offer the caller much faster service. Knowing the DNIS may allow the ACD to route the caller to particular agent or keep track of the success of various advertising campaigns. Ad agencies will routinely run the same ad in different towns using different 800 phone numbers. Picking up which number was called identifies which TV station the ad ran on.

The seven definitions that follow the definition "ACD" show some of the features which newer ACDs have. See also 800 SERVICE, ACD and AUTOMATIC CALL SEQUENCER.

AUTOMATIC CALLING UNIT ACU. A device that places a telephone call on behalf of a computer.

AUTOMATIC CALL INTERCEPT A feature of a Rolm ACD. This feature automatically forwards calls to an attendant if the dialed number is not installed or out of order. It can also intercept an attempted trunk call that is in violation of a Class of Service restriction. Automatic Call Intercept will also recall the attendant after a predetermined period of offshoot inactivity (e.g. flash or hold).

AUTOMATIC CALL RESCHEDULING When a call is unsuccessful, either no reply, or busy, the system will automatically dial the number again after a predetermined time.

AUTOMATIC CALL SEQUENCER A device for handling incoming calls. Typically it performs three functions. 1. It answers an incoming call, gives the caller a message, and puts them on "Hold." 2. It signals the agent (the person who will answer the call) which call on which line to answer. Typically, the call which it signals to be answered is the call which has been on "hold" the longest. 3. It provides management information, such as how many abandoned calls there were, how long the longest person was kept on hold, how long the average "on hold" was, etc.

There are three types of devices which handle incoming calls. The least expensive is the Automatic Call Sequencer which is traditionally used with key systems. It differs from Uniform Call Distributors (UCDs) and Automatic Call Distributors (ACDs) in that it has no internal switching mechanism and does not affect the call in any way. It simply recommends which call should be picked up and keeps statistical information on the progress of calls. A more expensive type of device is the UCD.

The most full-featured and expensive is the ACD. Distinctions between ACDs and UCDs and/or PBXs with features called UCDs and ACDs are blurring as UCDs get more sophisticated. The main difference, as we understand it, is that a UCD offers fewer options for routing an incoming call and answering calls in any particular order. ACDs typically produce the most detailed management information reports. One company also makes something called an Electronic Call Distributor. It is essentially an automatic call distributor.

AUTOMATIC CALLBACK When a caller dials another internal extension and finds it busy, the caller dials some digits on his phone or presses a special "automatic callback" button. When the person he's calling hangs up, the phone system rings his number and the number of the original caller and the phone system automatically connects the two together. This feature saves a lot of time by automatically retrying the call until the extension is free. See also CAMP ON. Wouldn't it be nice if they had this feature on long distance calls?

AUTOMATIC CIRCUIT ASSURANCE ACA is a PBX feature that helps you find bad trunks. The PBX keeps records of calls of very short and very long duration. If these calls exceed a certain parameter, the attendant is notified. The logic is that a lot of very short calls or one very long call may suggest that a trunk is hung, broken or out of order. The attendant can then physically dial into that trunk and check it.

AUTOMATIC COVER LETTER In a fax transmission, an automatic cover letter allows the user to automatically attach a cover letter to the document being sent. This is especially convenient when sending material directly from your PC.

AUTOMATIC DIALER or AUTODIALER A device which allows the user to dial pre-programmed telephone numbers by pushing one or two buttons. Sometimes referred to as a "repertory" dialer. Dialers can be bought as a separate device and added to a phone, however, today most telephone sets are outfitted with autodialers. There are four basic measures of an automatic dialer's efficiency. 1. What's the longest number it will dial automatically? This is important because using some of AT&T's long distance competitors requires dialing lots of numbers, with lots of pauses. 2. How many numbers will it dial? Some people like to have a dialer which dials hundreds of numbers. Others like a small one, just for their most frequently called numbers. 3. Will the dialer recognize dial tone? This is important because using a long distance company or dialing through a PBX requires one to recognize consecutive dial tones. 4. Can you "chain" dial? In other words, can you hit one speed dial button after another and have the machine dial through a complex network and throw in authorization codes, etc.?

AUTOMATIC DIALING See SPEED DIALING.

AUTOMATIC DIRECTORY PROPAGATION In electronic mail, automatic directory propagation is the ability to update addresses automatically in one domain after manually entering address changes in another domain, whether on the same LAN or another LAN connected by a gateway. In general, automatic directory propagation can be peer-to-peer, where changes in any post office are sent to all other post offices, or master-to-slave, where changes in the master post office are sent to the slaves, but changes in the slave post office do not go to the master.

AUTOMATIC EQUALIZATION The process of compensating for distortion of data communications signals over an analog circuit.

AUTOMATIC EXCHANGE A term for a central office which automatically and electronically switches calls between subscribers without using an operator. Not a common term.

AUTOMATIC FACILITIES TEST SYSTEM AFACTS is a Rolm CBX feature. It is an automatic testing system for identifying faulty tie and central office trunks. AFACTS can pinpoint faulty trunks and generate exception and summary reports.

AUTOMATIC FALLBACK A modem's ability to negotiate an appropriate data rate with the modem on the other end of the link, depending on line quality. For example, if two 2400 baud modems can not pass data at 2400 baud, they would "fall back" to 1200 baud automatically in order to transmit data without excessive errors.

AUTOMATIC FREQUENCY CONTROL A circuit in a radio receiver which automatically brings the tuning units of the set into resonance with a wave which is partially tuned in.

AUTOMATIC GAIN This is an electronic circuit which automatically increases the volume when someone is speaking quietly and drops it when someone is speaking loudly. The idea is to keep the transmitted signal even. Most tape recorders, for example, have automatic gain circuits. This allows them to pick up voices of people in a room, even though the volume of each person's conversation arriving at the tape recorder is different. The problem with automatic gain circuits is they're always looking for something to amplify. Such that when it's quiet (and meant to be) the automatic gain circuit will also try and amplify the ambient noise in the room — to keep the sound level constant. All professionally recorded tapes are done on tape reorders with manual volume controls.

AUTOMATIC HOLD — STATION or INTERCOM When a user is having a conversation and receives another call, he may press the button to answer that new call. The call he was on originally is automatically put on hold.

AUTOMATIC IDENTIFIED OUTWARD DIALING AIOD. The toll calls placed by all extensions on the telephone systems are automatically recorded. This information allows bills to be sent, long distance lines to be chosen, etc. Some central offices, for example, can provide an itemized breakdown of charges (including individual charges for toll calls) for calls made by each CPE telephone extension. See CALL ACCOUNTING, CALL DETAIL RECORDING, SMDR and AIOD.

AUTOMATIC INTERCEPT CENTER AIC. A Bellcore definition: "The centrally located set of equipment that is part of an Automatic Intercept System (AIS) that automatically advises the calling customer, by means of their recorded or electronically assembled announcements, of the prevailing situation that prevents completion of connection to the called number."

AUTOMATIC LEVEL CONTROL ALC. A control system that adjusts the incoming signal to a predetermined level. Somewhat similar to automatic gain control. See AUTOMATIC GAIN CONTROL.

AUTOMATIC LIGHT CONTROL ALC. Vidicon camera control which automatically adjusts the target voltage to compensate for variations in light levels. See also AUTOMATIC GAIN.

AUTOMATIC LINE HOLD A PBX feature. As long as a phone does not go "on-hook," activation of various line pushbuttons will automatically place the first line on hold without the use of special "hold" button.

AUTOMATIC LINK ESTABLISHMENT ALE. The capability of an HF radio station to contact, or initiate a circuit, between itself and another specified radio station, without operator assistance and usually under computer control. ALE techniques include automatic signaling, selective calling, and automatic handshaking. Other automatic techniques that are related to ALE are channel scanning and selection, Link Quality Analysis (LQA), polling, sounding, message store and forward, address protection, and anti-spoofing.

AUTOMATIC MESSAGE ACCOUNTING AMA. 1. Service mark of AT&T. A system which records and documents billing information for long distance calls made by a corporate subscriber. The calls must be made to billable destinations to be documented. The information recorded is generally either 20% of all information (CCSA networks) or 100% of the information (all others). 2. The network functionality that measures, collects, formats, and outputs subscriber network-usage data to upstream billing OSs and other OSs (Operations Systems). Definition from Bellcore.

AUTOMATIC MESSAGE LINK The name of a Bell Atlantic service, which allows you to forward your calls directly to your company message-taking system so your customers can always leave messages.

AUTOMATIC MESSAGE SWITCHING A technique of sending messages to their appropriate destination through information contained in the message itself — typically in its "address."

AUTOMATIC NETWORK DIALING A Rolm feature which is said to simplify on-network calling among multiple business locations by providing single-step dialing for private networks and a single numbering/dialing plan.

AUTOMATIC NUMBER IDENTIFICATION ANI. Being able to recognize the phone number of the person calling you. You must have equipment at your office. And the network must have the ability to send the calling number to you. For a much longer explanation, see ANI, CALLER ID, CLASS, ISDN and System Signaling 7.

AUTOMATIC NETWORK RESTORAL Automatic network restoral is a term which reflects the ability of a network to restore service rapidly and automatically following a catastrophic failure, such as that of a network cable cut. The result is higher network availability and reliability.

AUTOMATIC OVERFLOW TO DDD Toll calls jump to expensive direct distance dialed calls, when all lower cost FX, WATS lines, etc. are busy.

AUTOMATIC PHONE RELOCATION The Automatic Phone Relocation feature now available on some phone systems allows a telephone to retain its personal and system programming when it is reconnected to another physical location.

AUTOMATIC PRIVACY When someone is speaking on a phone line or on an intercom, this feature ensures no one else can accidentally or deliberately butt into that conversation. If you did, however, want somebody else to come into the conversation (for example, someone to provide some additional information), there's usually another feature called Privacy Release. By pushing this button on the phone, other people who have the same extension button or intercom button on their phones can then push their buttons and join the conversation. Or you can bring them into your conversation by dialing them in. Most modern key systems come with Automatic Privacy. Many people don't like it, especially those who live in small offices. Some newer phone systems are coming standard without it. And you have to program it in, if you want it.

AUTOMATIC PROGRAM LOAD APL is a PBX feature that allows it to load its own software into RAM from a local device such as a hard disk or a floppy disk. All this takes place automatically without human intervention. APL is an important feature since it often determines how fast a PBX can get back into service after some sort of failure — usually a failure in commercial power.

AUTOMATIC PROTECTION SWITCHING Switching architecture designed for SONET to perform error protection and network management from any point on the signal path.

AUTOMATIC QUEUING Queuing is exactly as it sounds. Something you want is being used. So you get placed in line for that device. There are two types of queuing — automatic and manual. Manual is when you're put in queue by a person, for example an operator. Automatic is when you're put in queue by a machine, for example a PBX aided by its software.

AUTOMATIC RECALL 1. A central office feature which gives telephone subscribers the ability to automatically redial their last incoming call — without actually knowing that number. On some central offices it is now possible for the calling person to block the ability of someone they've called to automatically call them back.

2. A PBX feature which returns a call to the PBX attendant (or alerts the attendant) if a call extended to a telephone is not answered within a pre-set period of time. The most logical time is three rings, or 18 seconds. This feature allows the attendant to give the caller some information, take a message or connect the caller to someone else. Most hotel switches have this feature. And when the call doesn't get answered, the switch sends it back to the operator. The sad thing is that the hotel operator is usually so busy, he/she keeps you waiting another 20 or 30 seconds, irritating you.

AUTOMATIC RECOVERY Your telephone system dies — typically because its power is cut off. Once the power comes on, instructions in the machine direct it to reload its software so that within minutes the system can be back and running normally. Those "instructions" are normally not affected by power drops.

AUTOMATIC REPLICATION Also known as data replication. It refers to the process of automatically duplicating and updating data in multiple computers on a network. The word "automatically" in this case means that the process of duplication is handled automatically by the software responsible for the data. The idea is that if one or several of the machines do down, the company using the data will still have reliable delivery of data.

AUTOMATIC REROUTING This refers to the process by which an intelligent voice or data network can automatically route a call, or virtual circuit, around a network failure. With frame relay, PVCs represent a fixed path through the network. However, in the event of a network failure along the primary path over which the PVC is routed, the PVC will be automatically routed to a secondary network path until the primary path is physically restored.

AUTOMATIC RESTART 1. The mechanism whereby, after a power failure and then power resumes, a process automatically restarts. Restart is from the exact point of interruption. 2. System facilities that allow restart from the point of departure after system failure.

AUTOMATIC RINGDOWN TIE TRUNK A direct path signaling facility to a distant phone. Signaling happens automatically when you lift the receiver on either phone. See also MANUAL RINGDOWN TIE TRUNK.

AUTOMATIC ROLLBACK A feature of the Transaction Tracking System (TTS) that returns a database on a Novell NetWare local area network to its original state. When a network running under TTS fails during a transaction, the database is "rolled back" to its most recent complete state. This prevents the database from being corrupted by the incomplete transaction.

AUTOMATIC ROUTE SELECTION Your phone system automatically chooses the least cost way of sending a long distance call. See LEAST COST ROUTING and ALTERNATE ROUTING.

AUTOMATIC SCHEDULED TESTING AST. A method of testing switched access service (Feature Groups B, C, and D) where the customer provides remote office test lines and 105 test lines with associated responders or their functions' equivalent; consists of monthly loss and C-message noise tests and annual balance test.

AUTOMATIC SECURE VOICE COMMUNICATIONS NETWORK AUTO-SEVOCOM. A worldwide, switched, secure voice network developed to fulfill DoD long-haul, secure voice needs.

AUTOMATIC SEND/RECEIVE ASR. A data device in which the transmitting thing is different from the receiving part, thus enabling the device to receive calls and transmit them simultaneously. See ASR for a different definition. We're not sure precisely which one is right. Both could be.

AUTOMATIC SEQUENTIAL CONNECTION A service feature provided by a data service to connect automatically, in a predetermined sequence, the terminals at each of a set of specified addresses to a single terminal at a specified address.

AUTOMATIC SPEED MATCHING The ability of an asynchronous modem to automatically determine whether it is expected to communicate at 300, 1200 or 2400 bps.

AUTOMATIC TIME-OUT ON UNCOMPLETED CALL A PBX feature. If a phone stays "off-hook" without dialing for a predetermined time interval, or stays connected to a busy signal longer than the predetermined time interval, the intercom switching equipment will automatically connect this phone to intercept.

AUTOMATIC TOLL TICKETING A system which makes a record of the calling phone number, the called number, the time of day, the length of the call, etc. and then generates an instant phone bill for that call. Often used in hotel/motels.

AUTOMATIC TRAFFIC OVERLOAD PROTECTION ATOP. A Rolm feature defined as a dynamic form of line-load control, which automatically denies a dial tone during those periods when the Rolm CBX may become overloaded. One wonders why someone would create this feature.

AUTOMATIC VOICE NETWORK AUTOVON. The principal long-haul, unsecure (meaning it's not secure) voice communications network within the Defense Communications System.

AUTOMATIC VOLUME CONTROL A circuit in a radio receiver; automatically maintains various received transmissions at approximately the same volume.

AUTOMATIC WAKEUP The capability for the user to schedule a wake-up call to a predetermined telephone number, either one time or daily.

AUTOMATIC WAKEUP SERVICE The guest or the operator dials into a machine which records a request for a guest wakeup call the following morning. The auto wakeup machine is a glorified, programmable auto-dial answering machine. The machine is said to save hotels money and make wakeup calls more reliable, and certainly more anonymous.

AUTONET A packet-switched network implemented in the U.S. by ADP, Ann Arbor, MI 48106.

AUTOSCALING A drawing feature that automatically adjusts the axis units of a graph to the minimum and maximum numerical values of a set of data.

AUTOSEARCH See RECORDER.

AUTOSEED An United Kingdom definition. The process of selecting records from a database using pre-defined criteria and allocating the records to outbound or mailing campaigns.

AUTOSEVOCOM The AUTOmatic SEcure VOice COMmunications system of the U.S. Department of Defense. A worldwide, switched, secure voice network developed to fulfill DoD long-haul, secure voice needs.

AUTOTIMED RECALL When a user places a call on hold and forgets about it, Autotimed Recall will ring that user or the receptionist after a predetermined time. That time is usually programmable. It shouldn't be longer than 30 seconds, otherwise your customers, sitting endlessly on your eternity hold, will go nuts and go elsewhere.

AUTOTIMED TRANSFER This telephone system feature switches unanswered incoming calls to a backup answering position after a predetermined (usually adjustable) interval of time.

AUTOTYPE PROTOCOL Hayes Microcomputer definition for a file transfer protocol which allows the user to automatically "type" a disk file, the clipboard or the contents of Smartcom Editor in either plain text (ASCII) or ANSI.SYS format to a remote computer. Pacing, send lines and await character echo options are provided. If necessary, character set mapping translates between different code pages and systems (Macintosh or Windows text files, for example).

AUTOVON AUTOmatic VOice Network. The principal long-haul, unsecure voice communications network within the Defense Communications System.

AUXILIARY EQUIPMENT See also PERIPHERAL DEVICE or APPLICATIONS PROCESSOR.

AUXILIARY EQUIPMENT ACCESS The ability of a telephone system to interface with (i.e. talk to) auxiliary equipment such as a paging system or dial dictation system.

AUXILIARY LINE A telephone trunk in addition to the main number you rent from the phone company. Phone systems are often equipped for calls to hunt from a busy main number to one or more auxiliary lines (Incoming Service Group, or ISG). For example, The Telecom Library's main number is 212-691-8215. But The Telecom Library also has 8216, 8217, 8218 and several unmarked or coded trunks. These are auxiliary lines and they don't receive their own billing or listing from the phone company. Sometimes, people have single line private lines which "appear" on their phone and no one else's. Sometimes they call these auxiliary lines. Sometimes these are called private lines.

AUXILIARY NETWORK ADDRESS In IBM parlance, in ACF/VTM, any network address except the main network address, assigned to a logical unit which is capable of having parallel sessions.

AUXILIARY POWER An alternate source of electric power, serving as backup for the primary power at the station main bus or prescribed sub-bus. An off-line unit provides electrical isolation between the primary power and the critical technical load; an on-line unit does not. These are government definitions: A Class A power source is primary power source; i.e., a source that assures an essentially continuous supply of power. Types of auxiliary power service include: Class B: a standby power plant to cover extended outages (days); Class C: a quick-start (10 to 60 seconds) unit to cover short-term outages (hours); Class D: an uninterruptible (no-break) unit using stored energy to provide continuous power within specified voltage and frequency tolerances.

AUXILIARY RINGER This is a separate external telephone ringer or bell. It can be programmed to ring when a line or a telephone, or both ring; or, when Night Service is turned on.

AUXILIARY SERVICE TRUNK GROUPS A category of trunk groups that provides selected services for customer or operators and terminates on announcement systems, switchboards, or desks. Examples include Directory Assistance, Intercept, Public Announcement, Repair Service, Time, and Weather.

AUXILIARY STORAGE A mass storage device capable of holding a larger amount of information than the main memory (i.e. RAM) of the computer or telephone system, but with slower access time. For example — magnetic tape, floppy disks, etc.

AUTOVON The AUTOmatic VOice Network used worldwide by the US Department of Defense. The system includes conferencing and secure voice communications (scrambling), among other features.

AUU ATM User-to-User

AVAILABLE In automatic call distribution language, an agent state, between calls, when an agent, having finished the previous transaction, returns to accept the next inbound caller. See also AVAILABILITY.

AVAILABLE STATE According to Bellcore, an available circuit state occurs when all of the following are true:

1. The Bit Error Ratio (BER) is better than 1 in 10 to the nth power for a specific number of consecutive observation periods of fixed duration.

2. Block Error Ratio (BLER) is better than 1 in 10 to the nth power under the same conditions.

3. There are a specific number of consecutive observation periods of fixed duration without a severely errored unit time.

AVAILABILITY The amount of time a computer or a telephone system is available for processing transactions or telephone calls. Here's a more technical definition: The ratio of the total time a functional unit is capable of being used during a given interval to the length of the interval; e.g., if the unit is capable of being used for 100 hours in a week, the availability is 100/168. Contrast this with the term Reliability, which is different. See RELIABILITY.

AVAILABILITY REPORTS Availability reports show how often and for how long nodes, links or paths were unavailable due to outages between specified dates. They can be used to monitor network reliability and to calculate rebates for users.

AVALANCHE PHOTO DIODE APD. A fiber optic transmission device. A light detector that generates an output current many times the light energy striking its face. A photodiode that shows gain in its output power compared to the optical power that it receives through avalanche multiplication (signal gain) of the current that flows through a photosensitive device. This type of diode is used in receivers requiring high light sensitivity. See APD.

AVALANCHING The process by which an electrical signal is multiplied within a device by electron impact ionization.

AVC Automatic Volume Control. In radio it maintains constant sound level despite undesired differences in strength of incoming signal.

AVD Alternative Voice Data. See AVD CIRCUITS.

AVD CIRCUITS Alternate Voice Data Circuits. Telephone lines which have been electrically treated to handle both voice and data signals. Typically used on leased overseas circuits to save money.

AVERAGE CALL DURATION Divide the total number of minutes of conversation by the number of conversations. Bingo, that's your average call duration.

AVERAGE CUSTOMER ARRIVAL RATE Represents the number of entities (humans, packets, calls, etc.) reaching a queuing system in a unit of time. This average is denoted by the Greek letter lambda. One would prefer to know, if possible, the full distribution of the calls arriving.

AVERAGE DELAY The delay between the time a call is answered by the ACD and the time it is answered by a person. This typically includes time for an initial recorded announcement plus time spent waiting in queue. Average delay can be chosen as the criterion for measuring service quality.

AVERAGE HANDLE TIME AHT. The period of time an employee is occupied with an incoming call. This is the sum of talk time and after-call-work time.

AVERAGE HOLDING TIME The sum of the lengths (in minutes or seconds) of all phone calls during the busiest hour of the day divided by the number of calls. There are two definitions. The one above refers to average speaking time (it's the more common one). There's a second definition for "average holding time." This refers to how long each call was on hold, and thus not speaking. This second definition is typically found in the automatic call distribution business (ACD). Check before you do your calculations.

AVERAGE LATENCY The time required for a disk to rotate one-half revolution.

AVERAGE PULSE DENSITY In T-1 bipolar transmissions, refers to the number of "1" pulses per "0" conditions and is usually tied to a maximum number of "0"s in a row (i.e., FCC Part 68 requires 12.5% pulse density and no more than 80 consecutive "0"s where as AT&T Pub 62411 uses a formula and no more than 15 consecutive "0"s).

AVERAGE SPEED OF ANSWER ASA. How many seconds it takes an operator on average to answer a call.

AVERAGE TRANSFER DELAY Average time between the arrival of a packet to a station interface and its complete delivery to the destination station.

AVI Audio Video Interleaved. File format for digital video and audio under Windows. Use the "Media Player," which comes with Windows, to play AVI files. The AVI file format is cross-platform compatible, allowing .AVI video files to be played under Windows and other operating systems.

AVK Audio Video Kernel. DVI (Digital Video) system software designed to play motion video and audio across hardware and operating system environments.

AVSS Audio-Video Support System. DVI (Digital Video) system software for DOS. It plays motion video and audio.

AVOIDABLE COSTS A wonderful concept used by the regulated telephone industry. It refers to those costs which would be avoided (i.e. not incurred) if the service were not offered. Examples of costs to avoid are maintenance, taxes, labor, and other direct costs. The concept of Avoidable Costs is to allow the phone industry the justification to price a competitive service very low.

AVOX A code name for Northern Telecom's "dumb" (i.e. programmable) switch which it intends to release in the North America some time in mid 1992.

AVP A Northern Telecom word for Associated Voice Port.

AVP-100 Introduced in early April 1992, AT&T Microelectrics' three-chip set that supports Px64, MPEG and JPEG coding and compression schemes. Its support of these standards for full-motion video and audio, stored motion video and still image compression is expected to reduce the cost of video codec equipment and stimulate development of non-proprietary codecs. The chip set performs 25 billion operations per second most of which is motion estimation.

AVP-L A Northern Telecom word for Associated Voice Port and Line.

AVRS Automated Voice Response System. See IVR and VOICE RESPONSE SYSTEM.

AWC Area-Wide Centrex.

AWG American Wire Gauge. Standard measuring gauge for non-ferrous conductors (i.e. non-iron and non-steel). AWG covers copper, aluminum, and other conductors. Gauge is a measure of the diameter of the conductor. Also known as the Brown and Sharpe (B&S) Wire Gauge. A method of measuring the thickness of cable. The AWG numbering system is backwards: The higher the AWG number the thinner the wire. For example, heavy industrial wiring may be No. 2. Homes are typically wired with No. 12 or No. 14. Telephone systems typically use No. 22, No. 24 or No. 26. The thicker the wire, the more current it can carry further. The thicker the wire, the less resistance the current will encounter and therefore the longer it will travel. You need thicker phone cabling when your phones are further away. Some vendors save money by installing systems with thin wire. Make sure you specify.

AX.25 An amateur radio implementation of the X.25 protocol. Used by some private VANs (Value Added Networks) to avoid PTT (post, Telephone, and Telegraph Administration) monopolies (and thus high prices) on X.25 transmission and switching.

AXIAL RATIO Of a wave having elliptical polarization, the ratio of the major axis to the minor axis of the ellipse described by the tip of the electric field vector.

AXIAL RAY A ray that travels along the axis of an optical fiber.

AXIAL SLAB INTERFEROMETRY Synonym for Slab Interferometry.

AXIS The center of an optical fiber.

AZIMUTH The horizontal angle which the radiating lobe of an antenna makes in angular degrees, in a clockwise direction, from a north-south line in the northern hemisphere. In the southern hemisphere, the reference is the south-north line. Azimuth actually involves a lot more than antennas. For example, it covers the alignment of a recording head in a tape recorder.

B The local wireline cellular carrier. In one of its less intelligent decisions, the Federal Communications Commission decided to issue two cellular franchises in each city of the United States. They gave one to the local phone company and one to a competitor. This duopoly has naturally meant little real price competition. And perhaps one day, the FCC will issue other licenses and the price of cellular phone calls will drop dramatically. Meantime, the "A" carrier on your cellular phone is the local wireline carrier. And the "B" is the other one. See PCS.

B BATTERY A section of a phone system power supply that provides unfiltered Direct Current for operating relays and various other components. Typically 20 volts. See A BATTERY.

B CHANNEL A "bearer" channel is a fundamental component of ISDN interfaces. It carries 64,000 bits per seconds in both directions, is circuit switched and is able to carry either voice or data. Whether it does or not depends on how your local telephone company has tariffed its ISDN service. See BASIC RATE INTERFACE (BRI) and ISDN.

B CONNECTOR A commonly-used wire-splicing device consisting of a flexible plastic sleeve over a toothed metal cylinder that bites through insulation when crimped with pliers or special tool. It is about one inch long and can hold three or four wires. A gel-filled version is available for installation in damp or humid areas. B connectors are also known as chiclets, beans, beanies, and rodent rubbers.

B LINK Bridge Link. A CCS/SS7 signaling link used to connect STP (Signal Transfer Point) pairs that perform work at the same functional level. These links are arranged in sets of four (called quads).

B PORT The port which connects the outgoing primary ring and the incoming secondary ring of the FDDI dual ring. This port is part of a dual attached station or concentrator. See FDDI.

B-911 Basic 911. B-911 is a centralized emergency reporting system which may have many features but which does NOT provide ALI (Automatic Location Information) to the 911 operator. In most cases, it does not provide ANI (Automatic Number Identification) either. B-911 provides a common emergency response number and relies on Emergency Hold and Forced Disconnect to maintain effective service.

B-CDMA Broadband Code Division Multiple Access.

B-CRYPT A symmetric cryptographic algorithm designed by British Telecom.

B-DCS Broadband Digital Cross-connect System. B-DCS is a generic term for an electronic digital cross-connect system capable of cross-connecting signals at or above the DS3 rate.

B-ISDN Broadband ISDN. Normal ISDN tends to assume all "conversations" are in chunks of 64 Kbps. ITU-T recommendation I.113 [45] defines Broadband as "a service or system requiring transmission channels capable of supporting (transmission) rates greater than the primary rate." Thus, broadband ISDN is a new concept in information transfer, although exactly what it is isn't clear yet. It could assume information comes in chunks as large as 150-million bits per second. In another ITU-T recommendation (I.121 [47]), the ITU-T presents an overview of what it sees as B-ISDN capabilities:

"B-ISDN supports switched, semipermanent and permanent point-to-point and point-to-multipoint connections and provides on demand, reserved and permanent services. Connections in B-ISDN support both circuit mode and packet mode services of a mono- and/or multi-media type and of connectionless or connection-oriented nature and in a bidirectional or unidirectional configuration. A B-ISDN will contain intelligent capabilities for the purpose of providing advanced service characteristics, supporting powerful operation and maintenance tools, network control and management." CCITT (now called ITU) is to decide on an international standard for B-ISDN by 1996.

Bellcore says that "National and international standards bodies have made the Asynchronous Transfer Mode (ATM) the target solution for providing the flexibility required by B-ISDN. ATM provides a common platform capable of supporting both broadband and narrowband services ... The physical layer-transmission standard for B-ISDN is the Synchronous Optical Network (SONET), also known as the Synchronous Digital Hierarchy (SDH). See N-ISDN and SONET."

B3ZS Bipolar 3-Zero Substitution.

B8ZS Binary 8 Zero Substitution. A technique used to accommodate the ones density requirement for digital T-carrier facilities in the public network, while allowing 64 Kbps clear data per channel. Rather than inserting a one for every seven consecutive zeros, B8ZS inserts two violations of the bipolar line encoding technique for digital transmission links.

BABBLE Just what it sounds like — crosstalk from several interfering communications circuits or channels.

BABBLING TRIBUTARY "A station that continuously transmits meaningless messages," as defined by John McNamara, of DEC and author of "Local Area Networks, an introduction to the technology." Some people might argue this was another word for Harry Newton, the author who didn't know when to stop and wanted to make this dictionary the most comprehensive telecom dictionary ever.

BABT British Approvals Board for Telecommunications. You need their approval before you can sell telecom equipment in Great Britain.

BABYPHONE Feature allowing calls to an off-hook telephone to listen to room noises, for example, to check if a baby is crying.

BACK BOARD A piece of plywood mounted on a wall. Phone equipment is mounted on the plywood. It is more efficient to first mount phone equipment on plywood in the service bay, test it out while it's convenient and diagnostic tools are handy. Then take the phone equipment and the back board (which typically consists of the KSU, power supply and 66-blocks) and install them on the customer's premises. This "pre-installation" makes enormous sense — economically and reliably. Sadly, few installation companies do it.

BACK END Database server functions and procedures for manipulating data on a network.

BACK END PROCESSOR A server is often called a back end and a workstation is often called the front end. On a LAN (Local Area Network), A back-end processor runs on a server. It is responsible for preserving data integrity and handles most of the processor-intensive work, such as data storage and manipulation.

BACK HAUL Back haul is a verb. A communications channel is back hauling when it takes traffic beyond its destination and back. There are many reasons it might do this. The first is that it may be cheaper to go that route instead of going directly. You might, for example, have a full-time private line from New York Dallas. You might find it cheaper to reach Nashville by going to Dallas first, then dialing back to Nashville. The economics of backhauling may change from one moment to another as the line to Dallas is empty, close to full or full. Another reason for backhauling is that you may do it to accommodate changes in your calling or staffing patterns. You may have an automatic call distributor in Omaha and one in Chicago. A call from New York may come into your Omaha ACD, but when it gets there you may discover that there are no agents available to handle the call. So it may now make sense to back haul the call to the Chicago ACD, where an agent is available.

BACK PORCH The portion of a video signal that contains the color burst information. It occurs between the end of the horizontal synch pulse and the beginning of active video.

BACK PROJECTION When the projection is placed behind a screen (as it is in television and various video conferencing applications where the image is displayed on a monitor or a fabric screen) it is described as a back projection system. In these systems the viewer sees the image via the transmission of light as opposed to reflection used in front projection systems. Audiences generally prefer back projection systems since they seem brighter.

BACK TO BACK CHANNEL BANK The connection of voice frequency and signaling leads between channel banks to allow dropping (i.e. removing) and inserting (i.e. adding) of channels.

BACK TO BACK CONNECTION A connection between the output of a transmitting device and the input of an associated receiving device. When used for equipment measurements or testing purposes, this eliminates the effects of the transmission channel or medium.

BACK UP SERVER A program or device that copies files so at least two up-to-date copies always exist.

BACKBONE The backbone is the part of the communications network which carries the heaviest traffic. The backbone is also that part of a network which joins LANs together — either inside a building or across a city or the country. LANs are connected to the backbone via bridges and/or routers and the backbone serves as a communications highway for LAN-to-LAN traffic. The backbone is one basis for design of the overall network service. The backbone may be the more permanent part of the network. A backbone in a LAN, a WAN, or a combination of both dedicated to providing connectivity between subnetworks in an enterprise-wide network.

BACKBONE CLOSET The closet in a building where the backbone cable is terminated and cross connected to either horizontal distribution cable or other backbone cable.

BACKBONE NETWORK The part of a communications facility that connects primary nodes; a primary shared communications path that serves multiple users via multiplexing at designated jumping-off points. A transmission facility, or arrangement of such facilities, designed to connect lower speed channels or clusters of dispersed users or devices.

BACKBONE SUBSYSTEM See RISER SUBSYSTEM.

BACKBONE TO HORIZONTAL CROSS-CONNECT BHC. Point of interconnection between backbone wiring and horizontal wiring.

BACKBONE WIRING The physical/electrical interconnections between telecommunications closets and equipment rooms. Cross-Connect hardware and cabling in the Main and Intermediate Cross-Connects are considered part of the backbone wiring.

BACKCHARGING A phone fraud term. Backcharging is starting the clock on a phone call at the time a customer contacts the long-distant phone service provider — not when the person being called answers the phone — which is what it should be.

BACKFEED PULL A method used to pull cable into a conduit or a duct liner when the cable is long or when placing cable into controlled environmental vaults, central offices, or under streets. With this method, the cable pays off its reel at an intermediate manhole and is first pulled in one direction. The remaining cable is then removed from the reel, laid on the ground, and then pulled in the opposite direction.

BACKFILE CONVERSION The process of scanning in, indexing and storing a large backlog of paper or microform documents in preparation of an imaging system. Because of the time-consuming and specialized nature of the task, it is generally performed by a service bureau.

BACKFILLING To designate memory on an expanded memory card and make it available for use as conventional memory.

BACKGROUND See BACKGROUND PROCESSING.

BACKGROUND COMMUNICATION Data communication, such as downloading a file from a bulletin board, that takes place in the background while the user concentrates on another application (e.g. a spreadsheet) in the foreground.

BACKGROUND MUSIC This feature allows music to be played through speakers in the ceiling and/or through speakers in each telephone, throughout the office, or office-by-office, or selectively. Background music is typically played through paging speakers, but it can also be played through the speakers of speakerphones. In fact, the two — paging and background music — often go hand-in-hand. When you want to page someone, the music turns off automatically and comes back on when the paging is over. The same thing happens on airplanes. Background music is said to motivate workers, often into shutting it off.

BACKGROUND NOISE The noise you hear when nothing else is being transmitted. See also WHITE NOISE.

BACKGROUND PROCESSING The automatic execution of lower priority computer programs when higher priority programs are not using the computer's resources. A higher priority task would be completing calls. A lower priority task would be running diagnostics. Some PBXs have this feature. Some insist on running their diagnostics even though they are choked with calls. The smarter ones tone down their diagnostics when they get busier, which makes sense.

BACKGROUND PROGRAM A low priority program operating automatically when a higher priority (foreground) program is not using the computer system's resources.

BACKGROUND TASK A secondary job performed while the user is performing a primary task. For example, many network servers will carry out the duties of the network (like controlling who is talking to whom) in the background, while at the same time the user is running his own foreground application (like word processing). See also BACKGROUND PROCESSING.

BACKHAUL See BACK HAUL.

BACKOFF When a device attempts to transmit data and it finds trouble, the sending device must try again. It may not try again immediately. It may "back off" for a little time so the trouble on the line can be cleared. This happens with LANs. For example, an earlier attempt to transmit may have resulted in a collision in a CSMA/CD (Carrier Sense Multiple Access/Collision Detection) Local Area Network (LAN). So the device "backs off," waits a little and then tries again. How long it waits is determined by preset protocols.

BACKOFF ALGORITHM The formula built into a contention local area network used after collision by the media access controller to determine when to try again to get back onto the LAN. See also BACKOFF.

BACKPLANE The high-speed communications line to which individual components, especially slide-in cards, are connected. For example, all the extensions of a PBX are connected to line cards (circuit boards) which slide into the PBX's cage. At the rear of the PBX cage, there are several connectors. Each of these connectors is wired to the PBX's backplane, also called a backplane bus. This backplane bus is typically running at a very high speed, since it carries many conversations, address information and considerable signaling. These days, the backplane bus is typically a time division multiplexed line — somewhat like a train with many cars, each representing a time slice of another conversation (data, voice, video or image). The backplane's capacity determines the overall capacity of the switch.

BACKPLANE BUS See BACKPLANE.

BACKPRESSURE Propagation effects in a communications network of hop-by-hop flow control to upstream nodes.

BACKSCATTERING 1. In fiber optics, the scattering of light into a direction opposite to the original one.

2. Radio wave propagation in which the direction of the incident and scattered waves resolved along a reference direction (usually horizontal) are oppositely directed. A signal received by backscattering is often referred to as "backscatter."

BACKSLASH Also called a virgule, the backslash key achieved fame because Microsoft used it to bring distinguish between subdirectories in MS-DOS. This is a backslash: \

BACKUP A copy of computer data on an external storage medium, such as a floppy disk or tape. Computers and telephone systems (which are computers) are unreliable. They glitch and lose data for all sorts of unusual and impossible-to-predict reasons. Thus the necessity for backups. The theory is when (not "if") a glitch will occur and the PBX's database will disappear off the face of the earth. If this happens, you have a backup and you simply retrieve the back-up file, load it up and, presto, you're back live.

Only information changed (since the backup was made) is lost. Backups save time in restoring the system after a loss. Most modern PBXs work with a database and other extensive customized instructions the user loads in. Most PBX users forget to make and keep backups of their PBX data. They expect their vendor to make backups, but he rarely does. This carelessness costs weeks of aggravation, as the PBX's database and instruction set is manually (and painfully) put back together.

The method by which backups are maintained is also important. The medium should clearly be reliable, i.e. the best quality magnetic medium. The method of backing up is also important. For example, a streaming tape backup is less reliable than a file-by-file backup. In a streaming backup, the backup medium simply captures the original data one bit after another in one long stream. In a file-by-file backup, the data moves over in logical segments — command files, data files, etc. Streaming backups will work if their data is placed back on the same precise device from which they were originally taken. But, if they are placed on a different device (even though the same model number, etc.), they may barf because the tape assumes bad sectors are in the same place. This will probably not be true. Streaming tape backup devices are less expensive to buy and much faster to use. Avoid them.

BACK UP DOMAIN CONTROLLER A server in a network domain that keeps and uses a copy by a computer without interrupting its current or primary task. For Windows NT Server domains, refers to a computer that receives a copy of the domain's security policy and domain database, and authenticates network logons.

BACKUP LINK A resilient (fault tolerant) link which is not used until the primary link fails.

BACKUP RING The token ring cabling between MAUs or CAUs consists of the main ring and the backup ring. The data is normally transmitted on the main ring, but if an error occurs, the data can be transmitted on the backup ring until the main ring is repaired. In MAU networks the switching is done manually while in CAU (or CAM) networks it is done automatically.

BACKWARD CHANNEL In data transmission, a secondary channel whose direction of transmission is constrained to be opposite to that of the primary (or forward) channel. The direction of transmission in the backward channel is restricted by the control interchange circuit that controls the direction of transmission in the primary channel. The channel of a data circuit that passes data in a direction opposite to that of its associated forward channel. The backward channel is usually used for transmission of supervisory, acknowledgement, or error-control signals. The direction of flow of these signals is opposite to that in which information is being transferred. The bandwidth of this channel is usually less than that of the forward channel; i.e., the information channel.

BACKWARD LEARNING Routing algorithm based on assumed symmetric network conditions. Source node assumes best route to given destination is via neighbor node that was on best route from destination to source.

BACKWARD RECOVERY The reconstruction of an earlier version of a file by using a newer version of data recorded in a journal.

BACKWARD SIGNAL A signal sent in the direction from the called to the calling station, or from the original communications sink to the original communications source. The backward signal is usually sent in the backward channel and consists of supervisory, acknowledgement, or error control elements.

BACKWARD SUPERVISION The use of supervisory sequences from a secondary to a primary station.

BAD BLOCK A defective unit on a storage medium that software cannot read or write.

BAD LINE KEY When the PBX attendant encounters a bad trunk, he/she pushes this bad line button on the console, automatically flagging the trunk for later checking and repair.

BAD LINE REPORTING Automatically reports a poor connection without interrupting the current call.

BAD SECTORS Defective areas on a hard or soft disk. The MS-DOS FORMAT command locks out bad sectors so they are never used. Other operating systems have similar commands. See also HOT FIX.

BAF Billing format of the 0122 structure code defined by the Bellcore Automatic Message Accounting Format (BAF) Requirements TR#030#NWT-001100. This format identifies paths according to the resource they terminate on.

BAFFLE A partition used with a loud speaker to prevent air vibrations from the back of the diaphragm from cancelling out the vibrations from the front of the diaphragm. Particularly valuable in the reproduction of bass notes.

BAG PHONE A slang expression for a transportable cellular phone whose characteristics are 3 WATT output, heavy weight (for a portable), and a bag with a handle. Bag phones are not designed for carrying around. They are designed to carry from one place to another and used at that place for serious conversations. Their big "plus" is that they give off five times as much power as a handheld cellular phone. This makes them useful for semipermanent "installation" in places like construction sites, etc. They are as powerful as a car phone.

BAIC Barring of All Incoming Calls. A wireless telecommunications term. A supplementary service provided under GSM (Global System for Mobile Communications).

BAKELITE An obsolete insulating material of the phenolic (synthetic resin) group. Jewelry made of bakelite is now particularly prized.

BALANCE To equalize load or current between parts or elements of a telephone line or circuit. Balancing helps get the best out of a phone line. In more technical terms, balancing a line is to adjust the impedance of circuits and balance networks to achieve specified return loss objectives at junctions of two-wire and four-wire circuits.

BALANCED CIRCUIT Telephone circuit in which the two conductors are electrically balanced to each other and to the ground. A balanced electrical interface generally allows data to be transmitted over longer distances than does an unbalanced circuit. See BALANCE.

BALANCED CONFIGURATION Point-to-point network configuration in HDLC with two combined stations.

BALANCED ELECTRICAL INTERFACE An electrical interface on which each circuit consists of a separate pair of wires. A balanced electrical interface generally allows data to be transmitted over longer distances than does an unbalanced electrical interface.

BALANCED LINE A transmission line which has two conductors and a ground. When the voltages of the two conductors are equal in strength but opposite in direction, then you have a balanced line.

BALANCED MODE TRANSMISSION Data transmission with information conveyed by differences in voltages on two circuits to minimize effects of induced voltages.

BALANCED MODULATOR An amplitude modulating circuit that suppresses the carrier signal, producing an output consisting only of upper and lower sidebands.

BALANCED RETURN LOSS A measure of the effectiveness with which a balanced network simulates the impedance of the two-wire circuit at a hybrid coil. More generally, a measure of the degree of balance between two impedances connected to two conjugate sides of a hybrid set, network, or junction.

BALANCED TO GROUND In a two-conductor circuit, a balanced-to-ground condition exists where the impedance-to-ground on one wire equals the impedance-to-ground on the other. This is the preferred condition for decent data communications.

BALANCED TRANSMISSION LINE A line having conductors with equal resistance per unit length and equal capacitance and inductance between each conductor and ground. Coaxial cable, for example, is configured easily as a balanced transmission system by the use of resistance-to-ground terminators.

BALANCING NETWORK A network used in a set ending a four-wire circuit to match the impedance of the two-wire circuit. 2. Sometimes employed as a synonym for balun.

BALCONY A little platform up a telephone pole where people can work or sleep safely.

BALLAST Device that modifies incoming voltage and current to provide the circuit conditions necessary to start and operate electric discharge lamps, e.g. fluorescent bulbs.

BALUN BALanced/UNbalanced. An impedance matching transformer. Baluns are small, passive devices that convert the impedance of coaxial cable so that its signal can run on twisted-pair wiring. They are used often so that IBM 3270-type terminals, which traditionally require coaxial cable connection to their host computer, can run off twisted-pair. Works for some types of protocols and not for others. There is often some performance degradation with baluns. And the signal cannot run as far on twisted wire as it can on coaxial cable.

BANDWIDTH 1. In telecommunications, bandwidth is the width of a communications channel. In analog communications, bandwidth is typically measured in

Hertz — cycles per second. In digital communications, bandwidth is typically measured in bits per second (not bytes per second). A voice conversation in analog format is typically 3,000 hertz. In digital communications, encoded in PCM, it's 64,000 bits per second. Do confuse bandwidth with band. Let's say we're running a communications device in the 12 GHz band. What's its bandwidth? That's the space it's occupying. Let's say it's occupying from 12 GHz to 12.1 GHz. This means that it's occupying the space from 12,000,000,000 to 12,100,000,000. This means its bandwidth is one million cycles or one megahertz. Affiliated terms are narrow bandwidth and wideband circuit. These are not precise terms, except that wideband circuits are wider than narrow ones. 2. The capacity to move information. A person who can master hardware, software, manufacturing and marketing — and plays the oboe or some other musical instrument — is "high bandwidth." The term is believed to have originated in Redmond, WA in the headquarters of Microsoft. People there who are super-intelligent and have generally broad capabilities are said to have "high bandwidth.".

BAND ELIMINATION FILTER BEF. A filter that has a single continuous attenuation band, with neither the upper nor lower cut-off frequencies being zero or infinite.

BAND SPLITTER A multiplexer designed to split the available frequency band into several smaller channels. A band splitter can use time division or frequency division multiplexing.

BAND-STOP FILTER A device that bars passage of frequencies within its designed range(s), and allows passage of higher or lower frequencies, or both.

BAND, CITIZENS One of two bands used for low power radio transmissions in the United States — either 26.965 to 27.225 megahertz or 462.55 to 469.95 megahertz. Citizens band radio is not allowed in many countries, even some civilized countries. In some countries they use different frequencies. CB radios, in the United States, are limited by FCC rule to four WATTS of power, which gives each CB radio a range of several miles. Some naughty people boost their CBs with external power. The author of this dictionary has actually spoken to Australia while driving on the Santa Monica Freeway in Los Angeles. See also CB.

BAND, FREQUENCY The frequencies between the upper and lower bands. See also BAND. Here is the accepted explanation of "bands:"

Below 300 Hertz	— ELF —	Extremely low frequency
300—3,000 Hertz	— ILF —	Infra Low Frequency
3—30 kHz	— VLF —	Very Low Frequency
30—300 kHz	— LF —	Low Frequency
300—3,000 kHz	— MF —	Medium Frequency
3—30 MHz	— HF —	High Frequency
30—300 MHz	— VHF —	Very High Frequency
300—3,000 MHz	— UHF —	Ultra High Frequency
3—30GHz	— SHF —	Super High Frequency
30—300GHz	— EHF —	Extremely High Frequency
300—3,000 GHz	— THF —	Tremendously High Frequency

Frequency Ranges (GHz)
Band American European
P 0.2-1.0 0.2-0.375

Band	American	European
L	1-2	0.375-1.5
S	2-4	1.5-3.75
C	4-8	3.75-6
X	8-12.5	6-11.5
J	-	11.5-18
Ku 12.5-18	-	
K 18-26.5 18-30		
Ka 26.5-40	-	
Q	-	30-47

BANDED MEMORY In a PostScript printer, virtual printer memory is a part of memory that stores font information. The memory in PostScript printers is divided into banded memory and virtual memory. Banded memory contains graphics and page-layout information needed to print your documents. Virtual memory contains any font information that is sent to your printer either when you print a document or when you download fonts.

BANDED RATE A price range for regulated telephone service that has a minimum floor and maximum ceiling. The minimum covers the cost of service; the maximum is the rate filed in the price list.

BANDMARKING A continuous circumferential band applied to an insulated conductor at regular intervals for identification.

BANDPASS The range of frequencies that a channel will transmit (i.e. pass through) without excessive attenuation.

BANDPASS FILTER A device which transmits a band of frequencies and blocks or absorbs all other frequencies not in the specified band. Often used in frequency division multiplexing to separate one conversation from many.

BANDPASS LIMITER A device that imposes hard limiting on a signal and contains a filter that suppresses the unwanted products of the limiting process.

BANDWIDTH 1. The range of electrical frequencies a device can handle. The amount of bandwidth a channel is capable of carrying tells you what kinds of communications can be carried on it. A wideband circuit, for example, can carry a TV channel. A wideband circuit capable of providing one video channel can also provide 1,200 voice telephone channels. 2. The capacity to move information. A person who can master hardware, software, manufacturing and marketing — and plays the oboe or some other semi-obscure musical instrument — is "high bandwidth." The term is believed to have originated in Redmond, WA in the headquarters of Microsoft. People there who are super-intelligent and have generally broad capabilities are said to have "high bandwidth."

BANDWIDTH COMPRESSION A technique to reduce the bandwidth needed to transmit a given amount of information. Bandwidth compression is used typically in "picture type" transmissions — such as facsimile, imaging or video-conferencing. For example, early facsimile machines scanned each bit of the document to be sent and sent a YES or NO (if there was material in that spot or not). More modern machines simply skip over all the blank spaces and transmit a message to the receiving facsimile machine when to start printing dots again. A facsimile "picture" is made up of tiny dots, similar to printing photos in a magazine. Today, bandwidth compression is used to transmit voice, video and data. There are many techniques, few of which are standard. The key, of course, is that if you're going to compress a "conversation" at one end, you must "de-compress" it at the other end. Thus, in every bandwidth compressed conversation there must be two sets of equipment, one at each end. And they better be compatible.

BANDWIDTH LIMITED OPERATION The condition prevailing when the system bandwidth, rather than the amplitude (or power) of the received signal, limits performance. The condition is reached when the system distorts the shape of the signal waveform beyond specified limits. For linear systems, bandwidth-limited operation is equivalent to distortion-limited operation.

BANDWIDTH ON DEMAND Just what it sounds like. You want two 56 Kbps circuits this moment for a videoconference. No problem. Use one of the newer pieces of telecommunications equipment and "dial up" the bandwidth you need. An example of such a piece of equipment is an inverse multiplexer. Uses for bandwidth on demand include video conferencing, LAN interconnection and disaster recovery. Bandwidth on demand is typically done only with digital circuits (they're easier to combine). Bandwidth on demand is typically carved out of a T-1 circuit, which is permanently connected to the customer's premises from a long distance carrier's central office, also called a POP — Point of Presence.

BANG An exclamation point (!) used in a Unix-to-Unix Copy Program (UUCP) electronic mail address. People who are on AT&T Mail often give you their mail address as "Bang Their Name." My AT&T Mail address is Bang HarryNewton, i.e. !HarryNewton.

BANG PATH A series of UUCP nodes mail will pass through to reach a remote user. Node names are separated by exclamation marks nicknamed "bangs." The first node in the path must be on the local system, the second node must be linked to the first, and so on. To reach user 1 on sys2 if your computer's address is sys1 you would use the following address:

sys1! sys2! sys3! user1

BANK SWITCHING A way of expanding memory beyond an operating system's or microprocessor's address limitations by switching rapidly between two banks of memory. IN MS-DOS, a 64K bank of memory between 640K and one megabyte is set aside. When more money is needed, the bank, or page, is switched with a 64K page of free memory. This is repeated with additional 64K pages of memory. When the computer requires data or program instructions not now in memory, expanded memory software finds the bank containing the data and switches it with the current bank of memory. Although effective, bank switching results in memory access times that are slower than true, extended memory.

BAOC Barring of All Outgoing Calls. A wireless telecommunications term. A supplementary service provided under GSM (Global System for Mobile Communications).

BAR CODE A bunch of lines of varying width printed on something. The bar code is designed to be read optically by some data capturing device. Bar codes are turning up on letters. They are read by image scanning devices in the post office and allegedly help the mails move faster. Bar codes are on most things you buy now in supermarkets. By scanning those bar codes at the checkout counter, the supermarket knows what's being sold and not being sold. And presumably the supermarket, or its computer, can order supplies to keep the supermarket stocked with goods that are selling and not re-order those which aren't.

BARBIE, JANE The electronic "Voice With A Smile" on many telephone company intercept recordings. Ms. Barbie does her work for the Audichron Company of Atlanta, GA.

BARE WIRE An electrical conductor having no covering or insulation.

BARGE-IN Interrupting a call in progress.

BARGE-OUT Leaving a call in progress without notice.

BARIUM FERRITE A type of magnetic particle used in some recording media including floptical diskettes. See also FERRITE, HARD FERRITE and SOFT FERRITE.

BARREL An imaging term. Distortion that swells an image in the middle, narrows it at the top and the bottom.

BARREL CONNECTOR This connector is a cylindrical (barrel-shaped) connector used to splice together two lengths of thick Ethernet coaxial cable.

BARREL CONTACT A term in cabling. A barrel contact is an insulation displacement type contact consisting of a slotted tube that cuts the insulation when the wire is inserted.

BARREL DISTORTION When a screen is distorted — with the top, bottom and sides pushing outwards (like a beer barrel) — the screen is said to be suffering barrel distortion.

BARTON Enos Barton once said he was "disgusted" when told that it would be possible to send conversation along a wire. He later co-founded (with Elisha Gray) the Western Electric Company, which became AT&T's manufacturing subsidiary and was once the largest electrical equipment manufacturer in the US. In addition to phones, the company made sewing machines, typewriters, movie sound equipment, radio station gear, radar systems and guided missile parts. See also GRAYBAR.

BASE ADDRESS The first address in a series of addresses in memory, often used to describe the beginning of a network interface card's I/O space.

BASE AMOUNT A call center term. One of the historical patterns; what the monthly call volume would be if there were no long-term trend or seasonal fluctuation- in other words, the average number of calls per month.

BASE LOAD In trunk forecasting, an amount of telephone traffic measuring during a certain defined time. See BASE PERIOD.

BASE MEMORY What many people refer to as the first 640 kilobytes of memory in an MS-DOS PC.

BASE PERIOD In trunk forecasting, a time span of consecutive study during which a base load is determined.

BASE SCHEDULES A call center term. A fixed set of pre-existing schedules that you can use as a starting point in scheduling. And new schedules created are in addition to the base schedules.

BASE STAFF A call center term. The minimum number of people, or "bodies in chairs," required to handle the workload in a given period. The actual required number of staff is always greater than base the staff, because of various human factors such as the need for breaks and time off.

BASE STATION A wireless term. A base station is the fixed device a mobile radio transceiver (transmitter/receiver) talks to, to talk to a person or to get to the landline phone network, public or private.

BASE-1 SERVICE An MCI definition. MCI Service providing customers network management capabilities by allowing them to operate and administer their own telecommunications usage.

BASEBAND A form of modulation in which signals are pulsed directly on the transmission medium without frequency division. Local area networks as a rule, fall into two categories — broadband and baseband. The simpler, cheaper and less sophisticated of the two is baseband. In baseband LANs, the entire bandwidth (capacity) of the LAN cable is used to transmit a single digital signal. In broadband networks, the capacity of the cable is divided into many channels, which can transmit many simultaneous signals. While a baseband channel can only transmit one signal and that signal is usually digital, a broadband LAN can transmit video, voice and data simultaneously by splitting the signals on that cable using frequency division multiplexing. The electronics of a baseband LAN are simpler than a broadband LAN. The digital signals from the sending devices are put directly onto the cable without modulation of any kind. Only one signal is transmitted at a time. Multiple "simultaneous" transmissions can be achieved by a technique called time division multiplexing (see multiplexing). In contrast, broadband networks (which typically run on coaxial cable) need more complex electronics to decipher and pick off the various signals they transmit. Attached devices on a broadband network require modems to transmit. Attached devices to baseband networks do not.

Baseband LANs typically work with one high speed channel, which all the attached devices — printers, computers, databases — share. They share it by using it in turns — for example, passing a "token" to the next device. That token entitles the device with the token to transmit. IBM's LAN is a token ring passing local area network. Another way of sharing the baseband LAN is that each device, when it is ready to transmit, simply transmits into the channel and waits for a reply. If it doesn't receive a reply, it retransmits. Thus there are two main network or baseband access control schemes — Token Ring Passing and CSMA/CD. See also CSMA/CD, BROADBAND, ETHERNET and LOCAL AREA NETWORKS.

BASEBAND MODEM A modem which does not apply a complex modulation scheme to the data before transmission, but which applies the digital input (or a simple transformation of it) to the transmission channel. This technique can only be used when a very wide bandwidth is available. It and only operates over short distances where signal amplification is not necessary. Sometimes called a limited distance or short-haul modem.

BASEBAND SIGNALING Transmission of a digital or analog signal at its original frequencies, i.e., a signal in its original form, not changed by modulation.

BASEBOARD A term used in voice processing/computer telephony to mean a printed circuit board without any daughterboards attached.

BASEBOARD RACEWAY A floor distribution method in which metal or wood channels, containing cables, run along the baseboards of the building. The front panel of the baseboard channel is removable, and outlets may be placed at any point along the channel.

BASELINE 1. The line from which a graph is drawn. The base line is the X axis on vertically oriented graphs, the Y axis on horizontal bar graphs, or the line representing zero if the data contains both positive and negative numbers. 2. The imaginary line extending through a font and representing the line on which characters are aligned for printing. In conventional, alphanumeric fonts, the baseline is usually defined as the imaginary line touching the bottom of uppercase characters.

BASELINE SEQUENTIAL JPEG The most popular of the JPEG modes which employs the lossy DCT (Discrete Cosine Transform) to compress image data as well as lossless processes based on variations of DPCM (Differential Pulse Code Modulation). The "baseline" system represents a minimum capability that must be present in all Sequential JPEG decoder systems. In this mode image components are compressed either individually or in groups. A single scan pass completely codes a component or group of components.

BASIC Beginners All-purpose Symbolic Instruction Code. A programming language. BASIC is an easy language to learn. It's worth learning. Not all "Basics" are the same. A sort of de facto standard is Microsoft Basic. If you're wish to learn some programming, we recommend you begin with the latest version of Microsoft's Visual Basic, a Windows version of Basic. We've tried it. We're very impressed with it.

BASIC BUDGET SERVICE An inexpensive local phone service often restricted to people with limited incomes. It may or may not include any outgoing calls. It may include only a few outgoing calls.

BASIC CALL A call between two users that does not require Advanced Intelligent Network Release 1 features (e.g. a POTS call). Definition from Bellcore. See AIN.

BASIC CALL STATE MODEL BCSM. An abstraction of the ASC call processing activities for a basic two-party call. The BCSM is split into Originating and Terminating BCSMs.

BASIC EXCHANGE TELECOMMUNICATIONS RADIO SERVICE BETRS. A service that can extend telephone service to rural areas by replacing the local loop with radio communications, sharing the UHF and VHF common carrier and private radio frequencies.

BASIC MODE LINK CONTROL Control of data links by use of the control characters of the 7-bit character set for information processing interchange as given in ISO Standard 646-1983 and ITU-T Recommendation V.3-1972.

BASIC RATE INTERFACE BRI. There are two "interfaces" in ISDN: BRI and PRI. In BRI, you get two bearer B-channels at 64 kilobits per second and a data D-channel at 16 kilobits per second. The bearer B-channels are designed for PCM voice, video conferencing, group 4 facsimile machines, or whatever you can squeeze into 64,000 bits per second full duplex. The data D-channel is for bringing in information about incoming calls and taking out information about outgoing calls. It is also for access to slow-speed data networks, like videotex, packet switched networks, etc. One BRI standard is the "U" interface, which uses two wires. Another BRI standard is the "T" interface which uses four wires. See ISDN for a much fuller explanation.

BASIC SERVICE A telephone company service limited to providing local switching and transmission. Basic Service does not include equipment. The term Basic Service is unclear and varies between telephone companies and data communications service providers.

BASIC SERVICE ELEMENTS BSEs. An Open Network Architecture term. BSEs are services which value-added companies could get from their phone company. BSEs are optional basic network functions that are not required for an ESP to have a BSA, but when combined with BSEs can offer additional features and services. Most BSEs allow an ESP to offer enhanced services to their customers. BSEs fall into four general categories: Switching, where call routing, call management and processing are required; Signaling, for applications like remote alarm monitoring and meter reading; Transmission, where dedicated bandwidth or bit rate is allocated to a customer application; and Network Management, where a customer is given the ability to monitor network performance and reallocate certain capabilities. The selection of available BSEs is an ongoing process, with new arrangements being developed. ANI, Audiotext "Dial-It" Services, and Message Waiting Notification are all examples of BSEs. See AIN and OPEN NETWORK ARCHITECTURE.

BASIC SERVING ARRANGEMENT BSA. An old term defining the relationship of an enhanced service provider (value added provider) to the phone company providing the line/s. Under ONA (Open Network Architecture), a BSA is the basic interconnection access arrangement which offers a customer access to the public network (i.e. the normal switch phone service) and provides for the selection of available Basic Service Elements. It includes an ESP (Enhanced Service Provider) access link, the features and functions associated with that access link at the central office serving the ESP and/or other offices, and the transport (dedicated or switched) within the network that completes the connection from the ESP to the central office serving its customers or to capabilities associated with the customer's complementary network services. Each component may have a number of categories of network characteristics. Within these categories of network characteristics are alternatives from among which the customer must choose. Examples of BSA components are ESP access link, transport and/or usage. See OPEN NETWORK ARCHITECTURE.

BASIC TELEPHONY The lowest level of service in Windows Telephony Services is called Basic Telephony and provides a guaranteed set of functions that corresponds to "Plain Old Telephone Service" (POTS - only make calls and receive calls). See WINDOWS TELEPHONY SERVICES.

BASR Buffered Automatic Send/Receive.

BATCH FILE A text file for personal computers with the extension .BAT that contains MS-DOS commands. When you type the name of the file, DOS carries out the commands in the file. Many computer programs are installed on your hard disk or loaded using batch files, as are many LAN operating systems. Batch files simplify life. If used wisely, you can save yourself typing things over and over again. It also means you don't have to remember all the commands to do something, just the first one. Batch files can be used to load other programs or to change the parameters of your computer. Anything that can be done from DOS (and some things that can't) can be done from a batch file. Norton Utilities has an enhanced version of DOS's Batch file.

BATCH PROCESSING There are two basic types of data processing. One is batch processing. Also called deferred time processing and off-line processing. Batch processing occurs where everything relating to one complete job — such as preparing this week's payroll — is bunched together and transmitted for processing (locally, in the same building or long distance, across the country), usually by the same computer and under the same application program. Batch processing does not permit interaction between the program and the user once the program has been read (i.e. fed into) the computer. In batch processing with telecommunications (i.e. sending the task to be done over the phone line), network response time is not critical, since no one is sitting in front of a screen waiting for a response. On the other hand, accuracy of communications is very critical, since no one is sitting in front of a screen checking entries and responses.

The second type of processing is called INTERACTIVE or REAL TIME processing. Under this method of processing, a user sends in transactions and awaits a response from the distant computer before continuing. In this case, response time on the data communications facility is critical. Seconds count, especially if a customer is sitting at the other end of a voice call awaiting information on whether there's space on that airline flight, for example. See BATCH FILE.

BATCH FILE A batch file on a computer contains sequential instructions to perform one task after another. Batch files on a MS-DOS machine are identified by the extension .BAT. When the MS-DOS operating system sees them, it recognizes the file and executes the instructions inside the file. DOS has a special (though limited) language for writing programs in. There are also programs for converting DOS batch files into .EXE or .COM files. This makes them run faster.

BATCH JOB FILE See BATCH FILE.

BATTERIES A,B AND C In ancient times, when vacuum tubes were still in use, the A battery (often about 6 volts) heated the filament or cathode to boil off electrons, the B battery (usually several hundred volts), positive with respect to the cathode, sucked the negative electrons to the plate, while the C battery, a few volts negative with respect to the cathode, tended to repel the electrons back toward the cathode. By varying a small signal voltage riding on the C battery, the flow of electrons to the plate could be controlled to generate a much larger voltage.

BATTERY All telephone systems work on DC (direct current). DC power is what you use to talk on. Often the DC power is called "talking battery." Most key systems and many PBXs plug directly into an AC on the wall, but that AC power is converted by a built-in power supply to the DC power the phone system needs. All central offices (public exchanges) used rechargeable lead acid batteries to drive them. These batteries perform several functions: 1. They provide the necessary power. 2. They serve as a filter to smooth out fluctuations in the commercial power and remove the "noise" that power often carries. 3. They provide necessary backup power should commercial power stop, as in a "blackout" or should it get very weak, as in a "brownout."

In short, "battery" is the term used to reference the DC power source of a telephone system. Often called "Talking Battery." 2. Storage battery used with central office switching systems and PBXs serving locations which cannot tolerate outages. Batteries serve the following purposes: Act as a filter across the generator or power rectifier output to smooth out the current and reduce noise; provide a cushion against periodic overloads exceeding the generator/rectifier capacity; supply emergency power for a limited time in event of commercial power failure. See also AC, AC POWER, BATTERY RESERVE and CENTRAL OFFICE BATTERY.

BATTERY BACKUP A battery which provides power to your phone system when the main AC power fails especially during blackouts and brownouts. Hospitals, brokerage companies, airlines and hotel reservation services must have battery backup because of the integral importance of their phone systems to their business.

BATTERY ELIMINATOR A device which has a rectifier and (hopefully) a filter. This device will convert AC power into the correct DC voltages necessary to drive a telephone system. Such a battery eliminator, or power supply, should deliver "clean" power, i.e. with little "noise" and of low impedance.

BATTERY RESERVE The capability of the fully charged battery cells to carry the central office power load imposed when commercial power fails and the primary power source (generators/rectifiers) is out of service. Properly described in terms of the number of hours the batteries can furnish operating power for dependent CO apparatus for a demand equal to that on the CO during its busy hour. A busy-hour reserve of eight hours is typical for a telephone office battery plant.

BAUD RATE A measure of transmission speed over an analog phone line — i.e. a common POTS line. (POTS stands for Plain Old Telephone Service). Imagine that you want to send digital information (say from your computer) over a POTS phone line. You buy a modem. A modem is a device for converting digital on-off signals, which your computer speaks, to the analog, sine-wave signals your phone line "speaks." For your modem to put data on your phone line means it must send out an analog sine wave (called the carrier signal) and change that carrier signal in concert with the data it's sending. Baud rate measures the number of number of changes per second in that analog sine wave signal. According to Bell Labs, the most changes you can get out of a 3 KHz (3000 cycles per second) voice channel (which is what all voice channels are) is theoretically twice the bandwidth, or 6,000 baud.

Baud rate is often confused with bits per second, which is a transfer rate measuring exactly how many bits of computer data per second can be sent over a telephone line. You can get more data per second — i.e. more bits per second — on a voice channel than you can change the signal. You do this through the magic of coding techniques, such as phase shift keying. Advanced coding techniques mean that more than one bit can be placed on a baud, so to speak. To take a common example, a 9,600 bit per second modem is, in reality, a 2,400 baud modem with advanced coding such that four bits are impressed on each baud. The continuing development of newer and newer modems point to increasingly advanced coding techniques, bringing higher and higher bit per second speeds. My latest modem, for example, is 28,800 bits per second.

BAUDOT CODE The code set used in Telex Transmission, named for French telegrapher Emile Baudot (1845-1903) who invented it. Also known by the CCITT approved name, International Telegraph Alphabet 2. The Baudot code has only five bits, meaning that only 32 separate and distinct characters are possible from this code, i.e. 2 x 2 x 2 x 2 x 2 equals 32. By having one character called Letters (usually marked LTRS on the keyboard) which means "all the characters that follow are alphabetic characters," and having one other key called Figures (marked FIGS), meaning "all characters that follow are numerals or punctuation characters," the Baudot character set can represent 52 (26 x 2) printing characters. The characters "space," "carriage return," "line feed" and "blank" mean the same in either FIGS or LTRS. TDD devices (Telecommunications Devices for the Deaf) use the Baudot method of communications to communicate with distant TDD devices over phone lines. See also ASCII, EBCDIC, MORSE CODE and UNICODE, which are other ways of encoding characters into the ones or zeros needed by computers.

BAY A telephone industry term for the space between the vertical panels or mounting strips ("rails") of the rack. One rack may contain several bays. A bay is another place you put equipment.

BBN Bolt, Beranek, and Newman, Inc. The Cambridge, MA company responsible for development, operation and monitoring of the ARPANET, and later, the Internet core gateway system, the CSNET Coordination and Information Center (CIC), and NSFnet Network Service Center (NNSC).

BBS Bulletin Board System. Another term for an electronic bulletin board. Typically a PC, modem/s and communications bulletin board software attached to the end of one or more phone lines. Callers can call the BBS, read messages and download public domain software. The person who operates a BBS is called a system operator, commonly shortened to SYSOP (pronounced "sis-op"). See also ELECTRONIC BULLETIN BOARD.

BCC 1. Bellcore Client Company. What Bellcore calls its owners — the seven regional Bell operating companies and their operating phone company subsidiaries. 2. Block Check Character. A control character appended to blocks in character-oriented protocols and used for figuring if the block was received in error. BCC is especially used in longitudinal and cyclic redundancy checking. As a packet (or in IBM jargon, a frame) is assembled for transmission, the bits are passed through an algorithm to come up with a BCC. When the packet is received at the other end, the receiving computer also runs the same algorithm. Both machines should come up with the same BCC. If they do, the transmission is correct and the receiving computer sends an ACK — a positive acknowledgement. If they don't, an error has occurred during transmission, and they don't have the same bits in the packet. The receiver transmits a signal (a NAK, for negative acknowledgement) that an error has occurred, and the sender retransmits the packet. This process goes on until the BCC checks.

BCD Binary Coded Decimal. A system of binary numbers where each digit of a number is represented by four bits. See BINARY.

BCH Bose, Chaudhuri and Hocquenghem error correction code. Named after the three guys who invented it.

BCM 1. Bit Compression Multiplexer. 2. Basic Call Model (a term from the

Bellcore discussion of Advanced Intelligent Networks). See AIN.

BCR Business Communications Review, a good magazine based in Hinsdale, IL. To get a sub, call 1-800-BCR-1234.

BDLC Burroughs Data Link Control, a bit oriented protocol.

BEACON A token ring frame sent by an adapter indicating that it has detected a serious ring problem, such as a broken cable or a MAU. An adapter sending such frames is said to be beaconing. See BEACONING.

BEACON INITIATIVE A "plan and rationale to help bring the information highway to Canadian businesses and consumers. The central theme of the initiative is an open collaborative effort with all interested players to bring enhanced interactive data, image and video services to Canadians." That's what the press release of April 5, 1994 said. Companies in the Beacon Initiative include BC Telephone, AGT Limited, SaskTel, Manitoba Telephone System, Bell Canada. NBTel, Maritime Tel & Tel. Island Telephone, Newfoundland Telephone and Stentor Communications.

BEACONING Token Ring process to recover the network when any attached station has sensed that the ring is inoperable due to a hard error. Stations can withdraw themselves from the ring if necessary. A station detecting a ring failure upstream transmits (beacons) a special MAC frame used to isolate the location of the error using beacon transmit and beacon repeat modes. See BEACON.

BEAM A way to exchange information between Newton users. Beaming uses the small built-in infrared unit at the top of the Newton MessagePad to send anything that's on one MessagePad to another MessagePad, or to a Sharp Wizard. This can be done across a conference table.

BEAM DIAMETER The distance between the diametrically opposed points on a plane perpendicular to the beam axis at which the irradiance is a specified fraction of the beam's peak irradiance. The term is most commonly applied to beams that are circular or nearly circular in cross-section.

BEAM DIVERGENCE As through the air telecom signal go further, they diverge. Beam divergence measures that divergence.

BEAMSPLITTER A device for dividing an optical beam into two or more separate beams, often a partially reflecting mirror.

BEANS Telco slang for B-connectors, which are about the size and shape of common beans. See B CONNECTOR.

BEAT FREQUENCY An old radio term: The frequency resulting when an oscillation of one frequency is "beat" or heterodyned against an oscillation of different frequency. The figure given is normally in cycles per second.

BEAT RECEPTION An old radio term. The resultant audible frequency when two sources of unequal undamped electrical oscillations of constant amplitude act simultaneously in the same circuit. See BEAT FREQUENCY.

BEATING The phenomenon in which two or more periodic quantities having slightly different frequencies produce a resultant having periodic variations in amplitude.

BECN Backward Explicit Congestion Notification. This bit notifies the user that congestion-avoidance procedures should be initiated for traffic in the opposite direction of the received frame. It indicates that the frames that the user transmits on this logical connection may encounter congested resources. In other words, slow down, you move too fast. Your bits may not get through or get delayed.

BED OF NAILS CORD A description of a type of alligator clip that attaches to the end of a craft test set, also called a butte set.

BEF Band Elimination Filter. A filter that has a single continuous attenuation band, with neither the upper nor lower cut-off frequencies being zero or infinite.

BEHIND SWITCH MODE An AT&T Merlin term. A mode of operation in which the communications system control unit is connected to (is "behind") another communications system. In other words, running Merlin behind Centrex.

BEL A relative measurement, denoting a factor of ten change. Rarely used in practice; most measurements are in decibels (0.1 bel).

BELDEN A major manufacturer of communications cable. Belden is such a high quality manufacturer and has set many cabling standards that some many other manufacturers follow their specs.

BELL A bell in a telephone instrument rings when a 20 Hz signal of about 90 volts AC is applied to the subscriber loop. In contrast, the normal voltage applied to a subscriber loop and used for speaking and listening is 48 volts DC.

BELL 103 AT&T specification for a modem providing asynchronous originate/answer transmission at speeds up to 300 bits per second (300 baud). This is the most common standard for modems running with personal computers. Every dial service in the U.S. adheres to this standard. The second most common standard is Bell 212. See the next few definitions.

BELL 201 AT&T specification for a modem providing synchronous data transmission at 2,400 bits per second.

BELL 202 AT&T specification for a modem providing asynchronous data transmission at speeds up to 1,800 bits per second. Requires four-wire line for full duplex transmission.

BELL 208 AT&T specification for a modem providing synchronous data transmission at speeds up to 4,800 bits per second.

BELL 209 AT&T specification for a modem providing synchronous data transmission at speeds up to 9,600 bits per second.

BELL 212 AT&T specification for a modem providing full duplex asynchronous or synchronous data transmission at speeds up to 1,200 bits per second on the voice dial-up phone network. This is the second most common standard for modems running with personal computers. The first is Bell 103.

BELL 43401 Bell Publication defining requirements for transmission over telco-supplied circuits that have dc continuity (that are metallic).

BELL ATLANTIC Formed as a holding company after the AT&T Divestiture. Includes Bell of Pennsylvania, C&P Telephone Companies of D.C., Maryland, Virginia, and West Virginia, Diamond State Telephone (MD), New Jersey Bell and several Bell Atlantic business activities. Check out Bell Atlantic's logo. It has a wonderful, small wave in the "A" in Atlantic. Very charming. Very subtle.

BELL COMMUNICATIONS RESEARCH Bellcore. Formed at Divestiture to provide certain centralized services to the seven Regional Bell Holding Companies (RHCs) and their operating company subsidiaries. Also serves as a coordinating point for national security and emergency preparedness communications matters of the federal government. Bellcore does not work on customer premise equipment or other areas of potential competition among its owners — the seven Regional Bell Operating companies. Bellcore also works on standardizing methods by which customers of long distance companies will reach their favorite long distance companies. At time of writing, around 8,000 people worked at Bellcore, mostly in northern New Jersey. Bellcore has the unenviable task of trying to service the needs of the seven competitors, which own it. Its annual budget is around $1 billion, paid for by the seven Bell regional operating companies. It does work on ISDN and common channel signaling standards. See also BELLCORE.

BELL COMPATIBLE A term sometimes applied to modems. A modem is said to be "Bell compatible" if it conforms to the technical specifications set forth by AT&T for the various devices, such as Bell 212.

BELL OPERATING COMPANY BOC. A BOC is one the 22 regulated telephone companies of the former Bell System, which was broken apart (the Divestiture of the Bell System) at midnight on December 31, 1983.

At Divestiture, the Bell operating companies were grouped into seven Regional Holding Companies (RHCs). According to the terms of the Divestiture Agreement between the Federal Courts, the Federal Government and AT&T, the divested companies must limit their activities to local telephone services, directory service, customer premise equipment, cellular radio and any other ventures as the Federal Court may approve from time to time. BOCs are specifically limited from manufacturing equipment and from providing long distance service. See also REGIONAL BELL OPERATING COMPANY.

BELL SPEAK A term coined by Michael Marcus for insider jargon spoken by "real" telephone people — those who practiced pre-divestiture. Such old jargon is usually incomprehensible to anyone in today's telephone industry who is younger than 46.

BELL SYSTEM The entire AT&T organization prior to when it was broken up — at the end of 1984. The Bell System included Bell Labs, Long Lines, Western Electric and the 23 Bell operating companies.

BELLBOY A public paging system run by local Bell phone companies. The name survived for many years and only drew criticism in the middle to late seventies with the rise of the Women's Liberation movement. It's now not used. Shucks.

BELLCORE Bell Communications Research. Formed at Divestiture to provide certain centralized services to the seven Regional Bell Holding Companies (RBOCs) and their operating company subsidiaries. Also serves as a coordinating point for national security and emergency preparedness, and communications matters of the federal government. Bellcore does not work on customer premise equipment (e.g. the telephone set) or other areas of potential competition between its owners — the seven Regional Bell Operating Companies. It is a key player in the design of AIN — the Advanced Intelligent Network. You'll find many AIN definitions in this dictionary. You can acquire Bellcore documents from Bellcore — Document Registrar, 445

South Street, Room 2J-125, P.O. Box 1910, Morristown, NJ 07962-1910. Fax 201-829-5982. See also BELL COMMUNICATIONS RESEARCH. www.bellcore.com

BELLCORE AMA FORMAT BAF. The standard data format for AMA (Automatic Message Accounting) data to be delivered to the Revenue Accounting Office (RAO) in Advanced Intelligent Network Release 1.

BELLCORE MULTI-VENDOR INTERACTIONS MVI. The process for coordinating the efforts of Bellcore, the Bell Operating telephone companies and vendors to address technical issues associated with Advanced Intelligent Network.

BELLMAN-FORD-ALGORITHM Shortest-path routing algorithm that figures on number of hops in a route to find shortest-path spanning tree.

BELLSOUTH CORPORATION The largest regional Bell holding company formed at the Divestiture of AT&T. Includes Southern Bell and South Central Bell and several other BellSouth businesses.

BELOW-THE-LINE Expenses incurred that are charged to shareholders of regulated operating telephone companies, not ratepayers.

BENCHMARK A standardized task to test the capabilities of various devices against each other for such measures as speed.

BEND LOSS A form of increased attenuation caused by allowing high-order signals to radiate from the side of the fiber. The two common types of bend losses are those occurring when the fiber is curved and microbends caused by small distortions of the fiber imposed by poor cabling techniques.

BENDING RADIUS The smallest bend which may be put into a cable under a stated pulling force. Bending radius affects size of bends in conduit, trays or ducts. It affects pulley size. It affects the size of openings at pull boxes where loops may form. Very critical in all aspects of cable laying, especially with under-carpet cabling and fiber optic cable.

BEP Back End Processor.

BER 1. Bit Error Rate. The ratio of error bits to the total number of bits transmitted. If the BER gets too high, it might be worth while to go to a slower baud rate. Otherwise, you would spend more time retransmitting bad packets than getting good ones through. The theory is that the faster the speed of data transmission the more likelihood of error. This is not always so. But if you are getting lots of errors, the first — and easiest — step is to drop the transmission speed. See also BIT ERROR RATE. 2. A LAN term, which means Basic Encoding Rules. Rules for encoding data units described in ASN.1. (Abstract Syntax Notation One. LAN "grammar," with rules and symbols, that is used to describe and define protocols and programming languages. ASN.1 is the OSI standard language to describe data types.) BER is sometimes incorrectly lumped under the term ASN.1, which properly refers only to the abstract syntax description language, not the encoding technique.

BEST PATH An internetworking term: The optimal route between source and destination end stations through a wide area network. Determined through routing protocols such as RIP and OSPF, best path can be based on lowest delay, cost or other criteria.

BERNOULLI Daniel Bernoulli was the 18th century Swiss mathematician who first expressed the principle of fluid dynamics — the basis of Bernoulli "boxes" also called disk cartridges. A Bernoulli box, which is a mass storage device, uses both floppy and hard disk technologies. Bernoulli disks are removable. They physically look like large floppy disks.

BERT Bit Error Rate Test, or Tester. A known pattern of bits is transmitted, and errors received are counted to figure the BER. The idea is to measure the quality of data transmission. The bit error rate is the ratio of received bits that are in error, relative to the number of bits received. Usually expressed in a power of 10. Sometimes called Block Error Rate Tester.

BETA 1. Refers to the final stages of development and testing before a product is released to market. "Alpha" is the term used when a product is in preliminary development. "Her baby is in beta," according to Peter Lewis of the New York Times, means she is expecting soon. In the software industry, beta has been known to last a year or more. Microsoft's Bill Gates has given the word "beta" a whole new meaning by having as many as 500,000 "beta testers" for his Windows 95 operating system. At this level, beta testing is no longer testing, it's marketing. And it's positively brilliant. See BETA TEST. 2. Business Equipment Trade Association (UK).

BETA SITE A place a beta test is conducted. See BETA and BETA TEST.

BETA TEST Typically the last step in the testing of a product before it is officially released. A beta test is often conducted with customers in their offices. Some customers pay for the equipment or software they get under a beta test; some don't. Some beta tests stay in (if they work). Some don't. Most products don't work when they're first introduced. So beta tests are a good idea. Unfortunately, most manufacturers don't do sufficient beta testing. They want to get their product to market before the competition does. This often means we now have two or three new products on the market, none of which work reliably or do exactly what they're meant to do. Our rule: always wait several months after a product is introduced before buying it. By then the major bugs will have been fixed. The test before the beta test is called the Alpha. It isn't that common. See BETA.

BETAZED A planet in the second Star Trek TV series, inhabited by Betazoids, beings with great powers of empathy and telepathy.

BETRS Basic Exchange Telecommunications Radio Service. A service that can extend telephone service to rural areas by replacing the local loop with radio communications, sharing the UHF and VHF common carrier and private radio frequencies.

BEZEL The metal or plastic part — in short, the frame — that surrounds a cathode ray tube — a "boob" tube.

BEZS Bandwidth Efficient Zero Suppression. N.E.T.'s patented T-1 zero suppression technique; maintains Bell specifications for T-1 pulse density without creating errors in end-user data; uses a 32 kbps overhead channel.

BFT Binary File Transfer. BFT is a method of routing digital files using facsimile protocols instead of traditional modem file transfer protocols. See BINARY FILE TRANSFER for a fuller explanation.

BFV Bipolar violations: The digital data format consists of pulses of opposite polarity. No two consecutive pulses should be the same polarity; if two are detected in a row, the term is a violation, which is also a warning flag.

BGP Border Gateway Protocol. An interdomain routing protocol that is an alternative to EGP (Exterior Gateway Protocol). BGP is defined by RFC 1105.

BH Bandwidth Hog. A term defined by Philip Elmer-DeWitt, technology editor of Time Magazine in 1994, who spearheaded the launch of Time Online, the first fully electronic national magazine. He defined BH "as a person who uses the online medium like a bullhorn and attracts like-minded people who then rove in a pack, filling them with up with screeds." (Screed is a long discourse or essay.)

BHC Backbone to Horizontal Cross-connect. Point of interconnection between backbone wiring and horizontal wiring.

BI A Latin prefix meaning twice.

BIAS 1. A systemic deviation of a value from a reference value. 2. The amount by which the average of a set of values departs from a reference value. 3. An electrical, mechanical, magnetic, or other force field applied to a device to establish a reference level to operate the device. 4. Effect on telegraph signals produced by the electrical characteristics of the terminal equipment.

BIAS DISTORTION Distortion affecting a two-condition (binary) coding in which all the significant intervals corresponding to one of the two significant conditions have uniformly longer or shorter durations than the corresponding theoretical durations. The magnitude of the distortion is expressed in percent of a perfect unit pulse length.

BIAS GENERATOR A CBX printed circuit card that generates a signal that reduces idle channel noise for all coders installed in the CBX.

BIAS POTENTIAL The potential impressed on the grid of a vacuum tube to cause it to operate at the desired part of its characteristic curve.

BICONIC Fiber Optic Connector developed by AT&T.

BICONICAL ANTENNA An antenna consisting of two conical conductors having a common axis and vertex. Excitation occurs at the common vertex. If one of the cones is flattened into a plane, the antenna is called a discone.

BIDIRECTIONAL BUS A bus that may carry information in either direction but not in both simultaneously.

BIDIRECTIONAL COUPLERS Fiber optic couplers that operate in the same way regardless of the direction light passes through them.

BIDIRECTIONAL PRINTING A typewriter always prints from left to right. So did the early computer printers. The newer computer printers will print from left to right, drop down a line, then print from right to left. This increases the printer's speed.

BIG-ENDIAN A networking term. A format for storage or transmission of binary data in which the most significant bit (or byte) comes first. The reverse convention is called little-endian.

BIGAMY The only crime in which two rites make a wrong.

BIFURCATED ROUTING Routing that may split one traffic flow among multiple routes.

BILATERAL SYNCHRONIZATION A synchronization control system between exchanges A and B in which the clock at exchange A controls the received data at exchange B and the clock at exchange B controls the received data at exchange A. Normally implemented by deriving the receive timing from the incoming bit stream.

BILDSCHIRMTEXT German word for interactive videotex. The German Bundespost likes this service. But the German version isn't as successful as the French because the French gave away the videotex terminals. And the Germans didn't. Also, the French really encourage videotex entrepreneurs by giving a real piece of the action — 60% of the collected revenues.

BILL OF MATERIALS A list of specific types and amounts of direct materials expected to be used to produce a given job or quantity of output.

BILLBOARD Electronic sales pitches that come up on your computer screen at any time.

BILLBOARD ANTENNA A broadside antenna array with flat reflectors.

BILLED NUMBER SCREENING You (at home or your business) establish who can and cannot charge a call to your phone by making an agreement with your local telephone company to screen your calls. (e.g. Refusal of all collect call requests.)

BILLED TELEPHONE NUMBER BTN. The primary telephone number used for billing regardless of the number of telephone lines associated with that number.

BILLIBIT Someone's absolutely awful term for one billion bits. Also (and better) called a gigabit.

BILLING INCREMENT The increments of time in which the phone company (long distance or local) bills. Some services are measured and billed in one minute increments. Others are measured and billed in six or ten second increments. The billing increment is a major competitive weapon between long distance companies. Short billing increments become important to you, as a user, when your average calls are very short — for example, if you're making a lot of very short data calls (say for credit card authorizations). Being billed for a lot of six second calls is a lot cheaper than being billed for a lot of one minute calls.

BILLING MEDIA CONVERTER A Billing Media Converter, as made by the Cook division of Northern Telecom, provides a means of transporting Automatic Message Accounting (AMA) data from DMS-10 central offices to regional accounting offices with the physical transfer of magnetic tapes. The BMC is polled.

BILLING TELEPHONE NUMBER A Billing Telephone Number is the number to which calls to given location are billed. It is the seven-digit number with the area code followed by an alphanumeric code assigned by the local telephone company (e.g. NPA-NXX-XXXX).

BILLING VALIDATION SERVICE See BVA and BVS

BILLION In North America, a billion is a thousand million. In many countries overseas, a billion is a million million.

BINARIES Binary, machine readable forms of programs which have been compiled or assembled. As opposed to source language forms of programs.

BINARY Where only two values or states are possible for a particular condition, such as "ON" or "OFF" or "One" or "Zero." Binary is the way digital computers function because they can only represent things as "ON" or "OFF." This binary system contrasts with the "normal" way we write numbers — i.e. decimal. In decimal, every time you push the number one position to the left, it means you increase it by ten. For example, 100 is ten times the number 10. Computers don't work this way. They work with binary notation. Every time you push the number one position to the right it means you double it. In binary, only two digits are used — the "0" (zero) and the "1" (the one). If you write the number 10101 in binary, and you want to figure it in decimal as we know it, here's how you do it. 1 is one thing; Zero x 2 = zero; 1 times 2 x 2 = 4; 0 x 2 x 2 x 2 = 0; 1 x 2 x 2 x 2 x 2 = 16. Therefore the total 10101 in binary = 1 + 0 + 4 + 0 + 16 = 21 in decimal.

Binary notation differs slightly from notation used in ASCII or EBCDIC. In ASCII and EBCDIC, the binary values are used for coding of individual characters or keys or symbols on keyboards or in computers. So each string of seven (as in ASCII) or eight (as in EBCDIC) ones and zeros is a unique value — but not a mathematical one.

ASCII uses a seven bit coding scheme. Thus, the maximum number of different things you can code using seven bits is 128, i.e. 2 x 2 x 2 x 2 x 2 x 2 x 2 = 128. The maximum number represented by a byte (8 bits) or the IBM EBCDIC coding system is 256. i.e. 2 x 2 x 2 x 2 x 2 x 2 x 2 x 2 = 256. See BINARY CODED DECIMAL, BINARY FILE and BINARY TRANSFER.

BINARY CODE A code in which every elememt has only one of two possible values, which may be the presence or absence of a pulse, a pulse, a one or a zero, or high or a low condition for a voltage or current.

BINARY CODED DECIMAL BCD. A system of binary numbering that uses a 4-bit code to represent each decimal digit from 0 to 9 and multiple 4-bit patterns for higher numbers. The decimal numbers 0 to 9 are represented by the four-bit binary numbers from 0000 to 1010.

BINARY DIGIT A number in the binary system of notation.

BINARY FILE A file containing information that is in machine-readable form. It is an application. Or it can only be read by an application. See BINARY TRANSFER.

BINARY FILE TRANSFER BFT. The transmission of binary files, documents and electronic data exchange information between fax devices.

BINARY NOTATION Any notation that uses two different characters, usually the binary digits O and 1.

BINARY SYMMETRIC CHANNEL A channel designed so that the probability of changing binary bits in one direction is the same as the probability of changing them back to the correct state.

BINARY SYNCHRONOUS COMMUNICATIONS BISYNC or BSC. 1. In data transmission the synchronization of the transmitted characters by timing signals. The timing elements at the sending and receiving terminal define where one character ends and another begins. There are no start or stop elements in this form of transmission. 2. Also a uniform discipline or protocol for synchronized transmission of binary coded data using a set of control characters and control character sequences.

BINARY TO DECIMAL CONVERSION Conversion from base 2 to base 10. See BINARY.

BINARY TRANSFER A method of transferring binary files to a remote computer. When binary files are transferred via telecommunications, they must not be converted, changed or translated in any way during the transfer process otherwise they will be destroyed. Many electronic mail services, such as CompuServe or MCI Mail, have ways of "attaching" binary files to electronic mail, such that the binary file will not be affected or changed in any way during transmission. You can also compress binary files (binary or not) and transmit.

BINARY TRANSFER A transfer between two computers from files that may not be text based information, and therefore, if sent as ASCII characters, would not be received properly. A Binary Transfer keeps the integrity of the data by sending it in some manner of Error Correcting Protocol such as SNA, or XMODEM.

BIND A request to activate a session between two logical units (LUs).

BINDER A helically applied colored thread, yarn, or plastic ribbon used to confine and sometimes separate and identify groups of fibers or wires in a cable. Binders are usually used for holding assembled cable components in place.

BINDER GROUP A group of wires within a large cable that can be distinguished from other groups because it is wrapped with colored threads. Normal telephone color-coding provides for only 25 pairs of wire, so binder groups allow multiple pairs of the same color wire to be in one cable. A 50-pair cable has blue and orange binder groups; a 75-pair cable has blue, orange, and green groups. Since several wire pairs have the same color markings, installers must be careful when stripping cable insulation so they do not destroy the binder threads.

BINDERY A Novell NetWare database containing definitions for entities such as users, groups, and workgroups. The bindery contains three components: objects, properties, and property data sets. Objects represent any physical or logical entity, including users, user groups, file servers, print servers, or any other entity given a name. Properties are the characteristics of each bindery object, including passwords, account restrictions, account balances, internetwork addresses, list of authorized clients, workgroups, and group members. Property data sets are values assigned to entities bindery properties.

BINDING A Windows 95 definition. Binding is a process that establishes the communication channel between a protocol driver and a network adapter driver.

BINDING POST A screw with a small nut. You take your wires and join them together on a binding post by wrapping them together around the screw and then tightening the nut on them. These days, 66-blocks have effectively replaced binding posts. 66-blocks are easier and faster to use.

BIOS Basic Input/Output System of desktop computers. The BIOS contains the buffers for sending information from a program to the actual hardware device the information should go to.

BIOS ENUMERATOR A Windows 95 term. Bios enumerator is responsible, in a Plug and Play system, for identifying all hardware devices on the motherboard of the computer. The BIOS supports an API that allows all Plug and Play computers to be queried in a common manner.

BIOSENSORS Devices such as fingerprint readers and signature recognition systems.

BIP-N Bit Interleaved Parity N. A method of error monitoring. With even parity, an N bit code is generated by the transmitting equipment over a specified portion of the signal in such a manner that the first bit of the code provides even parity over the first bit of all N-bit sequences within the specified portion, etc. Even parity is generated by setting the BIP-N bits so that there are an even number of 1s in each of all N-bit sequences including the BIP-N.

BIPOLAR The predominant signaling method used for digital transmission services, such as DDS and T-1. The signal carrying the binary value alternates between positive and negative. Zero and one values are represented by the signal amplitude at either polarity, while no-value "spaces" are at zero amplitude.

BIPOLAR CODING The T carrier line coding system that inverts the polarity of alternate "one" bits.

BIPOLAR SIGNAL A signal having two polarities, both of which are not zero. It must have two-state or three-state binary coding scheme. It is usually symmetrical with respect to zero amplitude.

BIPOLAR VIOLATION The presence of two consecutive "one" bits of the same polarity on the T carrier line. See also BIPOLAR CODING.

BIRD A satellite.

BIRTHDAYS

January 4, 1847 Thomas Edison born

February 16, 1982 Michael Allen Newton born

February 20, 1980 Claire Elizabeth Newton born

February 23, 1965 Michael Dell (Dell Computer) born

March 3, 1847 Alexander Graham Bell born

March 11, 1933 Ben Rosen (Compaq, SRX, etc.) born

March 15, 1949 Gerry Friesen born

April 6, 1939 John Sculley (Apple) born

April 27, 1791 Samuel Morse born

May 11, 1948 International Communications Association born

June 10, 1942 Harry Newton born in Sydney Australia

June 13, 1961 TeleCommunications Association born

June 19, 1924 Ray Noorda (Novell) born

June 25, 1952 Paula Friesen born

June 27, 1968 Carterfone decision handed down by FCC

July 4, 1943 Susan Newton born

August 31, 1962 President Kennedy signed Communications Satellite Act
September 2, 1936 Andy Grove (Intel)

September 12, 1948 Communications Managers Association

October 28, 1955 Bill Gates (Microsoft)

November 13, 1954 Scott McNealy (Sun Microsystems)

December 10, William G. McGowan, founder of MCI

BIS The French term for "second" or "encore." It is used by the CCITT/ITU to designate the second in a family of related standards. "ter" designates the third in a family. See V SERIES.

BICSI Building Industry Consulting Service International, a professional organization. For those who acquire certain requisite education and experience by BICSI, the association makes them a RCDD, Registered Communication Distribution Designer. BICSI is at 813-397-1991.

BISDN Also spelled B-ISDN. Broadband ISDN. See ISDN. This is a vaguely defined term. It basically means any circuit capable of transmitting more than one Basic rate ISDN, i.e. 144 kbps. One definition I read recently suggested that BISDN is "a set of public network services that are delivered over ATM, including data, voice, and video. BISDN will provide services such as high-definition television (HDTV), multi-lingual TV, voice and image storage and retrieval, video conferencing. high-speed LANs, and multimedia." See B-ISDN for a longer explanation.

BISTABLE TRIGGER CIRCUIT A trigger circuit that has two stable states.

BISYNC (pron. Bye-sink). BISYNChronous Transmission. A half-duplex, character-oriented, synchronous data communications transmission method originated by IBM in 1964. See SYNCHRONOUS.

BISYNCHRONOUS TRANSMISSION Also called BISYNC. A data character-oriented communications protocol developed by IBM for synchronous transmission of binary-coded data between two devices. BISYNC uses a specific set of control characters to synchronize the transmission of that binary coded data. See also BINARY SYNCHRONOUS COMMUNICATION.

BIT Bit is a contraction of the term BInary digiT. It is the smallest unit of information (data) a computer can process, representing either high or low, yes or no, or 1 or O. It is the basic unit in data communications. A bit can have a value of zero (a mark) or one (a space).

BIT BUCKET Slang for throwing out bits — into a wastepaper bucket.

BIT BUFFER A section of memory capable of temporarily storing a single BInary uniT (bit) of information. Used to make data transmission accurate or consistent.

BIT CHECK A bit added to a digital signal and used for error checking, i.e. a parity bit. See also PARITY.

BIT DURATION The time it takes one bit to pass a point on the transmission medium. Used to measure delay times, especially in high speed communications.

BIT ERROR The value of an encoded bit can be changed due to a transmission problem (e.g. noise on the line) and then interpreted incorrectly by the receiver.

BIT ERROR RATE BER. The percentage of received bits in error compared to the total number of bits received. Usually expressed as a number to the power of 10. For example, 10 to the fifth power means that one in every 100,000 bits transmitted will be wrong. In transmitting data a high error rate on the transmission medium (i.e. some noise), doesn't mean there'll be lots of problems with the final transmission. It just means there'll have to be lots of re-transmissions — "until one gets it right." These re-transmissions reduce the amount of data transmitted in a unit of time and therefore, increase the time needed to send that information. If the BER gets too high, it might be worth while to go to a slower transmission rate. Otherwise, you would spend more time retransmitting bad packets than getting good ones through. The theory is that the faster the speed of data transmission the more likelihood of error. This is not always so. But if you are getting lots of errors, the first — and easiest — step is to drop the transmission speed.

BIT INTERLEAVING A form of TDM for synchronous protocols, including HDLC, SDLC, BiSync and X.25. Bit interleaving retains the sequence and number of bits, so that correct synchronization is achieved between both ends. See BIT INTERLEAVING/MULTIPLEXING.

BIT INTERLEAVING/MULTIPLEXING In multiplexing, individual bits from different lower speed channel sources are combined one bit at a time/one channel at a time into one continuous higher speed bit stream. Compare with byte interleaving/ multiplexing.

BIT ORIENTED Used to describe communications protocols in which control information may be coded in fields as small as a single bit.

BIT ORIENTED PROTOCOL BOP. A data link control protocol that uses specific bit patterns to transfer controlling information. Examples are IBM's Synchronous Data Link Control (SDLC) and the ITU-T High-Level Data Link Control (HDLC). Bit-oriented protocols are normally used for synchronous transmission only. Bit-oriented protocols are code transparent (meaning they work regardless of the character encoding method used), since no encoded characters are used in the control sequence.

BIT ORIENTED TRANSMISSION An efficient transmission protocol that encodes communications control information in fields of bits rather than characters or bytes.

BIT PARITY A binary bit appended to an array of bits to make the sum of all the bits always odd or always even. See PARITY.

BIT PATTERN A group of bits arranged in specified ways to represent numbers, letters or symbols, forming a unique binary number for each character. For example, the 7-bit ASCII code produces 128 different characters, i.e. 2 x 2 x 2 x 2 x 2 x 2 x 2 = 128.

BIT RATE The number of bits of data transmitted over a phone line per second. You can usually figure how many characters per second you will be transmitting — in asynchronous communications — if you divide the bit rate by ten. For example, if you are transmitting at 1200 bits per second, you will be transmitting 120 characters per second. In real life, it's never this simple, however. The total bits transmitted will depend on re-transmissions, which depends on the noise of the line, etc. See BAUD RATE.

BIT ROBBING A technique to signal in-band in digital facilities, which typically use out of band signaling, e.g. Signaling System 7. In bit robbing, we steal bits from the speech path a few line-signal bits. The remaining bits are adequate to recreate the original electrical analog signal (and ultimately, the original sound). Bit robbing typically uses the least significant bit per channel in every sixth frame for signaling. See BIT STUFFING and ROBBED BIT SIGNALING.

BIT SPECIFICATIONS Number of colors or levels of gray that can be displayed at one time. Controlled by the amount of memory in the computer's graphics controller card. An 8-bit controller can display 256 colors or levels of gray; a 16-bit controller, 64,000 colors: a 24-bit controller, 16.8 million colors.

BIT STREAM A continuous stream of data bits transmitted over a communications line with no break or separators between the characters.

BIT STUFFING Process in some data communications protocols where a string of "one" bits is broken by an inserted "zero." This inserted zero is added by the sender and stripped by the receiver. The idea of inserting the zero is to avoid confusing the receiver into thinking the series of one bits mean something else, like a flag control character. See ZERO STUFFING.

BIT TRANSFER RATE The number of bits transferred per unit time. Usually expressed in Bits Per Second (BPS).

BITBLT BIT BLock Transfer. Microsoft Windows relies intensively on a type of operation called bit block transfer (BitBLT) to redraw rectangular areas of the image on the computer's screen. Generally, BitBLT operations are accomplished by software routines in the video driver, a cheap, but slow method that uses many of your CPU's clock cycles. If you add a separate video controller with a special processor to handle BitBLT, you will be able to offload video tasks from your main CPU and make your computer run faster.

BITMAP Representation of characters or graphics by individual pixels arranged in row (horizontal) and column (vertical) order. Each pixel can be represented by one bit (simple black and white) or up to 32 bits (high-definition color). Bitmapped images can be displayed on screens or printed. See BIT SPECIFICATIONS.

BITMAPPED GRAPHICS Images which are created with matrices of pixels, or dots. Also called raster graphics. See BITMAP.

BITNET Because It's Time NETwork. An academic computer network based originally on IBM mainframes connected with leased 9600 bps lines. BITNET has recently merged with CSNET, The Computer+Science Network (another academic computer network) to form CREN: The Corporation for Research and Educational Networking. The network connects more than 200 institutions and has more than 900 computational nodes.

BITNIK A person who uses a coin-operated computer terminal installed in a coffee house to log into cyberspace.

BITRONIX Hewlett Packard's term for its bidirectional parallel port communications "standard." It introduced this standard with its 600 dps LaserJet 4 plain paper printer in the fall of 1992. It is hoping other manufacturers will adopt the standard. The big plus of the standard is that it allows a printer to tell a connected computer that it (the printer) has run out of paper, or the paper has jammed, etc. Having that communications back and forth will allow the user to clear the problem and get the printer and up and running faster. It will also stop the computer locking up.

BITS Building Integrated Timing Supply. A clock, or a clock with an adjunct, in a building that supplies DS1 and/or composite clock timing reference to all other clocks in that building.

BITS PER SECOND The number of bits passing a specific point per second.

A KILObit is one thousand bits per second.

A MEGAbit is one million bits per second (thousands of kilos).

A GIGAbit is one billion bits per second (thousands of millions).

A TERAbit is one trillion bits per second (thousands of billions).

A PETAbit is equal to 10 to the 15th or 1,000 terabits.

BITSLAG All the useless rubble on the Net one has to plow through to get to the rich information core.

BIX A Northern Telecom tradename for an in-building termination and cross-connect system for unshielded twisted pair cables.

BL Business Line

BLACK BODY A totally absorbing body that does not reflect radiation (i.e. light). In thermal equilibrium, a black body absorbs and radiates at the same rate; the radiation will just equal absorption when thermal equilibrium is maintained.

BLACK BOX An electronic device that you don't want to take the time to understand. As in, "We'll put the data through a black box that will put it into X.25 format." The term has recently come also to mean PBX switches. While "Black Box" is a generic term, The Black Box Corporation of Pittsburgh, PA, has had the audacity (and brilliance) to register the term as a trademark.

The Phone Phreak community has used the term black box to describe a device that's put on phone lines in electromechanical central office areas (they don't work under ESS offices). To the phone phreak community, a black box made up of a resistor, a capacitor and a toggle switch that would "fool" the central office into thinking the phone had not been picked up when receiving a long distance call. Since the call was not "answered," the call could not be billed. Clever, eh? (Illegal, too.) See BLUE BOX and RED BOX.

BLACK FACSIMILE TRANSMISSION 1. In facsimile systems using amplitude modulation, that form of transmission in which the maximum transmitted power corresponds to the maximum density of the subject copy. 2. In facsimile systems using frequency modulation, that form of transmission in which the lowest transmitted frequency corresponds to the maximum density of the subject copy.

BLACK LEVEL The lowest luminance level that can occur in video or television transmission and which, when viewed on a monitor, appears as the color 'black.'

BLACK MATRIX Picture tube in which the color phosphors are surrounded by black for increased contrast.

BLACK RECORDING 1. In facsimile systems using amplitude modulation, that form of recording in which the maximum received power corresponds to the maximum received power corresponds to the maximum density of the record medium.

2. In a facsimile system using frequency modulation, that form of recording in which the lowest received frequency corresponds to the maximum density of the record medium.

BLACK SIGNAL 1. In facsimile, the signal resulting from the scanning of a maximum-density area of the subject copy. 2. In cryptographic systems, a signal containing only unclassified or encrypted information.

BLANK A character on teletype terminals that does not punch holes in paper tape (except for feed holes to push the paper through). Also the character between words, usually called a "Space" is referred to in IBM jargon as a Blank.

BLANKING The suppression of the display of one or more display elements or display segments.

BLANKING INTERVAL Period during the television picture formation when the electron gun returns from right to left after each line (horizontal blanking) or from top to bottom after each field (vertical blanking) during which the picture is suppressed.

BLANKING PULSES The process of transmitting pulses that extinguish or blank the reproducing spot during the horizontal and vertical retrace intervals.

BLAST BLocked ASynchronous Transmission.

BLEND To have outbound and inbound phone calls answered by the same agents. See the next two definitions.

BLENDED AGENT A call center person who answers both incoming and makes outgoing calls. This idea of a blended agent is a new concept in a Call Center. In the past call centers have typically kept their inbound and outbound agents separate. The reason? Management felt that the necessary skills were very different and no one could master both.

BLENDED CALL CENTER A telephone call center whose agents both receive and make calls. In other words, a call center whose phone system acts both as an automatic call distributor and a predictive dialer.

BLER Block Error Ratio. The ratio of the blocks in error received in a specified time period to the total number of blocks received in the same period.

BLERT BLock Error Rate Test.

BLINKING An intentional periodic change in the intensity of one or more display elements or display segments.

BLF The Busy Lamp Field is a visual display of the status of all or some of your phones. Your BLF tells you if a phone is busy or on hold. Your Busy Lamp Field is typically attached to or part of your operator's phone. See BUSY LAMP FIELD.

BLIND TRANSFER Someone transfers a call to someone else without telling the person who's calling. Also called Unsupervised Transfer.

BLISTER PACK A pocketed polyvinyl chloride shipping container with a snap-on cover.

BLOB Binary Large OBjects. When a database includes not only the traditional character, numeric, and memo fields but also pictures or other stuff consuming of large space, a database is said to include BLOBs — binary large objects.

BLOCK In data communications, a group of bits transmitted as a unit and treated as a unit of information. Usually consists of its own starting and ending control deliminators, a header, the text to be transmitted and check characters at the end used for error correction. Sometimes called a Packet.

BLOCK CHARACTER CHECK BCC. The result of transmission verification algorithm accumulated over a transmission block, and normally appended at the end, e.g. CRC, LRC.

BLOCK DIAGRAM A graphic way to show different elements of a program or process by the use of squares, rectangles, diamonds and various shapes connected by lines to show what must be done, when it must be done and what happens if it's done this way or that. In short, it shows how all the small decision points add up to the whole process.

BLOCK ERROR RATIO BLER. The ratio of the blocks in error received in a specified time period to the total number of blocks received in the same period.

BLOCK MISDELIVERY PROBABILITY The ratio of the number of misdelivered blocks to the total number of block transfer attempts during a specified period.

BLOCK-MODE TERMINAL INTERFACE BMTI. A device used to create (and break down) packets to be transmitted through a ITU-T X.25 network. This device is needed if block-mode terminals (such as IBM bisync devices) are to be connected to the network without an intermediate computer.

BLOCK MULTIPLEXER CHANNEL An IBM mainframe input/output channel that allows interleaving of data blocks.

BLOCK PARITY The designation of one or more bits in a block as parity bits whose purpose is to ensure a designated parity, either odd or even. Used to assist in error detection or correction, or both.

BLOCK TRANSFER The process of sending and receiving one or more blocks of data.

BLOCK TRANSFER ATTEMPT A coordinated sequence of user and telecommunication system activities undertaken to effect transfer of an individual block from a source user to a destination user. A block transfer attempt begins when the first bit of the block crosses the functional interface between the source user and the telecommunication system. A block transfer attempt ends either in successful block transfer or in block transfer failure.

BLOCK TRANSFER EFFICIENCY The average ratio of user information bits to total bits in successfully transferred blocks.

BLOCK TRANSFER FAILURE Failure to deliver a block successfully. Normally the principal block transfer failure outcomes are: lost block, misdelivered block, and added block.

BLOCK TRANSFER RATE The number of successful block transfers made during a period of time.

BLOCK TRANSFER TIME The average value of the duration of a successful block transfer attempt. A block transfer attempt is successful if 1. The transmitted block is delivered to the intended destination user within the maximum allowable performance period and 2. The contents of the delivered block are correct.

BLOCKED CALLS DELAYED A variable in queuing theory to describe what happens when the user is held in queue because his call is blocked and he can't complete it instantly.

BLOCKED CALLS HELD A variable in queuing theory to describe what happens when the user redials the moment he encounters blockage.

BLOCKED CALLS RELEASED A variable in queuing theory to describe what happens when the user, after being blocked, waits a little while before redialing.

BLOCKING When a telephone call cannot be completed it is said that the call is "blocked." Blocking is a fancy way to say that the caller is "receiving a busy." There are many places a call can be blocked: at the user's own telephone switch — PBX or key system, at the user's local central office or in the long distance network. Blocking happens because switching or transmission capacity is not available at that precise time.

The number of calls you try compared to the number of times you get blocked measures "the grade of service" on that network. Blocked calls are different from calls that are not completed because the called number is busy. This is because numbers that are busy are not the fault of the telephone switching and transmission network. One might think the fewer blocked calls, the better. From the user's point of view, the answer is obviously YES, it is better. Less blockage, fewer busies and less frustration. But as one designs a switching and transmission network for less and less blocking, the network becomes more and more expensive. Logarithmically so. We keep adding extra circuits and extra equipment. Thus, in any telecommunications network design there is always a trade-off: What are you prepared to pay, compared to what can you tolerate?

Everyone designs their network with different trade-offs depending on what they and their users or customers, can tolerate and/or are willing to pay. Most companies are willing to pay more for better service if someone explains the logic of telephone design to them. Many network salesmen, however, don't believe this. They practice the sales "theory" of selling better service for less money. This doesn't work in business, and especially not in telephony.

The "Grade of Service" is a measurement of blocking. It varies from almost zero (best, but most expensive case, no calls blocked) to one (worst case, all calls blocked). Grade of Service is written as P.05 (five percent blocking). "Blocking" used to be a technical term but has now become a sales tool especially among PBX manufacturers, who increasingly claim their switch to be "non-blocking." This means it will not, they claim, block a call in the switch.

There are several flaws in this logic: First, it's not logical or useful to buy a non-blocking PBX if the chances of being blocked elsewhere — the local lines, the local exchange or the long distance network — are very high. Second, a true non-blocking PBX can be very expensive, perhaps too much power and too much money for most peoples' needs. Third, most manufacturers define "non-blocking" differently. One defines it strictly in terms of switching capability and ignores the fact that his PBX might not have sufficient other "things," like devices which ring bells on phones (to indicate an incoming call) or devices which deliver dial tone to a phone (to indicate the PBX is ready to receive instructions).

BLOCKING FACTOR The number of records in a block; the number is computed by dividing the size of the block by the size of each record contained therein. Each record in the block must be the same size.

BLOCKING FORMULAS Specific probability distribution functions that closely approximate the call pattern of telephone users probable behavior in failing to find idle lines.

BLOWER A microphone.

BLOWFISH The name of the scrambling algorithm behind Philip Zimmerman's powerful encryption scheme called Pretty Good Privacy, or PGP, which lets you converse in total privacy over normal phone lines. See PGP for a fuller explanation.

BLOWING YOUR BUFFER Losing one's train of thought. This happens when the person you're speaking with won't let you get a word in edgewise or just said something so astonishing that your brain gets derailed. "Damn, I just blew my buffer!"

BLOWN FIBER A method for installing optical fibers in which fibers are blown through glass.

BLOWN FUSE A broken fuse.

BLU Northern Telecom word for Basic Link Unit.

BLUE ALARM Used in T-1 transmission. Also known as the AIS (Alarm Indication Signal). The blue alarm is turned on when two consecutive frames have fewer than three zeros in the data bit stream. A blue alarms sends 1's (ones) in all bits of all time slots on the span. See T-1 and AIS.

BLUE BOX A device used to steal long distance phone calls. The classic blue box was slightly larger than a cigarette container. It had a touchtone pad on the front and a single button on top. Typically, you went to a coin phone and dialed an 800 number. While the distant number was ringing, you punched the single button on the top of the blue box. That button caused the blue box's speaker to emit a 2600 Hz tone. This disconnected the ringing at the other end but left the user inside the long distance network. The user then punched in a series of digits on the touchtone pad. The phone network heard those tones and sent the call according to the instructions in the tones. The tones duplicated the tones which the touchtone pads of long distance operators emitted. They are different from those emitted by normal telephones. The first blue box was "discovered" at MIT in a small utility box that was painted blue, thus the term blue box. When they were young, Steve Jobs and Steve Wozniak, founders of Apple Computer, sold blue boxes, which Wozniak built. People who used blue boxes in their salad days included characters with adopted pseudonyms like Dr. No, The Snark and Captain Crunch, who got his name from the free 2600 Hz whistle included as a promotion in boxes of Captain Crunch breakfast cereal. With the advent of CCIS, Common Channel Interoffice Signaling (i.e. out-of-band signaling), blue boxes no longer work.

BLUE COLLAR COMPUTER A colloquial term for a handheld computer which is used by "blue collar" workers for tasks such taking inventory, tracking goods, etc. Such computer may have a pen, a large pen-sensitive or touch-sensitive screens, a bar code scanner and a modem. It may be able to capture signatures — useful for confirmation of the delivery of goods.

BLUE GROMMET The rubber collar over the joint between the handset and the armored cable on a pay phone. Blue identifies a "hearing aid compatible" handset.

BLUE PAGES Section of phone directory commonly used for government phone numbers, as distinct from white and yellow pages.

BM Burst Modem.

BMTI Block Mode Terminal Interface. A device used to create (and break down) packets to be transmitted through a ITU-T X.25 network. This device is needed if block-mode terminals (such as IBM bisync devices) are to be connected to the network without an intermediate computer.

BNA Burroughs Network Architecture. Communications architecture of Burroughs, now Unisys.

BNC A bayonet-locking connector for slim coaxial cables, like those used with Ethernet. BNC is an acronym for Bayonet-Neill-Concelman. Don't ask who Neill and Concelman are. Someone also says it also stands for British National Connector.

BNC BARREL CONNECTORS These connectors join two lengths of thin Ethernet coaxial cable together. See also BNC.

BNC CONNECTORS The connectors for thin Ethernet coaxial cable are BNC connectors. BNC connectors are used on thin Ethernet cable. The BNC connectors on each end of thin Ethernet cable connect to T-connectors, barrel connectors, and other network hardware. See BNC.

BNC FEMALE TO N-SERIES FEMALE ADAPTER The BNC female to N-Series female adapter is a connector which enables you to connect thin coaxial cable to thick coaxial cable. The BNC female connector attaches to the thin cable and the N-Series male connector attaches to the thick Ethernet cable.

BNC T-CONNECTORS The top of the T in a BNC T-connector functions as a barrel connector and links two lengths of thin Ethernet coaxial cable; the third end connects to the SpeedLink/PC 16.

BNC TERMINATORS 50-ohm terminators are used to block electrical interference on a Ethernet coaxial cable network and to terminate the network at certain spots. You attach a BNC terminator to one plug on a T-connector if you will not be attaching a length of cable to that plug. You may also need to use a BNC terminator with a grounding wire to ground the network. See BNC.

BNR Bell Northern Research. Northern Telecom's research arm.

BNS 1000/2000 AT&T's Broadband Networking Systems using fast-packet, cell relay switching providing dynamic bandwidth allocation on demand with interfaces to a variety of LAN routers, including AT&T's LCS200, Wellfleet, Cisco Systems and NCR StarWAN products.

BnZS CODE A bipolar line code with n zero substitution.

BOARD 1. Short for printed circuit board. Phone systems have boards for all sorts of purposes — from boards to serve trunk lines, to boards to serve proprietary phone sets, to boards that serve T-1 lines, etc. Computers also have boards — ones for SCSI ports, for floppy and hard disks, for CD-ROMs, etc. In display/monitor terminology a board refers to the adapter (or controller) that serves as an interface between the computer and monitor.

2. An SCSA term. Any hardware module that controls its own physical interface to the SCbus or SCxbus. From a programming point of view, a board is an addressable system component that contains resources.

BOB New software from Microsoft, which describes it as a "superapplication" for Windows designed for consumers intimidated by computer technology. According to Microsoft, users will use Bob to write letters, send e-mail, manage their household finances, keep addresses and dates and launch full-blown Windows applications, all under the guidance of cartoon characters.

BOC Bell Operating Company. The local Bell operating telephone company. These days there are 22 Bell Operating Companies. They are organized into (i.e. owned by) seven Regional Bell holding companies, also called RBOCs, pronounced "R-bocks," or RHCs. See BELL OPERATING COMPANY.

BODY The main informational part of a message. The information, not the address and the addressing information. There can be single or multiple parts to a body. For example, a single part could be text, or multiple parts could include text and graphics, or voice and graphics, etc. See BODY PART 14.

BODY PART 14 BP 14. An X.400 messaging term. A non-specific, identifying body part. A binary attachment with identifying header to explain the nature of the content such as a particular spreadsheet, word processor, etc,

BOF Business Operations Framework. A wireless telecommunications term. A document compiled to describe the operations of a telecommunications business entity in a specific area.

BOGON Something that is stupid or nonfunctional.

BOIC Barring of Outgoing International Calls. A wireless telecommunications term. A supplementary service provided under GSM (Global System for Mobile Communications).

BOLT PATTERN The pattern that the bolts on the back of the device make. The idea is that if you attach something to the device, you don't want to mess up its warranty by opening the box and putting your stuff inside. So you design your stuff to fit the bolt pattern. This does not mess up the warranty. His product is designed to fit the bolt pattern, but not to intrude into the box.

BOND The electrical connection between two metallic surfaces established to provide a low resistance path between them.

BONDING 1. In electrical engineering, the process of connecting together metal parts so that they make low resistance electrical contact for direct current and lower frequency alternating currents. 2. The process of establishing the required degree of electrical continuity between two or more conductive surfaces that are to be joined. 3. The process by which all building and equipment electrical grounds are joined together to eliminate differences in electrical ground potentials. 4. A new group know as the Bandwidth ON Demand INteroperability Group (BONDING). The group's charter is to develop common control and synchronization standards needed to manage high speed data as it travels through the public network. This will allow equipment from vendors to interoperate over existing Switched 56 and ISDN services. Version 1.0 of the standard, approved on August 17, 1992, describes four modes of inverse multiplexer (I-Mux) interoperability. It allows inverse multiplexers from different manufacturers to subdivide a wideband signal into multiple 56- or 64- Kbps channels, pass these individual channels over a switched digital network, and recombine them into a single high-speed signal at the receiving end.

BONG A tone that long distance carriers and value added carriers make in order to signal you that they now require additional action on your part — usually dialing more digits. See also VOICE MODEM.

BONTs Broadband Optical Network Terminations.

BOOKING FACTOR Booking factor is a percentage of the frame relay links used by frame relay paths, based on the sum of the Committed Information Rates (CIRs) of all the frame relay paths (FRPs) on the frame relay link (FRL).

BOOKMARK A gopher or Web file that lets you quickly connect to your favorite pre-selected page. Appropriately named. The way it works: You connect to a home page. You decide you'd like to return at some other time. So you command your internet surfing software to mark this web site with a "bookmark." Next time you want to return to that web site, you simply go to your bookmarks, click on which one you want. And bingo, you're there. A bookmark is also known as a hot list. Most Web browsers have book marks or hot lists.

BOOLEAN EXPRESSION An expression composed of one or more relational expressions; a string of symbols that specifies a condition that is either true or false.

BOOLEAN LOGIC Boolean Logic is named after the 19th century mathematician, George Boole. Boolean logic is algebra reduced to either TRUE or FALSE, YES or NO, ON or OFF. Boolean logic is important for computer logic because computers work in binary — TRUE or FALSE, YES or NO, ON or OFF.

BOOLEAN OPERATORS See BOOLEAN LOGIC. Boolean operators are AND, OR, XOR, NOR, NOT. The result of an equation with one or more of the boolean operators is that the result will either be true or false.

BOOLEAN VALUED EXPRESSION An expression that will return a "true" or "false" evaluation.

BOOT Abbreviation for the verb to bootstrap. A technique or device designed to bring itself into a desired state where it can operate on its own. For example, one type of boot is a routine whose first few instructions are sufficient to bring the rest of itself into memory from an input device. See BOOTSTRAP.

BOOT PRIORITY Which disk drive the computer looks to first for the files it needs to get started. Modern PCs start their boot cycle with the hard disk and then move to the floppy disk drive. Older PCs started their boot cycle with the floppy disk drive.

BOOT ROM A read-only memory chip allowing a workstation to communicate with the file server and to read a DOS boot program from the server. Workstations can thus operate on the network without having a disk drive. These are commonly called diskless PCs or diskless workstations.

BOOTP Boot Protocol. A TCP/IP protocol, which allows an internet node to discover certain startup information such as its IP address.

BOOTSTRAP The process of starting up a computer. Think about the following explanation in regard to your desktop MS-DOS machine. Usually, when the computer is turned on, it goes to a location of permanent Read Only Memory (See ROM) for instructions. These instructions, in turn, load the first instructions from the disk telling the computer what tasks to start performing. The name of this process comes from the expression "pulling oneself up by one's own bootstraps." The typical personal computer BOOT (startup) throws a message on the screen instructing the user to "insert a disk."

To confuse matters, there are WARM boots and COLD boots. Cold boots occur when the ac power switch on the computer is turned on. Warm boots occur when you hit the reset button (or CTL/ALT/DELETE) while the ac power switch stays on. A warm boot — reset — is done when you're changing disks or programs, or have done something dumb, like tried to access a drive that didn't access, or tried to print without connecting up to a printer.

You do a cold boot when the machine locks up rock hard and a warm boot doesn't work. To do a cold boot with your computer, turn the ac power off, count to ten and then turn it on. Remember: never leave disks in your computer when you're turning it on and off. The surge of electricity might destroy the disks. When modems give trouble, do a cold boot on them. In fact, when phone systems give trouble, do a cold boot on them also. See also BOOT RAM, DEVICE DRIVER and MS-DOS.

BOOT LOADER A Windows NT term. Defines the information needed for system startup, such as the location for the operating system's files. Windows NT automatically creates the correct configuration and checks this information whenever you start your system.

BOOT PARTITION A Windows NT term. The volume, formatted for either an NTFS, FAT, or HPFS file system, that contains the Windows NT operating system and its support files. The boot partition can be (but does not have to be) the same as the system partition.

BOP Bit Oriented Protocol. See BIT ORIENTED TRANSMISSION.

BORDER GATEWAY PROTOCOL BGP. An Internet protocol defined by RFC 1163. BGP is a Transmission Control Protocol/Internet Protocol (TCP/IP) routing protocol for interdomain routing in large networks.

BORSCHT A group of functions provided in Line Circuits (LC). It stands for B: Battery supply to subscriber line. O: Overvoltage protection. R: Ringing current supply. S: Supervision of subscriber terminal. C: Coder and decoder. H: Hybrid (2 wire to 4 wire conversion). T: Test.

Borscht is a group of functions provided to an analog line from a line circuit of a digital central office switch. An analog electronic switch can omit C and possibly H. A line circuit on a switch with a metallic matrix (SXS, Xbar, 1,2,3ESS) only detects call originations and disconnects itself.

BOTTOM LINE A phrase that can mean net profit, the lowest possible price that someone will take or the basic meaning with all the frills and nonsense cut away.

BOTTLE A water-tight device shaped like a glass bottle which contains amplifiers, regenerators and other equipment and used at regular distances along an underwater cable.

BOUNCE What your e-mail does when it cannot get to its recipient. It bounces back to you, unless it goes off into the ether, never to be found again.

BOUNCED MAIL Mail that is returned to the originator due to an incorrect E-mail address.

BOUND MODE In an optical fiber, a mode whose field decays monotonically in the transverse direction everywhere external to the core and which does not lose power to radiation. Except in a single-mode fiber, the power in bound modes is predominantly contained in the core of the fiber.

BOUNDARY CONDITIONS Boundary conditions are those that are found at the cusp of valid and invalid inputs and parameters. Many faults are found in a computer telephony system's ability to handle boundary conditions, especially when the computer telephony system is under load. For example, for a network that expects a switch to reset a trunk port within two seconds, the associated boundary conditions would be found at 1.9 to 2.1 seconds.

BOUNDARY FUNCTION Capability in SNA sub-area node to handle some functions that nearby peripheral nodes are not capable of handling.

BOUNDARY NODE In IBM's SNA, a sub-area node that can provide certain protocol support for adjacent sub-area nodes, including transforming network addresses to local addresses, and vice versa, and performing session level sequencing and flow control and less intelligent peripheral nodes.

BOWSER General Magic's mascot, a rabbit.

BP 14 Body Part 14, an X.400 electronic messaging term referring to a non-specific body part, commonly used to transfer binary attachments.

BPAD Bisynchronous Packet Assembler/Disassembler.

BPI Bytes Per Inch. How many bytes are recorded per inch of recording surface. Typically used in conjunction with magnetic tape.

BPON Broadband Passive Optical Network.

BPP Bits Per Pixel. The number of bits used to represent the color value of each pixel in a digitized image.

BPS Bits Per Second. A measure of the speed of data communications. There are many ways to measure bits per second. So don't assume that just because one LAN or other data communications system has a faster bits per seconds, it will transmit your information faster. You have to factor in speed of writing and reading from the disk and the accuracy of transmission. All data communications schemes have error-checking systems, some better than others. Typically such systems force a re-transmission of data if a mistake is detected. You might have a fast, but "dirty" (i.e. lots of errors) transmission medium, which may need lots of re-transmissions. Thus, the "effective" bps of data communications network may actually be quite low. See also BAUD.

BPSK Binary phase shift Key.

BRA Basic Rate Access. A Canadian term for the ISDN 2B+D standard, which is called BRI in the U.S. — Basic Rate Interface.

BRAGG REFLECTOR A device designed to finely focus a semiconductor laser beam. Dennis Hall, a professor at the University of Rochester's Institute of Optics in New York, told the Economist Magazine in the Spring of 1993 that he and his colleague Gary Wicks have etched into the surface of his gallium-arsenide laser a grating of 600 concentric grooves, each a quarter of a millionth of a meter apart. The grating acts as what is known as a Bragg reflector. As the waves of laser light pass through each of its ridges, they are reflected by each of its ridges, a process which causes them to come together into an even, circular beam.

BRAID A fibrous or metallic group of filaments interwoven cylindrically to form a covering over one or more insulated conductors.

BRAIN FART A definition from Wired Magazine: A byproduct of a bloated mind producing information effortlessly. A burst of useful information. "I know you're busy on the Microsoft story, but could give us a brain fart on the Mitnik burst?" Variation of old hacker slang that had more negative connotations.

BRAINERD, PAUL S. Founder of Aldus Corporation of 1984, Mr. Brainerd is reputed to be "the father of desktop publishing." His program Aldus PageMaker allowed the average PC user to produce professional-looking documents.

BRANCH A path in the program which is selected from two or more paths by a program instruction. "To branch" means to choose one of the available paths.

BRANCH FEEDER A cable between the distribution cable and the main feeder cable to connect phone users to the central office. An outside plant term.

BRANCHING FILTER A device placed in a waveguide to separate or combine different microwave frequency bands.

BRANDING A term for identifying the Operator Service Provider (OSP) to the caller. Picture calling from your hotel room. You dial long distance. You have no idea which carrier you're using. But a message comes on: "Thanks for using MCI." Now you know. That's called branding.

BRCS Business and Residence Customer Services. An approach that the AT&T 5ESS switch employs to provision revenue-generating services.

BREADBOARD A circuit board made by hand, usually in building a prototype. No one knows where the word breadboard came from. Maybe because it looks a little like a breadboard?

BREAK An interruption. As in "Make and Break." Make means contacts which are usually open, but which close during an operation. "Make and Break" accurately describes rotary dialing.

BREAK IN The attendant can interrupt conversations and announce an emergency or an important call.

BREAK KEY A Break Key is found on some PCs. It is usually used to interrupt the current task running on a remote host. Break is not an ASCII character, it is simply a period of start (space) polarity.

BREAK OPTIMIZATION A call center term. The automatic adjustment of break start times for schedules in the Daily Workfile so as to more closely match staff to workload in each period of the day. The program can thus improve upon the originally scheduled break arrangement because it now has information about schedule exceptions, newly added schedules, and additional call volume in AHT (Average Handle Time) history. See BREAK PARAMETERS.

BREAK OUT BOX A testing device that permits a user to cross-connect and tie individual leads of an interface cable using jumper wires to monitor, switch, or patch the electrical output of the cable. The most common break out box in our industry is probably the RS-232 box. Some of these boxes have LEDs (Light Emitting Diodes), which allow you to see which lead is "live." See also BREAKOUT BOX.

BREAK PARAMETERS A call center term. A group of scenario assumptions you set to govern the placement of breaks in employee scheduling. These are typically: * Earliest allowable break start time * Latest allowable break start time * Duration of the break * Whether the break is paid or unpaid

BREAK TEST ACCESS Method of disconnecting a circuit, which has been electrically bridged, to allow testing on either side of the circuit. Devices that provide break test access include: bridge clips, plug-on protection modules, and plug-on patching devices. Break test access also provides a demarcation point.

BREAKDOWN VOLTAGE The voltage at which the insulation between two conductors breaks down.

BREAKING STRENGTH The amount of force needed to break a wire or fiber.

BREAKOUT A wire or group of wires in a multi-conductor configuration which terminates somewhere other than at the end of the configuration.

BREAKOUT BOX A device that is plugged in between a computer terminal and its connecting cable to re-configure the way the cable is wired. When hooking up a terminal that is wired as if it were a computer itself (such as a VT-100), a break out box is used to break out, or fan out the 25 connections in the RS-232 cable. Each wire in the break out box goes through a switch that can be turned off, and a wire jumper is provided to connect each pin on one side to one or the other pin on the other side. This allows you, for example, to switch pins 2 & 3, thus fooling two computer devices into thinking one is talking to a terminal. (Now you have the essence of a null modem cable.) Break out boxes are necessary because there is no such thing as "standard" pinning on an RS-232 cable. To connect one computer to a printer one minute and to another computer the next minute, usually requires totally different wiring in the RS-232 cable, i.e. two sets of cables. This lack of standardization is why you'll always see dozens of RS-232 cables lying around where computers are used.

BRI Basic Rate Interface. There are two subscriber "interfaces" in ISDN. This one and PRI (Primary Rate Interface). In BRI, you get two bearer B-channels at 64 kilobits per second and a data D-channel at 16 kilobits per second. The bearer B-channels are designed for PCM voice, slow-scan video conferencing, group 4 facsimile machines, or whatever you can squeeze into 64,000 bits per second full duplex. The data (or D) channel is for bringing in information about incoming calls and taking out information about outgoing calls. It is also for access to slow-speed data networks, like videotex, packet switched networks, etc. See BASIC RATE INTERFACE and ISDN.

BRICK A large hand-held cellular phone or handheld two-way radio. In more technical language, a "brick" is a station in the mobile service consisting of a hand-held radiotelephone unit licensed under a site authorization. Each unit can work while being hand-carried.

BRIDGE First, we'll explain bridge as a noun. A bridge is a data communications device that connects two or more networks and forwards packets between them. The bridge may use similar or dissimilar media and signaling systems such as Ethernet, Token-Ring, and X.25. It operates at the data-link layer of the OSI model. Bridges sometimes work within a PC and sometimes within a special purpose computer. Bridges read and filter data packets and frames. A bridge is also called a data link relay or level 2 relay." When used for connecting LANs, a bridge connects LANs at the Medium Access Control (MAC) sub-layer of the OSI model's Data Link Layer. Bridges forward packets destined for another LAN. Bridges can be classified as source routing bridges, which are used in IBM environments, or transparent bridges, which operate primarily in non-IBM environments. A third bridging method, Source Routing Transparent (SRT), enables a bridge to act as both a transparent and a source routing bridge. In voice and videoconferencing, a bridge connects three or more telecommunications channels so that they can all communicate together. In video conferencing, bridges are often called MCUs — Multipoint Conferencing Units. One feature of some video bridges is their ability to figure who's speaking and turn the camera onto that person and have that person be on everyone's screen.

Second, we'll explain bridge as a verb, as in "to bridge." Imagine a phone line. It winds from your central office through the streets and over the poles to your phone. Now imagine you want to connect another phone to that line. A phone works on two wires, tip and ring (positive and negative). You simply clamp each one of the phone's wires to the cable coming in. That's called bridging. Imagine bridging as connecting a phone at a right angle. When you do that, you've made what's known as a "bridged tap." The first thing to know about bridging is that bridging causes the electrical current coming down the line to lose power. How much? That typically depends on the distance from the bridged tap to the phone. A few feet, there's no significant loss. But that bridged tap can also be thousands of feet. For example, the phone company could have a bridged tap on your local loop, which joined to another long-defunct subscriber. If you want the cleanest, loudest phone line, the local loop to your phone should not be bridged — but be a direct run from your central office to your phone. Bridging can be a real problem with digital circuits. Circuits above 1 million bits per second — e.g. T-1 and Ethernet — should never, ever be bridged. Because of the power loss, they simply won't work or will work so poorly they won't be worth having. ISDN BRI channels are also digital. But they were specifically designed to work with the existing telephone cable plant, which has a huge number of bridged circuits. Telephone companies typically will install ISDN BRI circuits with up to six bridged taps and about 6,000 feet of bridged cabling. But that's a rule of thumb. Once they get an ISDN BRI circuit installed, the first thing a phone company will do is to check it out. Below I've excerpted some words from a Nynex Networking & Technology Planning document, called "Network Loops and Customer Premises Wiring."

Says Nynex, the design objective for the ISDN Basic Access DSL (Digital Subscriber Loop) is to allow transmission through as much as practical of the North American loop plant. The majority of this loop plant was built using the "Resistance Design" rules to control the total signaling resistance and transmission loss. Up to a working length of loop of 18 kilofeet, mixed gauges of wire are used to limit the total de resistance typically to 1300 ohms. This corresponds to a maximum loss at 1000 Hz of about 9 dB. Total length of bridged taps is limited to 6 kft. Note that not every network loop meets Resistance Design criteria and some bridged tap lengths, even for Resistance Design nonloaded loops, appear as quarter-wave length shorting stubs for critical DSL transmission frequencies. To limit resistance and loss for loops longer than 18 kft, coarser gauge wire used and 88 mH loading coils are placed at 6 kft intervals. The series inductive loading combines with the cable shunt capacitance acts as a low pass filter with a sharp cutoff about 3000 Hz, and effectively prevents high frequency DSL operation (what ISDN requires). About one quarter of the total loop plant was loaded in 1988. The customer-network interface for Basic Access is at the end of this loop plant, at the intersection with the customer on-premises wiring. Note that customers are free to construct their own premises wiring and to purchase wiring from any source. There is potential for reduced DSL transmission performance due to inappropriate cable types, gauge changes or excessive bridged taps existing at the customer end of the loop. This may create opportunity for significant exposure to induced noise and crosswalk plus increased transmission loss. In recognition of the relatively uncontrolled customer portion of the DSL cable pair, the members of the T-1 work group typically used 1000 feet of customer wiring as a target for analytical transmission studies. For problems dealing with direct current, a nominal de resistance of 100 ohms was typically used to represent customer wiring. Planners must therefore take into account the possible effects of customer premises wiring on DSL operation when the customer premises is located near the extremes of the DSL loop operating range or when unusual premises wiring conditions exist. See INTERNETWORKING, LOADING COIL, ROUTERS, SOURCE ROUTING, and TRANSPARENT ROUTING.

BRIDGE AMPLIFIER An amplifier installed on a CATV trunk cable to feed branching cables.

BRIDGE BATTERY A small supplementary battery on a laptop which holds the contents of the memory and the system status for a few minutes while you replace a drained battery. NEC uses the term on its UltraLite Versa laptops.

BRIDGE EQUIPMENT Equipment which connects different LANs, allowing communication between devices. As in "to bridge" several LANs. Bridges are protocol-independent but hardware-specific. They will connect LANs with different hardware and different protocols. An example would be a device that connects an Ethernet network to a Starlan network. With this bridge it is possible to send signals between the two networks, and only these two networks.

These signals will be understood only if the protocols used on each LAN are the same, e.g. XNS or TCP/IP, but they don't have to be the same for the bridge to do its job for the signals to move on either LAN. They just won't be understood. This differs from gateways and routers. Routers connect LANs with the same protocols but different hardware. The best examples are the file servers that accommodate different hardware LANs. Gateways connect two LANs with different protocols by translating between them, enabling them to talk to each other. The bridge does no translation. Bridges are best used to keep networks small by connecting many of them rather than making a large one. This reduces the traffic faced by individual computers and improves network performance.

BRIDGE LIFTER A device that removes, either electrically or physically, bridged telephone pairs. Relays, saturable inductors, and semiconductors are used as bridge lifters.

BRIDGE TAP An undetermined length of wire attached between the normal endpoints of a circuit that introduces unwanted impedance imbalances for data transmission. Also called bridging trap or bridged tap. See BRIDGED TAP.

BRIDGED RINGING A system where ringers on a phone line are connected across that line.

BRIDGED TAP A bridged tap is multiple appearances of the same cable pair at several distribution points. A bridged tap is any section of a cable pair not on the direct electrical path between the central office and the user's offices. A bridged tap increases the electrical loss on the pair — because a signal traveling down the pair will split its signal between the bridge and main pairs. You can't run high-speed digital circuits, e.g. T-1, over cable that has bridged taps in it. But you can run ISDN circuits over cable with a limited number of bridged taps. See BRIDGE and LOADING COIL.

BRIDGING Bridging across a circuit is done by placing one test lead from a test set or a conductor from another circuit and placing it on one conductor of another circuit. And then doing the same thing to the second conductor. You bridge across a circuit to test the circuit by listening in on it, by dialing on it, by running tests on the line, etc. You can bridge across a circuit by going across the pair in wire, by stripping it, etc. You can bridge across a pair (also called a circuit path) by installing external devices across quick clips on a connecting block.

BRIDGING ADAPTER A box containing several male and female electrical connectors that allows various phones and accessories to be connected to one cable. Bridging adapters work well with 1A2 key systems and single line phones, but usually not with electronic or digital key systems and electronic or digital telephones behind PBXs.

BRIDGING CLIP A small piece of metal with a U-shape cross-section which is used to connect adjacent terminals on 66-type connecting blocks.

BRIDGING CONNECTION A parallel connection by means of which some of the signal energy in a circuit may be extracted, usually with negligible effect on the normal operation of the circuit. Most modern phone systems don't encourage bridging connections, since the negligible is rarely negligible.

BRIDGING LOSS The loss at a given frequency resulting from connecting an impedance across a transmission line. Expressed as the ratio (in decibels) of the signal power delivered to that part of the system following the bridging point before bridging, to the signal power delivered to that same part after the bridging.

BRIDLE CARDS Propietary Basic Rate ISDN Dual Loop Extension lets ISDN service be provided up to 28,000 feet away. See ISDN.

BRIGHTNESS An attribute of visual reception in which a source appears to emit more or less light. Since the eye is not equally sensitive to all colors, brightness cannot be a quantitative term.

BRITE CARDS AND SERVICES Basic Rate Interface Transmission Extension lets telephone companies extend service from ISDN-equipped central offices to conventional central offices. See ISDN.

BRITTLE Easily broken without much stretching.

BROADBAND A transmission facility that has a bandwidth (capacity) greater than a voice grade line of 3 kHz. (Some say that to be "broadband" it should be 20 kHz.) Such a broadband facility — typically coaxial cable — may carry numerous voice, video and data channels simultaneously. Each "channel" will take up a different frequency on the cable. There'll be "guardbands" (empty spaces) between the channels to make sure each channel doesn't interfere with its neighbor. A coaxial CATV cable is the "classic" broadband channel. Simultaneously it carries many TV channels. Broadband cables are used in some office LANs. But more common are the baseband variety which have the capacity for one channel only. Everything on that cable to be transmitted or received must use that one channel. That one channel is very fast, so each device needs only to use that high speed channel for only a little of the time. The problem is getting onto the channel. See BASEBAND.

BROADCAST To send information to two or more receiving devices simultaneously — over a data communications network, a voice mail, electronic mail system, a local TV or radio station or a satellite system.

BROADCAST LIST A list of two or more system users to whom messages are sent simultaneously. Master Broadcast Lists are shared by all system users and are set up by the System Administrator. Personal Lists are set up by individual subscribers.

BROADCAST MESSAGE A message from one user sent to all users. Just like a TV station signal. On LANs, all workstations and devices receive the message. Broadcast messages are used for many reasons, including acknowledging receipt of information and locating certain devices. On voice mail systems, broadcast messages are important announcement messages from the system administrator that provide information and instructions regarding the voice processing system. Broadcast messages play before standard Voice Mail or Automated Attendant messages.

BROADCAST NET A British Telecom turret feature that allows each trader single key access to a group of outgoing lines. This is designed primarily for sending short messages to multiple destinations. The "net" function allows the user to set up and amend his broadcast group.

BROADCAST STORM A pathological condition that may occur in a TCP/IP network that can cause large number of broadcast packets to be propagated unnecessarily across an enterprise-wide network, thereby causing network overload. Broadcast storms happen when users mix old TCP/IP routers with routers supporting the new releases of TCP/IP protocol. Routers use broadcast packets to resolve IP addressing requests from stations on LANs. If a station running an old version of TCP/IP sends such a request, TCP/IP routers in an enterprise-wide network misunderstand it and send multiple broadcasts to their brother and sister routers. In turn, these broadcasts cause each router to send more broadcasts, and so on. This chain reaction can produce so many broadcast messages that the network can shut down. It should be noted that this is extremely rare and it happens only in TCP/IP networks that use two specific TCP/IP protocol releases.

BROADCAST TRANSMISSION A fax machine feature that allows automatic transmission of a document to several locations.

BROKER A company (or person) that buys and sells equipment often without taking ownership. A broker does not test or refurbish the equipment. Often, it never sees the equipment it buys and sells. Instead, it has the equipment shipped from the supplier to the customer, relying on the supplier to have tested and refurbished the equipment. Its specialty is knowing who has what equipment nationwide and selling it, possibly, at below-market price. See SECONDARY EQUIPMENT.

BROKERNET A virtual private dedicated network offering from New York

Telephone and provided within Manhattan aimed at brokerage, banking and message industries. It uses digital switching to provide virtual private lines, specifically "hot line" service.

BRONZE Allow of copper and tin, widely used and known since ancient times. Copper content in bronze varies between 89% and 96%.

BROUTER Concatenation of "bridge" and "router." Used to refer to devices which perform both bridging and routing functions. In local area networking, a brouter is a device that combines the dynamic routing capability of an internetwork router with the ability of a bridge connect dissimilar local area networks (LANs). It has the ability to route one or more protocols, such as TCP/IP and XNS, and bridge all other traffic.

BROWNOUT When you lose all your electricity, it's called a blackout. When your voltage drops more than 10% below what it's meant to be, it's a brownout.

BROWSER 1. Software which moves documents on the World Wide Web to your computer. A Web Browser is software which allows a computer user (like you and me) to "surf" the Internet. It lets us move easily from one World Wide Web site to another. Every time we alight on a Web Page, our Web Browser moves a copy of documents on the Web to your computer. A Web Browser uses HTTP — the HyperText Transfer Protocol. Invisible to the user of a Web Browser, HTTP is the actual protocol used by the Web Server and the Client Browser to communicate over the Internet. The most famous Web Browser is Netscape. See BROWSING, INTERNET and SURF. 2. A developed tool used to inspect a class hierarchy in an object-oriented software system.

BROWSING The act of searching through automated information system storage to locate or acquire information without necessarily knowing of the existence or the format of the information being sought.

BRUSH A computer imaging term. A paint package's most basic image-creation tool. Most packages let you select a variety of sizes and shapes. Many let you customize shapes.

BSA See both BASIC SWITCHING ARRANGEMENT and OPEN NETWORK ARCHITECTURE.

BSC 1. Binary Synchronous Communication. A set of IBM operating procedures for synchronous transmission used in teleprocessing networks. 2. Base Station Controller. A wireless telecommunications term. The BSC is a device that manages radio resources in GSM (Global System for Mobile Communications), including the BTS, for specified cells within the PLMN (Public Land Mobile Network).

BSD Berkeley Software Distribution. Term used when describing different versions of the Berkeley UNIX software, as in "4.3BSD UNIX".

BSE 1. Basic Switching Element. See OPEN NETWORK ARCHITECTURE. 2. Basic Service Elements. A term used in voice processing to describe technical telephone system features such as ANI, DID trunks, call forwarding, stutter dial tone, suppressed ringing, and directory database access.

BSGL Branch Systems General Licence. A British term. A licence that must be obtained by any organisation seeking to link a private network to the British PSTN (Public Switched Telephone Network). A separate licence must be held on each site.

BSI British Standards Institution. The UK standards body responsible for input to European and international standards setting bodies like ISO and the ITU-T.

BSIC Base Station Identity Code. An attribute of a GSM (Global System for Mobile Communications) cell which is a code allowing a distinction between local cells having the same radio frequency.

BSP Bell System Practice. A very defined way of writing and presenting instruction and installation manuals. BSPs also establish standards for splicing cable, for installing phones, answering phones, collecting debts, finding phonetaps, climbing poles. They are (or once were) the instruction manuals that dictated how to do everything. Divestiture has changed the rules. BSPs are not as important as they were when AT&T handed down all the BSPs.

BSS Base Station System. A wireless telecommunications term. A GSM (Global System for Mobile Communications) device charged with managing radio frequency resources and radio frequency transmission for a group of BTSs. See also GSM.

BT British Telecom.

BTA 1. Basic Trading Area. A wireless telecommunications term. Several BTAs make up Metropolitan Trading Area, an area defined by the FCC for the purpose of issuing licenses for PCS. Each MTA consists of several Basic Trading Areas (BTAs). 2. Broadband Telecommunications Architecture, an architecture introduced by General Instrument's Broadband Communications Division at the Western Cable Television Show on December 1, 1993. General Instrument said the plant is built to 750 MHz and can support reduced node size and add services such as video-on-demand, telephony, interactivity, data services, etc. 3. Business Technology Association (was NOMDA/LANDA)

BTAM Basic Telecommunications Access Method. One of IBM's early host-based software programs for controlling remote data communications interface to host applications, supporting pre-SNA protocols. See IBM.

BTI British Telecom International.

BTL Bell Telephone Laboratories.

BTN Billed Telephone Number or Billing Telephone Number. The primary telephone number used for billing, regardless of the number of phone lines associated with that number. According to Bellcore, BTN is sometimes known as a screening telephone number, the BTN is a telephone number used by the AMA process as the calling-party number for recording purposes.

BTOS A UNIX program which translates binary files into ASCII.

BTRIEVE Btrieve is a key-indexed database record management system. You can retrieve, insert, update, or delete records by key value, using sequential or random access methods. First introduced in 1983, Btrieve was one of the first databases designed for LANs. Novell bought the company in the late 1980s. Now called NetWare Betrieve, it is included with most versions of NetWare 2.x and NetWare 3.x. There are Btrieve developer products for DOS, OS/2 and Windows.

BTRL British Telecom Research Laboratories.

BTS Base Transceiver Station. A wireless telecommunications term. A GSM

(Global System for Mobile Communications) device used to transmit radio frequency over the air interface.

BTSM BTS (Base Transceiver Station) Management. A wireless telecommunications term. Devices configured to manage BTS functions and equipment.

BTU Basic Transmission Unit.

BTV See Business Television.

BTW By The Way. An acronym used in electronic mail on the Internet to save words or to be hip, or whatever.

BUFFER 1. In data transmission, a buffer is a temporary storage location for information being sent or received. Usually located between two different devices that have different abilities or speeds for handling the data. The buffer acts like a dam, capturing the data and then trickling it out at speeds the lower river can handle without, hopefully, flooding or overflowing the banks. A buffer can be located in the sending or receiving device. 2. A coating material used to cover and protect the fiber. The buffer can be constructed using either a tight jacket or loose tube technique.

BUFFER COATING Protective material applied to fibers. Increases apparent fiber size. May be more than one layer. Stated in microns. Usually thicker or multi-coated on tight-buffer cables.

BUFFER MEMORY Electronic circuitry where data is kept during buffering. See BUFFER.

BUFFER STORAGE Electronic circuitry where data is kept during buffering. See BUFFER.

BUFFERED REPEATER A device that amplifies and regenerates signals so they can travel farther along a local area cable. This type of repeater also controls the flow of messages to prevent collisions.

BUG 1. A concealed microphone or listening device or other audiosurveillance device. 2. To install the means for audio surveillance. 3. A semiautomatic telegraph key. 4. A problem in software or hardware. The original computer bug, a moth, is enshrined at the Washington Navy Yard. It was the cause of a hardware failure in an early computer in 1945. The story goes like this: a team of top Navy scientists was developing one of the world's first electronic computers. Suddenly, in the middle of a calculation, the computer ground to a halt, dead. Engineers poured over every wire and every inch of the massive machine. Finally, one of the technicians discovered the cause of the problem. Buried deep insides its electronic innards, crushed between two electric relays, lay the body of a moth. These days, "bugs" in telecom or computer systems are not insects. They're indescribable glitches that adversely affect smooth operations. Bugs usually originate in software. Some programmers call bugs "undocumented features." And they are, indeed. All the above is the navy likes to put out. In actual fact, the word "bug" for problem in design has been around for eons. It's mentioned in a 1910 book called, "Edison, His Life and Inventions" by Frank Lewis Dyer. The book talks about Edison harassing his employees to "get all the bugs out."

BUG MIX A silly term for the precise collection of bugs in a particular piece of software.

BUG RATE The frequency with which new bugs are found during the testing cycle is referred to as the bug rate. As these bugs are fixed, and as time passes, bugs will become more and more difficult to find, and new bugs will be found less frequently, i.e., the bug rate decreases. Usually, when the bug rate drops to zero and all major bugs (and most of the minor bugs) have been fixed, a product is ready for the next stage in its lifecycle.

BUILDING ENTRANCE AREA The area inside a building where cables enter the building and are connected to riser cables within the building and where electrical protection is provided. The network interface as well as the protectors and other distribution components for the campus subsystem may be located here. Typically this area is the end of the local telephone company's responsibility. From here on it's your responsibility. You should protect your equipment inside the building from spikes and surges and other electrical nonsenses which the phone company's cables might bring in. For the best disaster protection, it's wise to have two building entrances by which your telecommunications cables can enter. And they should enter from separate telephone central offices. Some telephone companies, e.g. New York Telephone, are now tariffing such services.

BUILDING FOOTING The concrete base under the foundation of a building in which copper wire may be laid to form an electrical ground.

BUILDING INTEGRATED TIMING SUPPLY BITS. A clock, or a clock with an adjunct, in a building that supplies DS1 and/or composite clock timing reference to all other clocks in that building.

BUILDING OUT The process of adding a combination of inductance, capacitance,and resistance to a cable pair so that its electrical length may be increased by a desired amount to control impedance characteristics.

BUILDING STEEL The structural steel beams that make up the frame of a building. If the steel frame is buried deep in the earth, it can be used as an electrical ground. But you'd better be careful: Unbalanced three-phase power is also probably using the frame as a ground, and you may pick up huge quantities of 60 hz hum.

BULK BILLING A method of billing for long distance telephone services where no detail of calls made is provided. WATS is a bulk billed service. Therein lies the problem for the cost conscious user. There's no verification of calls made. See CALL DETAIL RECORDING.

BULK STORAGE Lots of storage. Usually reels of magnetic tape or hard disks.

BULLETIN BOARD SYSTEM A fancy name for an electronic message system running on a microcomputer. Call up, leave messages, read messages. The system is like a physical bulletin board. That's where the name comes from. Some people call bulletin board systems electronic mail systems. See also BBS.

BULK ENCRYPTION Simultaneous encryption of all channels of a multichannel telecommunications trunk.

BUMPER BEEPER Radio beacon transmitter, hidden in or on a vehicle for use with radio tailing equipment.

BUNCHED FRAME-ALIGNMENT SIGNAL A frame-alignment signal in which the signal elements occupy consecutive digit positions.

BUNDLE 1. A group of fibers or wires within a cable sharing a common color-code. 2. In T-1, specifically M44 Multiplexing, a bundle consists of 12 nibbles (4 bits) and may represent 11 channels of 32 Kbps compressed information plus a delta channel. A bundle is typically a subset of a DSI and treated as an entity with its own signaling delta channel.

BUNDLE FODDER Junk software included on CD-ROMs or packaged with peripherals such as modems and designed to bulk up the presumed value of the total package to entice an unsuspecting consumer to buy. See SHOVELWARE.

BUNDLED Combining several services under one telephone tariff item at a single charge.

BUNDLED RATES Several service combined into one offering for one charge.

BURDEN TEST A semi-legitimate test used in regulation to determine if the offering of a new or continued service will cause consumers of other services to pay prices no higher than if the service were not offered. In other words, the question is "Who carries the Burden?" It's sometimes called the "avoidable cost test."

BURFORD COURIER An MCI definition. A communications software package developed for use with Wang VS mainframes enabling users to communicate directly with MCI International's Telex messaging services.

BURN-IN To run new devices and printed circuits cards, often at high temperatures, in order to pinpoint early failures. The theory is all semiconductor devices show their defects — if any — in the first few weeks of operation. If they pass this "burn-in" period, they will work for a long time, so the theory goes. "Burn-in" should probably be 30-days under full power and working load. Burn-in should also take place in a room with lots of heat and at least 50% humidity, since this will simulate the poorly-ventilated places most people install telephone systems.

BURN OUT A condition, where stress causes agents to be apathetic and lethargic, caused by intensity of calling, lack of variety and poor working conditions. It is particularly associated with outbound cold calling and inbound complaint handling, both of which are stressful for agents if not carefully managed.

BURN RATE The speed at which a new company using up its cash en route to developing a product before it turns cash positive.

BURNING A POLE Slang expression to describe when an installer accidentally slides down a telephone pole.

BURRUS DIODE A surface-emitting LED with a hole etched to accommodate a light-collecting fiber. Named after its inventor, Charles Burrus.

BURST 1. In data communication, a sequence of signals, noise, or interface counted as a unit in accordance with some specific criterion or measure. 2. To separate continuous-form or multipart paper into discrete sheets.

BURST ISOCHRONOUS Isochronous burst transmission. See ISOCHRONOUS.

BURST MODE A way of doing data transmission in which a continuous block of data is transferred between main memory and an input/output device without interruption until the transfer has been completed.

BURST SWITCHING In a packet-switched network, a switching capability in which each network switch extracts routing instructions from an incoming packet header to establish and maintain the appropriate switch connection for the duration of the packet, following which the connection is automatically released. In concept, burst switching is similar to connectionless mode transmission, but it differs from the latter in that burst switching implies an intent to establish the switch connection in near real time so that only minimum buffering is required at the node switch.

BURST TRAFFIC Burst traffic is many phone calls (usually incoming telephone calls) that simultaneously arrives at a computer telephony system. Burst traffic tests are usually performed as part of a systems load and stress testing. Burst traffic tests are particularly important for computer telephony systems as usually they must perform a lot of processing to set up to handle a call. The arrival of many calls simultaneously, such as in response to a television sales offer (or when Oprah asks you to call 1-800-xxxxxxx to vote on whether OJ is guilty on innocent), can place significant strain on a computer telephony system.

BURST TRANSMISSION 1. A method of transmission that combines a very high data signaling rate with very short transmission times. 2. A method of operating a data network by interrupting, at intervals, the data being transmitted. The method enables communication between data terminal equipment and a data network operating at dissimilar data signaling rates.

BURSTY INFORMATION Information that flows in short bursts with relatively long, silent intervals between.

BURSTY SECONDS Bursty seconds is a measure of the amount of time spent at maximum data transfer rate.

BUS An electrical connection which allows two or more wires or lines to be connected together. Typically, all circuit cards receive the same information that is put on the BUS. Only the card the information is "addressed" to will use that data. This is convenient so that a circuit card may be plugged in "anywhere on the Bus." See also BACKPLANE and BUS NETWORK.

BUS ENUMERATOR A Windows 95 term. A new type of driver required for each specific bus type, responsible for building ("enumerating") the hardware tree on a Plug and Play system.

BUS HOG A device connected to a transmission bus which, after gaining access to the transmission medium, transmits a large number of messages regardless of whether other devices are waiting.

BUS MASTER A VME board (usually a CPU) that can contend for, seize and control the VME bus for the purpose of accessing bus resources such as voice boards or even other CPU's. See VME.

BUS MOUSE Mouse that takes up an expansion slot in a PC, rather that a serial port (those are called "serial mice"). There are generally more expansion slots available than serial ports.

BUS NETWORK All communications devices share a common path. Typically in a bus network, a "conversation" from each device is sampled quickly and interleaved using time division multiplexing. Bus networks are very high-speed — millions of bits per second — forms of transmission (e.g. on a local area network) and switching. They often form the major switching and transmission backbone of a modern PBX. The printed circuit cards which connect to each trunk and each line are plugged into the PBX's high-speed "backbone" — i.e. the bus network. See also BUS.

BUS SLAVE A VME board(usually a subsystem or I/O board) which can only respond to VME bus accesses mapped to its address. Slaves can usually interrupt the VME bus on one of 7 levels. See VME.

BUS SPEED The speed at which the computer's CPU (central processing unit) communicates with other elements of the computer. For example, the speed at which data moves between the CPU and your serial ports.

BUS TOPOLOGY A network topology in which nodes are connected to a single cable with terminators at each end.

BUSINESS AUDIO At one stage business audio was thought to involve voice annotating spreadsheets. Now it means making phone calls through and by your PC.

BUSINESS ID An MCI definition. A five-digit numeric code identifying the business to which a customer is assigned. The first two digits indicate division number, the third indicate service type, and the fourth and fifth indicate billing cycle. These are assigned during order entry and passed to MCI A/R with the customer install/ transaction.

BUSINESS TECHNOLOGY ASSOCIATION An association formerly known as Nomda/Landa.

BUSINESS TELEVISION BTV. Point-to-multipoint videoconferencing. Often refers to the corporate use of video for the transmission of company meetings, training and other one-to-many broadcasts. Typically uses satellite transmission methods and is migrating from analog to digital modulation techniques.

BUSINESSVIEW A Rolm term. Businessview for Call Centers is a centralized system for collecting, integrating, analyzing and reporting call center data.

BUSY In use. "Off-hook". There are slow busies and fast busies. Slow busies are when the phone at the other end is busy or off-hook. They happen 60 times a minute. Fast busies (120 times a minute) occur when the network is congested with too many calls. Your distant party may or may not be busy, but you'll never know because you never got that far.

BUSY BACK A busy signal.

BUSY CALL FORWARDING When you call a busy phone extension, your call is automatically sent to another predetermined telephone extension.

BUSY HOUR The hour of the day (or the week, or the month, or the year, — check) during which a telephone system carries the most traffic. For many offices, it is 10:30 A.M. to 11:30 A.M. The "busy hour" is perhaps the most important concept in traffic engineering — the science of figuring what telephone switching and transmission capacities one needs. Since the "busy hour" represents the most traffic carried in a hour, the idea is if you create enough capacity to carry that "busy hour" traffic, you will be able to carry all other traffic. In actuality, one never designs capacity sufficient to carry 100% of the busy hour traffic. That would be too expensive. So, the argument then comes down to, "What percentage of my peak busy or busy hour traffic am I prepared to block?" This percentage might be as low as half of one percent or as high as 10%. Typically, it's between 2% and 5%, depending on what business you're in and the cost to you — in lost sales, etc. — of blocking calls.

BUSY HOUR USAGE PROFILE The busy hour usage profile identifies how a system will normally be used (i.e., who the users are and what type of transactions they are performing) during the busy hour. Different things that users of CT systems do stress the CT system in different manners. For example, sending a broadcast message in voice mail (where one message is automatically sent to many recipients) may force the system to perform 10 times as much disk I/O as sending message to single recipients. Or, updating an account balance in an IVR transaction forces strain on the IVR to mainframe link. Or, setting up conference calls across a switch or network stresses the use of the network database resources. Understanding and characterizing the type and mix of calls that will take place during the busy hour is key to designing and placing a real-world load on the CT system. Load testing a system should always incorporate tests using the busy hour call profile.

BUSY LAMP A light on a telephone showing a certain line or phone is busy. See BUSY LAMP FIELD.

BUSY LAMP FIELD A device with rows of tiny lights that shows which phones in a telephone system have conversations on them, which phones are ringing, which phones are on hold. Each light corresponds to a telephone extension on the system. The busy lamp field usually sits attached to the attendant's console, telling the attendant if an extension is busy, free, on hold, etc. The benefit of having a busy lamp field is that the operator doesn't have to dial the number to find out what's happening with the extension. This saves the attendant time in handling incoming calls and gives the caller better service. A busy lamp field is often combined with DSS (Direct Station Select.) Next to each light on the busy lamp field there is a button which the operator can push which will dial the corresponding extension (i.e. directly select it) and will typically transfer the call automatically. This button is like an autodial button. This saves the time of dialing the two, three or more numbers of the extension. These days, busy lamp fields are often built into phones on a key system, and everyone, not just the operator, can have one. This gives everyone information on what's happening in the system. It makes transferring calls, etc. easier. See also DIRECT STATION SELECT.

BUSY OUT To cause a line to return a busy signal to a caller. Busying out lines going into a computer is useful when the computer is not available, i.e. during maintenance periods. This way callers do not get connected to modems with no computers to talk to. This is also known as "taking the phone off the hook." In a voice phone system with trunks that rotary (or hunt) on, sometimes busying one or more broken trunks out helps calls rotary on to trunks that are still working. This way, someone doesn't end up on your third trunk with endless ringing, while your 4th, 5th, 6th etc. trunks are free, leaving them wondering where you are and wondering why you're not getting any calls.

BUSY OVERRIDE A feature of some PBXs which allows the attendant or other high priority user to barge in on a telephone conversation. A warning tone is usually thrown into the conversation to alert the parties of an override. The feature is also called "Barge-In." Sometimes when conversations are overridden, only the person within the organization can hear the barge-in.

BUSY SEASON An annual recurring and reasonably predictable period of maximum busy hour requirements — normally three months of the year, and typically the three months preceding Christmas.

BUSY SIGNAL A signal indicating the line called is busy. The busy signal is generated by the central office. There are two types of busy signals. See BUSY.

BUSY TEST A method of figuring whether something which can carry traffic is actually doing so or whether it's broken or free and available for use.

BUSY VERIFICATION OF STATION LINES 1. An attendant can confirm that a line is actually in use by establishing a connection (dialing in and listening) to that apparently busy line. 2. In the public switched telephone network, a switching system service feature that permits an attendant to verify the busy or idle state of station lines and to break into the conversation. An alternating tone of 440 Hz is applied to the line for 2 seconds, followed by a 0.5-second burst every 10 seconds to alert both parties that the attendant is connect to the circuit.

BUTT SET See BUTTINSKY.

butt splice Connecting the ends of two wires with a "butt splice connector," from such manufacturers as AT&T and 3M.

BUTTINSKY Or Butt Set. The one-piece telephone carried on the hips of telephone technicians. It's called buttinsky or butt set because it allows technicians to "butt in" on phone calls, not because the device is worn on their butts. Butt sets used to be essentially telephones without ringers. But now they are much more sophisticated. They will pulse out in rotary or dial out in touchtone and allow you to talk or to monitor a call. They will run computerized tests on the line. Some even have the equivalent of an asynchronous computer terminal built in, which can be used to talk to a distant computer over a phone line. This distant computer could assign them their next jobs, allow them to check and assign features (touchtone, rotary, hunt), report the time spent on this job, etc. In short, the terminal and the computer could replace a raft of clerks and a deluge of paperwork.

The derivation of the term "buttinsky" has long been lost in history. Butt can also mean to attach the end of something to the end of something else. If the clips of a butt set are attached to a pair of wires, it is a "butt" connection. There are those people who also think that the term buttinsky came from some middle European language — Polish or Yiddish — and is slang for someone who butts in a lot, which is what you can do with a Butt Set. I shall keep researching this one. If you can help, let me know, please.

BUTTON CAPS Interchangeable plastic squares fit over the buttons of electronic telephones, and are used to label the features programmed onto each programmable button location. Button caps can be either pre-printed or have clear windows which allow features, lines, and Autodial numbers to be labelled on the button.

BUZZ 1. To check the continuity of a cable pair by putting an audible buzzer on one end and then checking with a "buttinsky" to see if you can hear the buzz and thus identify the correct cable pair. 2. A feature of a Rolm CBX which lets the user signal one Rolm desktop product without picking up the handset. Only one buzz per extension is permitted.

BUZZER An electromechanical device that makes a buzzing noise when power is applied, often used to signal someone to answer an intercom call. Battery-powered buzzers were once used to help trace phone circuits. TONE GENERATORS are more common today, but old terminology is still used, as in "buzzing out a line."

BUZZER LEADS The wires inside a telephone intended for the connection of a buzzer, usually as part of an intercom system.

BVA AT&T's exclusively-owned Billing Validation Application database. Today, BVA contains all the Regional Bell Operating Companies (RBOCs) calling cards, and other billing information such as billed number screening and payphone numbers. The RBOCs and AT&T access that database today. Prior to Divestiture three market players, the RBOCs, AT&T and most Independent Companies, dominated the "O" Operator Services business which provided alternate billing arrangements such as collect calls, bill to third number and charging calls to calling cards. The three market players still exclusively employ BVA which allows them to validate or authorize alternate billing arrangements. No other long distance carrier or a company needing access to the data for billing validation can use the system. The database is owned by AT&T and is updated daily by the RBOCs and Independent Companies with local exchange information, billing number screening and calling card information. The scenario is further complicated by the 1984 AT&T Plan of Reorganization's exclusive BVA access restrictions. In other words, the three original market players (AT&T, the RBOCs and Independent Companies) have exclusive access to BVA for a predetermined contract length. In most cases these arrangements run into the 1990's. See BVS.

BVS Business Validation Service. US West Service Link was the first in the nation to develop and make available a nationwide Billing Validation Service open to any company that needs to verify the legitimacy of their callers' requests to place charge calls to their local telephone calling cards. US West Service Link developed BVS in 1987 and turned up the system for "on-line" customers in early 1988. Today, the US West BVS system is a national validation source containing calling card data of customers served by the RBOCs, GTE, Southern New England Telephone, United Telecommunications, Cincinnati Bell, Rochester Telephone and Telecomm Canada, a consortium representing all of Canada's local telephone operating companies. In all, more than 60 million records are stored. US Sprint, MCI and ITI are among the carriers using BVS. BVS uses X.25 and SS7 protocol. See BVA.

BX.25 AT&T's rules for establishing the sequences of events and the specific types and forms of signals required to transfer data between computers. BX.25 includes the international rules known as X.25 and more.

BYPASS A term coming from the idea of using a method of local communications other than the local telephone company. The theory is you bypass the local phone company for typically two reasons: 1. Because the phone company is too expensive. 2. Because the phone company can't get you the bandwidth, the quality, the fast delivery or the service you want.

Bypass means you might be transmitting between two of your offices in the same city, perhaps between your office and your factory, etc. You might also be transmitting directly to your friendly long distance telephone company, which then carries your calls to distant cities. Bypass means you might be using one, several or many technologies, including your own private microwave, your own cable (metal or fiber), using the local CATV company, using the local bypass company, of which there are now dozens.

Bypass is a word created by the local telephone industry to sound very threatening. The theory is major users will bypass their local phone company, depriving their phone company of needed revenues. This will drive the phone company close to imminent bankruptcy, or at the very least, to the state regulators for huge rate increases, hurting everyone. The reality of this threat has not been proven. Nevertheless, the rhetoric frightens sufficient regulators to look at the evils of bypass and to outlaw it, or at least severely restrict it — as several states have done. This will strengthen the phone company's local monopoly, the objective of the exercise in the beginning. The reality is that bypass in all its forms is expanding, under encouragement from large users and from the FCC. See also 700 SERVICE.

BYPASS CABLING Bypass cabling or relays are wired connections in a local area ring network that permit traffic between two nodes that are not normally wired next to each other. Such bypass cabling might be used in an emergency or while other parts of the system are being serviced. Usually such bypass relays are arranged so that any node can be removed from the ring and the two nodes on either side of the removed node can then talk.

BYPASS TRUNK GROUP A trunk group circumvents one or more tandems in its routing ladder.

BYTE A popular microcomputer magazine, which derives its name from the true meaning of BYTE, which is eight bits of information composed of zeros or ones, one of which may include a parity bit. Most character sets, e.g. ASCII or EBCDIC, use one byte per character of information such as a letter, a number or digit, a punctuation mark or a symbol, such as $. A byte is to a bit what a word is to a character. In some circles a byte is called an octet. See BYTE COUNT.

BYTE COUNT The number of 8-bit bytes in a message. Since ASCII characters typically have 8-bits, the byte count is also called the character count.

BYTE COUNT PROTOCOL A class of data link protocols in which each frame has a header containing a count of the total number of data characters in the body of the frame.

BYTE MULTIPLEXER CHANNEL An IBM mainframe input/output channel that allows for the interleaving, or multiplexing, of data in bytes. Compare with block multiplexer channel.

BYTE MULTIPLEXING A byte (or character) from one channel is sent as a unit and bytes from different channels follow in successive time slots.

BYTE STUFFING The process whereby dummy bytes are inserted into a transmission stream so that the net data transmission rate will be lower than the actual channel data rate. The dummy bytes are identified by a single controlling bit within the byte.

BYTE TIMING CIRCUIT Optional X.21 circuit used to maintain byte or character synchronization.

BZT Bundesamt fur Zulassungen in der Telekommunikation. The name of the German telecom approval authority. It was established in 1982 under the name of the Central Approvals Office for Telecommunications. The name was changed to BZT on March 10, 1992. It is currently based in Saabrucken.

C The programming language AT&T uses for several of its central office switches. It is also used as the programming language of choice for interactive voice response (voice processing) systems. C operates under UNIX, MS-DOS and other operating systems. It is very powerful and is becoming somewhat of a standard for programming telecom switches. AT&T writes its C programs under the operating system UNIX, because UNIX is a true multi-tasking system.

C BAND Portion of the electromagnetic spectrum used heavily for satellite transmission. The uplink frequency is at 6 GHz and the downlink is at 4 GHz. Contrast with KU BAND.

C BATTERY A source of low potential used in the grid circuit of a vacuum tube to cause operation to take place at the desired point on the characteristic curve.

C LEAD The third of three wires which make up trunk lines between central office switches. There are three wires — positive, negative, and the "c lead." The purpose of the "c lead" is to control the grounding, holding and releasing of trunks.

C MESSAGE WEIGHTING This definition from James Harry Green, author of the excellent Dow Jones Handbook of Telecommunications. C Message Weighting is a factor in noise measurements to approximate the lesser annoying effect on the human ear of high and low-frequency noise compared to mid-range noise.

C WIRE C Wire is what the phone company calls the last piece of its wire that comes into your house or office. It is typically the piece of underground cable that comes in from its pedestal on the street to your network interface box on the side of your house or building.

C&C Computers and Communications. An NEC slogan which focused on the deployment of computer and telephony elements to create an integrated environment. Later on, NEC changed it to "Computing and Communicating" and expanded it into a "Fusion" strategy. See FUSION.

C++ A high-level programming language developed by Bjarne Stroustrup at AT&T's Bell laboratories. Combining all the advantages of the C language with those of object-oriented programming, C++ has been adopted as the standard house programming language by several major software vendors, such as Apple Computer.

C2 Command and Control. The exercise of authority and direction by a properly designated commander over assigned forces in the accomplishment of the mission. Command and control functions are performed through an arrangement of personnel equipment, communications, facilities, and procedures employed by a commander in planning, directing, coordinating, and controlling forces and operations in the accomplishment of the mission. See C3.

C3 Command, Control and Communications. The capabilities required by military commanders to exercise command and control of their forces. See C2.

C7 European equivalent of the North American System Signaling 7. C7 is not 100% compatible with North American System Signaling 7 and that's where gateway switches come in. These switches convert the signaling between one and the other and do it in real time.

C&C NEC Corp.'s idea of combining Computers and Communications into something wondrous. Not well defined.

C-DTE Character mode Data Terminal Equipment. A term to describe most PCs (personal computers) and printer-terminals that use asynchronous signals for data communications.

C-LINK A signaling link used to connect mated pairs of Signal Transfer Points (STPs). An Ericsson term.

C-MESSAGE WEIGHTING A type of telephone weighting network that allows for equal attenuation of all frequencies within the voice band in the same manner as it appears to be attenuated by the media.

C/A CODE The standard Clear/Acquisition GPS (Global Positioning Code) — a sequence of 1023 pseudo-random, binary biphase modulations on the GPS carrier at the chip rate of 1,023 MHz. Also known as the "civilian code." See GPS.

CA Call Appearance

CAAGR Compound Annual Average Growth.

CABLE May refer to a number of different types of wires or groups of wires capable of carrying voice or data transmissions. The most common interior telephone cable has been two pair. It's typically called quad wiring. It consists of four separate wires each covered with plastic insulation and with all four wires wrapped in an outer plastic covering. Quad wiring is falling into disrepute as it is increasingly obvious that it does not have the capacity to carry data at high speeds. The wire and cable business is immense. The assortment of stuff it produces each year is mind-boggling. In telecommunications, there is one rule: The quality of a circuit is only as good as its weakest link. Often that "weak link" is the quality of the wiring or cabling (we used the words interchangeably) that the user himself puts in. Please put in decent quality wiring. Don't skimp. See CATEGORY OF PERFORMANCE.

CABLE ACT OF 1984 An Act passed by Congress that deregulated most of the CATV industry including subscriber rates, required programming and fees to municipalities. The FCC was left with virtually no jurisdiction over cable television except among the following areas: (1) registration of each community system prior to the commencement of operations; (2) ensuring subscribers had access to an A-B switch to permit the receipt of off-the-air broadcasts as well as cable programs; (3) carriage of television broadcast programs in full without alteration or deletion; (4) non-duplication of network programs; (5) fines or imprisonment for carrying obscene material; and (6) licensing for receive-only earth stations for satellite-delivered via pay cable. The FCC could impose fines on CATV systems violating the rules. This Act was superseded by the Cable Reregulation Act of 1992.

CABLE ASSEMBLY A completed cable and its associated hardware ready to install.

CABLE BAYS Lots of cable arranged like bays in a harbor.

CABLE BUSINESS A magazine on cabling run by Steve Paulov and family in Mesquite (Dallas), TX. A great magazine. 214-270-0860.

CABLE CUTOFF WAVELENGTH For a cabled single-mode optical fiber, Cable Cutoff Wavelength specifies a complex inter-relation of specified length, bend, and deployment conditions. It is the wavelength at which the fiber's second order mode is attenuated a measurable amount when compared to a multimode reference fiber or to a tightly bent single-mode fiber.

CABLE DIAMETER Expressed in millimeters or inches. Affects space occupied, allowable bend radius, reel size, length on a reel and reel weight. Also affects selection of pulling grips.

CABLE DOG Slang expression. In the West, lifelong cable installer who seeks no upward mobility. In the East, worker who deals with underground cable.

CABLE/INFORMATION TECHNOLOGY CONVERGENCE FORUM This forum is a new organization of the cable television, telephone, computer and switching network industries. The Forum was created to promote greater communication between vendors in the information technology industry, cable television companies and CableLabs, the research and development consortium serving most of the cable operators in North America. The Convergence Forum, based in Louisville, Colo., was conceived and sponsored by CableLabs. Companies that have agreed to join the Forum include Apple Computer, Bay Networks, Cisco Systems, Compaq, Digital Equipment Corp., Fore Systems and LANCity.

CABLE LOSS The amount of radio frequency (RF) signal attenuated (lost) while it travels on a cable. There are many reasons for cable loss, including the cable's shape, its type, its size, its length and what it's made of. For coaxial cable, higher frequencies have greater loss than lower frequencies and follow a logarithmic function. Cable losses are usually calculated for the highest frequency carried on the cable. See ATTENUATION.

CABLE MAPPING Cable mapping is the task of trying to track every single pair of wire or circuit from beginning to end. You will need to know where all cables reside, not just the circuits that are in use. Cable mapping is critical for any organization — from company to university — which has a lot of cables floating around. Installing more of it — when there are plenty of spare pairs — is stupid and expensive. Thus, the need for cable mapping.

CABLE MODEM Modem designed for use on TV coaxial cable circuit. The idea is simple: Put the cable modem on a home cable TV line, provide the subscriber a circuit on which he can dial up Prodigy, CompuServe, America On Line, the Internet, etc. And charge a little extra for the privilege.

CABLE PLANT A term which refers to the physical connection media (optical fiber, copper wiring, connectors, splicers, etc.) in a local area network. It is a term also used less frequently by the telephone to mean all its outside cables — those going from the central office to the subscribers' offices.

CABLE PROTECTION There are three basic types of protection in addition to standard plastic cladding:

ElectroMagnetic (EM) Shielding: Prevents passive coupling. EM shielding can be a metallic conduit or metal wrapping-with appropriate grounding-on the wires.

Penetration-Resistant Conduit: Used to secure the cable from cutting or tapping. Note, however, not all penetration-resistant conduits provide EM shielding.

Pressurized Conduit: Detects intrusion by monitoring for pressure loss. Fiber optic cable is extremely difficult to tap and if tapped, the intrusion can be detected through signal attenuation. But since fiber optic cable can be cut, penetration-resistant conduit is recommended to protect the cable.

CABLE RACKING Framework fastened to bays to support cabling between them.

CABLE REREGULATION ACT OF 1992 Reregulation Bill 1515 passed Congress in October 1992, forcing the FCC to reregulate cable television and cable television rates (after the Cable Act of 1984 effectively de-regulated the cable TV industry). After the Act was passed, the FCC forced the industry to reduce its rates by 10% in 1993 and then again by 7% in 1994.

CABLE RISER Cable running vertically in a multi-story building to serve the upper floors.

CABLE RUN Conduit used to run cables through a building. Also, path taken by a cable or group of cables.

CABLE SHIELD A metallic component of the cable sheath which prevents outside electrical interference and drains off current induced by lightning.

CABLE TELEVISION RELAY STATION CARS. A fixed or mobile station used for the transmission of television and related audio signals, signals of standard and FM broadcast stations, signals of instructional television fixed stations, and cablecasting from the point of reception to a terminal point from which the signals are distributed to the public.

CABLE TYPE The type of cable used. Also called the media. Examples are coaxial, UTP (Unshielded Twisted Pair), STP (Shielded Twisted Pair) and fiber. Factors including cost, connectivity and bandwidth are important in determining cable type. Choosing cable is getting more and more complex. Our tip: Choose and buy well in advance of when you'll need it. The cable you want will not always be in stock.

CABLE VAULT Room under the main distribution frame in a central office building. Cables from the subscribers lines come into the building through the cable vault. From here they snake their way up to the main distribution frame. The cable vault looks like a bad B-movie portrayal of Hell, replete with thousands of dangerous black snakes. Cable vaults are prime targets for the spontaneous starting of fires. They should be protected with Halon gas, but usually aren't because some parts of the phone industry think Halon is too expensive.

CABLE WEIGHT Expressed in lbs. per 1000 (without reel weight included). Affects sag, span and size of messenger in aerial applications.

CABLEGRAM SERVICE An MCI definition. An MCI International service which provides cablegram communication to International destinations through the use of a computerized message switching center in New York City.

CABLEPORT Intel Corporation's

new technology, which brings high speed multimedia-rich interactive services to personal computers in the home via cable.

CABLESPAN A Tellabs Operations, Inc. product which deliver two-way voice and data services over coaxial cable used by cable TV operators. Tellabs is in Lisle, In.

CABLEWAY An opening in a work surface that allows access to cords or cables from below, or mounting of an electrical receptacle or telephone jack. Cableways typically come with removable plastic grommets.

CAC Customer Administration Center. A type of terminal used by a PBX user to maintain and troubleshoot his PBX.

CACHE A cache is high-speed memory designed to hold upcoming to-be-accessed and/or recently-accessed data. A cache speeds up a computer's operation because high-speed memory sends information to and from the computer's central microprocessor much faster than a hard disk could. Cache memory gives the computer user the impression that the computer and its programs are actually running a lot faster than they are theoretically capable of. Cache memory comes in RAM on a computer's motherboard and on hard disk controller cards. The value of a cache is directly related to how good the software is that runs it. There are wide variations in the quality of caching software. A cache is especially important in a LAN file server. It can be used to "speed up" access to a database stored on the file server, thereby saving workstation users time and aggravation. Caches work because of a phenomenon known as the locality principle which states that a von Neumann CPU (i.e. one that performs instructions one after another) tends to access the same memory locations over and over again. A cache works like this: when the CPU needs data from memory, the cache hardware and software checks to see if the information is already in the cache. If it is, it grabs that information. This is called a cache hit. If it isn't, it's called a cache miss and the computer has to access the disk, which is slower. Data retrieved during a cache miss is often written into the cache. See also CACHE MEMORY.

CACHE CONTROLLER A chip, such as the Intel 82385, that manages the retrieval, storage and delivery of data to and from memory or the hard disk.

CACHE HIT When the data you want is actually in cache. Thus you don't have to access your hard disk and your computing is fast. See CACHE and CACHE MEMORY.

CACHE MEMORY Available Random Access Memory that you set up to allow your computer to "remember" stuff — so the next time your computer wants that information, it can find it fast from RAM, instead of searching through a hard disk which is slow. This high speed cache memory eliminates the CPU wait state. When the CPU reads data from main memory, a copy of this data is stored in the cache memory. The next time the CPU reads the same address, the data is transferred from the cache memory instead of from main memory. Novell's NetWare, for example, uses cache memory to improve file server access time. In NetWare, cache memory contains the directory and file caches, along with the FAT (File Allocation Table), the turbo FAT, the Hash table, and an open space for other functions. See also CACHE.

CACHE MISS When the caching software guesses wrongly and you have to read your data off your hard disk rather than reading it from the cache. See also CACHE and CACHE MEMORY.

CAD 1. Computer Aided Dispatch. 2. Computer Aided Design. A computer and its related software and terminals used to design things. A CAD system might be as simple as computerized drafting tools or as complex as detailed layouts of integrated circuits. CAD systems often have terminals on peoples' desks and a central maxi-computer in the company's main computer room. CAD terminals are often run over LANs (local area networks) or through telephone systems. The terminals are often moved, thus having universal wiring and a universal switching system — a LAN or a phone system — is extremely useful.

CAD/CAM Computer Aided Design/Computer Aided Manufacturing. See CAD.

CADB Calling Area Data Base. An MCI definition. An MCI System that stores reference data for various MCI Systems and reconciles MCI Calling Areas with those of Bell.

CADDY The shell of an optical disc. Protects it from grubby fingerprints, and includes write protection devices. AKA case.

CADENCE In voice processing, cadence is used to refer to the pattern of tones and silence intervals generated by a given audio signal. Examples are busy and ringing tones. A typical cadence pattern is the US ringing tone, which is one second of tone followed by three seconds of silence. Some other countries, such as the UK, use a double ring, which is two short tones within about a second, followed by a little over two seconds of silence.

CADS Code Abuse Detection System.

CAE Computer Aided Engineering.

CAGE ANTENNA An antenna having conductors arranged cylindrically.

CAGR Compound Annual Growth Rate.

CAI 1. Computer Assisted Instruction. See also CAD for a discussion on telecom needs. 2. A British Term. Common Air Interface. The CT2/telepoint international standard which allows any compliant equipment, i.e. a wireless handset, to be used on any network of the same type. CAI-compliant telepoint handsets from different vendors may therefore be used on a telepoint network.

CAIRO Microsoft's planned heavy duty successor to Windows NT. Cairo is due out the later part of the decade. It is rumored to include a radically new file structure that will let you easily find information among many thousands of files.

CALENDAR ROUTING A call center term for directing calls according to the day of the week and time of day. See also SOURCE/DESTINATION ROUTING, SKILLS BASED ROUTING and END-OF-SHIFT ROUTING.

CALIBRATE To test and reset a measuring or timing device against a standard to make sure it is functioning correctly.

CALL My definition: Two people on the phone. One calls the other. People who speak on phones are called "parties." No one knows why. Bellcore's definition: An arrangement providing for a relation between two or more simultaneously present users for the purpose of exchanging information.

CALL ABANDONS Also called ABANDONED CALLS. Call Abandons are calls that are dropped by the calling party before their intended transaction is completed. The call may be dropped at various points in the process. The point in the call at which the call is abandoned will have varying impacts on a computer telephony system. Many callers upon hearing an automated system will hang up. For systems that expended significant energy in setting up to answer a call, a large percentage of call abandons can negatively impact the call capacity of the system.

CALL ACCEPTED SIGNAL A control signal transmitted by the called equipment to indicate that it accepts an incoming call.

CALL ACCOUNTING SYSTEM A computer, a magnetic storage device (floppy or hard disk), software and some mechanical method of attaching itself to a telephone system. A call accounting system is used to record information about telephone calls, organize that information and upon being asked, prepare reports — printed or to disk. The information which it records (or "captures") about telephone calls typically includes from which extension the call is coming, which number it is calling (local or long distance), which circuit is used for the call (WATS, MCI, etc.), when the call started, how long it lasted, for what purpose the call was made (which client? which project?). A call accounting system might also include information on incoming calls — which trunk was used, where the call came from (if ANI or interactive voice response was used), which extension took the call, if it was transferred and to where and how long it took.

There are eleven basic uses for call accounting systems:

1. Controlling Telephone Abuse. It's the 90-10 rule. 10% of your people sit on long distance calls all day to their friends and family. The others work. Some people still think WATS calls are free. Knowing who's calling where and how much they're spending is useful. Often they appreciate being told they're spending money. Big money...and they stop.

2. Controlling Telephone Misuse. I figured once you could call between two major cities for five cents a minute and $1 a minute. That's a 20-fold difference! Often you need different lines. Often a company has different lines. Sometimes the phone system makes the dialing decision. Sometimes the person makes the dialing decision. Whoever's doing it can be wrong. A call accounting system is a good check to see if you're spending money needlessly.

3. Allocating telephone calling costs among departments and divisions. Telephones — voice, data, video and imaging — are some of your biggest expenses. They're a cost that should be allocated to the products you're making, or the departments or divisions in your company. Telephone costs can determine which product is profitable. Which isn't. Item: A software company recently dropped one of its three "big" software packages because phone calls for support got too expensive.

4. Billing Clients and Projects back for telephone charges incurred on their behalf. Every lawyer, government contractor, etc. does it. Makes sense.

5. Sharing and Resale of long distance and local phone calls, as in a hotel/motel, hospital, shared condominium, etc. Someone's got to send out the bills. And it's not the phone company. In fact, with a call accounting system you can be your own phone company!

6. Motivation of Salespeople. The more phone calls they make the more they sell.

This rule is as obvious as the nose on your face. You WANT salespeople to make more calls? Hang a list of all their calls on the wall. Give prizes to those make the most! Or those who make more than last week. Or those who set a new record.

7. Personnel Evaluation. Which employees are doing better at being productive on the phone (however you define "productive"). You want them to get on and off the phone fast? Or you want them to stay on and coddle your customers? You can now correlate phone calls with income — from service or just straightout sales.

8. Network Optimization. Two fancy words for figuring which is the best combination of MCI, AT&T, MCI, Sprint, Wiltel, etc. lines. And which is the best combination of all the various services each offer. A rule of thumb: There's a 20-fold difference in per minute telephone calling costs between any two major cities in the US. And — amazing — you won't hear any difference in quality, despite the huge difference in price. I think it's the biggest price difference in any product anywhere. It's amazing.

9. Phone System Diagnostics. Is the phone system working as well as it should? Are all the lines working? Are all the circuit packs (circuit cards) working? Call accounting systems can tell you which lines you're getting no traffic on. Or which line carried the 48 hour call to Germany (it's happened). Either way, you can figure quickly which lines are working and which aren't.

10. Long Distance Bill Verification. Was the bill accurate we received from our chosen long distance phone company? Mostly it isn't. In fact, there's no such thing as an accurate phone bill. That's an oxymoron. Using your call accounting systems to check your long distance gives you some peace of mind. It's cheap peace of mind. Everyone should have one.

11. Tracing Calls. True story: Every third or fourth Friday afternoon a large factory in the south received bomb threats. They'd clear the factory, search the factory and not find anything. By the time they'd checked, it was too late to start up production. One day they checked their call accounting records. The calls were coming from a phone on the factory floor. The whole thing was a ruse to get an afternoon off...And now that many phones give you the number of who's calling, call accounting systems are turning out to be great for checking the effectiveness of regional ad campaigns, figuring the profitability of direct mailings and even figuring the profitability of individual customers.

CALL ANNOUNCEMENT A telephone operator or person acting as a telephone operator can announce a call to the called party before putting the call through. All modern phone systems have this feature.

CALL ATTEMPT A try at making a telephone call to someone. Tally up call attempts and compare them to completions and you'll have some idea of corporate frustration and thus, the need for more lines or more phone equipment. The measures in this in call attempts,calls answered, calls overflowed, and calls abandoned.

CALL BACK A security procedure in which a user, dials into access a system and requests service. The system then disconnects and calls the user back at a preauthorized number to establish the access connection. Same as dial-back. See also INTERNATIONAL CALL BACK.

CALL BARRING The ability to prevent all or certain calls from reaching to or from a phone.

CALL BEFORE DIG A preventive maintenance measure in which signs are posted near buried cables advising people to phone before digging in the area.

CALL BLENDING A phone system has a bunch of people answering and making calls. The calls are coming (say in response to an ad). The calls are going out, courtesy of a dialing machine (perhaps a predictive dialer). The idea is to keep the calls at a constant level. The idea is to blend incoming with outgoing calls. Some predictive dialers have call blending. Others don't. They need a dedicated workforce. Call blending automatically transfers staff members between outbound and inbound programs as call volumes change. Some predictive dialers let you choose which workstations will be used for call blending, to avoid training of every staff member.

CALL BLOCK A name for a Pacific Bell (and possibly other local telephone companies') service which helps you avoid unwanted calls by rejecting calls from numbers you specify. BellSouth describes its service called "Call Block" as "prevents the number received from getting through again. It also lets the subscriber pre-select up to six phone numbers to be blocked.

CALL BLOCKING Check into a hotel. Dial a 0+ call. You're connected to an Alternate Operator Service company. But you know their rates may be high. You ask to be connected to AT&T or MCI, or whoever is the carrier of your choice. Sadly, the AOS cannot connect and neither can (nor will) your hotel's operator. This is called "Call Blocking." The FCC has disbarred the practice. But it continues. See also CALL SPLASHING.

CALL CARD A British term. A paper record, used in manual telebusiness systems, to record the results of a call.

CALL CENTER A place where calls are answered and calls are made. A call center will typically have lots of people (also called agents), an automatic call distributor, a computer for order-entry and lookup on customers' orders. A Call Center could also have a predictive dialer for making lots of calls quickly. The term "call center" is broadening. It now includes help desks and service lines. For more information on Call Centers, please read CALL CENTER Magazine. 212-691-8215. See CALL CENTRE.

CALL CENTRE A British term. An area in an organisation where business is conducted by phone in a methodical and organised manner. Call centres are typically based on the integration of a computerised database and an automatic call distribution system. (Note that this definition contains British spellings.) See CALL CENTER.

CALL CLEAR PACKET An information packet that ends an X.25 communications session, performing the equivalent of hanging up the phone.

CALL CLEARING The process by which a call connection is released from use.

CALL COLLISION 1. Contention that occurs when a terminal and a DCE simultaneously transfer a call request and an incoming call specifying the same logical channel. The DCE will proceed with the call request and cancel the incoming call. 2. That condition arising when a trunk or channel is seized at both ends simultaneously, thereby blocking a call.

CALL COMPLETION RATE The ratio of successfully completed calls to the total number of attempted calls. This ratio is typically expressed as either a percentage or a decimal fraction.

CALL CONTROL Call control is the term used by the telephone industry to describe the setting up, monitoring, and tearing down of telephone calls. There are two ways of doing call control. A person or a computer can do it via the desktop telephone or a computer attached to that telephone, or the computer attached to the desktop phone line (i.e. without the actual phone being there). That's called First Party Call Control. Third-party call control controls the call through a connection directly to the switch (PBX). Generally third-party call control also refers to the control of other functions that relate to the switch at large, such as ACD queuing, etc.

CALL CONTROL PROCEDURE Group of interactive signals required to establish, maintain and release a communication.

CALL CONTROL SIGNAL Any one of the entire set of interactive signals necessary to establish, maintain, and release a call.

CALL DATA Call data refers to any data about a phone call that is passed by a switch to an attached computer telephony system. Call data is usually used by the computer telephony application to process the call more intelligently. Call data may be passed In-Band, over the same physical or logical link as the call — usually via tones, or Out-Of-Band, over a separate link — usually a serial link. Call data may also be passed as part of the data designed to control telephone networks, such as SS7 (Signaling System 7) links. In addition to information about the call, status about the call and even control over the call, can be available as part of the call data link services. Call data almost always includes what number dialed the call (ANI) and/or what number called (DNIS). More complex call data links used for "PBX integration" may also indicate why the call was presented (such as forwarded on busy), tell what trunk the call is coming in on, or to pass message waiting on or off indications, and other functions. Full blown computer telephony links, such as are now being offered by many switching vendors, enhance the call data path, providing additional status information about calls and can even provide a level of call control to the attached computer telephony system. The above definition courtesy of Steve Gladstone, author of a great book called Testing Computer Telephony Systems, available from 212-691-8215.

CALL DELAY The delay encountered when a call reaches busy switching equipment. In normal POTS telephone service, the delay is considered OK if no more than one and a half percent of the calls are delayed by three seconds during the busy hour.

CALL DETAIL RECORDING CDR. A feature of a telephone system which allows the system to collect and record information on outgoing and incoming phone calls — who made/received them, where they went/where they came from, what time of day they happened, how long they took, etc. Sometimes the data is collected by the phone system; sometimes it is pumped out of the phone system as the calls are made. Which ever way, the information must be recorded elsewhere — dumped right into a printer or into a PC with call accounting software. See also CALL ACCOUNTING SYSTEM.

CALL DIVERTER 1. A device which when connected to a called telephone number intercepts calls to that number and connects them to a telephone operator or prerecorded message. 2. An ancillary device which is connected to a telephone line. The device will, when the called telephone rings, initiate a telephone call on another line to a different telephone number. The calling party may or may not be aware that his call has been diverted to another telephone.

CALL DURATION The time from when the call is actually begun (i.e. answered) to the instant either party hangs up. Call Duration is an important concept for traffic engineering.

CALL ESTABLISHMENT The process by which a call connection is created.

CALL FORWARDING A service available in many central offices, and a feature of many PBXs and some hybrid PBX/key systems, which allows an incoming call to be sent elsewhere. There are many variations on call forwarding: Call forwarding busy. Call forwarding don't answer. Call forwarding all calls, etc.

Call forward is a useful feature. For example, you're going to a meeting but you're expecting an important call. Pick up your phone, punch in some digits and all your calls will go to the new number — perhaps the phone outside the meeting room. The big disadvantage is that many people return to their offices but forget they forwarded their calls elsewhere. As a result, they usually miss a whole bunch of important calls. Some electronic phones now have a reminder light or message on them saying "all calls are being forwarded." Some people program their PBXs to cancel all call forwards at noon and at midnight every day. This makes sense.

Call forwarding is used to send calls to voice mail systems. For example, tell your PBX that if your phone isn't answered in four rings, send that call to your voice mail.

If you are getting call forwarding service from a central office in North America, the code to begin call forwarding is 72# and the number you want to be forwarded to. To cancel it, you punch in 73#.

CALL FRAME Harris' PBX to computer link. Harris' protocol for linking its PBX to an external computer and having that computer control the movement of calls within a Harris PBX. See also OPEN APPLICATION INTERFACE.

CALL HANDOFF A cellular phone term. Call handoff happens when a wireless call is transferred to another cell site in mid-conversation.

CALL HOLD If you hang the phone up, you lose the caller. Call hold — a feature of most phone systems — allows you to "hold" the call, so the other person can't hear you. You can then return to the conversation by pushing a button on your phone, typically the button flashing which shows which line the person is sitting on hold. Call hold is useful when you have someone on another line calling you.

CALL IDENTIFIER A network utility that is an identifying name assigned by the originating network for each established or partially established virtual call and, when used in conjunction with the calling DTE address, uniquely identifies the virtual call over a period of time.

CALL IN ABSENCE HORN ALERT A cellular car phone feature that sounds your car's horn when you are receiving a call.

CALL IN ABSENCE INDICATOR A cellular car phone feature that ensures that power to the cellular phone is not lost if the car's ignition is turned off.

CALL IN PROGRESS OVERRIDE A cellular car phone feature that keeps power to the phone during a call even though you've turned off the car's ignition.

CALL LETTERS Certain combinations of letters assigned to radio stations by the FCC. The group of letters assigned the U.S. by the International Radiotelegraph Convention are all three and four letter combinations beginning with N and/ or W and all combinations of KDA to KZZ inclusive.

CALL ME CARD A special AT&T Card number which permits others to call you, and only you, and have the call charged to your telephone. Give an AT&T CALL ME Card to your very best customers to encourage them to call you. A Call Me Card is like having a private unlisted 800 toll-free number.

CALL ME MESSAGE A Rolm/IBM feature on their CBX that allows internal users to leave other users a message showing the time, date and the caller's extension number.

CALL MIX Call mix is the pattern of call types (each call type defines what the caller will do for that call) that goes into creating a busy hour call profile or other call profile. A voice mail system's busy hour call profile call mix may consist of 10% call abandons, 20% login and send one message, 30% login and listen to one message, and so on. Varying the call mix can often be useful to stress particular parts of a system. For example, a call mix of 100% call abandons is frequently used to stress a computer telephony system's ability to handle high traffic call setup scenarios. This definition courtesy of Steve Gladstone, author of the book Testing Computer Telephony Systems, available from 212-691-8215.

CALL MODEL An abstraction of the call processing functionality of the architecture and the relationship that exists between the functionality of the Service Switching FE in an ASC and the Service Logic and Control FE in a SLEE (Service Logic Execution Environment). The call model consists of two components: Connection View and Basic Call State Model. Definition from Bellcore in reference to Advanced Intelligent Network.

CALL NOT ACCEPTED SIGNAL A call control signal sent by the called terminal to indicate that it does not accept the incoming call.

CALL PACKET A block of data carrying addressing and other information that is needed to establish an X.25 switched virtual circuit (SVC).

CALL PARK The phone call is not for you. Or maybe it is, but you don't want to answer it on your phone. Put it into CALL PARK, then you or anyone else can answer it from any other phone. Call Park is similar to placing a call on hold, but your retrieve the call by dialing a code, rather than by pressing a line button. The attendant may have a call for you, but you're not there. So he places the call in Call Park, pages you and tells you the call is in Call Park. You pick up the nearest phone, dial one or two digits (the code for grabbing the call out of Call Park) and you have the call. It's faster than looking for you, then telling you to hang up while she transfers the call.

CALL PICKUP A phone is ringing but it's not yours. With call pickup, you can punch in a button or two on your phone and answer that person's ringing phone. Saves time. See CALL PICKUP GROUP.

CALL PICKUP GROUP All the phones in an area that can be answered by each other by simply punching in a couple of digits. See CALL PICKUP.

CALL PROCESSING The system and process that sets up the intended connection in a switching system. The system scans the trunk and/or station ports for any "requests" for service. Upon detecting a request, the system checks the stored instructions and look-up tables and sets the connection up accordingly.

CALL PROGRESS The status of the telephone line; ringing, busy ring/no answer, voice mail answering, telephone company intercept, etc. See CALL PROGRESS ANALYSIS and CALL PROGRESS TONE.

CALL PROGRESS ANALYSIS As the call progresses several things happen. Someone dial or touchtones digits. The phone rings. There might be a busy or operator intercept. An answering machine may answer. A fax machine may answer. Call progress analysis is figuring out which is occurring as the call progresses. This analysis is critical if you're trying to build an automated system, like an interactive voice response system.

CALL PROGRESS SIGNALING All telephone switches use the same three general types of signals: + Event Signaling initiates an event, such as ringing. + Call Progress Signaling denotes the progress (or state) of a call, such as a busy tone, a ringback tone, or an error tone. + Data Packet Signaling communicates certain information about a call, for example, the identify of the calling extension, or the identity of the extension being called.

CALL PROGRESS TONE A tone sent from the telephone switch to tell the caller of the progress of the call. Examples of the common ones are dial tone, busy tone, ringback tone, error tone, re-order, etc. Some phone systems provide additional tones, such as confirmation, splash tone, or a reminder tone to indicate that a feature is in use, such as confirmation, hold reminder, hold, intercept tones.

CALL QUEUING Incoming or outgoing calls may be queued pending an answer. The idea of call queuing is to save money. See also CALLBACK QUEUING.

CALL RECORD The data record of a call transaction. The record is made up of event details that typically include date, time, trunk(s) used, station(s) used and duration. In an ACD, these events may also include time in queue, call route used, system disposition flag, inbound or outdialed digits and wrap-up data entered.

CALL REFERENCE Information element that identifies to which call a Layer 3 message pertains.

CALL RELEASE TIME The time it takes from sending equipment a signal to close down the call to the time a "free condition" appears and the system is ready for another call.

CALL REORIGINATION Caller reorigination allows a caller with a telephone debit card account number or a telephone credit card account to make unlimited calls without hanging up and redialing their access and their account numbers. At the end the first call, the caller remains on the line. The caller then presses the pound key (the # key) for a prescribed number of seconds and receives a confirmation tone (which sounds like a high-pitched dial tone). After receiving the tone, the caller immediately dials their next phone number. And so on. Sometimes you can hit the # button after the person you were talking to has hung up. My experience has been that it's better to hit the # before the person has hung up. Just tell them what you're doing. All this allows the card account holder to make a series of calls without ever hanging up and redialing the often lengthy access card account numbers. This saves a lot of time for callers with a long list of calls to make. It also saves money for callers from hotels, which charge for each connection to the long distance provider, but don't charge based on the length of the call (especially if it's a local call or toll-free 800 call). The prescribed number of seconds that the user needs to hold down the pound key is configurable. Depending on the application the time may range from 1 to 5 seconds. With most carriers, it's two to three seconds. The above definition was kindly provided by Karen Shelton, Systems Engineer, IEX Corporation, Richardson, TX.

CALL RESTRICTOR Equipment inserted in a telephone line or trunk which restricts outgoing calls in some way. Usually from making a toll call.

CALL REQUEST PACKET In packet data switching, a call request packet carries information, such as sender and recipient identification, that is needed to establish an X.25 circuit. In more technical terms, a call request packet is sent by the originating data terminal equipment (DTE) showing requested network terminal number (NTN), network facilities and either X.29 control information or call user data.

CALL RETURN A name for a Pacific Bell (and possibly other local telephone companies') service which allows you to dial the last caller, even if you did not answer the telephone.

CALL SCREENING There are several definitions. Here are two. 1. A PBX feature that looks at the digits dialed by the caller to figure whether the call should be completed. 2. A receptionist or secretary answers the "executive's" phone and checks out that the person calling is important enough be put through to the almighty executive whose calls are being screened.

CALL SECOND A unit for measuring communications traffic. Defined as one user making one second of a phone call. One hundred call seconds are called "ccs," as in Centum call seconds. "ccs" is the U.S. standard of telephone traffic. 3600 call-seconds = 1 call hour. 3600 call-seconds per hour = 36 CCS per hour = 1 call-hour = 1 erlang = 1 traffic unit. See also ERLANG and TRAFFIC ENGINEERING.

CALL SELECTOR A local phone company service which alerts the subscriber with a distinctive ring that one of the six numbers your pre-selected is calling.

CALL SEQUENCER A call sequencer, also called an Automatic Call Sequencer, is a piece of equipment which attaches to a key system or a PBX. The Call Sequencer's main function is to direct incoming calls to the next available person to answer that phone. It typically does this by causing lights on telephones to flash at different rates. The light with the fastest flashing is the one whose call has been waiting longest. This call is answered first. Call Sequencers also might answer the phone, deliver a message and put the person on hold. They might keep statistical tabs of incoming calls, how fast they were answered, how long the people waited, how many people abandoned (hung up while they were on hold waiting for their call to be answered by a human being), etc. Call Sequencers are usually simple and inexpensive. Better, but much more expensive devices for answering incoming phone calls are Automatic Call Distributors. These are the devices which typically answer when you call an airline. See AUTOMATIC CALL DISTRIBUTOR.

CALL SETUP The first six PICs (Point In Call) of the Originating BCSM (Basic

Call State Model), or the first four PICs of the Terminating BCSM. Definition from Bellcore in reference to Advanced Intelligent Network.

CALL SETUP TIME The amount of time it takes for a circuit-switched call to be established between two people or two data devices. Call set-up includes dialing, wait time and time to move through central offices and long distance services. You don't pay for call set-up, but you will need extra lines to take care of it. See also ANSWER SUPERVISION and TRAFFIC ENGINEERING.

CALL SHEDDING In many states, laws require that a real-life breathing person be available for a phone call being outdialed with an automated device. The reason these laws were enacted is because a lot of times call-center managers have their predictive dialers going so crazy in search of human answerers that they don't have an agent ready when someone does actually pick up the phone. Most systems simply hang up the connection when this occurs. This is called "call shedding" and is illegal in many states.

CALL SPILL-OVER In common-channel signaling, the effect on a traffic circuit of the arrival at a switching center of an abnormally delayed call control signal relating to a previous call, while a subsequent call is being set up on the circuit.

CALL SPLASHING A "splash" happens when an Alternate Operator Service (AOS) company, located in a city different to the one you're calling from, connects your call to the long distance carrier of your choice in the city the AOS operator is in. Let's say you're calling from a Hotel in Chicago. You ask AT&T handle your call. The AOS, located in Atlanta, "splashes" your call over to AT&T in Atlanta. But you're calling Los Angeles. Bingo. Your AT&T call to LA is now more expensive than it would be — if you had been connected to AT&T in Chicago.

CALL SPLITTING A feature allowing a phone user to speak privately with either party of a conference call by alternating between the two. Call splitting by an attendant allows the attendant to speak to the called person privately while effectively putting the calling person on hold, or vice versa.

CALL STALKER An AT&T PC-based product which gives the 911 attendant the phone number and address of the person calling.

CALL STORE The temporary memory used in a stored program control switch (SPC) to hold records of calls in progress. These records are then transferred to permanent memory.

CALL STREAM British Telecom's premium rate service.

CALL TAG A term used in the secondary telecom equipment marketplace. A ticket directing a freight carrier (e.g., UPS) to pick up equipment at another site. The company issuing the ticket pays the freight charge. Normally used to return defective equipment, it ensures the dealer a quick return and an accurate tracking mechanism.

CALL TRACE A name for local telephone company service which permits the tracing of the last call received and holds the results for later use by an authorized law enforcement agency. (Results of the trace are not available to the customer.)

CALL TRANSFER Allows you to transfer a call from your phone to someone else's. On some phones you do this by punching in a bunch of numbers. Some you do it by hitting the "transfer" button and then the number you want to send the call to. The fewer buttons and numbers you have to punch, the easier it will be for your people.

If you're choosing a telephone system, check how easy it is to transfer a call. It is the most commonly used (and misused) feature on a phone system. How many times have you been told, "I'll transfer you to Mr. Smith, but if we get disconnected, please call back on extension 234." If your people are saying this to your customers or prospects, you are giving the outside world the wrong impression of your business. And since 97% of your prospects' contact with your company is first through your phone system, you could be losing precious business.

CALL TYPE A call center term used in Rockwell ACDs. A portion of your call center traffic corresponding to one or more ACD gates or splits. This division of the total ACD traffic is the level at which forecasting and scheduling are done. At setup time, each Call Type is defined in the ACD by a unique three-letter code and specific gate or split number(s) that identifies the corresponding ACD report data.

CALL USER DATA In packet data networking technology, user information transmitted in a call request packet to the destination data terminal equipment (DTE).

CALL WAITING Call Waiting is a feature of phone systems that lets you know someone is trying to call you. You're speaking on the phone. A call comes in for you. You might hear a beep in your ear or see a light on your phone turn on. Or you might hear a beep and see a message come across the screen of your phone. When you hear the beep, you can, if you wish, put the present call on hold and answer the new one. Or you can ignore the new one, hoping it will go away, and perhaps send it to your attendant/operator, or voice mail. Call Waiting can be done manually by your telephone system operator. Or it can be a service which you buy as a monthly from your local phone company.

A major problem with call waiting is if you're on a data call from your PC, the call waiting "beep" will often cause your modem to hang up, thus destroying your data call. There are two solutions to this, the obvious one being turn off call waiting. Some phone systems will allow you to turn it off. The less obvious one is modify your modem's initialization string. Here's how. In all Hayes and Hayes-compatible modems, there's a S10 register. It tells the modem how long before it hangs up after losing carrier. In Hayes modems, the S10 register is set for 1.4 seconds. The typical call waiting tone is 1.5 seconds. Solution, increase the S10 register to six seconds (to be sure). Use your communications software. Go into terminal mode, then type: ATS10=60. You must put this command in every time you power up, because the Hayes 1200 modem (and others) have volatile memory. But the Hayes 2400 and higher speed asynchronous modems have non-volatile memory. They remember the six seconds after they've been switched off. The command to write this to memory is ATS10=60&W. The "&W" means write it to memory.

CALLBACK 1. A feature of some voice and data telephone systems. You dial someone. Their phone or computer is busy. You hit a button or code for "callback." When their phone becomes free, the phone system will call you and them simultaneously. You can only use this call-back feature on things internally in your phone system — calling other people, calling long distance lines (which might be busy), calling the dictation pool, etc. See CALL WAITING, CALLBACK MODEM and CALLBACK QUEUING. 2. A quick way of referring to international callback, which works thus: Calling the United States from many countries abroad is far more expensive than calling those countries from the United States. A new business called International Callback has started. It works like this. You're overseas. You dial a number in the United States. You let it ring once. It won't answer. You hang up. You wait a few seconds. The number you dialed in the U.S. knows it was you calling. There is a piece of equipment on that number that "hears" it ring and knows it's you since no one else has that number. That was your special signal that you want to make a call. A switch attached to that line then calls you instantly. When you answer (overseas, obviously) it conferences you with another phone line in the United States and gives you U.S. dial tone. You can then touchtone from overseas your American number, just as if you would, were you in the U.S. There are huge savings. U.S. international callback operators can offer as much as 50% savings on calls from South America, where international calling rates are very high. The process of international callback is being automated with software and dialing devices. International callback is also helping to bring down the high cost of calling the U.S. from overseas. A company called kallback in Seattle, WA has received a service mark from the U.S. Patent and Trademark Office for the words "callback" and "kallback" and sends letters to and threatens law suits against companies who use "their" words. See CALLBACK.

CALLBACK MODEM A modem that calls you back. Here's how it works. You dial into a network. A modem answers. You put your password in. It accepts the password. It says "Please hang up. I will now call you back." You hang up. It calls you back. There are two reasons for doing this instead of allowing you to just go straight into the network. 1. It's better security. You have to be at a pre-determined place — an authorized phone number. 2. It may save on phone calls. The modem uses the company's communications network, which is probably cheaper than what the person calling in can use.

CALLBACK QUEUE The queue used to hold callers who have requested a busy pool or extension. See CALLBACK QUEUE.

CALLBACK QUEUING An option on a telephone system which allows outgoing calls to be put in line for one or several trunks. When a trunk becomes available, the phone system calls the user, his phone rings and then the phone system dials the distant party on the trunk it grabbed before calling the user. Phone systems typically have two types of queuing. The first is called Hold-On Queuing. With this, the user dials his long distance number, the phone system searches for the correct trunk, finds it's not available and tells the user with a beep or message. The user then elects to stay on the line and wait. The instant the trunk becomes free, the phone system connects the user to it. The second type of queuing is called Callback Queuing. The user hangs up and the phone system calls you back, as we explained above.

There are tradeoffs between the two types of queuing. Callback queuing obviously can tolerate longer queues. The longer you wait, the more chance you have of reaching a very low-cost trunk. But users don't like waiting so long for a trunk. And when the call does come, it may likely reach a phone, newly-deserted by a user who's gone to the bathroom.

In contrast, hold-on queuing is more efficient of the user's time, but less efficient of the user's trunks. The less time you wait, the less chance you have of reaching a low-cost trunk. Life is a trade-off. Queuing is no exception. See also QUEUING.

CALLBRIDGE Rolm to non-IBM computers open architecture interface. A method of connecting a Rolm CBX (telephone system) to a non-IBM computer, so that the computer may "talk" to the PBX and make certain things happen, e.g. moving a screen of client information around simultaneously with the phone call from the client. This feature is especially useful in customer service and customer order-entry environments — for example with direct mail order catalog companies, etc. See OPEN APPLICATION INTERFACE.

CALLDISPLAY A member of the RolmCenter family of products. It is a software product that runs on an IBM PS/2 under the SCO Xenix operating system. CallDisplay enhances the Rolm Automatic Call Distribution (ACD) current status and system summary displays. It operates in the Rolm 9751 CBX, the Rolm CBX II 9000 and the Rolm CBX II 8000 environments.

CALLED DTE A DTE which receives a call from another DTE.

CALLED LINE IDENTIFICATION FACILITY A service feature provided by a network (private or public), which enables a calling terminal to be notified by the network of the address to which the call has been connected. See CALLER ID.

CALLER ID Your phone rings. A name pops upon on your phone's screen. It's the name of the person calling you. Or it may be just the caller's phone number. It's called Caller ID and the information about name and/or calling phone number is passed to your phone by your telephone company's central switch. There are basically two forms of "caller ID" — one provided by your local phone company and one provided by your long distance company (chiefly on 800 calls). Caller ID, generic term, is a term most commonly applied to the service your local phone company provides, usually called CLASS. In CLASS, the information about who's calling and/or their phone number is passed to your phone between the first and second ring signaling an incoming call. See also CLASS and ANI.

CALLER INDEPENDENT VOICE RECOGNITION Having a voice response unit recognize the voice of a caller without having been trained on the caller's voice.

CALLED LINE IDENTIFICATION SIGNAL A sequence of characters transmitted to the calling terminal to permit identification of the called line.

CALLED PARTY SUBADDRESS Information element that is passed transparently by the SPCS (if certain conditions are met) and can be used to further identify the destination party.

CALLED PARTY CAMP-ON A communication system service feature that enables the system to complete an access attempt in spite of issuance of a user blocking signal. Systems that provide this feature monitor the busy user until the user blocking signal ends, and then proceed to complete the requested access. This feature permits holding an incoming call until the called party is free.

CALLING A procedure which consists of transmitting address signals in order to establish a link between devices that want to talk to each other.

CALLING CARD A credit card issued by Bell operating companies, AT&T, MCI, Sprint and other phone companies (local and long distance) and used for charging local and long distance calls. Typically, the number on your calling card is the phone number at which you receive bills (home or business phone) plus a four digit Personal Identification Number (PIN number). Increasingly often it's not. I prefer to carry a calling card with digits completely different to my phone number since this provides me with greater security. It's harder for someone to figure out my calling card. Some phone companies — local and long distance — charge more for a call made with a Calling Card. Some don't. Bell Canada claims they trademarked the term "Calling Card" in Canada. If they did, good luck protecting it, since the term "calling card" is generic. See BREAKAGE, DEBIT CARD and PREPAID CALLING CARD.

CALLING DTE A DTE (Data Terminal Equipment) which places a call to another DTE.

CALLING LINE ID You are called. As the call comes in, you receive the phone number of the person calling you. Calling Line ID is another term for AUTOMATIC NUMBER IDENTIFICATION. Calling Line ID is used increasingly for the phone numbers of local calls, while ANI tends to be used for the phone numbers of distant phone numbers. Essentially they're the same. See also ANI, CALLING NUMBER DISPLAY, ISDN and SIGNALING SYSTEM 7.

CALLING LINE IDENTIFICATION FACILITY A service feature, provided by a network, that enables a called terminal to be notified by the network of the address from which the call has originated. See CALLING LINE ID.

CALLING NUMBER DISPLAY Your phone has a LCD (Liquid Crystal Display) or LED (Light Emitting Diode) display. When your phone rings, it will show which telephone number (internal or external) is calling you. Some phone systems allow you to add the person's name to the calling number display. See also ANI and CALLER ID.

CALLING PARTY The person who makes (originates) the phone call.

CALLING PARTY CAMP-ON A feature that enables the system to complete an access attempt in spite of temporary unavailability of transmission or switching facilities. Systems that provide this feature monitor the system facilities until the necessary facilities become available, and then proceed to complete the requested access. Such systems may or may not issue a system blocking signal to let the caller know of the access delay.

CALLING PARTY IDENTIFICATION A telephone company service which tells the person being called the number and sometimes the name of the person calling them. They can then decide to answer or not answer it. See ANI, which stands for Automatic Number Identification.

CALLING PARTY NUMBER Information element that identifies the number of the originating party. An AIN term.

CALLING PARTY SUBDIVIDERS Information element that is passed transparently by the SPCS (if certain conditions are met) and can be used to further identify the originating party. An AIN term.

CALLING SEQUENCE A sequence of instructions together with any associated data necessary to perform a call.

CALLING TONE See CNG.

CALLPATH IBM's announced telephone system link to IBM's computers. See CALLPATH SERVICES ARCHITECTURE, CALLPATH CICS, and CALLPATH HOST.

CALLPATH CICS Enabling software that connects your telephone systems with your IBM 370 or 390 (i.e. the mainframe version of CallPath/400, which works on the AS/400 platform).

CALLPATH CALLCOORDINATOR CallCoordinator is IBM's integrated call management application that uses CallPath Services APIs to integrate data processing applications with telephone systems. IBM has versions of CallCoordinator for MVS CICS, OS/2 and Windows workstations. CallCoordinator provides features such as Intelligent Answering (based on ANI, DNIS, or Calling Line ID), Coordinated Voice and Data Transfer, Consultation (both voice and data), Conferencing (both voice and data), Transfer Load balancing between a single or multiple telephone systems, Outbound dialing, Event logging for Management Information Reporting, Personal Dialing Directory (Windows Only), Personal telephony facilities (answer phone, disconnect, transfer, etc.), Integration with CallPath DirectTalk/2 and CallPath DirectTalk/6000, Customizable Application Programming Interfaces. CallCoordinator integrates with existing 3270 or 5250 applications, and on the workstation versions, has the ability to communicate with existing applications via Dynamic Data Exchange or standard LAN communications protocols (such as TCP/IP). See CALLPATH SERVICES ARCHITECTURE.

CALLPATH SERVICES ARCHITECTURE CSA is IBM's architecture that defines the protocols for communication between computers and telephone switches. CallPath Services Architecture, announced in 1991, provides an Application Programming Interface (API) that enables a call management application to interact with telephone systems, with little regard to the protocols or communications interface provided by the telephone system. The idea is that with CallPath a call will arrive at a computer terminal simultaneously with the database record of the caller. And such call and database record can be transferred simultaneously to an expert, a supervisor, etc. CallPath has especial value in telephone call centers. As of writing, IBM provided connectivity to PBXs (AT&T Definity Generic 3, Northern Telecom Meridian 1, ROLM 9751, Siemens Hicom, NEC), central office switches (AT&T 5ESS and Northern Telecom DMS-100), and has agreements with other PBX manufactures that provide CallPath connectivity for Aspect, Ericsson, SDX, Telenorma, and Cortelco. IBM's CallPath products provide support for locally attached applications and client/server applications. IBM has CallPath APIs available for mainframes, minicomputers and workstations, in particular IBM System 390 and ES9000, AS/400, RISC System/6000, OS/2 workstations, Windows workstations, Sun Solaris, HP UX, and SCO UNIX workstations. See OPEN APPLICATION INTERFACE and DIRECTTALK.

CALLPOWER A Rockwell ACD term. An integrated voice and data workstation for use in combining ACD capabilities with host computer database management.

CALLWARE CallWare is a company in Salt Lake City, UT, which makes computer telephony software that runs on the Novell NetWare operating system. CallWare software includes voice mail, autoattendant, IVR database lookup, etc.

CAM 1. Call Applications Manager. The name of the Tandem software interface which provides the link between a call center switch telephone switch (either a PBX or an ACD) and all Tandem NonStop (fault tolerant) computers. CAM supports most major PBXs and automatic call distributors. 2. Computer-Aided Manufacture. The actual production of goods implemented and controlled by computers and robots. Often used in conjunction with CAD. Only a few factories are completely automated. Usually, there is some human intervention in the actual construction of the product, often to make sure a part is placed in the robot correctly. 3. Controlled Attachment Module. Intelligent Token-Ring hub.

CAMA Centralized Automatic Message Accounting. See CAMA/LAMA.

CAMA/LAMA Centralized Automatic Message Accounting/Local Automatic Message Accounting. Specific versions of AMA in which the ticketing of toll calls is done automatically at a central location for several COs (CAMA) or only at the local office for that office's subscribers.

CAMCORDER A camera and a video recording system packaged as a whole.

CAMEO Macintosh-based personal videoconferencing system, announced by Compression Labs in January of 1992. Developed jointly with AT&T and designed to work over ISDN lines and, most recently, Ethernet LANs. The Cameo transmits 15 fps of video and needs an external handset for audio.

CAMP-ON You're calling a telephone an extension or you want to transfer a call to a phone but it's busy. This telephone system feature will allow you to lock the call you're trying to transfer onto the line that's busy. When it becomes free, the phone will ring and the "camped-on" call will be connected automatically.

CAMPUS BACKBONE Wiring between buildings.

CAMPUS ENVIRONMENT An environment in which users — voice, video and data — are spread out over a broad geographic area, as in a university, hospital, medical center, prison. There may be several telephone systems. There may be several LANs on a campus. They will be connected with bridges and/or routers communicating over telephone, microwave or fiber optic cable.

CAMPUS SUBSYSTEM The part of a premises distribution system which connects buildings together. The cable, interbuilding distribution facilities, protectors, and connectors that enable communication among multiple buildings on a premises.

CANCEL By touching the "cancel" button on a phone system you're telling the phone system to ignore the last command you gave it. That command might have been transfer, hold, park, etc. The "cancel" button is often mistakenly confused with the "release" button. The "release" button acts the same as hitting "Enter" on a computer system, i.e. it tells the system to go ahead and do what you just told it to do, no matter how stupid your command. In short, "Cancel" means kill the last command. You use when you make a mistake. "Release" means "Enter" — Do it and do it now.

CANCEL CALL WAITING On a touchtone phone in North America, you typically can cancel the feature, Call Waiting, by touchtoning *70.

CANNIBALIZE To devour a phone system by stripping parts from it to repair another system. A common technique for maintaining equipment whose original manufacturer no longer supplies parts. Before you cannibalize, check out the monthly publication Telecom Gear. That publication lists sources of secondary telecom equipment. Good stuff, too.

CAP 1. Competitive Access Provider. An alternative, competitive local exchange carrier such as MCI Metro and MHS. 2. Customer Administration Panel. A simplified alternative to CAC, which is a Customer Administration Center. These are

AT&T words. 3. Computer Aided Professional Publishing. The computerization of professional publishing (as opposed to desktop operations), including true color representation of the layout on the workstation screen. 4. Cellular Array Processor.

CAPS Competitive Access Providers.

CAP'N CRUNCH see CAPTAIN CRUNCH.

CAPACITANCE The capacity of a medium (wire, cable, resistor, bus) to store an electrical charge. Capacitance is measured in farads.

CAPACITIVE COUPLING The transfer of energy from one circuit to another by virtue of the mutual capacitance between the circuits. The coupling may be deliberate or inadvertent. Capacitive coupling favors transfer of higher frequency components, whereas inductive coupling favors transfer of lower frequency components.

CAPACITY 1. The information carrying ability of a telecommunications facility. What the "facility" is determines the measurement. You might measure a date line's capacity in bits per second. You might measure a switch's capacity in the maximum number of calls it can switch in one hour, or the maximum number of calls it can keep in conversation simultaneously. You might measure a coaxial cable's capacity in bandwidth. 2. The measure of the amount of electrical energy a condenser can store up. The unit of capacity is the farad.

CAPACITY TRANSFER CONTROL A Northern Telecom term for a feature which permits single allocation of capacity to be shared among members in a digital switched broadcast connection. For teleconferencing, for instance, a conference leader can transfer transmission capacity among the digital ports in the circuits. 95% of such transfers will take place within 10 seconds.

CAPCODE A capcode is a four or seven digit number on either side or rear of the casing of a pager, the type you wear on your belt. This number is a paging system necessity to know how to generate the right sequence of tones to alert the pager.

CAPS 1. Code Abuse Prevention System. 2. Competitive Access Providers to the local telephone network i.e., Teleport or Metropolitan Fiber System.

CAPSIZING When downsizing, rightsizing and upsizing fail. Contributed by Fred Schindler of IBM.

CAPSTAN 1. A flangeless pulley used to control speed and motion of magnetic tape through a recorder or playback unit. 2. A rotating drum or cylinder used for pulling cables by exerting traction upon a rope or pull line passing around the drum.

CAPTAIN Character And Pattern Telephone Access Information Network System. A form of videotext developed in Japan and operated through the public switched telephone network. Displays are on a TV set. It's interactive.

CAPTAIN CRUNCH At one point in the 1960s, a breakfast cereal had a promotion. It was a toy whistle. When you blew the whistle, it let out a precise 2,600 Hz tone. If you blew that whistle into the mouthpiece of a telephone after dialing any long distance number, it terminated the call as far as the AT&T long distance phone system knew, while still allowing the connection to remain open. If you dialed an 800 number, blew the whistle and then touchtoned in a series of tones (called MF tones) you could make long distance and international calls for free. The man who discovered the whistle was called John Draper and he picked up the handle of Cap'n Crunch in the nether world of the late 1960s phone phreaks. A marvelous account of the exploits of phone phreaks was published in the October 1971 issue of Esquire Magazine. That article described how the Cap'n would call himself (he needed two lines) — choosing to route the connection through Tokyo, India, Greece, South Africa, South America, London, New York and California — to make his second phone next to him ring. He'd have a wonderful time talking to himself, albeit with a round-the-world delay (despite the speed of light) of as long as 20 seconds. Later, AT&T closed the loophole Cap'n Crunch had discovered. AT&T turned from in-band signaling to out-of-band signaling. Cap'n Crunch's legacy (he got put in jail four times during the 1970s) is System Signaling 7, a system of immense benefit to us all. See 2600 TONE, MULTI-FREQUENCY SIGNALING and SIGNALING SYSTEM 7.

CAPTIVE EFFECT An effect associated with the reception of frequency-modulated signals in which, if two signals are received on or near the same frequency, only the stronger of the two will appear in the output. The complete suppression of the weaker carrier occurs at the receiver limiter, where it is treated as noise and rejected. Under conditions where both signals are fading randomly, the receiver may switch from one to the other.

CAPTURE EFFECT An effect associated with the reception of frequency-modulated signals in which, if two signals are received on or near the same frequency, only the stronger of the two will appear in the output. The complete suppression of the weaker carrier occurs at the receiver limiter, where it is treated as noise and rejected. Under conditions where both signals are fading randomly, the receiver may switch from one to the other.

CAPTURE RATIO The ability of a tuner or receiver to select the stronger of two signals at or near the same frequency. Expressed in decibels, the lower the figure, the better.

CAR PHONE The type of cellular phone that's installed in a vehicle. There are four types of cellular phones being sold today — mobile, transportable, portable and handheld. A car phone (also called a mobile unit) is attached to the vehicle, its power comes from the vehicle's alternator (or battery if the car if not running) and the car phone has an external antenna, which works best if it's mounted in the middle of the highest point of the car and wired directly with no breaks in the wire. Many window-mounted antennas have a break in their wiring. The wiring ends at the inside. There is no electrical connection between the inside of the window and the antenna glued onto the outside of the window. The "connection" is done through signal radiation. In North America, the car phone transmits with a standard three watts of power.

CARBON BLOCK A device for protecting cable from lightning strikes. The carbon block consists of two electrodes spaced so that any voltage above the design level is arced from line to ground. Carbon block protectors are used commonly in both local customer offices and central offices. They are effective, but can be destroyed if high voltage is directly applied — as in a direct strike by lightning. A more expensive, but more effective method of protection is the gas tube. These are glass capsules that are connected between the circuit and the ground. When a voltage higher than the design voltage strikes the line, the gas ionizes and conducts the excess voltage to ground. When the voltage is gone, the protector restores itself to normal. Gas tubes, however, take a tiny time to ionize. This may not be fast enough for very sensitive things, like PBX circuit cards. So gas tube protectors are often equipped with diodes, which clamp the interfering voltage to a safe level until the gas tube ionizes.

CARBON FIBER A strong synthetic material that is low in mass with excellent damping characteristics, used in the manufacture of tonearms.

CARBON RHEOSTAT A rheostat using carbon as the resistance material. See RHEOSTAT.

CARBON TRANSMITTER The microphone of an telephone set from yesteryear which uses carbon granules and a diaphragm. The diaphragm responds to our voice and varies the pressure on the granules and hence, their resistance. If your carbon mike isn't working well, the humidity has got to it, tap it lightly on your desk. The carbon granules will line up and it will work much better. Carbon microphones are very reliable but are being increasingly replaced with more sensitive electret microphones.

CARD AUTHORIZATION CENTER CAC. A computer directly linked to MCI switches for authorization and determination of billing center ID for MCI card calls.

CARD CAGE A frame in a telephone system or computer for mounting circuit cards, power supply, backplane and other equipment.

CARD DIALER A device attached to a telephone which accepts a special plastic card and then automatically dials the number on the card as indicated by the holes punched in it. A card dialer is now obsolete except for unusual applications, like systems whereby you carry your card with you and use it as a security device.

CARD SERVICES The software layer above Socket Services that coordinates access to PCMCIA cards, sockets and system resources. Card Services is a software management interface that allows the allocation of system resources (such as memory and interrupts) automatically once the Socket Services detects that a PC Card has been inserted. This is called "hot swapping." The idea is that you can slide PCMCIA cards in and out of PC at will and your Socket and Card services will recognize them and respond accordingly. It's a great theory. In practice, it doesn't work because certain cards, like network cards, simply can't be connected and disconnected at will. Socket Services is a BIOS level software interface that provides a method for accessing the PCMCIA slots of a computer. Card Services is a software management interface that allows the allocation of system resources (such as memory and interrupts) automatically once the Socket Services detects that a PC Card has been inserted. Both of these specifications are contained in the PCMCIA Standards document. You do not need either Socket or Card Services to successfully use PCMCIA cards in your desktop or laptop. You simply need the correct device drivers and the proper memory exclusions. See PCMCIA, SOCKET SERVICES and SLOT SIZES.

CARD SLOT A place inside a phone system or computer into which you slide a printed circuit board. See BOARD.

CARDBUS The new name for the computer bus into which you slide PCMCIA cards. These cards are increasingly known as CardBus. The new CardBus, which will combine the PCI bus, will have a 32-bit interface and suport 132 Mbps. See PCMCIA.

CARET The symbol ^ which is found above 6 on most keyboards. Also used to indicate the "Ctrl" key in some instruction manuals.

CAROT Centralized Automatic Reporting On Trunks. A test and maintenance facility associated primarily with electronic toll switching systems like the AT&T Communication's #4-ESS. CAROT is a computerized system that automatically accesses and tests trunks for a maximum of fourteen offices simultaneously. It enables rapid routine testing of all trunks to ensure quick identification of faults and potential failures.

CARPEL TUNNEL SYNDROME Carpel tunnel syndrome is a serious disorder of the arm caused by fast, repetitive work, such as typing without support for your wrists or with insufficient time for rest. In carpel tunnel syndrome, the tendons passing through the wrist bones swell and press on the median nerve. Surgery to take pressure off the nerve can relieve numbness and pain, but it's not always effective and many victims remain permanently disabled.

CARRIAGE RETURN By hitting this key, the printing head or the cursor on your screen will return to the left hand margin. Usually hitting a Carriage Return or the "Enter" key includes a line feed, i.e. the paper will move up one line or the cursor will drop down one line. "Usually" does not mean always. So check. You can usually correct the problem of not having a line feed with a carriage return by moving a dip switch on the printer, changing one of the parameters of the telecommunications software program (the part where it says something about auto linefeed) or changing the computer's operating system (by doing a "Config" or the like). In most microcomputers, a Carriage Return is equivalent to a "Control M," or ASCII 13. A line feed is a "Control J".

CARRIER 1. A company which provides communications circuits. Carriers are split into "private" and "common." A private carrier can refuse you service. A "common" carrier can't. Most of the carriers in our industry — your local phone company, AT&T, MCI, US Sprint, etc. — are common carriers. Common carriers are regulated. Private carriers are not. 2. An electrical signal at a continuous frequency capable of being modified to carry information. It is the modifications or the changes from the carrier's basic frequency that become the information carried. Modifications are made via amplitude, frequency or phase. The process of modifying a carrier signal is called modulation. A carrier is modulated and demodulated (the signal extracted at the other end) according to fixed protocols. Some of the wideband (i.e. multi-frequency) circuits are also called "carriers." T1, which typically has 24-channel PCM voice circuits, is known as a carrier system.

CARRIER BAND The range of frequencies that can be modulated to carry information on a specific transmission system.

CARRIER BYPASS A long distance phone company provides a direct link between its own switching office and a customer's office, thus bypassing the local phone company. Bypass is done to save the customer or the long distance company money. Bypass is also done to get service faster. Sometimes the local phone company simply can't deliver fast enough.

CARRIER COMMON LINE CHARGE Also called Access Charge. The charge which long distance phone companies pay to local phone companies to complete their long distance calls. These charges typically are much more than the local phone company gets from its normal business and residential users for completing local phone calls of the same distance. High access charges are designed to help the local phone company financially. That they do. They also encourage bypass and may, in the long term, be self-defeating.

CARRIER DETECT CIRCUITRY Electronic components which detect the presence of a carrier signal and thus determine if a transmission is about to happen. Used in modems.

CARRIER FREQUENCY The frequency of a carrier wave. The frequency of an unmodulated wave capable of being modulated or impressed with a second (information-carrying) signal. In frequency modulation, the carrier frequency is also referred to as the "center frequency."

CARRIER IDENTIFICATION CODES CIC. Three digit numbers used by end-user customers to reach the services of interexchange carriers through equal access arrangements. The primary carrier of choice is reached by dialing "1" plus the area code and called party number. Secondary IX carriers can still be reached by dialing 10 plus the CIC assigned to the carrier desired. CIC numbers are used to dial around the carrier presubscribed to the calling telephone (e.g. 10-XXX or 950-0XXX where XXX is the CIC).

CARRIER LEAK The unwanted carrier remaining after carrier suppression in a suppressed carrier transmission system.

CARRIER LIAISON COMMITTEE CLC. A committee formed to help industry participants work together to resolve the issues of implementing 800 Portability. CLC is sponsored by the Exchange Carriers Standards Association (ECSA) and is comprised of the LECs (local exchange carriers), long distance carriers and users of 800 service.

CARRIER LOSS In T-1, carrier loss means too many zeros. A carrier loss in T-1 is said to occur when 32 consecutive zeros appear on the network. Carrier is said to return when the next 1 is detected.

CARRIER NOISE LEVEL The noise level resulting from undesired variations of a carrier in the absence of any intended modulation.

CARRIER POWER (OF A RADIO TRANSMITTER) The average power supplied to the antenna transmission line by a transmitter during one radio frequency cycle taken under the condition of no modulation. Does not apply to pulse modulation or frequency-shift keying.

CARRIER PROVIDED LOOP MCI is responsible for ordering coordinating, maintaining, and billing the local loop.

CARRIER SELECT KEYS Buttons at the bottom of a payphone used to choose a long distance carrier.

CARRIER SELECTION As a result of Judge Greene's Modified Final Judgment which lead to the breakup of the Bell System, most local phone companies must offer their customers (business and home) the opportunity to select which long distance company they would like to be use on a "primary" basis. That means when you dial 1+ (one plus) you get that carrier. To use any other long distance company you have to dial more digits, e.g. 1-0288 (for AT&T). See NANP.

CARRIER SENSE In a local area network, a PC or workstation uses its network card to detect if another station is transmitting. See CSMA.

CARRIER SENSE MULTIPLE ACCESS CSMA. In local area networking, CSMA is a way of getting onto the LAN. Before starting to transmit, personal computers on the LAN "listen" to make sure no other PC is transmitting. Once the PC figures out that no other PC is transmitting, it sends a packet and then frees the line for other PCs to transmit. With CSMA, though stations do not transmit until the medium is clear, collisions still occur. Two alternative versions (CSMA/CA and CSMA/CD) attempt to reduce both the number of collisions and the severity of their impact. See CSMA/CA and CSMA/CD.

CARRIER SENSE MULTIPLE ACCESS WITH COLLISION AVOIDANCE CSMA/CA. A protocol that requires the PC to sense if another PC is transmitting. If not, it begins transmitting. Under CSMA/CA, a data station that intends to transmit sends a jam signal; after waiting a sufficient time for all stations to pick up the jam signal, it sends a transmission frame; if while transmitting, it detects another station's jam signal, it stops transmitting for a designated time and then tries again.

CARRIER SENSE MULTIPLE ACCESS/COLLISION DETECTION A network control scheme. It is a contention access control scheme. It "listens" for conflicting traffic to avoid data collisions. The Ethernet LAN uses CSMA/CD, then waits a small amount of time and then tries again. See CSMA/CD and ETHERNET.

CARRIER SHIFT 1. A method of keying a radio carrier for transmitting binary data or teletypewriter signals, which consists of shifting the carrier frequency in one direction for a marking signal and in the opposite direction for a spacing signal. 2. In amplitude modulation, a condition resulting from imperfect modulation whereby the positive and negative excursions of the envelope pattern are unequal, thus effecting a change in the power associated with the carrier. There can be positive or negative carrier shift.

CARRIER SIGNAL A continuous waveform (usually electrical) whose properties are capable of being modulated or impressed with a second information-carrying signal. The carrier itself conveys no information until altered in some fashion, such as having its amplitude changed (amplitude modulation), its frequency changed (frequency modulation) or its phase changed (phase modulation). These changes convey the information.

CARRIER SYNCHRONIZATION In a radio receiver, the generation of a reference carrier with a phase closely matching that of a received signal.

CARRIER SYSTEM A system where several different signals can be combined onto one carrier by changing some feature of the signals transmitting them (modulation) and then converting the signals back to their original form (demodulation). Many information channels can be carried by one broadband carrier system. Common types of carrier systems are frequency division, in which each information channel occupies an assigned portion of the frequency spectrum; and time division, in which each information channel uses the transmission medium for periodic assigned time intervals.

CARRIER TERMINAL The modulation, demodulation and multiplex equipment used to combine and separate individual channels at the ends of a transmission system.

CARRIER TO NOISE RATIO CNR. In radio receivers, the ratio, expressed in decibels, of the level of the carrier to that of the noise in the receiver bandwidth before any nonlinear process such as amplitude limiting and detection takes place.

CARRIER WAVE The radio frequency wave generated at a transmitting station for the purpose of carrying the modulated or audio frequency wave.

CARRIED LOAD The traffic that occupies a group of servers on a LAN.

CARRIED TRAFFIC The part of the traffic offered to a group of servers that successfully seizes a server on a LAN.

CARS Cable Television Relay Service Station. A fixed or mobile station used for the transmission of television and related audio signals, signals of standard and FM broadcast stations, signals of instructional television fixed stations, and cablecasting from the point of reception to a terminal point from which the signals are distributed to the public.

CARTERFONE A device for connecting a two-way mobile radio system to the telephone network invented by Thomas Carter. It was electrically connected to the base station of the mobile radio system. Its electrical parts were encased in bakelite. When someone on the radio wanted to speak on a "landline" (the phone system), the base station operator would dial the number on a separate phone then place the telephone handset on the Carterfone device. The handset was acoustically, not electrically, connected to the phone system. No more than 4,000 Carterfones were ever installed, yet the Bell System thought they were the most dangerous device ever invented. Tom Carter died in Gun Barrel, TX where he lived, in the early part of 1991. He died not a rich man. See CARTERFONE DECISION.

CARTERFONE DECISION In the summer of 1968 the FCC said that the Carterfone and other customer phone devices could be connected to the nation's phone network — if they were "privately beneficial, but not publicly harmful." The Carterfone decision was a landmark. It allowed the connection of non-telephone company equipment to the public telephone network. This decision marked the beginning of the telephone interconnect business as we know it today. The Carterfone decision made a lot of lawyers rich before all the rules on connection to the network got cleared up, and finally codified in something called Part 68 of the FCC's Rules. See CARTERFONE, NATA and NETWORK HARM.

CARTRIDGE 1. A device which holds magnetic tape of some kind. 2. A device to translate (transduce) stylus motion to electrical energy in a phonograph. It comes in three basic types — moving magnetic coil, induced magnet and ceramic. A phono cartridge is also call a pickup. Most record players use ceramic cartridges because they have higher output than the three magnetic types and can work with a less powerful (i.e. cheaper) amplifier.

CAS 1. Centralized Attendant Service. One group of switchboard operators answers all the incoming calls for several telephone systems located throughout one city. CAS is used by customers with several locations in the same geographic area, i.e. retail stores, banks. 2. Communicating Applications Specification. A high-level API (Application Programming Interface) developed by Intel and DCA that was introduced in 1988 to define a standard software API for fax modems. CAS enables software developers to integrate fax capability and other communication functions into their applications.

CASCADE 1. To connect the output of a device into the input of another device, which then may in turn be connected to another device. Image the organization of a company. At the top is the president. Reporting to him are three vice presidents. Reporting to each of these vice presidents are five directors. Reporting to each of these directors are five managers. If each of these positions were a piece of network gear, you'd have a classic cascaded topology. 2. A Windows term. When windows cascade, they are arranged in an overlapping pattern so that the title bar of each window remains visible.

CASCADE AMPLIFICATION The method of successively using two or more vacuum tubes for amplification at radio, intermediate or audio frequencies.

CASCADED STARS Local area network topology in which a centralized multiport repeater serves as the focal point for many other multiport repeaters.

CASCADED TOPOLOGY See CASCADE.

CASCADING FAULTS Faults that cause other faults. Typically faults in a network causing other faults.

CASCADING MENU A Windows term. A menu that is a submenu of a menu item. Also known as a hierarchical menu.

CASCADING NOTIFICATION A feature of some sophisticated voice mail systems. Let's say someone leaves a message for you in your voice mail box. Your voice mail system then automatically goes out to find you, i.e. to notify you. It may start by lighting your message light, calling your home phone number, calling your cellular phone, calling your beeper, etc. I like this feature because when I want you, I want you. And a little mechanized help is much appreciated. I first saw the feature in Macrotel's MVX voice mail series.

CASE Computer Aided Software Engineering. CASE is a new, faster, more efficient way of writing software for some applications. The idea with CASE is to sketch out relations between databases, events, and options and then have the computer write the code.

CASE METHOD A traditional way of load testing computer telephony systems, the case method involves gathering many individuals together in a room full of telephones along with several cases of an appropriate libation (frequently beer), and using these individuals to simulate real users calling into (or being called by) the computer telephony system. Case method testing usually continues until all the cases have been consumed, the testing is completed, it becomes too late in the evening to continue, or the perspective of the gathered individuals becomes too subjective to be of use any longer to those conducting the test. This definition courtesy of Steve Gladstone, author of the book Testing Computer Telephony Systems, available from 212-691-8215.

CASE SENSITIVE This means that uppercase letters must be typed in uppercase on your keyboard, and that lowercase letters must be typed in lowercase. It is important to key in your data in the exact combination of upper or lower case characters. Inputting in the wrong case could make your entry invalid for some fields (for example, password). DOS and Windows are much less case sensitive than Unix, for example.

CASE TOOLS These tools provide automated methods for designing and documenting software programming. Computer-aided software engineering (CASE) sketches relations between databases, events, and options. It then provides a language in which the computer writes the code, letting programmers develop applications faster. It's new and seems to work in limited instances.

CASSEGRAIN ANTENNA An antenna in which the feed radiator is mounted at or near the surface of a concave main reflector and is aimed at a convex secondary reflector slightly inside the focus of the main reflector. Energy from the feed unit illuminates the secondary, reflects it back to the main reflector, which then forms the desired forward beam. This technique is adapted from optical telescope technology and allows the feed monitor radiator to be more easily supported.

CASSETTE TAPE A slow, inefficient method of storing and retrieving data which uses the same technology as audio cassettes — like the Sony Walkman. Some PBXs use cassette tape to backup their user programming and database.

CASTELLATION A series of ribs and metallized indentations that defines edge contact regions.

CAT 1. An AT&T Merlin term. Call Accounting Terminal. A stand-alone unit with a built-in microprocessor and data buffer that provides simple call accounting at a relatively low cost. 2. Shortened way of saying "Category," as in Cat 1 cabling. See CATEGORY OF PERFORMANCE.

CATEGORY 1 See CATEGORY OF PERFORMANCE.

CATEGORY 2 There's no such thing as Category 2. See CATEGORY OF PERFORMANCE for a fuller explanation.

CATEGORY 3 Cabling and cabling components designed and tested to transmit cleanly 16 megahertz of communications. Used for voice and data/LAN traffic to 10 megabits per second. Category 3 technical specifications are defined by FCC Part 68, ANSI/EIA/TIA-568, TIA TSB-36 and TIA TSB-40. Category 3 safety requirements are defined by UL 1459 (Telephone), UL 1863 (Wire and Jacks) and NEC 1993, Article 800-4. See CATEGORY OF PERFORMANCE for a fuller explanation.

CATEGORY 4 Cabling and cabling components designed and tested to transmit cleanly 20 megahertz of communications. Few people today buy Category 4 cabling and cabling components. Category 4 technical specifications are defined by FCC Part 68, EIA/TIA-568, TIA TSB-36, and TIA TSB-40. Category 4 safety requirements are defined by UL 1459 (Telephone), UL 1863 (Wire and Jacks) and NEC 1993, Article 800-4. See CATEGORY OF PERFORMANCE for a fuller explanation.

CATEGORY 5 Cabling and cabling components designed and tested to transmit cleanly 100 megahertz of communications. Used for voice and data/LAN traffic to 100 megahertz. Category 5 technical specifications are defined by FCC Part 68, EIA/TIA-568, TIA TSB-36, and TIA TSB-40. Category 4 safety requirements are defined by UL 1459 (Telephone), UL 1863 (Wire and Jacks) and NEC 1993, Article 800-4. See CATEGORY OF PERFORMANCE for a fuller explanation.

CATEGORY OF PERFORMANCE As we try and push more and data faster and faster down a pair or two of wires, so the quality of the wires and the components they connect to has become increasingly important. You can't shove 100 million bit per second down junky phone lines. As a result, the telecommunications industry has defines cabling and cabling component standards. The idea is that if your stuff conforms to the standard, users will be able to achieve the data rates and reliability they want. Some standards specify physical characteristics, such as thickness of cable, plastic material used in the outer jacket, etc. These "Category of Performance" standards, which the telecommunications industry has adopted, in the main do not specify materials. They specify tests which the cabling and cabling components must pass. There were originally five categories of tests. But now there are effectively only two categories that anyone buys — Category 3 and Category 5. In simple terms, if you want voice and data to 10 megabits per second, i.e. standard Ethernet, then buy Category 3. If you are looking to the future when you may be transmitting 100 million bits per second on your local area network, then you should buy Category 5. Today the difference in price is about 20% to 30%. In other words, Cat 5 is 20% to 30% more expensive than Cat 3. In my unhumble opinion, all LAN cable going in today should be Cat 5, while all voice cable going in should be Cat 3, which will happily support ISDN BRI, when that happens in the not too distant future.

Let's talk about how they measure Cat 3 and Cat 5. First, you should understand that all the tests are self-certifying, which means that while there are standards, each manufacturer is himself responsible for conforming. No one will put a manufacturer in jail if his Cat 5 stuff doesn't perform to Cat 5 standards. The only thing likely to happen to the manufacturer is that the world will find out his stuff is garbage and he'll go broke.

The concept of the test is simple. The test for cable and components is a swept frequency test. Cat 3 must pass all signals from one through 16 megahertz. (Note megahertz, not megabits). In Cat 5, it must pass signals from one through 100 megahertz. Cat 3 and Cat 5 cables and components are designed to support any applications intended to operate over those frequencies. That includes all forms of modulation of any carrier waves within those frequencies and all forms of digital pulses. Handling digital pulses is more difficult since digital pulsing typically uses a much broader range of frequencies (than simply modulating one or two carrier waves as in AM or FM modulation). Digital pulsing needs a broader range of frequencies in order to get its edges more square. Interestingly, both Cat 3 and Cat 5 cabling are the same thickness, namely 24 gauge. The twist structure on Cat 5 is tighter. Insulation is better. Connecting hardware is definitely different. Below is Harry's quick rule of thumb for what you should buy based on what you want to transmit, as against the swept frequency test:

Category	Data Rate Supported
1,2	Voice (Obsoleted in early 1995)
3	10 Mbps
4	20 Mbps
5	100 - 155 Mbps

150 ohm STP-A Full bandwith video

If you make the following Mistakes, your nice new Cat 5 cables probably won't work at 100 Mbps.

● Use Staples - NEVER!

● Use Tie Wraps - other than VERY loosely to hold a bundle in place. Velcro is a better idea.

● Untwist the wire before you punch it down on the block or terminate it on a jack - the twists should be right up to the termination!

● Strip more jacket off the wire than is needed to terminate it.

● Pull too hard on the cable - especially around a corner.

● Pull on a cable to straighten out a kink or loop. Always go back and untwist it!

● Stuff too many cables in too small a conduit.

See COMMERCIAL BUILDING TELECOMMUNICATIONS WIRING STANDARD.

CATENET A network in which hosts are connected to networks are interconnected by gateways (routers). The Internet is an example of a catenet.

CATHODE The heated element which emits electrons in a vacuum tube. It may be a filament, or may be a separate element, heated by proximity to a filament. It is maintained at a negative potential in respect to the anode or plate. Cathodes have other applications, also.

CATHODE RAY The beam of electrons emitted by a cathode. See CATHODE RAY TUBE.

CATHODE RAY TUBE CRT. A TV screen. A CRT is a tube of glass, used in television, oscilloscope and computer terminals, from which air has been removed (i.e. vacuum tube). At the back of the CRT is an electron gun which directs an electron beam to the front of the tube. The inside front of the tube has been coated with fluorescent material which reacts to and lights up once the electron beams hit. CRTs are very reliable if they are vented, since the electron gun gets hot. CRTs have a "memory." They will memorize what's been left on their screen for a while, i.e. the image is burned into the screen. And you'll see it even though the screen is turned off. In short, turn your screen off when you're not using it. Or run a "CRT-saving" program which varies the image on the screen.

CATI Computer Assisted Telephone Interviewing, a market research term for a call center based on the use of a computerized database.

CATLAS AT&T software standing for Centralized Automatic Trouble Locating and Analysis System. CATLAS is used as a maintenance tool for locating and diagnosing problems in AT&T electronic central offices.

CATS Consortium for Audiographics Teleconferencing Standards, San Ramon, CA. 510-831-4760. CATS describes itself as a non-profit corporation dedicated to promoting standards for this technology, which it describes as enhancing audioconferencing by allowing people at different sites to work together in real time to create, manipulate, edit, annotate and reference still images. Now called IMTC.

CATV Community Antenna TeleVision or CAble TeleVision. CATV is a broadband transmission facility. It generally uses a 75-ohm coaxial cable which simultaneously carries many frequency-divided TV channels. Each channel is separated by guard channels. See ADDRESSABLE PROGRAMMING and BROADBAND.

CAU 1. Northern Telecom term for Connection Arrangement Unit. 2. Controlled Access Unit. Intelligent Token-Ring hub.

CAVITY A volume defined by conductor-dielectric or dielectric-dielectric reflective boundaries, or a combination of both, and having dimensions designed to produce specific interference effects (constructive or destructive) when excited by an electromagnetic wave.

CB Why 10-4, good buddy, that stands for Citizens Band. Also known as Children's Band, not because of Radio Shack's toy walkie talkies, but for the inane chatter that sometimes goes on in these channels. In short, CB is low-power (up to four WATTS permitted) public radio. You do not need permission from the FCC to transmit or receive at these frequencies. Thus CB's great popularity. CB went through a boom (perhaps a craze?), then it ran out of radio frequencies and public enthusiasm. Its original frequencies were 26.965 to 27.225 Mhz. Now the FCC's given it new frequencies — 462.55 to 469.95 MHz. These new frequencies are much better, clearer and less congested. If you buy a CB set, make sure you get one that operates in these higher frequencies. In some countries they use different frequencies. CB radio is not allowed in many countries, even some civilized countries, though it will obviously work there.

CBDS Connectionless Broadband Data Service. The European version of SMDS. A draft standard written by ETSI as a recommendation to ITU-T.

CBEMA Computer Business Equipment Manufacturers Association. A lobbying group created to protect the interests of its members.

CBF Computer Based Fax.

CBK Change BacK.

CBR Constant Bit Rate. It refers to processes such as voice that require a constant, repetitive or uniform transfer of information.

CBTA Canadian Business telecommunications Alliance. The largest organization of business telecom users in Canada.

CBX Computerized Branch eXchange. CBX is a registered trademark of the ROLM Corporation, Santa Clara, CA. Rolm is now owned by Siemens and IBM, but largely by Siemens. What CBX is to Rolm, PBX or PABX is to other companies. The term CBX has not received wide acceptance, except at Rolm.

CBX II A Rolm communications controller for larger systems. Two versions exist: the CBX II 8000 (16-bit CPU) and the CBX II 9000 (32-bit CPU).

CC 1. Call Control. A wireless telecommunications term. A term used to refer to circuit communications management. 2. Country Code. The portion of an international telephone number used to identify the country of the called party. That country code may be one, two or three digits. An international phone number consists of a Country Code (CC) and a NSN (National Significant Number). Until December 31, 1996, the CC can be up to three digits and the NSN up to 11 digits — for a total of no more than 12 digits. After December 31, 1996, the CC stays at up to 3 digits and the NSN goes to up to 14 digits, for a total of no more than 15 digits.

CCBM Came Clear By Magic. This term created (but not contributed) by Nynex. This is pseudo-technical lingo used by Nynex when they repair something that they broke (i.e. the problem was their fault), but they are unwilling to admit it was their fault. They say this "CCBM" to interconnect companies who are trying to get their customers' phone lines fixed.

CCC 1. Clear Coded Channel. A 64 kbps channel in which all 64 kbps is available for data. 2. Clear Channel Capability. The bandwidth of a data transmission path available to end users after control and signaling bits are accounted for.

3. Communications Competition Coalition. Lobbying organization established to encourage competition in telecommunications in Canada.

CCD 1. Charge Coupled Device. The "eyes" of a scanner or "digital camera." CCDs are small electronic devices with arrays of light-sensitive elements. The number of these elements and the width determine the scanner's or camera's resolution. Light is bounced off the image onto the CCD, which translates the varying intensities of the reflected light into digital data. CCD technology is used also in "digital still cameras" such as the Sony Mavica. The small size of the array itself — approximately microchip size — and the high resolution — around 1,000 by 1,018 elements — of these cameras have greatly improved "image acquisition" capabilities and opened up new applications in manufacturing quality control and in medicine. 2. Change Coupled Device.

CCDN Corporate Consolidated Data Network. It is the name for IBM's main internal data communications network. It used to be managed by IBM. It's now managed by Advantis, an IBM spin-off company, which is majority-owned by IBM and the rest by Sears.

CCFL Cold Cathode Fluorescent Lamp. A technology several laptop computer manufacturers use to light their LCD screens.

CCIA Computer and Communications Industry Association. A trade organization of computer, data communications and specialized common carrier services companies headquartered in Arlington VA. It runs seminars, does lobbying and generally tries to take care of the common interests of its members. See CBEMA.

CCIR Comite' Consultatif International des Radiocommunications (Consultative Committee on International Radiocommunications France). Also used to describe 625-line television system used primarily in Western Europe. The US system of TV is 525. The high definition TV is scheduled to be 1,125.

CCIR 601 An internationally agreed-upon standard for the digital encoding of component color television that was derived from the SMPTE RP125 and the EBU 324E standards. It uses the 4:2:2 sampling scheme for Y, U and V with luminance sampled at 13.5 MHz and chrominance (U and V components) sampled at 6.75 MHz. After sampling, 8-bit digitizing is used for each channel. These frequencies are used because they work for both 525/60 (NTSC) and 625/50 (SECAM and PAL) television systems. The system specifies that 720 pixels be displayed on each line of video. The D1 digital videotape format conforms to CCIR 601. See CCIR 656.

CCIR 656 The international standard defining the electrical and mechanical interfaces for digital TV operating under the CCIR 601 standard. It defines the serial and parallel interfaces in terms of connector pinouts as well as synchronization, blanking and multiplexing schemes used in these interfaces.

CCIS Common Channel Interoffice Signaling. A way of carrying telephone signaling information along a path different from the path used to carry voice. CCIS occurs over a separate packet switched digital network. CCIS is separate from the talk path. A special version of CCIS is called Signaling System #7. SS#7 is integral to ISDN. CCIS offers basically two benefits: first, it dramatically speeds up the setting up and tearing down of phone calls. Second, it allows much more information to be carried about the phone call than what is carried on in-band (old-fashioned) signaling. That information can include the calling number, a message, etc.

Signaling for a group of voice telephone circuits is done on CCIS by encoding the information digitally on one of the voice circuits. In the previous method of signaling — the one replaced by CCIS — multi-frequency tones were sent down the same talkpath and the conversation would eventually travel. By taking the signaling information out of the talk path, the "phone phreak" community could no longer get free calls by using so-called "blue boxes" which duplicated the multi-frequency tones used by switching machines. CCIS is a much more efficient method of signaling, since it doesn't require a full voice grade channel just to check if the called party in LA is free and whether the call coming in from New York should be put through. See also COMMON CHANNEL SIGNALING, SYSTEM SIGNALING 7, ISDN and COMMON CHANNEL INTEROFFICE SIGNALING.

CCITT Comite Consultatif Internationale de Telegraphique et Telephonique, which, in English, means the Consultative Committee on International Telegraphy and Telephony. The CCITT is one of the four permanent parts of the International Telecommunications Union, the ITU, based in Geneva Switzerland. The scope of its work is now much broader than just telegraphy and telephony. It now also includes telematics, data, new services, systems and networks (like ISDN). The ITU is a United Nations Agency and all UN members may also belong to the ITU (at present 182), represented by their governments. In most cases the governments give their rights on their national telecom standards to their telecommunications administrations (PITs). But other national bodies (in the US, for example, the State Department) may additionally authorize Recognized Private Operating Agencies (RPOAs) to participate in the work of the CCITT. After approval from their relevant national governmental body, manufacturers and scientific organizations may also be admitted, as well as other international organizations. This means, says the ITU, that participants are drawn from the broad arena. The activities of the CCITT divide into three areas:

Study Groups (at present 15) to set up standard ("recommendations") for telecommunications equipment, systems, networks and services.

Plan Committees (World Plan Committee and Regional Plan Committee) for developing general plans for a harmonized evolution of networks and services.

Specialized Autonomous Groups (GAS, at present three) to produce handbooks, strategies and case studies for support mainly of developing countries.

Each of the 15 Study Groups draws up standards for a certain area - for example, Study Group XVIII specializes in digital networks, including ISDN. Members of Study Groups are experts from administrations, RPOAs, manufacturing companies, scientific or other international organizations - at times there are as many as 500 to 600 delegates per Study Group. They develop standards which have to be agreed upon by consensus. This, says the ITU, can sometimes be rather time-consuming, yet it is a democratic process, permitting active participation from all CCITT member organizations.

The long-standing term for such standards is "CCITT recommendations." As the name implies, recommendations have a non-binding status and they are not treaty obligations. Therefore, everyone is free to use CCITT recommendations without being forced to do so. However, there is increasing awareness of the fact that using such recommendations facilitates interconnection and interoperability in the interest of network providers, manufacturers and customers. This is the reason why CCITT recommendations are now being increasingly applied — not by force, but because the advantages of standardized equipment are obvious. ISDN is a good example of this.

CCITT has no power of enforcement, except moral persuasion. Sometimes, manufacturers adopt the CCITT specs. Sometimes they don't. Mostly they do. The CCITT standardization process runs in a four-year cycle ending in a Plenary Session. Every four years a series of standards known as Recommendations are published in the form of books. These books are color-coded to represent different four cycles. In 1980 the CCITT published the Orange Books, in 1984 the Red Books and, in 1988, the Blue Books. The CCITT is now more commonly called the ITU, after its parent. See CCITT STUDY GROUPS and CCITT V.XX below.

The CCITT has now been incorporated into its parent organization, the International Telecommunication Union (ITU). Telecommunication standards are now covered under Telecommunications Standards Sector (TSS). ITU-T (ITU-Telecommunications) replaces CCITT. For example, the Bell 212A standard for 1200 bps communication in North America was referred to as CCITT V.22. It is now referred to as ITU-T V.22.

CCITT STUDY GROUPS The CCITT operates as a series of groups considering specialist areas. Key study groups applicable to networking and communications are: Study Group VII responsible for terminal equipment for telematic services, including fax and higher level OSI standards; Study Group X covering Languages and methods for telecommunications applications; Study Group XI covering ISDN, telephone network including V-series Recommendations; Study Group XVIII covering digital networks including ISDN. See CCITT above and ITU-T.

CCITT V.XX A set of evolving telecom standards. For more on those standards, see under the letter "V."

CCMS A Rolm term. It stands for Call Center Management System.

CCIU Northern Telecom word for Conference Control Interface Unit.

CCO SYSTEM DEC VAX and IBM mini/mainframe telecommunications management software from the folks at Telco Research Nashville, TN. Includes cost allocation, directory, inventory management, problem recovery, traffic statistics, trouble tickets, work orders, student resale, tenant resale, bill verification, cable and wire, and network optimization applications. Also has a PC-based graphical interface to Telco Research's mini/mainframe telemanagement system.

CCR Customer Controlled Reconfiguration. An AT&T service that lets users make changes in their digital access and cross connect (DACS) network configurations at a DSO Level in either real time or according to a preplanned schedule.

CCS One hundred call seconds or one hundred seconds of telephone conversation. One hour of telephone traffic is equal to 36 CCS (60 x 60 = 3600 divided by 100 = 36) which is equal to one erlang. CCS are used in network optimization. Lee Goeller calls CCS an obsolete traffic unit. He says "When given traffic in CCS, always divide by 36 immediately. It is not obvious that 5 trunks cannot carry 185 CCS, but you don't have to be a rocket scientist to know that you can't average 5.14 calls on a five trunk group." See also TRAFFIC ENGINEERING.

CCS/SS7 A Bellcore term for Common Channel Signal/System Signaling 7. See SYSTEM SIGNALING 7.

CCSA Common Control Switching Arrangement. A private network set up by AT&T for very large users and using parts of the public switched network. One important feature of a CCSA is that any user anywhere in a CCSA network can reach any other user by dialing only seven digits. Only very large customers subscribe to this service. It's expensive. AT&T has fewer than 100 customers.

CCSA ACCESS A PBX feature which allows a PBX user to get into a CCSA network. See CCSA.

CCS7 COMMON CHANNEL SIGNALING 7. See ISDN.

CCT CONTINUITY CHECK TONE.

CCTV Closed Circuit TV.

CCU 1. Communication Control Unit. A processor, often a minicomputer, associated with a host mainframe computer that performs a number of communications-related functions. Compare with cluster control unit. 2. Camera Control Unit.

CD 1. Carrier Detect. CD is a signal generated by dial-up modem. CD indicates its connection status. If your CD light is on, then your modem is speaking to another modem. 2. Compact Disc. A 4.5 inch diameter disk containing digital audio or digital computer information, which can be played back and (now recorded) on a laser-equipped player. It was introduced by Sony and Philips in 1982. A compact disc originally came in only one flavor — read only. And most music tapes can only be listened to, not recorded to. For music it was a major breakthrough. It recorded music digitally (that is, coded as the zeros and ones of computer-speak) instead of trying to make an electrical copy of the sound waves themselves as devices like audio cassettes and LP records had. The Economist described the CD well. It said, "Instead of using a needle, the sound was plucked from the CD's surface by a tiny beam of laser light and then processed by a microcomputer. To the ear, the leap in performance between a compact disc and a long-playing record was even greater than the difference between color and black and white TV was to this eye."

Each month, a division of Ford Motor Co. publishes a CD-ROM inventory of 300,000 parts for its 2,400 dealers. A CD can typically hold up to 650 megabytes of information. That is the equivalent of 1,500 floppies or 250,000 pages of print. Most computer CD-ROM drives can play audio CD disks — if they have the software and the speakers. Audio CD players, though, cannot play computer CD-ROM discs. But most computer CD-ROM players can play CD audio discs. As CD-ROM have become more popular and their makers have tried to do more and more with them, so CD-ROM formats have proliferated and some are not compatible with each other. See CD-R, CD-ROM, CD-I, CD-V and WORM.

CD-AUDIO Sometimes called "Redbook audio," is the digital sound representation used by CD-ROMs. CD audio is converted to analog sound output within the CD-ROM drive. The sampling frequency for CD audio is 44.1 KHz.

CD I See CD-I below.

CD-I Compact Disc Interactive. Geared toward home entertainment, the drive connects to a television.

CD-PLUS A format for CDs created by Sony and PHilips Electronics which makes the multimedia track on CDs invisible to CD players. The problem: there are few enhanced CDs — discs for both CD player and CD-ROM drives. The reason: the format prior to CD-Plus puts the multimedia data on track one, which listeners must skip over on their CD players. Thus the new format.

CD-R CD Recordable. A standard and technology allowing you to write to and read from a Compact Disc, but not erase or change what you record. This technology is compatible with existing CDs, i.e. you are able to read these discs in existing CD-players, and often in both PC and Macintosh machines. See CD-ROM and MULTI-SESSION.

CD-ROM Compact Disc Read Only Memory. Also called CD or CD-ROM. The familiar 4.7 inch Compact Disc which you see in the audio stores, but now made for computers. These discs hold huge amounts of data — as much as 660 megabytes per disk, or 330 pages of ASCII test. Put into a computer drive, time to retrieve information off the CD-ROM is much slower than from a hard disc. But CD-ROMs are catching up. Most of today's newer CD-ROMs can now be used in multimedia applications and virtually all CD-ROM drives available today support the Multimedia PC or MPC standard. As of writing, the first desktop device to record CD-ROM disks were beginning to appear. They cost several thousand dollars, but are, of course, coming down in price. 1993 was the first year where sales of encyclopedias on CD-ROM exceeded the number of sales of encyclopedias on paper. See CD, CD-ROM XA, CD-V, CD-WO and SHOVELWARE.

CD-ROM XA Stands for Compact Disc - Read Only Memory eXtended Architecture. Microsoft's extensions to CD-ROM that let you interleave audio with data. Though it is not a video specification, limited video can be included on disc. Demand for multimedia applications is increasing use of CD-ROM XA. To use it, you must have a drive that reads the audio portions of the disc and audio card in your computer that translates the digital into sound. Not all drives can recognize the extensions. See CD-WO.

CD-V Compact Disc Video. A format for putting 5 minutes of video on a 3-inch disc. This format has come and gone. Video is shifting towards CD-ROM XA.

CD-WO Compact Disc Write Once. A CD-ROM version of the WORM (Write Once Read Many) technology. For companies performing all CD-ROM publishing in-house, this format is useful for creating test discs before sending the master for duplication. CD-WO discs conform to ISO 9660 standards and can be played in CD-ROM drives.

CDAR Customer Dialed Account Recording.

CDCS Continuous Dynamic Channel Selection.

CDDI Copper Distributed Data Interface is a version of FDDI (Fiber Distributed Data Interface— a 100 million bit per second local area network) that runs on unshielded twisted-pair cabling rather than optical fiber.

CDEV Control panel DEVice. An Apple Macintosh term.

CDFP Centrex Data Facility Pooling.

CDFS Compact Disc File System, which controls access to the contents of CD-ROM drives in PCs.

CDH INTERFACE An interface once required by the Bell System to protect their phone lines from "foreign" (i.e. non-AT&T) phone equipment. CDH devices were eventually ruled a total waste of money and the phone companies refunded the money — at least to the subscribers who asked. If you still have the stuff installed, you may be due a huge refund. Watch out for the statute of limitations.

CDLC Cellular Data Link Control. A public domain data communications protocol used in cellular telephone systems. In other words, you can attach a data terminal to a cellular telephone and send and receive information. There are more 5,000 modems using CDLC on the Vodaphone Cellular System in the UK, where it is the de facto standard for cellular data communications. Features like improved synchronization field, forward error correction, bit interleaving, and selective retransmission make CDLC ideal for cellular transmissions, according to Millidyne who makes the CDLC modems in the US.

CDMA 1. Call Division Multiple Access. 2. Code Division Multiple Access, also called Spread Spectrum, is a name for a new form of digital cellular phone service. Motorola, a leading cellular manufacturer, says CDMA is a spread spectrum technology that assigns a code to all speech bits, sends a scrambled transmission of the encoded speech over the air and reassembles the speech to its original format. The major benefits of CDMA is increased capacity (up to 10 times analog) and more efficient use of spectrum. More importantly, CDMA technology provides three features that improve system quality: 1) The "soft hands-off" feature ensures that a call is connected before handoff is completed, reducing the probability of a dropped call. 2) Variable rate vocoding allows speech bits to be transmitted at only the rates necessary for high quality which conserves the battery power of the subscriber unit. 3) Multipath signal processing techniques combines power for increased signal integrity. Additional benefits to the subscriber include increased talk times for handportable units, more secure transmissions and special service options such as data, integrated voice and data, fax and tiered services.

CDMA works by combining each phone call with a code which only one cellular phone plucks from the air. Business Week said CDMA works "by spreading all signals across the same broad frequency spectrum and assigning a unique code to each. The dispersed signals are pulled out of the background noise by a receiver which knows the code. This method, developed by a San Diego company called Qualcomm Inc. is very new. According to the Wall Street Journal, CDMA systems are said to offer up to 20 times more call handling capacity than the conventional cellular systems by assigning a special electronic code to each call signal, allowing more calls to occupy the same space and be spread over an entire frequency band. Much of the equipment to support CMDA, like cellular switches, however, have not yet been developed."

CDMA is about to be used in inside-building wireless PBX conversations by companies including SpectraLink of Boulder, CO. SpectraLink's explanation: "One of several technologies used to separate multiple transmissions over a finite frequency allocation. CDMA operates in conjunction with spread spectrum transmission. Spread spectrum takes the original information signal and combines it with a correlating code, resulting in a signal which occupies a much greater band-width than the original. By assigning a unique correlating code to each transmit-ter, several simultaneous conversations can share the same frequency allocation. The process of using spread spectrum in conjunction with individual correlating codes is known as Code Division Multiple Access." See also CODE DIVISION MULTIPLE ACCESS.

CDO Community Dial Office. A small automatic central office switching system that is completely unattended. Routine maintenance is provided by a traveling technician once or twice each year, or as troubles develop. Such an office usual-ly serves a small community with a few hundred lines in a rural area.

CDPD Cellular Digital Packet Service. A technology that folds packets of data into envelopes (packets) that are sent at very high speeds during pauses in cellular phone conversations. By adding CDPD to an existing analog cellular system (most systems worldwide are cellular), cellular operators can transmit data eight times faster without having to go to the trouble of building a whole new digital world. CPDP is new and just becoming available.

CDPD is a new, open standard for the use cellular as a means of wireless data transmission. The technology allows data files to be broken into packets and sent along idle channels of existing (but CDPD-upgraded) cellular voice networks. CPDP was originally developed by IBM and is backed by a group of companies including Ameritech, AT&T, McCaw Cellular, Motorola and Nynex Mobile. CDPD lets you send data at 19.2 Kbps over an enhanced cellular network. It uses a full voice channel, but it can move your connection from one channel to another to avoid congesting voice communications. The drawback to CDPD is that it requires you to have CDPD modem and your cellular supplier to upgrade its base stations to CDPD, which not all are willing to do. On July 21, 1993, the group of cellular carrier that supports the Cellular Digital Packet Data (CDPD) project released the complete version 1.0 of its open specification designed to enable customers to send computer data over an enhanced cellular network. The group said the pack-et data approach is ideally suited to those applications that require the transmis-sion of short bursts of data, for example, authorizing a credit card number, exchanging e-mail messages or making databases queries. The cellular networks deploying CDPD will enable mobile workers to use a single device to handle all of their voice and packet data needs. This version of the specification includes input from parties that reviewed the earlier release (0.8 and 0.9). The new version pro-vides details of the CDPD architecture, airlink, external network interfaces, encryption and authentication, network support services, network applications services, network management, radio resource management and radio media access control. To get a copy of specification, call CDPD Project Coordinator Tom Solazzo at Pittiglio Rabin Todd & McGrath 714-545-9400 extension 235. See CDPD FORUM.

CDPD FORUM The CDPD Forum Inc. is an industry association that brings together companies with an interest in CDPD. It is based in Chicago on 312-644-6610 or 800-335-CDPD.

CDR Call Detail Recording (as in Call Accounting) or Call Detail Record, as a record generated by customer traffic later used to bill the customer for service. See CALL ACCOUNTING.

CDR EXCLUDE TABLE A table listing local central office codes which are not monitored (i.e. ignored) by a call accounting system.

CDV Compression Labs Compressed Digital Video, a compression technique used in satellite broadcast systems. CDV is the compression technique used in CLI's SpectrumSaver system to digitize and compress a full-motion NTSC or PAL analog TV signal so that it can be transmitted via satellite in as little as 2 MHz of bandwidth. (A normal NTSC signal takes 6 Mhz.)

CE MARK A type of pan-European equipment approval. Obtaining the CE Mark allows a product to be sold into 18 European countries without any further in-country testing. Several country regulatory bodies are set up to do the testing and thus the certification. These bodies are called "notified bodies." When one company, Larscom, reported one of its NDSUs had been granted a CE Mark, it said that the European "Notified Body" issuing the approval for its product was the British Approval Board for Telecommunications (BABT).

The CE Mark will become a requirement for all telecommunications terminal equipment (TTE) products sold into the European Union, effective January 1, 1996. Countries covered are Austria, Belgium, Demark, Finland, France, Germany, Greece, Ireland, Italy, Luxemburg, the Netherlands, Portugal, Spain, Sweden, and the United Kingdom. CE marketing confirms that a product has been tested and meets the essential requirements of the European Telecom Directive to market it throughout the EU. The European TTE Directive 91/263/EEC specifies approved products to meet appropriate telecommunications technical standards. These include personal safety, protection of public networks, interoperation with public network equipment, and electromagnetic compatibility.

CEBIT CeBIT is the world's largest computer and office automation show. It attracts 600,000 or so people to Hannover, Germany in March or so of each year. It is also called the Hannover Fair. It is about five times the size of Comdex, which is North America's largest computer show. Many of the "booths" at Hannover are really small buildings, which are used year-round. May of the "booths" are three stories high, with an open air restaurant on the top floor. Space at the show is sometimes rented for four years.

CED 1. CallEd station iDentification. A 2100 Hz tone with which a fax machine answers a call. See CNG. 2. Capacitance Electronic Disc. System of video recording a grooved disc, employing a groove-guided capacitance pickup.

CED COMPRESSION A method of compression used in faxing.

CEDAR A Rolm desktop computer phone that is part IBM PC, part Rolm phone.

CEI Comparable Efficient Interface. The idea is that the telephone industry will let all its information providers have this interface — defined by technical specs and pricing — and, if it does, then the phone companies can themselves use this information to become information providers themselves. The concept has merit. Implementation has been agonizingly slow.

CEILING DISTRIBUTION SYSTEMS Cable distribution system that use the space between a suspended or false ceiling and the structural floor for running cable. Methods used in ceiling distribution systems include zone, home-run, raceway, and poke-through.

CEO Chief Executive Officer.

CEKS Centrex Electronic Key Set.

CELL 1. The basic geographic unit of a cellular system. It derived its name "cell" from the honeycomb pattern of cell site installations. Cell is the basis for the generic industry term "cellular." A city or county is divided into smaller "cells," each of which is equipped with a low-powered radio transmitter/receiver. The calls can vary in size depending upon terrain, capacity demands, etc. By controlling the transmission power, the radio frequencies assigned to one cell can be limited to the boundaries of that cell. When a cellular phone moves from one cell toward another, a computer at the Mobile Telephone Switching Office (MTSO) monitors the movement and at the proper time, transfers or hands off the phone call to the new cell and another radio frequency. The handoff is performed so quickly that it's not noticeable to the callers. For a longer explanation, see CMTS. 2. The basic unit of a battery, consisting of plates, electrolyte and a container. A chemical device that produces electricity through electrolysis.

CELL INTERARRIVAL VARIATION CIV. An ATM term. "Jitter" in common parlance, CIV measures how consistently ATM cells arrive at the receiving end-station. Cell interarrival time is specified by the source application and should vary as little as possible. For constant bit rate (CBR) traffic, the interval between cells should be the same at the destination and the source. If it remains constant, the latency of the ATM switch or the network itself (also known as cell delay) will not affect the cell interarrival interval. But if latency varies, so will the interarrival interval. Any variation could affect the quality of voice or video applications.

CELL RELAY A form of packet switching using fixed length packets which results in lower processing and higher speeds. Cell relay is a generic term for a protocol based on small fixed packet sizes capable of supporting voice video and data at very high speeds. Information is handled in fixed length cells of 53 octets (bytes). A cell has 48 bytes of information and 5 bytes of address. The objective of cell relay is to develop a single high-speed network based on a switching and multiplexing scheme that works for all data types. Small cells (like 53 bytes) favor low-delay, a requirement of isochronous service. The downside to small cells is that the address information is almost 10 percent of the total packet. That's a high overhead. See ATM.

CELL REVERSAL The reversal of the polarity of the terminals of a battery cell as the result of discharging.

CELL SITE A transmitter/receiver location, operated by the WSP (Wireless Service Provider), through which radio links are established between the wireless system and the wireless unit. The area served by a cell site is referred to as a "cell". A cell site consists of an antenna tower, transmission radios and radio controllers. The cell site of an analog cellular radio system handles up to 5,000 users (but not all at once).

CELL SITE CONTROLLER The cellular radio unit which manages the radio channels within a cell.

CELL SWITCHING A term that refers to how cellular calls are switched. Cellular systems are built to accommodate moving phones — ones in cars, buses, etc. These phones are low-powered. The "movingness" and the low power of the phones poses major design constraints on the design of cellular switching offices, which are called Mobile Telephone Switching Office (or MTSO). First, you have to build many cellular switching sites. That way each phone is close to a cell site. Thus there's always a cell site which can pick up the transmission. Second, because of the closeness of the cell sites, any phone conversation may be simultaneously heard by several MTSOs. As a result, the MTSO constantly monitors signal strength of both the caller and the receiver. When signal strength begins to fade, the MTSO locates the next best cell site and re-routes the conversation to maintain the communications link. The switch from cell site to another takes about 300 milliseconds and is not noticeable to the user. All switching is handled by computer, with the control channels telling each cellular unit when and where to switch.

The Cellular Mobile Telephone System is a low-powered, duplex, radio/telephone which operates between 800 and 900 MHZ, using multiple transceiver sites linked to a central computer for coordination. The sites, or "cells", named for their honeycomb shape, cover a range of three to six, or more, miles in each direction. Their range is limited only by certain natural or man-made objects.

The cells overlap one another and operate at different transmitting and receiving frequencies in order to eliminate cross-talk when transmitting from cell to cell. Each cell can accommodate up to 45 different voice channel transceivers. When a cellular phone is activated, it searches available channels for the strongest signal and locks onto it. While in motion, if signal strength begins to fade, the telephone will automatically switch signal frequencies or cells as necessary without operator assistance If it fails to find an acceptable signal, it will display an "out of service" or "no service" message, indicating that it has reached the limit of its range and is unable to communicate.

Each mobile telephone has a unique identification number which allows the Mobile Telephone Switching Office (MTSO) to track and coordinate all mobile phones in its service area. This ID number is known as the Electronic Security Number (ESN). The ESN and Telephone Number are NOT the same. The ESN is a permanent number engraved into a memory chip called a PROM or EPROM, located in the telephone chassis. This number cannot be changed through programming as the telephone number can, although it can be replaced. Each time the telephone is used, it transmits its ESN to the MTSO by means of DTMF tones during the dialing sequence. The MTSO can determine which ESN's are good or bad, thus individual numbers can be banned from use within the system. See CELLULAR RADIO.

CELL SPLITTING A means of increasing the capacity of a cellular system by subdividing or splitting cells into two or more smaller cells.

CELLPHONE A British term for a cellular telephone — whether car-based or handheld.

CELLULAR DATA LINK CONTROL CDLC is a public domain data communications protocol used in cellular telephone systems. In other words, you can attach a data terminal to a cellular telephone and send and receive information. There are more 5,000 modems using CDLC on the Vodaphone Cellular System in the UK, where it is the de facto standard for cellular data communications. Features like improved synchronization field, forward error correction, bit interleaving, and selective retransmission make CDLC ideal for cellular transmissions, according to Millidyne who makes the CDLC modems in the US.

CELLULAR DIGITAL PACKET DATA CDPD is an open standard developed by a group of cellular carriers led by McCaw. The specification provides a standard for using existing cellular networks for wireless data transmission. Packets of data are sent along channels of the cellular network. See CDPD for a much more detailed explanation.

CELLULAR FLOOR METHOD A floor distribution method in which cables pass through floor cells, constructed of steel or concrete, that provide a ready-made raceway for distributing power and communication cables.

CELLULAR DIGITAL PACKET DATA GROUP In the summer of 1993, a group of cellular carriers that supports the Cellular Digital Packet Data (CDPD) project has released the complete - version 1.0 - of its open specification designed to enable customers to send computer data over an enhanced cellular network. According to the group, the packet data approach is ideally suited to those applications that require the transmission of short bursts of data, for example, authorizing a credit card number, exchanging e-mail messages or making databases queries. The cellular networks deploying CDPD will enable mobile workers to use a single device to handle all of their voice and packet data needs. The 1.0 specification provides network and customer equipment manufacturers the parameters for building to this nationwide approach that sends packets of data over existing cellular networks. This version of the specification includes input from parties that reviewed the earlier release (0.8 and 0.9) and provides details of the CDPD architecture, airlink, external network interfaces, encryption and authentication, network support services, network applications services, network management, radio resource management and radio media access control. Copies of the specification can had from CDPD Project Coordinator Tom Solazzo at Pittiglio Rabin Todd & McGrath, 714-545-9400 extension 235.

CELLULAR GEOGRAPHIC SERVICE AREA CGSA. The geographic area served by the wireless (cellular) system within which a WSP is authorized to provide service.

CELLULAR MOBILE TELEPHONE SERVICE See CMTS.

CELLULAR PHONE SERVICE See CMTS.

CELLULAR PROTOCOLS Conventions and procedures which relate to the format and timing of device communications. In data transmission communications, there are currently three major protocols, which are converging into a de facto standard: MNP, SPCL, and PEP.

CELLULAR RADIO A mobile radio system. In the old days, there was one central antenna and everything homed in on that and emanated from it. With cellular radio, a city is broken up into "cells," each maybe no more than several city blocks. Every cell is handled by one transceiver (receiver/transmitter). As a cellular mobile radio moves from one cell to another, it is "handed" off to the next cell by a master computer, which determines from which cell the strength is strongest. Cellular mobile radio has several advantages:

1. You can handle many simultaneous conversations on the same frequencies. One frequency is used in one cell and then re-used in another cell. You can't do this on a normal mobile radio system.

2. Because one cellular system can accommodate many more subscribers than a normal mobile radio system, and therefore because it can achieve certain

economies of scale, it has the potential of achieving much lower transmission costs.

3. Because the transceiver is always closer to the user than in a normal mobile system, and the user's radio device thus needs less power, the device can be cheaper and smaller. Cellular radios started at over $5,000 and are now well under $500. From the first portable units, weight has already dropped to under one pound. There are several units that will fit in your breast pocket and not overly stretch your suit.

The following are specific cellular radio terms, or general telecom terms that mean something special in cellular radio:

A/B Switch Permits user to select either the wireline (B system) or the nonwireline (A system) carrier when roaming.

Alphanumeric memory Capability to store names with phone numbers.

Call-in-absence horn alert User-activated feature that sounds car horn upon receiving a call.

Call-in-absence indicator Feature that displays what calls came in while user was absent.

Call-in-progress override Insures that power to the phone is not lost if the car's ignition is turned off.

Call restriction Security feature that limits phone's use without completely locking it. Variations might include dial from memory only, dial last number only, seven-digit dial only, no memory access, etc.

Call timer Displays information on call duration and quantity. Variations might include present call, last call, total number of calls, or total accumulated time since last reset. Call-timer beep serves as a reminder to help keep calls brief. It might be set to go off once a minute, ten seconds before the minute, for example.

Continuous DTMF (touch-tones) Sends DTMF (dual-tone, multi-frequency) tones — also called touchtones — allowing access to voice mail and answering machines that require long-duration tones. "Continuous" means you get the tone so long as your finger is on the button. This may seem obvious to you and me, except that some "modern" phones just give a short tone no matter how long you keep your finger on the touchtone button.

Dual NAM Allows user to have two phone numbers with separate carriers (see multi-NAM).

Electronic lock Provides security by completely locking phone so it can't be used by unauthorized persons.

Expanded spectrum Full 832-channel analog cellular spectrum currently available to users.

Hands-free operation Allows user to receive calls and converse while leaving handset in cradle (similar to office speakerphone).

Hands-free answering Phone automatically answers incoming call after a fixed number of rings and goes to hands-free operation.

Memory linkage Allows programming specific memory locations to dial a sequence of other memory locations.

Multi-NAM A cellular telephone term to allow a phone to have more than two phone numbers, each of which can be on a different cellular system if desired. This lets the user register with both carriers in home city, expanding available geographic coverage.

Mute Silences the telephone's microphone to allow private conversations without discontinuing the phone call. Audio mute turns off the car stereo automatically when the phone is in use, and turns it back on when the call is completed.

NAM Numerical Assignment Module. Basically, your cellular phone number, although it refers specifically to the component or module in the phone where the number is stored.

On-hook dialing Allows dialing with the handset in the cradle.

Roaming Using any cellular system outside your home system. Roaming usually incurs extra charges.

Scratch pad Allows storage of phone numbers in temporary memory during a call. Silent scratch pads allows number entry into scratch pad without making beep tones.

Signal strength indicator Displays strength of cellular signal to let user know if a call is likely to be dropped.

Speed dialing Dialing phone number from memory by pressing a single button.

Standby time Maximum time cellular phone operating on battery power can be left on to receive incoming calls.

Talk time Maximum time cellular phone operating on battery power can transmit.

Voice-activated dialing Your cellular phone recognizes your words and dial accordingly. You say "Dial Mom" and it dials mom.

CELLULAR RADIO SWITCHING OFFICE The electronic switching office which switches calls between cellular (mobile) phones and wireline (i.e. normal wired) phones. The switch controls the "handoff" between cells and monitors usage. Different manufacturers call their equipment different things, as usual.

CELLULAR SWITCHING See CELL SWITCHING.

CELLUPLAN II A proposed national standard to place packets of data between idle spaces on a cellular voice network.

CELP Code Excited Linear Prediction. An analog-to-digital voice coding scheme. Sun is proposing the use of CELP so that a user could send realtime voice communications over local area or wide are network — bypassing the phone system!

CEMH Controlled Environment ManHole. Environmental control of the CEMH is maintained by a heat pump (a fancy name for an airconditioner — cooler and heater).

CEN/CENELEC Comite European de Normalisation/Comite European e Normalisation ELECtrotechnique) Two committees that have combined to address the standardisation of information technology. The main part of their work is aimed at the development of functional standards for OSI and related standards. Its membership comprises national standards bodies such as the UK's BSI as well as other European standards bodies.

CENLEC European Electrical Standards Institute (Comite European de Normalization Electrique).

CENTEL CORPORATION A telephone company serving over one million customer lines. It's based near the Chicago O'Hare Airport. During 1992 it was absorbed by Sprint.

CENTRAL OFFICE Telephone company facility where subscribers' lines are joined to switching equipment for connecting other subscribers to each other, locally and long distance. Also called CO, as in See-Oh. Sometimes the term central office is the same as the overseas term "public exchange." Sometimes, it means a wire center in which there might be several switching exchanges.

CENTRAL OFFICE BATTERY A group of wet cells joined in series to provide 48 volts DC. Central office batteries are typically charged off the main 120 volts AC. The batteries have two basic functions. 1. To provide a constant source of DC power for eight hours or so after AC powers drops, and 2. To isolate the central office from glitches on the AC line.

CENTRAL OFFICE CODE Part of the national numbering plan, the central office code is the second three digits of a subscriber's telephone number, which identifies the local switching office. Here is Bellcore's definition: A 3-digit identification under which up to 10,000 station numbers are subgrouped. Exchange area boundaries are associated with the central office code that generally have billing significance. Note that multiple central office codes may be served by a central office. Also called NXX code or end office code.

CENTRAL OFFICE CONNECTION COC. An MCI charge (monthly and installation) for each local access channel. If no access channels are provided, one COC is charged for each serving MCI terminal.

CENTRAL OFFICE OVERRIDE A third party may interrupt or join in your conversation.

CENTRAL OFFICE TRUNK 1. A trunk between central offices. It may be between major switches or between a major and a minor switch.

2. A trunk between public and private switches.

CENTRAL PROCESSING UNIT CPU. The part of a computer which performs the logic, computational and decision-making functions. It interprets and executes instructions as it receives them. Personal computers have one CPU, typically a single chip. It is the so-called "computer on a chip." That chip identifies them as an 8-bit, 16-bit or 32-bit machine.

Telephone systems, especially smaller ones, are not that different. Typically they have one main CPU — a chip — which controls the various functions in the telephone. Today's telephone systems are in reality nothing more than special purpose computers. As phone systems get bigger, the question of CPUs - - central processing units — becomes harder to figure. The design of phone systems has, of late, tended away from single processor-controlled telephone systems (as in single processor controlled PCs). There are several reasons for this move. First, it's more economical for growth. Make modules of "little" switches and join little ones together to make big ones. Second, it's more reliable. It's obviously better not to rely on one big CPU, but to have several. In short, the issue of Central Processing Units — CPUs — is blurring. But the concept is still important because by understanding how your telephone switch works (its architecture), you will understand its strengths and weaknesses.

CENTRALIZED ATTENDANT SERVICE Calls to remote (typically branch) locations are automatically directed to operators at a central location. Imagine four retail stores in a town. There are three branch stores and one main, downtown store, each having their own local phone numbers, which customers call. It's clearly inefficient to put operators at each of the stores — when one group is busy, the other will be free, etc. What this feature does is to direct all the calls coming into each of the stores into one bank of operators, who then send those calls back to the outlying stores.

Despite the extra schlepping of calls around town, having one large group of operators is cheaper than maintaining many small groups. Each store has its own local Listed Directory Number (LDN) Service. Special Release Link Trunk circuits connect each unattended location (each store) to the main attendant location. These trunks are only temporarily used during call processing. An incoming call to an unattended store seizes such a trunk circuit for completion of the call to the centralized attendant, who then uses the same trunk circuit to process the call to the remote location's internal extension. (After all if the caller was calling that store, they obviously want to talk to someone in that store.) The circuit is then released and is available for other calls. Since such special trunk circuits are only used during that part of a call that requires connection between locations, such trunks are more efficient than normal tie trunk circuits.

CENTRALIZED AUTOMATIC MESSAGE ACCOUNTING CAMA. The recording of toll calls at a centralized point.

CENTRALIZED ORDERING GROUP COG. An organization provided by some communications service providers (like a local phone company) to coordinate services between the companies and vendors.

CENTREX Centrex is a business telephone service offered by a local telephone company from a local central office. Centrex is basically single line telephone service delivered to individual desks (the same as you get at your house) with features, i.e. "bells and whistles," added. Those "bells and whistles" include intercom, call forwarding, call transfer, toll restrict, least cost routing and call hold (on single line phones).

Think about your home phone. You can often get "Custom Calling" features. These features are typically fourfold: Call forwarding, Call Waiting, Call Conferencing and Speed Calling. Centrex is basically Custom Calling, but instead of four features, it has 19 features. Like Custom Calling, Centrex features are provided by the local phone company's central office.

Phone companies peddle Centrex is leased to businesses as a substitute for that business buying or leasing its own on-premises telephone system — its own PBX, key system or ACD. Before Divestiture in 1984, Centrex was presumed dead. AT&T was, at that time, intent on becoming a major PBX and key system supplier. Then Divestiture came, and the operating phone companies recognized they were no longer part of AT&T, no longer had factories to support, but did have a huge number of Centrex installations providing large monthly revenues. As a result, the local operating companies have injected new life into Centrex, making the service more attractive in features, price, service and attitude. Here are the main reasons businesses go with Centrex as opposed to going with a stand-alone telephone system:

1. Money. Centrex is typically cheaper to get into (the central office already

exists). Installation charges can be low. Commitment can also be low, since most Centrex service is leased on a month-to-month basis. So it's perfect for companies planning an early move. There may be some economies of scale, also. Some phone companies are now offering low cost, large size packages.

2. Multiple locations. Companies with multiple locations in the same city are often cheaper with Centrex than with multiple private phone systems and tie lines, or with one private phone system and OPX lines. (An OPX line is an Off Premise eXtension, a line going from a telephone system in one place to a phone in another. It might be used for an extension to the boss's home.)

3. Growth. It's theoretically easier to grow Centrex than a standalone PBX or key system, which usually has a finite limit. With Centrex, because it's provided by a huge central office switch, it's hard, theoretically, to run out of paths, memory, intercom lines, phones, tie lines, CO lines, etc. The limit on the growth of a Centrex is your central office, which may be many thousands of lines.

4. Footprint Space Savings. You don't have to put any switching equipment in your office. All Centrex switching equipment is at the central office. All you need at your office are phones.

5. Fewer Operators because of Centrex's DID features. Fewer operator positions saves money on people and space.

6. Give better service to your customers. With Centrex, each person has their own direct inward dial number. Many people prefer to dial whomever they want directly rather than going through a central operator. Saves time.

7. Better Reliability. When was the last time a central office crashed? Here are some of the features built into modern central offices: redundancy, load-sharing circuitry, power back-up, on-line diagnostics, 24-hour on-site personnel, mirror image architecture, 100% power failure phones, complete DC battery backup and battery power. Engineered to suffer fewer than three hours down time in every 40 years.

8. Non-blocking. Trunking constraints are largely eliminated with Centrex, since a central office is so large.

9. Minimal Service Costs. Repair is cheap. Service time is immediate. People are right next to the machine 24-hours a day. Phones and wires are the only things that require repair on the customers' premises. You can easily plug new phones in, plug them out yourself. All other equipment is in the central office. You need not hold inventory or test equipment.

10. No technological obsolescence. Renting Centrex means a user has the ultimate flexibility — ability to jump quickly into new technology. Central offices are moving quickly into new technologies, such as ISDN.

11. Ability to manage it yourself. You can now get two important features previously available only on privately-owned self-contained phone systems (like PBXs): 1. The ability for you, the user, to make changes to the programming of your own Centrex installation without having to personally call a phone company representative. 2. The ability to get call detail accounting by extension and then have reports printed by a computer in your office. The phone company does this call accounting by installing a separate data line which carries Centrex call records back to the customer as those calls are made.

The above arguments are pro-Centrex. There are also anti-Centrex arguments. And there's plenty of evidence to argue exactly the opposite. For example, central offices often run out of capacity. The "big" key to Centrex traditionally comes down to price. And, in fact, in some cities the price of Centrex lines is lower than "normal" PBX lines. Of course, you can buy Centrex lines and attach your own PBX or key system to those Centrex lines. The big disadvantage of Centrex is that there are no specialized Centrex phones able to take better advantage of Centrex central office features than normal electronic phones can.

Centrex is known by many names among operating phone companies, including Centron and Cenpac. Centrex comes in two variations — CO and CU. CO means the Centrex service is provided by the Central Office. CU means the central office is on the customer's premises. See the following CENTREX definitions.

CENTREX CALL MANAGEMENT A Centrex feature that provides detailed cost and usage information on toll calls from each Centrex extension, so you can better manage your telephone expenses.

CENTREX CO Indicates that all equipment except the attendant's position and station equipment is located in the central office. See CENTREX.

CENTREX CU Indicates that all equipment including the dial switching equipment, is located on the customer's premises. See CENTREX.

CENTREX CCRS Centrex Customer Rearrangement System. Computer software from New York Telephone that allows their Centrex customers to make certain changes in their own line and features arrangements. Other phone companies have similar services under different names.

CENTREX EXTEND SERVICE The name of a Bell Atlantic service. If you maintain offices in multiple locations — or have work-at-home employees — this service allows you to tie all your locations into one phone system. So everyone in your company can take advantage of Centrex features and services on a cost-efficient, call-by-call sharing basis. With Centrex Extended Service, you can even tie non-Centrex locations into your Centrex system.

CENTREX LAN SERVICE Put a modem on a dedicated central office line. Connect that line to a switch. Bingo you have a switched, relatively high-speed service that can connect synchronous and asynchronous terminals and other equipment at speeds up to 19.2 Kbps. Centrex LAN service works with existing wiring Centrex central office to customer premise wiring. Centrex LAN is a name given this service by New York Telephone. Other phone companies have similar services under different names. It's not a very successful service, since it's very slow. Compare 19,200 bits per second to Ethernet, which is 10 million bits per second!

CENTREX SMDI Have you ever called someone and been forwarded to their voice mail, and then had to enter their extension again. This is because their voice mail does not know where the call originated. The voice mail system does not know who you just called, All it knows is that it just received another call. SMDI is simply a modem link back to the central office supplying your Centrex system. This modem link will feed a computer at your location the information about incoming calls as they are forwarded through your system. It feeds the originating number and why the call is transferred, so you know whether the user didn't answer their phone, or that it was busy.

To indicate the health of the SMDI link, it generates a heartbeat message every few seconds. If you don't receive a heartbeat within the time window, you know there is a problem with the SMDI link and know to restart the link. The one good thing about SMDI is the option that your voice mail system can control the status of message waiting indicators on the user's phone. They can either have a message waiting lamp on their phone, or use the "stutter dial tone" which causes a broken dial tone when the user picks up their phone.

Problems to watch out for... Since SMDI is a communications link, it can be broken. If the SMDI link goes down, make sure you build in the old two step method of finding out what extension the caller was attempting to call. Make sure you also offer a user directory in case the caller does not know the extension number. When the link goes down, make sure the system does not continue to spend the message waiting status commands down an inactive link. SMDI stands for Standard Message Desk Interface or Simplified Message Disk Interface. See also SMDI.

CENTRONICS The name of the printer manufacturer whose method of data transmission between a computer and a parallel printer has become an industry standard. See CENTRONICS PRINTER STANDARD.

CENTRONICS PRINTER STANDARD The Centronics standard was developed by the Centronics company which makes computer printers. The Centronics standard is a 36-pin single plug/connector with eight of the 36-pins carrying their respective bits in parallel (eight bits to one character), which means it's much faster than serial transmission which sends only one bit a time. There are several types of Centronics male and female plugs and receptacles. So know which you want before you buy. The pinning — the location of and function of each of the 36-individual wires, is standard from one Centronics cable to another.

The Centronics printer standard has been adopted by many printer and PC companies, including IBM. It is a narrower standard than the RS-232-C standard. The Centronics works only between a computer and a printer. It won't work over phone lines, unless conversion is done at either end. However, it is standard and has none of the dumb interface problems the RS-232-C standard does.

CENTUM CALL SECOND 1/36th of an erlang. The formula for a centum call second is the number of calls per hour multiplied by their average duration in seconds, all divided by 100.

CEPT Conference des administrations Europeenes des Postes et Telecommunications (European Conference of Postal and Telecommunications Administrations). Standards-setting body whose membership includes European Post, Telephone, and Telegraphy Authorities (PTTs). It in turn participates in relevant areas of the work of CEN/CENELEC. It was originally responsible for the NET standards, but these have subsequently been passed on to ETSI.

CEPT FORMAT Defines how the bits of a PCM carrier system of the 32 channel European type T-1/E-1 will be used and in what sequence. To correctly receive the transmitted intelligence, the receiving end equipment must know exactly what each bit is used for. CEPT format uses 30 VF channels plus one channel for supervision/control (signaling) and one channel for framing (synchronizing). All 8 bits per channel are used to code the waveshape sample. For a much better explanation, see T-1.

CERB Centralized Emergency Reporting Bureau. A Canadian term similar to PSAP — Public Safety Answering Position. See PSAP.

CERN European Laboratory for Particle Physics Research in Geneva, Switzerland.

C.E.R.T. Computer Emergency Response Team. Founded in 1988 by the Pentagon's Advanced Research Projects Agency, after a program written by a graduate student jammed more than 6,000 Internet-connected computers nationwide. C.E.R.T. is based at the Software Engineering Institute of the Carnegie Mellon University in Pittsburgh. C.E.R.T. is Internet's "the fire department." It counsels computer operators on how to keep viruses and intruders out of their computers.

CERTIFIED Several companies in the "secondary" industry test used equipment, parts and/or systems. They have various ways of testing them. Typically they test with working phones operating for extended periods at different temperatures. The idea is to check that this used equipment works the way it's meant to work — to the original manufacturer's design specification. Once these tests have been completed a secondary dealer will "certify" such equipment, usually in writing. Such certification carries the assurance that the used equipment works as it's meant to. Sometimes certified equipment is upgraded to the most current revision level of hardware and software. Sometimes it's not. You, the buyer, must check. Certified equipment typically carries a guarantee — that guarantee being as good, obviously, as the company that backs it.

CERTIFIED EQUIPMENT A term used in the secondary telecom equipment business. Equipment carrying the written assurance that it will perform up to the manufacturer's specifications. It qualifies for addition to existing maintenance contracts.

CESIUM CLOCK A clock containing a cesium standard as a frequency-determining element. It's a very accurate clock. See CESIUM STANDARD.

CESIUM STANDARD A primary frequency standard in which a specified hyperfine transition of cesium-133 atoms is used to control the output frequency. Its accuracy is intrinsic and achieved without calibration.

CEV Controlled Environmental Vault. A below ground room that houses electronic and/or optical equipment under controlled temperature and humidity.

CFA Carrier Failure Alarm. The alarm which results from an out-of-frame or loss of carrier condition and which is combined with trunk conditioning to create a CGA.

CFAC Call Forward All Calls.

CFAMN Call Forwarding Address Modified Notification.

CFB 1. Call Forward Busy. 2. Call Forwarding on mobile subscriber Busy. A wireless telecommunications term. A supplementary service provided under GSM (Global System for Mobile Communications).

CFDA Call Forward Don't Answer.

CFGDA Call Forward Group Don't Answer.

CFM Cubic Feet per Minute. A measure of how much air you move through the fan of a PC.

CFNRc Call Forwarding on mobile subscriber Not Reachable. A wireless telecommunications term. A supplementary service provided under GSM (Global System for Mobile Communications).

CFNRy Call Forwarding on No Reply. A wireless telecommunications term. A supplementary service provided under GSM (Global System for Mobile Communications).

CFO Chief Financial Officer.

CFP Channel Frame Processor.

CFRP Carbon Fiber Reinforced Plastic. A light and durable material, which has been used (for the wings of advanced fighter jets) in the defense business and which Toshiba introduced in 1991 as casing for a line of notebook sized computer laptops.

CFUC Call Forwarding UnConditional. A wireless telecommunications term. A supplementary service provided under GSM (Global System for Mobile Communications).

CFV Call For Votes. Begins the voting period for a Usenet newsgroup. At least one (occasionally two or more) email addresses is customarily included as a repository for the votes.

CFW Call Forward.

CGA 1. Carrier Group Alarm. A service alarm generated by a channel bank when an out-of-frame (OOF) condition exists for some predetermined length of time (generally 300 milliseconds to 2.5 seconds). The alarm causes the calls using a trunk to be dropped and trunk conditioning to be applied.

2. Color Graphics Adapter. An obsolete IBM standard for displaying material on personal computer screens. The simplest (and conventional) CGA displays 320 horizontal picture elements, known as pels or pixels, by 200 pels vertically. There is also an Enhanced CGA, which is 640 x 400, or 128,000 pixels per screen. Older portables may use CGA monochrome mode. CGA has essentially been obsoleted by VGA. See MONITOR and VGA.

CGI'S Common Gateway Interfaces. An Internet term. Programs or Scripts, usually executed on the Server, that perform actions when the user clicks on certain buttons or parts of the Web Screen. CGI actually refers to the pre-defined way in which these programs communicate with the Web Server but has lately come to refer to the programs themselves.

CGM Computer Graphics Metafile. A standard format that allows for the interchanging of graphics images.

CGSA Cellular Geographic Service Area. The actual area in which a cellular company provides cellular service. CGSAs are usually made up of multiple counties and often cross state lines.

CGSA RESTRICTION If you own a cellular phone, you are prevented from making calls outside your own local Cellular Geographic Service Area. This restriction is an option that is available to subscribers in most cellular cities.

CHAD 1. The little solid round dots of paper made when paper tape is punched with information. 2. CHAnge Display.

CHAD TAPE Punched tape used in telegraphy/teletypewriter operation. The perforations, called "chad," are severed from the tape, making holes representing the characters.

CHADLESS TAPE 1. Punched tape that has been punched in such a way that chad is not formed. 2. A punched tape wherein only partial perforation is completed and the chad remains attached to the tape. This is a deliberate process and should not be confused with imperfect chadding. See CHAD.

CHAINING A programming technique linking one activity to another, as in a chain. Each link in the chain may contain a pointer to the next link, or there may be a master control or program instructing the programs to link together.

CHAIN MAILBOXES Mailboxes that are connected together to provide a service or a number of messages (e.g. Directory, Product Information, etc.).

CHANNEL 1. Typically what you rent from the telephone company. A voice-grade transmission facility with defined frequency response, gain and bandwidth. Also, a path of communication, either electrical or electromagnetic, between two or more points. Also called a circuit, facility, line, link or path. 2. An SCSA term. A transmission path on the SCbus or SCxbus Data Bus that transmits data between two end points. 3. A channel of a GPS (Global Positioning System) receiver consists of the circuitry necessary to tune the signal from a single GPS satellite.

CHANNEL ATTACHED Describing the attachment of devices directly to the input/output channels of a (mainframe) computer. Devices attached to a controlling unit by cables rather than by telecommunications circuits. Same as locally attached (IBM).

CHANNEL BANK A multiplexer. A device which puts many slow speed voice or data conversations onto one high-speed link and controls the flow of those "conversations." Typically the device that sits between a digital circuit — say a T-1 — and a couple of dozen voice grade lines coming out of a PBX. One side of the channel bank will be connections for terminating two pairs of wires or a coaxial cable — those bringing the T-1 carrier in. On the other side are connections for terminating multiple tip and ring single line analog phone lines or several digital data streams. Sometimes you need channel banks. Sometimes, you don't. For example, if you're shipping a bundle of voice conversations from one digital PBX to another across town in a T-1 format — and both PBXs recognize the signal — then you will probably not need a channel bank. You'll need a Channel Service Unit (CSU). If one, or both, of the PBXs is analog, then you will need a channel bank at the end of the transmission path whose PBX won't take a digital signal. See CHANNEL SERVICE UNIT and T-1.

CHANNEL CAPACITY A measure of the maximum possible bit rate through a channel, subject to specified constraints.

CHANNEL IDENTIFICATION Information element that requests or identifies the channel to be used for a call. An AIN term.

CHANNEL GATE A device for connecting a channel to a highway, or a highway to a channel, at specified times.

CHANNEL LOOPBACK In network management systems, diagnostic test that forms a loop at the multiplexer's channel interface that returns transmitted signals to their source. See also LOOPBACK.

CHANNEL MODE An AT&T term for a method of communications whereby a fixed bandwidth is established between two or more points on a network as a semi-permanent connection and is rearranged only occasionally.

CHANNEL MODEM That portion of multiplexing equipment required to derive a desired subscriber channel from the local facility.

CHANNEL PACKING A technique for maximizing the use of voice frequency channels used for data transmission by multiplexing a number of lower data rate signals into a single higher speed data stream for transmission on a single voice frequency channel.

CHANNEL QUEUE LIMIT Limit on number of transmit buffers used by a station to guarantee that some receive buffers are always available.

CHANNEL SEIZED The time when a connection is established between the cellular user's mobile equipment and the mobile telephone switching office (MTSO). Channel seizure occurs before the number dialed begins to ring.

CHANNEL SERVICE UNIT CSU. A device used to connect a digital phone line (T-1 or Switched 56 line) coming in from the phone company to either a multiplexer, channel bank or directly to another device producing a digital signal, e.g. a digital PBX, a PC, or data communications device. A CSU performs certain line-conditioning, and equalization functions, and responds to loopback commands sent from the central office. A CSU regenerates digital signals. It monitors them for problems. And it provides a way of testing your digital circuit. You can buy your own CSU or rent one from your local or long distance phone company. See also CSU and DSU.

CHANNEL SURFING Flipping channels on a TV set. A person who channel surfs is called a MOUSE POTATO.

CHANNEL TIER An AT&T term for the tier within the Universal Information Services network that partitions transmission capacity into channels and offers the channels to the nodes' higher tiers.

CHANNEL TIME SLOT A time slot starting at a particular instant in a frame and allocated to a channel for transmitting a character, in-slot signal, or other data. Where appropriate a modifier may be added.

CHANNEL TRANSLATOR Device used in broadband LANS to increase carrier frequency, converting upstream (toward the head-end) signals into downstream signals (away from the head-end).

CHANNELIZATION Subdividing a wideband channel into many smaller channels so it may carry many different streams of information.

CHAPTER 11 The Chapter 11 process is started when a company files a reorganization petition with the federal Bankruptcy Court. From that moment on, creditors are prevented from suing the company, and any creditor lawsuits in process are halted, pending the outcome of the Chapter 11 reorganization. Creditors of the company file claims with the Bankruptcy Court. A creditors committee, usually made up of the seven creditors who have filed the largest claims against the company, represents the interest of all creditors. Under Chapter 11 protection, the company's management usually continues to manage the company's business, subject to judicial review. In rare circumstances, such as fraud, a party may ask the court to appoint a trustee to manage the company during reorganization. The ultimate objective of a Chapter 11 reorganization is to restructure creditors' claims so that the company can move ahead with its business. Company management includes a negotiated partial payment to creditors. The plan also can include exchanges of debt for equity, a moratorium on repayment or a combination of these actions. In some cases, more than one plan may be proposed. For example, a creditor, or group of creditors, may develop its own plan. The complex process of reaching a consensual plan entails extensive negotiations among the company, its creditors and its shareholders.

Once developed, the company's reorganization plan — or one of the competing plans — must be accepted by specified margins of creditors and shareholders. Creditors representing two-thirds of the total dollar amount of bankruptcy claims against the company and 51 percent of the total number of those voting must accept the plan, and two-thirds of the amount of shares represented by shareholders voting on the plan must approve it for a plan to be accepted. Once accepted, the Bankruptcy Court reviews the plan to ensure that it conforms to certain additional statutory requirements before confirming it. With a restructured balance sheet, the company then emerges from Chapter 11 protection to implement the plan. Some companies emerge from Chapter 11 and become normal operating companies again. Some don't and move into Chapter 7 bankruptcy, which is complete and relatively immediate liquidation of the company (i.e. sale of all the company's assets).

CHAPTER 7 See Chapter 11.

CHARACTER A letter, a number or a symbol. A character is sometimes described by the digit represented by the bit pattern that makes up the Character. i.e., the letter A is ASCII code 65, a carriage return is ASCII code 13.

CHARACTER CELL In text mode on a PC, each pel is called a character cell. Character cells are arranged in rows and columns. A typical PC will support two text modes — 80 columns by 25 rows and 40 columns by 25 rows. The default text mode on virtually all PCs is 80 x 25.

CHARACTER CODE One of several standard sets of binary representations for the alphabet, numerals and common symbols, such as ASCII, EBCDIC, BCD.

CHARACTER DISTORTION In telegraphy, the distortion caused by transients that, as a result of previous modulation, are present in the transmission channel. It effects are not consistent. Its influence upon a given transition is to some degree dependent upon the remnants of transients affecting previous signal elements.

CHARACTER GENERATOR A functional unit that converts the coded representation of a character into the graphic representation of the character for display.

CHARACTER IMPEDANCE The impedance termination of an electrically uniform (approximately) transmission line that minimizes reflections from the end of the line.

CHARACTER INTERLEAVING A form of TDM used for asynchronous protocols. A 20% saving can be obtained by omitting the start and stop bits. This can be used either with extra channels or by carrying RS232-C control signals.

CHARACTER INTERVAL The total number of unit intervals (including synchronizing, information, error checking, or control bits) required to transmit any given character in any given communication system. Extra signals that are not associated with individual characters are not included. An example of an extra signal that is excluded in the above definition is any additional time added between the end of the stop element and the beginning of the next start element as a result of a speed change, buffering, etc. This additional time is defined as a part of the intercharacter interval.

CHARACTER SET A group of letters, numbers, and symbols that have some relationship in common. For example, the ASCII character set contains characters that make up the ASCII coding scheme. See ASCII.

CHARACTER ORIENTED PROTOCOL A communications protocol in which the beginning of the message and the end of a block of data are flagged with special characters. A good example is IBM Corp's. Binary Synchronous Communications (BSC) protocol. Character-oriented protocols are used in both synchronous and asynchronous transmission.

CHARACTER ORIENTED WINDOWS (COW) INTERFACE An SAA-compatible user interface for OS/2 applications.

CHARACTER PRINTER A device which prints a single character at a time. Contrast with a line printer, which prints blocks of characters and is much faster.

CHARACTER SET All the letters, numbers and characters which a computer can use. The symbols used to represent data. The ASCII standard has 256 characters, each represented by a binary number from 1 to 256. This set includes all the letters in the alphabet, numbers, most punctuation marks, some mathematical symbols and some other characters typically used by computers.

CHARACTER STUFFING A technique used to ensure that transmitted control information is not misinterpreted as data by the receiver during character-based transmission. Special characters are inserted by the transmitter and then removed by the receiver.

CHARACTER TERMINAL A computer terminal that cannot show graphics, only text.

CHARACTERISTIC FREQUENCY A frequency that can be easily identified and measured in a given emission. A carrier frequency may, for example, be designated as the characteristic frequency.

CHARACTERISTIC IMPEDANCE The impedance of a circuit that, when connected to the output terminals of a uniform transmission line of arbitrary length, causes the line to appear infinitely long. A line terminated in its characteristic impedance will have no standing waves, no reflections from the end, and a constant ratio of voltage to current at a given frequency at every point on the line.

CHARACTERS PER SECOND CPS. A data transfer rate generally estimated from the bit rate and the character length. For example, at 2400 bps, 8-bit characters with Start and Stop bits (for a total of ten bits per character) will be transmitted at a rate of approximately 240 characters per second (cps). Some protocols, such as USR-HST and MNP, employ advanced techniques such as longer transmission frames and compression to increase characters per second.

CHARGED COUPLED DEVICE CCD. The full name of the term is Interline Transfer Charge-Coupled Device or IT CCD. CCD are used as image sensors in an array of elements in which charges are produced by light focused on a surface.

They consist of a rectangular array of hundreds of thousands of light-sensitive photo diodes. Light from a lens is focused onto the photo diodes. This frees up electrons (charges) which accumulate in the photo diodes. The charges are periodically released into vertical shift registers which move them along by charge-transfer to be amplified.

CHARLIE-FOXTROT Slang. Seriously beyond all hope. Very badly broken.

CHAT A common name for a type of messaging done over a network, involving short, usually one or two line messages sent from one node to another. Usually, a chatting facility is RAM-resident, meaning it can be "popped up" inside an application program. Users are usually notified of an incoming chat by a beep and a message at the bottom of their screens.

CHEAPERNET A slang name for the thin wire coaxial cable (0.2-inch, RG58A/U 50-ohm) that uses a smaller diameter coaxial cable than standard thick Ethernet. Thin Ethernet is also called "Cheapernet" due to the lower cabling cost. Thin Ethernet systems tend to have transceivers on the network interface card, rather than in external boxes. PCs connect to the Thin Ethernet bus via a coaxial "T" connector. Thin Ethernet is now the most common Ethernet coaxial cable, though twisted pair is gaining. Thin Ethernet is also referred to as ThinNet or ThinWire. See also 10BASE-T.

CHECK BIT A bit added to a unit of data, say a byte or a word, and used for performing an accuracy check. See also PARITY.

CHECK CHARACTERS Characters added to the end of a block of data which is determined by an algorithm using the data bits which are sent. The receiving device computes its own check characters. It compares them with those sent by the transmitter. If they do not match, the receiver requests the sender to send the block again. If the check characters match, then all the bits used to compute the check characters have been received properly.

CHECK-IN MAILBOX The Centigram VoiceMemo II mailbox used to assign names and passcodes for guests checking into a hotel.

CHECK-OUT MAILBOX The Centigram VoiceMemo II mailbox used to clear out guest mailboxes when the guest checks out of the hotel.

CHECKPOINT CYCLE HDLC error recovery cycle formed by pairing an F bit with a previous P bit or vice versa.

CHECKPOINTING HDLC error recovery based on pairing of P and F bits and giving the equivalent of a negative acknowledgment without using either REJ or SREJ.

CHECKSUM The sum of a group of data items used for error checking. Checksum is computed by the sending computer based upon an algorithm that counts the bits going out in a packet. The check digit is then sent to the other end as the tail, or trailer of the packet. As the packet is being received, the receiving computer goes through the same algorithm, and if the check digit it comes up with is the same as the one received, all is well. Otherwise, it requests the packet be sent again.

CHEESING When a buffered fiber cable appears to stretch during stripping and then cheeses (creeps) back into the outer jacket of the cable, to resume its original place.

CHEMICAL RECTIFIER A chemical device for changing alternating current to pulsating direct, usually used to storage battery charging.

CHEMICAL STRIPPING Soaking an optical fiber in a chemical to remove its coating.

CHEMICAL VAPOR DEPOSITION TECHNIQUE CVD. In optical fiber manufacturing, a process in which deposits are produced by heterogeneous gas-solid and gas-liquid chemical reactions at the surface of a substrate. The CVD method is often used in fabricating optical fiber preforms by causing gaseous materials to react and deposit glass oxides. The preform may be processed further in preparation for pulling into an optical fiber.

CHICAGO An early code word for Windows 95, due out originally in mid-1994. It finally appeared on August 24, 1995.

CHICLET 1. Another term for a B Connector. See B CONNECTOR.

2. IBM once came out with a PC that had small keys. The press said the PC had a chiclet keyboard, after the chewing gum.

CHIEF INFORMATION OFFICER The person responsible for planning, choosing, buying, installing — and ultimately taking the blame for — a company's computer and information processing operation. Originally, CIOs were called data processing managers. Then they became Management Information System (MIS) managers. Then, CIOs. The idea of calling them CIOs was to reflect a new idea that the information they controlled was a critical corporate advantage and one that could give the company a competitive edge over its competitors — if played correctly.

CHILD GROUP In some systems, a new group of users created under a parent group is called a child group. Child groups sometimes have more properties than their parent groups.

CHILL Ccitt HIgh Level Language. A computer language developed by the CCITT for the standardization of software in telecommunications switches. Not widely adopted. C is more widely adopted.

CHIME An electromechanical or electronic substitute for the conventional telephone bell, that sounds like a musical chime being struck, typically in a "bing-bong" sequence.

CHIMNEY EFFECT Picture a phone system. We have an upright, rectangular cabinet full of printed circuit cards and all getting hot. How to cool them? Simple, raise the machine a little off the ground, put holes in the bottom of the cabinet and holes in the top of the cabinet. Hot air rises. Bingo, air will rise through the top of the cabinet and cool air will get sucked in the bottom of the cabinet. And bingo, you don't need a fan. This natural cooling technique is called the Chimney Effect and many modern phone systems now use it.

CHIP 1. An integrated circuit. The physical structure upon which integrated circuits are fabricated as components of telephone systems, computers, memory systems, etc.

2. The transition time for individual bits in the pseudo-random sequence transmitted by the GPS satellite.

CHIP HEAD Anyone whose education, entertainment and employment is primarily derived from computer-based devices. Also called a BIT HEAD.

CHIRPING 1. A rapid change (as opposed to a long-term drift) of the wavelength of an electromagnetic wave. Chirping is most often observed in pulsed operation of a source. 2. A pulse compression technique that uses (usually linear) frequency modulation during the pulse.

CHOICE CHIP Your new TV will come with electronics that will allow you to program it not to receive certain programs, e.g. violent ones, you choose not to receive. The idea is that shows will be rated. Before they start, the show will broadcast a digital signal containing its rating. The "choice" chip in your TV will recognize the rating, check it against your instructions and block it or allow it through. The "choice" chip is so named as to give parents a choice of programs they and their children will watch. The provision for a choice chip was contained in telecommunications reform legislation passed by the Senate in mid-1995.

CHOKE An obsolete term: An inductance with either and air or iron core, designed to retard certain frequencies; as a radio frequency choke or an audio frequency choke.

CHOKE COIL A coil so wound as to offer a retarding or self inductance effect to an alternating current.

CHOKE PACKET Packet used for flow control. Node detecting congestion generates choke packet and sends it toward source of congestion, which is required to reduce input rate.

CHOOSER A desk accessory on the Apple Macintosh that allows a user to choose items such as a printer or file server by clicking on an icon of the device.

CHOPPER A device for rapidly opening and closing a circuit. An ancient radio term.

CHROMA The level of saturation or intensity of a color. Name sometimes applied to color intensity control in a receiver.

CHROMA KEY Method of electronically inserting the image from one video source into the picture from another video source using color for discrimination. A selected "key color" is replaced by the background image.

CHROMATIC DISPERSION Chromatic dispersion is one of the mechanisms that limits the bandwidth of optical fibers by producing pulse spreading because of the various colors of light traveling in the fiber. Different wavelengths of light travel at different speeds. Since most optical sources emit light containing a range of wavelengths, each of these wavelengths arrive at different times and thereby cause the transmitted pulse to spread as it travels down the fiber.

Chromatic dispersion is the sum of material and waveguide dispersion. Dispersion can be positive or negative because it measures the change in the refractive index with wavelength. Thus, the total chromatic dispersion can actually be zero (really close to zero). For example, step-index single-mode fibers have zero dispersion at 1300nm, almost exactly at the same wavelength where the optical loss of the fiber is at a minimum. This is what allows single-mode fibers to have low loss and high bandwidth.

CHROMINANCE The color portion of the video signal. Chrominance includes hue and saturation information but not brightness. Low chroma means the color picture looks pale or washed out; high chroma means the color is too intense, with a tendency to bleed into surrounding areas. Black, gray and white have a chrominance value of O. Brightness is referred to as luminance.

CHROMIUM DIOXIDE Tape whose coating is of chromium dioxide particles. Noted for its superior frequency output.

CHS Cylinder-Head Sector. The method of identifying a given location on a hard drive used by the original PC-AT BIOS (INT 13) and original IDE specification. Differences between details of the two methods resulted in the 528 MB limit on IDE drives. Enhanced IDE-compliant BIOSes can translate between the two methods, allowing drive sizes up to 8.4 GB. See ENHANCED IDE and IDE.

CHUCK HOLE Also known as Pot Hole. Slang for when your system hangs up on-line.

CHURN Cellular phone and beeper users drop their monthly subscriptions often. The industry calls This phenomenon "churn." Sometimes it's as high as 2% or 3% a month. It drives the cellular and beeper business mad. It's very expensive to sign up a new customer.

CHUTZPAH A New York Jewish word which means unmitigated gall (audacity). The word is best exemplified by the story of the 15-year old who goes into court having killed his father and mother and falls on the mercy of the court that he's now an orphan. Now that's Chutzpah! Telecom companies without competition show they understand the meaning of chutzpah very well in the way they typically treat their customers.

CI 1. Customer Interface. 2. Certified Integrator.

CI Labs Component Integration Labs. www.cilabs.org

CIC Carrier Identification Code. See CARRIER IDENTIFICATION CODE.

CICS Customer Information Control System. An IBM program environment designed to allow transactions entered at remote computers to be processed concurrently by a mainframe host. Also, IBM's Customer Information Control System software.

CID A generic term in Britain to identify a customer identity, client identity or contract identity. It is a single record and all the fields of information associated with it; for example, name, address, phone number, contact history and so on.

CIDB Calling Line Identification Delivery Blocking. A "feature" of central offices which lets you block the sending of your phone number to the person you're calling.

CIDR An internetworking term. Classless Inter-Domain Routing. A method for using the existing 32-bit Internet Address Space more efficiently.

CIF 1. A videophone ISDN standard which is part of the ITU-T's H.261/Px64 standard. It produces a color image of 288 non-interlaced luminance lines, each containing 352 pixels to be sent at a rate of 30 frames per second. The format uses two B channels, with voice taking 32 kbps and the rest for video. 2. CIF stands for Cost, Insurance and Freight are included. That means the seller pays the freight. The opposite of CIF is FOB, which stands for Free On Board. What this means is that you buy something, F.O.B. The seller puts it on a truck or railroad, plane, i.e. some carrier. He's responsible for getting it on the carrier. You — the buyer — are responsible for paying for the cost of the freight of getting you the goods you ordered.

CIGOS Canadian Interest Group on Open Systems. Canadian organization which promotes OSI.

CIIG Canadian ISDN Interest Group. Canadian organization which promotes ISDN.

CIM 1. Computer-Integrated Manufacturing. 2. An MCI definition. Customer Information Manager.

CIPHERTEXT The result of processing plaintext (unencrypted information) through an encryption algorithm. See CLIPPER CHIP.

CIR Committed Information Rate. It is used in the Frame Relay arena. CIR refers to the amount of data guaranteed to be transmitted over the carrier's network. The customer is always free to "burst" up to the port's speed but any amount of data over the CIR will be marked as DE or Discard Eligible. All data marked as DE will be discarded in the event of network congestion. CIR comes in increments of 16 Kbps (16-32-48-64) with 16 being the lowest. An example would be: A 56k frame relay connection with a CIR of 16k (very common) would allow the customer to transmit or burst data up to the full 56 Kbps. If they bursted up to the full 56k they would only be guaranteed delivery of 16k. See also COMMITTED INFORMATION RATE.

CIRCUIT The physical connection (or path) of channels, conductors and equipment between two given points through which an electric current may be established. Includes both sending and receiving capabilities. A circuit can also be a network of circuit elements, such as resistors, inductors, capacitors, semiconductors, etc., that performs a specific function. A circuit can also be a closed path through which current can flow.

CIRCUIT BOARD Same as a Printed Circuit Board, namely a board with microprocessors, transistors and other small electronics components. Such a board slides into a the slot in a telephone system or personal computer.

CIRCUIT BREAKER A special type of switch arranged to open a circuit when overloaded, without injury to itself. A circuit breaker is basically a re-usable fuse.

CIRCUIT IDENTIFICATION CODE CIC. The part of CCS/SS7 signaling message used to identify the circuit that is being established between two signaling points (14 bits in the ISDNUP).

CIRCUIT MODE 1. An AT&T term for the method of communications in which a fixed bandwidth circuit is established from point to point through a network and held for the duration of a telephone call.

2. An AIN term for a type of switching that causes a one-to-one correspondence between a call and a circuit. That is, a circuit or path is assigned for a call between each switching node, and the circuit or path is not shared with other calls.

CIRCUIT NOISE LEVEL At any point in a transmission system, the ratio of the circuit noise at that point to some arbitrary amount of circuit noise chosen as a reference.

CIRCUIT ORDER MANAGEMENT SYSTEM COMS. An automated processing system of MCI circuit- and service-related information. Processes hardwire service circuit orders from order entry through scheduling and completion. COMS also provides circuit order data, hardwire customer data, and circuit inventory data to other MCI systems in Finance, Engineering, and Operations.

CIRCUIT ORDER RECORD COR. Report generated by the COR Tracking System within NOBIS, indicating circuit installations, changes, and disconnects.

CIRCUIT PROVISIONING The telephone operating company process that somehow organizes to get you a trunk or other special service circuit.

CIRCUIT SEGREGATION Differentiating between services that are maintained by separate technicians or departments. Can be accomplished through visual and/or mechanical means.

CIRCUIT SWITCHED DIGITAL CAPABILITY CSDC. A service implemented by some regional Bell Operating Companies that offers users a 56-Kbps digital service on a user-switchable basis.

CIRCUIT SWITCHING The process of setting up and keeping a circuit open between two or more users, such that the users have exclusive and full use of the circuit until the connection is released. There are basically three types of switching — CIRCUIT, PACKET and MESSAGE.

• PACKET SWITCHING is like circuit switching in that you can also switch information between people or devices, but in packet switching (as in circuit switching), no circuit is left open on a dedicated basis. Circuit switching is like having your own railroad track for your conversation to travel on that's yours as long as you keep the connection open. Once you hang up, the next caller gets to use that track.

• PACKET SWITCHING is a data switching technique only. In packet switching, the addresses on your packets are read by the switches as they approach, and are switched down the tracks. The next packet is read to throw the switches to send THAT packet where it needs to go. The data conversation is sent in packets. Each packet can be sent along different tracks as they are open. The packets are assembled at the other end — typically in the last switching office before the packets reach the distant computer or distant user.

• MESSAGE SWITCHING sends a message from one end to the other. But it's not interactive, as in packet or circuit switching. In message switching, the message is typically received in one block, stored in one central place, then retrieved or sent in one clump to the other end.

CIRCUIT TIER An AT&T term for the tier within the Universal Information Services network that provides real-time circuit switching of channels.

CIRCUIT, FOUR WIRE A path in which four wires are presented to the terminal equipment (phone or data), thus allowing for simultaneous transmission and reception. Two wires are used for transmission in one direction and two in the other direction.

CIRCULAR EXTENSION NETWORK Permits two or more single-line phones connected to a PBX, each with its own extension, to operate like a "square" key telephone system. An incoming call directed to any non-busy phone in the group will ring at all of the non-busy phones. The first extension to answer will be connected to the incoming call. At any time, a non-busy extension can make or receive calls.

CIRCULAR HUNTING When calling a phone, the switching system makes a complete search of all numbers within the hunting group, regardless of the location within that group of the called number. For example, the hunt group is 231, 232, 233 and 234, the call is directed to 233. If it is busy, the equipment will search

234, 231, and 232 to find a non-busy phone or line. Essentially it goes around the ring, remembering where it last connected and then goes to the next line or phone in the circle. See also HUNT GROUP and TERMINATED HUNT GROUP.

CIRCULAR MIL The measure of sectional area of a wire.

CIRCULAR POLARIZATION In electromagnetic wave propagation, polarization such that the tip of the electric field vector describes a circle in any fixed plane intersecting, and normal to, the direction of propagation. The magnitude of the electric field vector is constant. A circularly polarized wave may be resolved into two linearly polarized waves in phase quadrature with their planes of polarization at right angles to each other.

CIRCULATOR 1. In networking, a passive junction of three or more ports in which the ports can be accessed in such an order that when power is fed into any port it is transferred to the next port, the port counted as following the last in order.

2. In radar, a device that switches the antenna alternately between the transmitter and receiver.

CIRCUMNAURAL A type of headphone that almost totally isolates the listener from room sounds.

CIS Contact Image Sensor. A type of scanner technology in which the photodetectors come in contact with the original document.

CISC Complex Instruction Set Computing. PC Magazine defines CISC as a microprocessor architecture that favors robustness of the instruction set over the speed with which individual instructions are executed. The Intel 486 and Pentium are both examples of CISC microprocessors. See also RISC — Reduced Instruction Set Computing. See RISC.

CISCOWORKS A series of router management applications developed and marketed by Cisco Systems for managing Cisco-based router networks.

CIT Computer Integrated Telephone is Digital Equipment Company's program, announced in October 1987, that provides a framework for functionally integrating voice and data in an applications environment so that the telephone and terminal on the desktop can be synchronized, the call arriving as the terminal's screen on the caller arrives. CIT uses the DEC VAX line of computers. According to DEC, CIT supports both inbound and outbound telecommunications applications. In an inbound scenario, the application may recognize the caller's originating phone number through Automatic Number Identification (ANI) and/or the dialed number through Dialed Number Identification Service (DNIS), match the information to corresponding data base records and automatically deliver the call and the data to the call center agent. In an outbound application, dialing can be automated, increasing the number of connected calls. In either scenario, the telephone calls and associated data can be simultaneously transferred to alternate locations within an organization, adding a new level of customer service to call center applications. Digital made its first CIT announcements at Telecom '87 in Geneva, Switzerland. The CIT product set, consisting of client and server software implementing a variety of switch-to-computer link protocols, and providing a robust applications interface, was first shipped in 1989. The company announced its latest release, CIT Version 2.1, in January 1991. See also OPEN APPLICATION INTERFACE.

CITIZENS BAND One of two bands used for low power radio transmissions in the United States — either 26.965 to 27.225 megahertz or 462.55 to 469.95 megahertz. Citizens band radio is not allowed in many countries, even some civilized countries. In some countries they use different frequencies. CB radios, in the United States, are limited by FCC rule to four WATTS of power, which gives each CB radio a range of several miles. Some naughty people boost their CBs with external power. The author of this dictionary has actually spoken to Australia while driving on the Santa Monica Freeway in Los Angeles. See also CB.

CIV Cell Interarrival Variation. An ATM term. See CELL INTERARRIVAL VARIATION

CIVDL Collaboration for Interactive Visual Distance Learning. A collaborative effort by 10 US universities that uses dial-up videoconferencing technology for the delivery of engineering programs.

CIX Commercial Internet Exchange; an agreement among network providers that allows them to exchange commercial traffic. A connection point between the commercial Internet service providers. Pronounced "kicks."

CLADDING 1. When referring to an optical fiber, a layer of material of lower refractive index, in intimate contact with a core material of higher refractive index. 2. When referring to a metallic cable, a process of covering with a metal (usually achieved by pressure rolling, extruding, drawing, or swaging) until a bond is achieved.

CLADDING DIAMETER The diameter of the circle that includes the cladding layer in an optical fiber.

CLADDING MODE In an optical fiber, a transmission mode supported by the cladding; i.e., a mode in addition to the modes supported by the core material.

CLADDING MODE STRIPPER A device for converting optical fiber cladding modes to radiation modes; as a result, the cladding modes are removed from the fiber. Often a material such as the fiber coating or jacket having a refractive index equal to or greater than that of the fiber cladding will perform this function.

CLADDING RAY In an optical fiber, a ray that is confined to the core and cladding by virtue of reflection from the outer surface of the cladding. Cladding rays correspond to cladding modes in the terminology of mode descriptors.

CLAIM PROCESS A technique used to determine which station will initialize an FDDI ring.

CLAIRE Harry Newton's favorite daughter. Why "favorite?" Simple. She's his only daughter. Her full name is Claire Elizabeth Newton.

CLAMN Called Line Address Modification Notification

CLAMPER An electronic circuit which sets the level of a signal before the scanning of each line begins to insure that no spurious electronic noise is introduced into the picture signal from the electronics of the video equipment.

CLAS Centrex Line Assignment Service. A service from New York Telephone and other Bell operating companies, which allows Centrex subscribers to change their class of service by dialing in on a personal computer, reaching the phone company's computer and then changing things themselves — without phone company personnel assisting or hindering.

Load your PC with communications software. Dial your local central office.

Change your Centrex phone numbers. Turn on, turn off features. Change pickup groups. Add numbers to speed dialing, etc. Your on-line changes are checked by the phone company's computers. If they make sense (i.e. one change doesn't conflict with another), they take effect by early the following day — at which time you can call up and get a report on which took, which didn't and who's got what. Saves calling in person. Is more accurate. And, best of all, saves money. Typically just one flat monthly charge. No charge for any of your changes.

CLASS 1. Custom Local Area Signaling Services. It is based on the availability of channel interoffice signaling. Class consists of number-translation services, such as call-forwarding and caller identification, available within a local exchange of Local Access and Transport Area (LATA). CLASS is a service mark of Bellcore. Some of the phone services which Bellcore promotes for CLASS are Automatic Callback, Automatic Recall, Calling Number Delivery, Customer Originated Trace, Distinctive Ringing/Call Waiting, Selective Call Forwarding and Selective Call Rejection. See also CALLING LINE IDENTIFICATION. 2. In an object-oriented programming environment, a class defines the data content of a specific type of object, the code that manipulates it, and the public and private programming interfaces to that code. See ANI and ISDN. 3. See also CLASS 1 and 2, below.

CLASS 1 Also called Class 1/EIA-578. It's an American standard used between facsimile application programs and facsimile modems for sending and receiving Class 1 faxes. The Class 1 interface is an extension of the EIA/TIA's (Electronics Industry Association and the Telecommunications Industry Association) specification for fax communication, known as Group III. Class 1 is a series of Hayes AT commands that can be used by software to control fax boards. In Class 1, both the T.30 (the data packet creation and decision making necessary for call setup) and ECM/BFT (error-correction mode/binary file transfer) are done by the computer. A specification being developed (fall of 1991) Class 2, will allow the modem to handle these functions in hardware. Industry analysts believe Class 2 will be the standard for the long haul, but approval is slow. Even so, some modem makers will shortly deliver data/fax modems. See also CLASS 1 OFFICE.

CLASS 1 OFFICE A regional toll telephone switching center. The highest level toll office in AT&T's long distance switching hierarchy. There are essentially five levels in the hierarchy, with the lowest level — Class 5 — being those central offices owned by the local telephone companies. Each of the classes can complete calls between themselves. But, if the routes are busy, then calls automatically climb the hierarchy. A Class 1 office is the office of "last resort."

CLASS 2 Also known as Class 2.0/EIA-592. An American standard used between facsimile application programs and facsimile modems for sending and receiving Class 2.0 faxes. This class places more of the task of establishing the fax connection onto the faxmodem, while continuing to rely on the host's processor to send and receive the image data. The Class 2 standard (known as PN-2388) is still under study by the EIA's (Electronic Industries Association) TR.29 committee, with further revisions expected. See CLASS 1.

CLASS 2 OFFICE The second level in AT&T's long distance toll switching hierarchy.

CLASS 3 OFFICE The third level in AT&T's long distance toll switching hierarchy.

CLASS 4 OFFICE The fourth level in AT&T's long distance toll switching hierarchy — the major switching center to which toll calls from Class 5 offices are sent. In U.S. common carrier telephony service, a toll center designated "Class 4C" is an office where assistance in completing incoming calls is provided in addition to other traffic. A toll center designated "Class 4P" is an office where operators handle only outbound calls, or where switching is performed without operator assistance.

CLASS 5 OFFICE An end office. Your local central office. The lowest level in the hierarchy of local and long distance switching which AT&T set up when it was "The Bell System." A class 5 office is a local Central Office that serves as a network entry point for station loops and certain special-service lines. Also called an End Office. Classes 1, 2, 3, and 4 are toll offices in the telephone network.

CLASS A CERTIFICATION A Federal Communications Commission (FCC) certification that a given make and model of computer meets the FCC's Class A limits for radio frequency emissions, which are designed for commercial and industrial environments. See CLASS B CERTIFICATION.

CLASS B CERTIFICATION A Federal Communications Commission (FCC) certification that a given make and model of computer meets the FCC's Class b limits for radio frequency emissions, which are designed to protect radio and television reception to residential neighborhoods from excessive radio frequency interference (RFI) generated by computer usage. Class B computers also are shielded more efficiently from external interface. Computers used at home are more likely to be surrounded by radio and television equipment. If you plan to use your computer at home, avoid computers that have only Class A certification (that is, they failed Class B).

CLASS n OFFICE The way a telephone company defines its switching facilities. Class 5 is an end office (local exchange), Class 4 is a toll center, Class 3 is a primary switching center, Class 2 is a sectional switching center, and Class 1 is a regional switching center. See CLASS 1, CLASS 2, CLASS 3, CLASS 4 and CLASS 5.

CLASS OF EMISSION The set of characteristics of an emission, designated by standard symbols, e.g., type of modulation of the main carrier, modulating signal, type of information to be transmitted, and also if appropriate, any additional signal characteristics.

CLASS OF OFFICE A ranking assigned to switching points in the telephone network, determined by function, interfaces and transmission needs.

CLASS OF SERVICE 1. Each phone in a system may have a different collection of privileges and features assigned to it, such as access to WATS lines. Class of Service assignments if properly organized, can become an important tool in controlling telephone abuse. 2. A subgrouping of telephone users for the sake of rate distinction. This may distinguish between individual and party lines, between Government lines and others, between those permitted to make unrestricted international dialed calls and others, between business or residence and coin, between flat rate and message rate, and between restricted and extended area service. 3. A category of data transmission provided in a public data network in which the data signaling rate, the terminal operating mode, and the code structure (if any) are standardized. This is defined within ITU-T Recommendations X.1.

CLASSICAL IP A set of specifications developed by the Internet Engineering Task Force (IETF) for the operation of LAN-to-LAN IP connectivity over an ATM network.

CLASSMARK A designator used to describe the service feature privileges, restrictions, and circuit characteristics for lines or trunks accessing a switch; e.g., precedence level, conference privilege, security level, zone restriction. See CLASS OF SERVICE.

CLC Carrier Liaison Committee. A committee formed to help industry participants work together to resolve the issues of implementing 800 Portability. CLC is sponsored by the Exchange Carriers Standards Association (ECSA) and is comprised of the LECs (local exchange carriers), long distance carriers and users of 800 service.

CLD COALITION Inc. Competitive Long Distance Coalition, a Washington, DC-based lobbying group.

CLEAR To cause one or more storage locations to be in a prescribed state, usually that corresponding to a zero or to the space character.

CLEAR CHANNEL 1. A digital circuit where no framing or control bits (i.e. for signaling) are required, thus making the full bandwidth available for communications. For example, a 56 Kbps circuit is typically a 64 Kbps digital circuit with 8 Kbps used for signaling. Sometimes called Switched 56, DDS or ADN. Each of the carriers have their own name for clear channel service. The phone companies are obsoleting the 56 Kbps service in favor of the more modern ISDN BRI, which has two 64 Kbps circuits and one 16 Kbps packet service, part of which is used for signaling on the 64 Kbps channels. 2. An SCSA term. A channel which is used exclusively for data transmission, with no bandwidth required for administrative messages such as signaling or synchronization. All SCbus data channels are clear.

CLEAR CONFIRMATION SIGNAL A call control signal to acknowledge reception of the DTE clear request by the DCE or the reception of the DCE clear indication by the DTE.

CLEAR COLLISION Contention that occurs when a DTE and a DCE simultaneously transfer a clear request packet and a clear indication packet specifying the same logical channel. The DCE will consider that the clearing is completed and will not transfer a DCE clear confirmation packet.

CLEAR TO SEND CTS. One of the standard attributes of a modem in which the receiving modem indicates to the calling modem that it is now ready to accept data. One of the standard pins used by the RS-232-C standard. In ITU-T V.24, the corresponding pin is called Ready For Sending.

CLEARINGHOUSE A service company that collects and processes roaming and billing information from a number of carriers. It then transfers the compiled data to the proper carriers for credits and billing.

CLEARLINE 1.5 A Sprint name for T-1 service. It is an all digital 1.544 Mbps private line service that connects two customer sites via dedicated T-1 access lines.

CLEARLINE 45 A Sprint name for DS-3 service. This high-capacity point-to-point private line service transmits voice, data, and video at 44.736 Mbps.

CLEARLINE FRACTIONAL 1.5 A Sprint name for all digital private line service which transmits voice, data, and video at speeds from 112/123 Kbps up to 672/768 Kbps - a fraction of a T-1, also called a DS-1. The service may be ordered in 56/64 Kbps increments from two channels (112/128 Kbps) to 12 channels (672/768 Kbps). Point-to-point service connects customer sites via dedicated T-1 access lines.

CLEAVING The controlled breaking of a fiber so that its end surface is smooth.

CLEOS Conference of the Lasers and Electro-Optics Society.

CLI Compression Labs, Inc. One of the foremost codec makers and developer of some of the first "low-bandwidth" codecs in the US. Their VTS 1.5 codec was one of the first two codes (the other was from NEC) to compress full-motion video to 1.5 Mbps (T-1 speed).

CLICK TONES Indicates acknowledgment by the cellular system that the cellular system's computer is processing the call.

CLICKSTREAMS The paths a user takes as he or she navigates cyberspace. Advertisers and online media providers are developing software that can accurately track user's clickstreams.

CLID Calling Number IDentification. Same as ANI (Automatic Number Identification), except CLID tends to refer to identification of local calling numbers. CLID tends to be referred to as a service of CLASS. See also CLASS and ANI.

CLIENT Clients are devices and software that request information. Clients are objects that uses the resources of another object. A client is a fancy name for a PC on a local area network. It used to be called a workstation. Now it is the "client" of the server. See also CLIENT SERVER, CLIENT SERVER MODEL, FAT CLIENT, MAINFRAME SERVER, MEDIA SERVER and THIN CLIENT.

CLIENT APPLICATION Any computer program making use of the processing resources of another program.

CLIENT OPERATING SYSTEM Operating System running on the client platform. See CLIENT.

CLIENT SERVER A computer on a local area network that you can request information or applications from. The idea is that you — the user — are the client and it — the slave — is the server. That was the original meaning of the term. Over time, client server began to refer to a computing system that splits the workload between desktop PCs (called "workstations") and one or more larger computers (called "servers") joined on a local area network (LAN). The splitting of tasks allow the use of desktop graphic user interfaces, like Microsoft's Windows or Apple Macintosh's operating system, which are easier to use (for most people) than the host/terminal world of mainframe computing, which placed a "dumb terminal" on a user's desk. That dumb terminal could only send and receive simple text-based material. And the less it sent, the faster it worked (lines were slow), so some of the "human interfaces" were very cryptic. You often were forced to spend weeks at school learning simple mainframe programs.

A good analogy of client-server computing, according to Peter Lewis of the New York Times is to think of client server as a restaurant where the waiter takes your order for a hamburger, goes to the kitchen and comes back with some raw meat and a bun. You get to cook the burger at your table and add your favorite condiments. In computerese, this is client/server, distributed computing, where some processing work is done by the customer at his or her table, instead of entirely in the kitchen (centralized computing in the old mainframe days). It sounds like more work, but it has many advantages. The service is faster. The food is cooked exactly to your liking, and the giant, expensive stove in the kitchen can be replaced by lots of cheap little grills. See CLIENT SERVER MODEL, DOWNSIZING, REENGINEERING and SERVER.

CLIENT SERVER MODEL In most cases, the "client" is a desktop computing device or program "served" by another networked computing device. Computers are integrated over the network by an application, which provides a single system image. The server can be a minicomputer, workstation, or microcomputer with attached storage devices. A client can be served by multiple servers.

CLIENT TELESCRIPT A General Magic term. Telescript that is integrated into the various client platforms including Macintosh, DOS/Windows, UNIX, PenPoint, and Newton.

CLIP Calling Line Identification Presentation, A wireless telecommunications term.A supplementary service provided under GSM (Global System for Mobile Communications).

CLIP ON TOLL FRAUD Clip on toll fraud occurs when someone connects a phone between someone else's phone (typically a coin phone) and the central office and makes unlawful toll calls. The term "clip on" comes because the telephone service thief "clips on" to the line. Clip on toll fraud is often done on COCOT (Customer Owned Coin Operated Telephone) phone lines because these lines do not enjoy the same protection from toll fraud which is afforded to coin phone lines which local telcos provide to their own coin phones.

CLIPBOARD A generic term for a place in software which holds text, pictures or images that you are copying or moving between applications. The clipboard is a temporary holding place only. When you cut or copy a new item it will replace the current clipboard contents. In other words, there's usually only one clipboard. Windows uses a clipboard and so does the Apple Macintosh.

CLIPBOOK A Windows NT term. Permanent storage of information you want to save and share with others. This differs from the Clipboard which temporarily stores information. You can save the current contents of the clipboard, which temporarily stores information. You can then share that information, allowing others to connect to the Clipboard. See CLIPBOOK PAGE.

CLIPBOOK PAGE A Windows NT term. A unit of information pasted into a local ClipBook. The ClipBook page is permanently saved. Information on a ClipBook page can be copied back onto the Clipboard and then pasted into documents. You can share ClipBook pages on the notework.

CLIPBOOK SERVICE A Windows NT term. Supports the ClipBook Viewer application, allowing pages to be seen by remote ClipBooks.

CLIPPER A circuit or device that limits the instantaneous output signal amplitude to a predetermined maximum value, regardless of the amplitude of the input signal. See CLIPPER CHIP.

CLIPPER CHIP A microprocessor chip, officially known as the MYK-78, which the Federal Government wants to add to phones and data communications equipment. The chip would ensure that conversations in Clipper-equipped communicating equipment would be private — from everybody except the Government. With a court-approved wiretap, an agency like the FBI, could listen in, since the Government would have the key to Clipper. On February 4, 194, the Clinton White House announced its approval of the Clipper chip and the "Crypto War" broke out — with many companies and individuals urging a stop to Clipper. In late Spring, 1994 an AT&T Bell Labs researcher revealed that he had found a serious flaw in the Clipper technology. As of writing it wasn't clear what would happen to the Clipper Chip. See NSA.

CLIPPING Clipping has two basic meanings. The first refers to the effect caused by a simplex (one way at a time) speakerphone. Here the conversation goes one way. When the other person wants to talk, the voice path has to reverse (to "flip"). While the flipping takes place, a few sounds are "clipped" from that person's conversation. This phenomenon happens on some long distance and many overseas channels. These channels are so expensive, they are simultaneously shared by many conversations. Gaps in your conversation are filled by other people's conversation. But when you start talking, the equipment has to recognize you're now talking, find some capacity for your conversation, and send it. In the process of doing this, your first word or part of your first word might be "clipped" and the conversation will sound "broken."

The second way your voice is clipped is what happens every day on the telephone. You're squeezing your own voice which typically spans 10,000 Hertz into a voice channel which is only 3,000 Hertz. This clips the extremes of your conversation — the higher sounds. As a result, your voice sounds flatter over the phone. As you become more economical and try to squeeze your voice into smaller capacity channels, so it becomes increasingly clipped.

CLIR Calling Line Identification Restriction, A wireless telecommunications term. A supplementary service provided under GSM (Global System for Mobile Communications).

CLLI CODE Pronounced silly code. When a phone company institutes trapping and tracing on a phone line, one of the pieces of information it can receive on incoming calls is the CLLI Code, a 11 character code that might look like "nycm-ny18dso." That says the call is coming in from New York City, Manhattan from a central office called 18DSO (which I happen to know is an AT&T 5E located on West 18th Street. See ANNOYANCE CALL BUREAU, TRAP and TRACE, and WIRE TAP.

CLM Career Limiting Move. An ill-advised activity. Trashing your boss while he or she is within earshot is a serious CLM.

CLOCK Exactly as it sounds. An oscillator-generated signal that provides a timing reference for a transmission link. A clock provides providing signals used in a transmission system to control the timing of certain functions such as the duration of signal elements or the sampling rate. It also generates periodic, accurately spaced signals used for such purposes as timing, regulation of the operations of a processor, or generation of interrupts. In short, a clock has two functions: 1. To generate periodic signals for synchronization on a transmission facility. 2. To provide a time base for the sampling of signal elements. Used in computers, a clock synchronizes certain procedures, such as communication with other devices. It simply keeps track of time, which allows computers to do the same things at the same time so they don't "bump into each other."

CLOCK BIAS The difference between the GPS clock's indicated time and true universal time. GPS is Global Positioning System. See GPS.

CLOCK CYCLE The time that elapses from one read or write operation to another in the main memory of a computer's central processing unit (CPU). The more tasks that can be accomplished per cycle, the more efficient the chip. Some chips like the i860 chip can execute two instructions and three operations per clock cycle.

CLOCK DIFFERENCE A measure of the separation between the respective time marks of two clocks. Clock differences must be reported as algebraic quantities measured on the same time scale. The date of the measurement should be given.

CLOCK SPEED Each CPU contains a special clock circuitry which is connected to a quartz crystal (same as the one in your watch). The quartz crystal's vibrations, which are very fast, coordinate the CPU's operation, keeping everything in step. CPU clock speeds are measured in megahertz, or MHz, which stands for "million cycles per second." The clock speeds of today's computer range from a slow of 4.77 MHz (the original IBM PC) to 25 MHz with some Intel 80386 based machines. Clock speed is a misleading term. It is only one way of measuring the speed of a computer. One other critical way is how fast you can read and write information to the hard disk. How important that is depends on whether you're running a program with lots of access to your hard disk (like a database program) or running a program which uses a lot of calculations in RAM, i.e. a spreadsheet.

CLOCK TOLERANCE The maximum permissible departure of a clock indication from a designated time reference such as Coordinated Universal Time.

CLOCKING In synchronous communication, a periodic signal used to synchronize transmission and reception of data and control characters.

CLOCKWISE POLARIZED WAVE An elliptically or circularly polarized electromagnetic wave in which the direction of rotation of the electric vector is clockwise as seen by an observer looking in the direction of propagation of the wave.

CLONE FRAUD A way of using cellular phones to steal phone calls. In clone fraud, a legitimate serial number is programmed into an imposter's cellular telephone. This allows unauthorized calling to go on until a huge bill appears on the mailbox of the bewildered subscriber to whom the serial number actually belongs. Crooks get the numbers because the numbers are broadcast with every cellular call and can be picked up by ordinary radio scanners, which you can often buy at your local electronics store. See CLONED PHONE and TUMBLING.

CLONED PHONE A cellular phone has two basic ways it identifies itself to the cellular phone company it wants to use — its own telephone number (which can be changed) and a special secret number that's embedded into silicon inside the phone. That number is called an Electronic Serial Number, or ESN. When the phone wants to make a call, it sends those numbers and the cellular carrier uses them to check if the call is authorized. But because the information is traveling through the air, anyone with a scanner can pick up the information and retransmit it later, thus creating a "cloned phone" and pretending that he's authorized to make the call. Of course, the owner of the cloned phone ultimately gets the bill and a nasty shock.

CLOSE COUPLING The condition in which two coils are placed in close magnetic relation to each other, thus establishing a high degree of mutual induction.

CLOSE TALK A voice recognition term. An arrangement where a microphone is fewer than four inches from the speaker's mouth.

CLOSED ARCHITECTURE Proprietary design that is compatible only with hardware and software from a single vendor of single product family. Contrast with OPEN ARCHITECTURE.

CLOSED END The end of a Foreign Exchange — FX — line which ends on a PBX, a key system or a telephone. The closed end is the end of the circuit beyond which a call cannot progress further. The other end of the FX circuit is called the "open end," because calls can progress further.

CLOSED LOOP SYSTEM A closed electrical circuit into which a standard signal is feed and received instantly. A measure of the difference between the input signal and the output signal is a measure of the error, and potentially what's causing it.

CLOSED USER GROUP A group of specified users of a data network that is assigned a facility that permits them to communicate with each other but precludes communications with other users of the service or services.

CLOSURE A cabinet, pedestal, or case used to enclose cable sheath openings necessary for splicing or terminating fibers.

CLOUD Some of the newer high-speed data, phone company-offered services resemble a local area network. You connect to them directly. To make a call, you don't actually dial a number as you do on a circuit-switched service, you just transmit, putting an address at the front of your transmission. The service reads the address and sends it where you want. Like a LAN, everything is connected and on line. The concept is get stuff sent from one place to another much faster than would be possible if you had to wait to dial, for the circuit to be set up, for the machine at the other end to answer, etc. In these high-speed services, the circuit is "always set up." The provider (the phone company) refers to its network as a "cloud." And when you see diagrams of these newer high-speed services, like SMUTS and frame relay, you see the carrier portion drawn as a cloud (like the one you see in the sky). Services with "clouds" are also called "connectionless." See the various definitions below beginning with CONNECTIONLESS.

CLNP Connectionless Network Protocol. An OSI network layer protocol that does not require a circuit to be established before data is transmitted. The OSI protocol for providing the OSI Connectionless Network Service (data gram service). CLNP is the OSI equivalent to Internet IP, and is sometimes called ISO IP.

CLTS ConnectionLess Transport Service.

CLUSTER 1. Collection of terminals or other devices in a single location. A cluster control unit and a cluster controller in IBM 3270 systems are devices that control the input/output operations of a group (cluster) of display stations. 2. Unit of storage allocation used by MS-DOS usually consisting of four or more 512-byte sectors. 3. Physical grouping of workstations that share one or more panel runs.

CLUSTER CONTROLLER A device that can control input/output operations of more than one device connected to it (e.g. a terminal). An interface between several bisynchronous devices and a PAD, NC or communication facility. The cluster controller handles remote communications processing for its attached devices. Most common types are IBM 327X.

CLUSTER SIZE An operating function or term describing the number of sectors that the operating system allocates each time disk space is needed.

CLUT An imaging term. Color Look-Up Table. The palette used in an indexed color system. Usually consists of 256 colors.

CM Configuration Management. A wireless telecommunications term. The tracking, coordination, and administration of software and hardware related to telecommunication or information systems. Versions are controlled and tracked.

CMC Common Messaging Calls. A messaging standard defined by the X.400 API Association. CMC 1.0 defines a basic set of calls to inject and extract messages and files and access address information. CMC is intended to define a useful common denominator across a wide variety of messaging systems. The idea is that an electronic mail system, no matter how crude, should be able to support a CMC front end. CMC's major "competition" is MAPI — Messaging Application Programming Interface — from Microsoft, though simple MAPI is almost identical to CMC.

CMIP Common Management Information Protocol. A protocol formally adopted by the International Standards Organization in Paris (ISO), used for exchanging network management information. Typically, this information is exchanged between two management stations. CMIP can, however, be used to exchange information between an application and a management station. CMIP has been designed for OSI networks, but it is transport independent. Theoretically, it could run across a variety of transports, including, for example, IBM's Systems Network Architecture. See CMIP/CMIS.

CMIP/CMIS Common Management Information Protocol/Common Management Information Services. An OSI network management protocol/service interface created and standardized by ISO for managing heterogeneous networks.

CMISE Common Management Information Service Element. A wireless telecommunications term. The functionality provided by CMIP in transporting network management information.

CMOL Short for "CMIP Over Logical Link Control". An implementation of the CMIP protocol over the second layer of the OSI protocol stack, to be proposed as a standard by 3 Com Corp. and IBM. The goal of CMOL is to create agents that require significantly less memory than CMIP implemented over OSI, or SNMP implemented over UDP.

CMOS Complementary Metal Oxide Semiconductor. A technology for making integrated circuits known for requiring less electricity. See also COMPLEMENTARY METAL OXIDE SEMICONDUCTOR.

CMOS RAM Complementary Metal Oxide Semiconductor Random Access Memory. Memory which contains a personal computer's configuration information. CMOS RAM must have continuous power to preserve its memory. This power is typically supplied by a lithium battery.

CMOS SETUP A program which prepares the system to work. CMOS setup records your PC's hardware configuration information into CMOS RAM. It must be modified when you add, change or remove hardware.

CMOT CMIP Over TCP/IP. An Internet standard defining the use of CMIP for managing TCP/IP local area networks.

CMP Communications Plenum Cable.

CMS 1. Call Management System. This is the AT&T label for their inbound call distribution management reporting package. CMS is found on the Horizon, the Merlin, S/75 and S/85 PBX/ACDs. CMS is the successor product to AEMIS/PRO 150/500.

2. Call Management Services. Canadian term for local calling features based on CLID (Calling Line Identification).

CMS 8800 Cellular Mobile Telephone Service (North American version).

CMTS CMTS stands for the Cellular Mobile Telephone System. The original and still, most common CMTS is a low-powered, duplex, radio/telephone which operates between 800 and 900 MHZ, using multiple transceiver sites linked to a central computer for coordination. The sites, or "cells,", named for their honeycomb shape, cover a range of one to six, or more, miles in each direction. The cells overlap one another and operate at different transmitting and receiving frequencies in order to eliminate crosstalk when transmitting from cell to cell. Each cell can accommodate up to 45 different voice channel transceivers. When a cellular phone is activated, it searches available channels for the strongest signal and locks onto it. While in motion, if the signal strength begins to fade, the telephone will automatically switch signal frequencies or cells as necessary without operator assistance. If it fails to find an acceptable signal, it will display an "out of service" or "no service" message, indicating that it has reached the limit of its range and is unable to communicate. Each cellular telephone has a unique identification number which allows the Mobile Telephone Switching Office (MTSO) to track and coordinate all mobile phones in its service area. This ID number is known as the Electronic Security Number (ESN). The ESN and cellular phone's telephone Number are NOT the same. The ESN is a permanent number engraved into a memory chip called a PROM or EPROM, located in the telephone chassis. This number cannot be changed through programming as the telephone number can, although it can be replaced. Each time the telephone is used, it transmits its ESN to the MTSO by means of DTMF tones during the dialing sequence. The MTSO may be able to determine which ESNs are good or bad, thus individual numbers can be banned from use within the system. See also CELL and CELLULAR.

CMY A computer imaging term. A color model used by the printing industry that is based on mixing cyan, magenta, and yellow. It's also referred to as CMYK, with the K denoting black. The K was added after printers discovered they could obtain a darker black using special black colorants rather than by combining cyan, magenta, and yellow alone. See also CMYK.

CMYK A computer imaging term. A color model used by the printing industry that is based on mixing cyan, magenta, yellow and black (called "K.") It used to be called CMY. The K was added after printers discovered they could obtain a darker black using special black colorants rather than by combining cyan, magenta, and yellow. CMYK is the basis of what's known now as "four-color" printing. But there is also five, six, seven and eight color printing, etc. Each of these "extra" colors are basically "colors" which are better printed as their own color rather than by printing a combination the basic three. Silver, copper, gold, aluminum, etc. are all printed traditionally as extra colors, and extra passes through the printer.

CNA Cooperative Network Architecture.

CNC Complementary Network Service. See OPEN NETWORK ARCHITECTURE.

CND Calling Number Delivery.

CNE Certified (local area) Network Engineer. When you graduate from Novell's third level class, you become a certified network engineer. It costs a small fortune to go to all the required Novell classes. As a result, there are few CNE around. They're a rare breed.

CNET Centre National d'etudes de Telecommunication. The French organization that approves telecommunications products for sale in France.

CNG Also called Auto Fax Tone, or Calling Tone. This tone is the sound produced by virtually all fax machines when they dial another fax machine. CNG is a medium pitch tone (1100 Hz) that lasts 1/2 second and repeats every 3 1/2 seconds. A fax machine will produce CNG for about 45 seconds after it dials. The CNG tone is useful for owners of fax/phone/modem switches. Such switches answer an incoming call. If they hear a CNG tone, they will transfer the call to a fax machine. If they don't, they'll transfer the call to a phone, answering machine or perhaps a modem. Depends on how they're set up. Some fax machines do not transmit a CNG tone with manually-dialed transmissions — i.e. where the caller picked up the handset on the fax machine, dialed and waited for high-pitched squeal before pushing his fax machine's "start" button. A manual dialed fax transmission will "fool" fax/voice switches. See CED and FACSIMILE.

CNM An ATM an d SMDS (Switched Megabit Data Service) term. Customer Network Management. All activities that customers perform to manage their communications networks. SMDS CNM service enables customers to directly manage many aspects of the SMDS service provided by telecommunications carriers. See CUSTOMER NETWORK MANAGEMENT.

CNO Corporate Networking Officer, a term invented by William Y. O'Connor, CEO of Ascom Timeplex.

CNR Telephone company term for re-scheduling a telephone installation appointment because the "Customer is Not Ready."

CNRI Corporation for National Research Initiatives.

CNS Complementary Network Service. CNSs are basic services associated with end user's lines that make it easier for Enhanced Service Providers (ESPs) to offer them enhanced services. Some examples of CNSs include Call Forwarding Busy/Don't Answer, Three Way Calling, and Virtual Dial Tone. See OPEN NETWORK ARCHITECTURE.

CO Central Office. In North America, a CO is that location which houses a switch to serve local telephone subscribers. Sometimes the words "central office" are confused with the switch itself. In Europe and abroad, the words "central office" are not known. The more common words are "public exchange." But those words tend to refer more to the switch itself, rather than the site, as in North America.

CO was the name of a magazine published by Telecom Library Inc., the publisher of this dictionary. See also CENTRAL OFFICE or PUBLIC EXCHANGE.

CO LINES These are the lines connecting your office to your local telephone company"s Central Office which in turn connects you to the nationwide telephone system.

CO LOCATION See COLOCATION.

CO SIMULATOR A desktop device which pretends to act like a mini-central office. The smallest version will consist of two lines and two REJ-11 jacks. Plug a phone into both jacks. Pick up one phone. You hear dial tone. Dial or touchtone two or three digits. Bingo, the second phone rings. You pick up the second phone. You can have a conversation with yourself or with a machine — like a voice processing system. Most central office simulators can simulate normal on-hook, off-hook, dialing, answering, speaking, etc. Some now can simulate caller ID features — including number of person calling.

CO-LOCATION The ability of a someone who is not the local phone company to put their equipment in the phone company's offices and join their equipment to the phone company's equipment. That "someone" who might co-locate their equipment on the phone company's premises might be an end-user or it might be another local or long distance telecommunications company. It might even be a competitor of the local phone company, i.e. another local phone company. The idea of co-location is to save money, give better service, ensure better interconnection, get technical problems solved faster, etc. Not all local phone companies offer their customers co-location. New York Telephone and New England Telephone are two that now do. Also spelled collocation. See also VIRTUAL CO-LOCATION.

COAM Customer Owned And Maintained equipment.

COASTING MODE In timing-dependent systems, a free-running operational timing mode in which continuous or periodic measurement of timing error is not available. In some systems, operation in this mode can be enhanced for a period of time by using clock or timing error (or correction) information obtained during a prior tracking mode to estimate clock or timing corrections to be made in the free-running mode.

COATED FILAMENT A vacuum tube filament coated with a metallic oxide to provide greater electron emission and longer life.

COATING A protective material (usually plastic) applied to the optical fiber immediately after drawing to preserve its mechanical strength and cushion it from external forces that can induce microbending losses.

COAXIAL CABLE A cable composed of an insulated central conducting wire wrapped in another cylindrical conducting wire. The whole thing is usually wrapped in another insulating layer and an outer protective layer. A coaxial cable has great capacity to carry great quantities of information. It is typically used to carry high-speed data (as in connections of 327X terminals to computer hosts) and in CATV (multiplexed TV stations).

COB Close Of Business.

COBOL Common Business Oriented Language. A very popular computer programming language for business applications.

COBRA An MCI definition. Surveillance and test equipment for LADNER monitoring: not yet functioning.

COBWEB SITE A World Wide Web site that hasn't been updated for a long time. A dead Web page.

COC Central Office Connection. Separately tariffed part of T-1 circuit.

COCOT Customer Owned Coin Operated Telephone. See also CLIP ON TOLL FRAUD.

CODE The system of dots and dashes used to represent the letters of the alphabet, numerals, punctuation and other symbols.

CODE BIT The smallest signaling element used by the Physical Layer for transmission on the fiber cable.

CODE BLOCKING A switch's ability to block calls to a specified area code, central office code or phone number.

CODE CALL ACCESS A very useful PBX feature. It allows attendants and extension users to activate, by dialing an access code followed by a two or three digit called code, customer-provided signaling devices throughout the premises. The signaling devices then issue a series of tones or visual coded signals corresponding to the called code. The called or paged party responds by dialing a meet-me answering code from any phone and is then connected to the paging party.

CODE COVERAGE Modern computer telephony systems are composed largely of software, or "code." Invariably this code has many different logic paths and options. During normal system usage, many code paths are used only infrequently, if at all, meaning that normal usage will really only test a small portion of the total system. Code coverage refers to the amount of the system code that has been accessed during the testing of the system. The greater the code coverage, the more code that has been tested. 100% code coverage means that all the code has been tested. The amount of code coverage that has been achieved is usually determined through the use of a code coverage tool. Code coverage tools are available for most computer operating systems. Code coverage is especially important for computer telephony applications because many features are only infrequently used or are turned on or off based on the user's class of service. Also, many features interact with other features and the use of one feature often turns off another. Functional anomalies frequently exist in little-used paths and feature interactions. Tests should be designed to make sure that all code paths have been accessed and are adequately exercised. This definition courtesy of Steve Gladstone, author of the book Testing Computer Telephony Systems, available from 212-691-8215.

CODE CONVERSION A process which converts the codes coming in from one network into codes that can be recognized on another network, such as converting from the Baudot code in a telex network to the ASCII code on the TWX network. Usually, the hardware will convert differences in transmission speed.

CODE DIVISION MULTIPLE ACCESS CDMA, also called Spread Spectrum, is a name for a new form of digital cellular phone service. The idea is that each phone call is combined with a code which only one cellular phone plucks from the air. Business Week said CDMA works "by spreading all signals across the same broad frequency spectrum and assigning a unique code — the company says one of 42 billion — to each. The dispersed signals are pulled out of the background noise by a receiver which knows the code. This method, developed by a San Diego company called Qualcomm Inc. is very new. Much of the equipment to support it — like the cellular switches have not yet been developed." CDMA is also being used by wireless PBXs. See CDMA for a longer and better explanation.

CODE EXCITED LINEAR PREDICTION CELP. An analog-to-digital voice coding scheme.

CODE INDEPENDENT DATA COMMUNICATION Data communication mode using a link procedure associated with the character and not dependent on the set of characters or the code used by the data source.

CODE LEVEL Number of bits used to represent a character.

CODE OF FEDERAL REGULATIONS CFR. CFR is a codification of the general and permanent rules published in the Federal Register. It is divided into 50 titles that represent broad areas subject to federal regulation. Title 47 of the CFR pertains to telecommunications and contains the rules covering Part 22 Common Carriers and Part 90 Private Carriers.

CODE VIOLATION Violation of a coding rule; for example, the AMI coding rule is corrupted by a bipolar violation.

CODEC Originally CODEC stood for CODer-DECoder, i.e. microprocessor chip. Now the PC industry thinks it stands for COmpression/DEcompression, i.e. an overall term for the technology used in digital video and stereo audio. The original CODEC (still in big use in today's telephony industry) converts voice signals from their analog form to digital signals acceptable to modern digital PBXs and digital transmission systems. It then converts those digital signals back to analog so that you may hear and understand what the other person is saying. In some phone systems, the CODEC is in the PBX and shared by many analog phone extensions. In other phone systems, the CODEC is actually in the phone. Thus the phone itself sends out a digital signal and can, as a result, be more easily designed to accept a digital RS-232-C signal.

CODEC CONVERSION The back-to-back transfer of an analog signal from one codec into another codec in order to convert from one proprietary coding scheme (for instance, that used by CLI) to one used by another codec manufacturer (PictureTel, VTEL, GPT, BT, NEC, etc). The analog signal, instead of being displayed to a monitor, is delivered to the dissimilar codec where it is redigitized, compressed and passed to the receiving end. This is obviously a bi-directional process. Conversion service is offered by carriers such as AT&T, MCI and Sprint.

CODED CHARACTER SET A set of unambiguous rules that establish a character set and the one-to-one relationships between the characters of the set and their coded representations.

CODED IMAGE A representation of an image in a form suitable for storage and processing.

CODED TRUNKS You buy several trunks. They hunt on. The main number is 555-3000. If the main number is busy, the call goes to the next line. There are two types of "next lines." One type can have an actual number, like 555-3001, which you can call directly. The other can be a coded trunk with no actual number and which you can't call directly. It's better to have no coded trunks because it's hard to test coded trunks. You can't dial them directly. Actual dial-able numbers are better.

CODER An analog-to-digital converter that changes analog voice signals to their digital equivalents. See CODEC.

CODIAL OFFICE CDO. A small central office designed for unattended operation in a distant community. Usually a community dial office is fairly small, rarely more than 10,000 lines.

CODING THEORY Mathematical theory describing how to encode data into streams of digital symbols at transmitter and decode it at receiver to maximize accuracy of data presented to user.

COHERENCE AREA In optical communications, the area in a plane perpendicular to the direction of propagation over which light may be considered highly coherent.

COHERENCE LENGTH The propagation distance over which a light beam may be considered coherent. See COHERENT LIGHT.

COHERENT LIGHT Light emitted from laser and some light-emitting-diodes. It is made up of light of a single frequency in which all the light waves are in phase (i.e., their wave peaks and troughs are all in alignment so the waves reinforce or amplify each other.)

COIL A number of turns of wire, so wound as to afford inductance.

COIL ANTENNA One consisting of one or more complete turns of wire. See LOOP ANTENNA.

COIN ACCEPTOR/REJECTOR A mechanical or electromechanical device that checks and validates the coins deposited in a coin pay phone. They measure the coin's size and weight and steel content. These coin acceptor/rejector units transmit the value of the coin deposits to the processing part of a smart payphone or they signal the information to the telephone company central office via coded tones.

COIN SUPERVISORY TRUNK GROUP A trunk group that lets a switchboard operator collect overtime monies due on coin phones and check for stuck coins.

COIN TELEPHONE A pay telephone that takes coins. The coin telephone was invented by William Gray, an American whose previous inventions included the inflatable chest protector for baseball players. Mr. Gray's first phone lacked a dial. Its instructions read:

"Call Central in the usual manner. When told by the operator, drop coin in proper channel and push plunger down."

In today's nomenclature, Mr. Gray's original phone is known as a post-pay coin phone. See also PAYPHONE and several entries following it.

COLD DOCKING Docking is to insert a portable computer into a base unit. Cold docking means the computer must begin from a power-off state and restart before docking. Hot docking means the computer can be docked while running at full power.

COLD START Everything starts from scratch. The power to the computer or telephone system is turned off. Everything in the system's volatile memory is erased.

A cold start may be needed on a microcomputer when something has happened to "lock up" the keyboard and the Reset button (if there is one) doesn't clear the problem completely. A Cold Start is also needed when you want to load a new operating system. When your phone system gives troubles you find hard to diagnose, turn it off, count to ten and turn it on. This cold boot to your phone system will often fix the problem, as it will typically do on a computer system.

COLLABORATION A multimedia term. Collaboration involves two or more people working together in real-time, or in a "store-and-forward" mode. Applications will enable a group of people to collaborate in real-time over the network using shared screens, shared whiteboards, and video conferencing. Collaboration can range from two people reviewing a slide set on line to a conference of doctors at different locations sharing patient files and discussing treatment options.

COLLABORATING Two or more people working together on a project to share information and ideas, view suggestions, and make modifications. Computers can enable users to collaborate in real-time over a network or phone line using tools such as shared documents, shared whiteboards, and video conferencing, or time-efficient workflow such as document forwarding.

COLLAPSED BACKBONE The backbone network connecting all network segments is contained within a hub, allowing for the possibility of speeds far exceeding the standard backbone media.

COLLOCATION See CO-LOCATION.

COLLECT CALL A telephone call in which the called person pays for the call. The person calling calls a number and asks that the call be made "collect." Sometimes collect calls are handled by live operators, sometimes by machines. In a collect call, the phone company has to get some authorization from the person receiving the call that he will pay for it. This may be done by saying "Yes" or hitting a button a touchtone phone.

COLLECTOR RING Metallic ring generally on the armature of a generator in contact with brushes for completing the circuit to a rotating member.

COLLIMATE The condition of parallel light rays.

COLLIMATION The process by which a divergent or convergent beam of electromagnetic radiation is converted into a beam with the minimum divergence or convergence possible for that system (ideally, a parallel bundle of rays).

COLLINEAR ANTENNA A cellular car antenna which looks like a pigtail, because it has a little curlicue in the middle. The curlicue is not a spring, but a clever bit of electro-mechanical magic known as a phasing network, which allows the antenna to boost the effective power of the transmitter's signal. Typically a collinear cellular car antenna is 13 inches high.

COLLISION The result of two workstations trying to use a shared transmission medium (cable) simultaneously. The electrical signals, which carry the information they are sending bump into each other. This ruins both signals and both will have to re-transmit their information. In most systems, a built in delay will make sure the collision does not occur again. The whole process takes fractions of a second. Collisions in LANs make no sound. Collisions do, however, slow a LAN down. See ALOHA, COLLISION DETECTION and CONTENTION.

COLLISION DETECTION The process of detecting that simultaneous (and therefore damaging) transmission has taken place. Typically, each transmitting workstation that detects the collision will wait some period of time and try again. Collision detection is an essential part of the CSMA/CD access method. Workstations can tell that a collision has taken place if they do not receive an acknowledgement from the receiving station within a certain amount of time (fractions of a second). See ALOHA, CONTENTION and ETHERNET.

COLLISION WINDOW The time it takes for a data pulse to travel the length of the network. During this interval, the network is vulnerable to collision.

COLOCATION A competing local phone company can locate its switches within a local exchange company's (LEC) central office. See also CO LOCATION.

COLOPHON Did you ever notice a paragraph at the end of a book describing the typefaces used, the production methods, and so forth? That little paragraph is called a colophon.

COLOR CODE A color system for circuit identification by use of solid colors, contrasting stripes, tracers, braids, surface marking, etc.

COLOR DIFFERENCE SIGNAL The first step in encoding the color television signal. The color difference signals are formed by subtracting the luminance information from each primary color: red, green or blue. Color difference conventions include the Betacam format, the SMPTE format, the EBU-N10 format and the MII format.

COLOR MODEL A technique for describing a color (see CMY, HSL, HSV, and RGB).

COLUMN A database definition: The logical equivalent of a field, a column contains an individual data item within a row or record.

COMBAT NET RADIO CNR. A radio operating in a network, providing a half-duplex circuit employing a single radio frequency or a discrete set of radio frequencies (frequency hopping). Combat net radios are primarily used for command and control of combat, combat support, and combat service support operations between and among ground, naval, and airborne forces.

COMCODE AT&T's numbering system for telecom equipment, replacing older KS-prefix numbers, and supplements standard industry part designations. Comcode No. 102092848 is touchtone Princess phone with a transparent plastic housing. How many would you like to order? See also KS NUMBER.

COMBINATION SYSTEM An alternative to upgrading older telephone equipment, combination systems makes it possible to add network-based features to an equipment-based telephone system.

COMBINATION TRUNK A central office trunk circuit which is available as either an incoming or outgoing circuit to the attendant and also available through dial access to internal phone users for outgoing calls.

COMBINED DISTRIBUTION FRAME CDF. A distribution frame that combines the functions of main and intermediate distribution frames. The frame contains both vertical and horizontal terminating blocks. The vertical blocks are used to terminate the permanent outside lines entering the station. Horizontal blocks are used to terminate inside plant equipment. This arrangement permits the association of any outside line with any desired terminal equipment. These connections are made with equipment. These connections are made with twisted pair wire, normally referred to as jumper wire, or with optical fiber cables, normally referred to as jumper cables. In technical control facilities, the vertical side may be used to terminate equipment as well as outside lines. The horizontal side is then used for jackfields and battery terminations.

COMBINED STATION MDLC station containing both a primary and a secondary and used in asynchronous balanced mode.

COMINT COMunications INTelligence.

COMMA-FREE CODE A code constructed such that any partial code word, beginning at the start of a code word but terminating prior to the end of that code word, is not a valid code word. The comma-free property permits the proper framing of transmitted code words, provided that: (a) external synchronization is provided to identify the start of the first code word in a sequence of code words, and (b) no uncorrected errors occur in the symbol stream. Huffman codes (variable length) are examples of comma-free codes.

COMMAND See COMMAND SET.

COMMAND AND CONTROL C2. The exercise of authority and direction by a properly designated commander over assigned forces in the accomplishment of the mission. Command and control functions are performed through an arrangement of personnel equipment, communications, facilities, and procedures employed by a commander in planning, directing, coordinating, and controlling forces and operations in the accomplishment of the mission.

COMMAND AND CONTROL SYSTEM The facilities, equipment, communications, procedures, and personnel essential to a commander for planning, directing and controlling operations of assigned forces pursuant to the missions assigned. See COMMAND, CONTROL and COMMUNICATIONS.

COMMAND BUFFER A segment of memory used to temporarily store commands. The command buffer only holds a copy of the last command issued.

COMMAND CONFERENCE SYSTEM A conference calling arrangement in a Northern Telecom PBX which allows a designated phone to originate a conference to and between a group of PBX extensions. Any phone that is busy when the conference begins is automatically connected to the conference as soon as that phone becomes free.

COMMAND, CONTROL AND COMMUNICATIONS C3. The capabilities required by military commanders to exercise command and control of their forces.

COMMAND LINE INTERPRETER CLI. A Rolm user interface to the CBX software and used for things like testing.

COMMAND NET A communications network which connects an echelon of command with some or all of its subordinate echelons for the purpose of command control. See C2 and C3.

COMMAND PATH The list of path names that tells MS-DOS where to look for files that aren't in the current directory.

COMMAND PORT In network management systems an interface used to monitor and control the system.

COMMAND PROCESSOR The MS-DOS program, COMMAND.COM, that contains all DOS's internal commands, like DIR, ERASE and REName. Once you have your hard disk set up, it's a good idea to made your COMMAND.COM "read only." This way it will be difficult for anyone to erase the file. If you don't have COMMAND.COM on your disk, or don't have it in a place where MS-DOS can find it, your disk will not boot (i.e. start) your computer. The command to make COMMAND.COM read only is

> ATTRIB +R COMMAND.COM

A mistake many novices make is to "open" COMMAND.COM using their word processor, find that it's full of "junk," then save the file. Saving COMMAND.COM with a word processor destroys COMMAND.COM. The next time you start your computer it will "hang." The solution: Boot from a floppy. Erase COMMAND.COM and REName COMMAND.BAK to COMMAND.COM. Reboot your machine again. This time it should work. If it doesn't, copy COMMAND.COM from your original MS-DOS disk.

COMMAND PROMPT The MS-DOS command prompt appears on the screen as the default drive letter followed by a greater-than > sign. The command prompt lets you know MS-DOS is ready to receive a command. You can use the PROMPT command to change the command prompt. The PROMPT I prefer is

> prompt.$_　　DATE $d　　TIME $t $_$P$g

And it looks like this

> DATE Tues 10-11-1994 TIME 14:49:00.00
>
> C:\BIN\HARRY>

Don't forget to type the period after the word "prompt."

COMMAND SAVE A Rockwell ACD term. The introduction of a new demand command defines up to 10 commands per terminal position to enhance the productivity of both IST and non-IST supervisors.

COMMAND SET In computer telephony, a command set is a collection of special software instructions that do special jobs. These software instructions are often called function calls. For example, the command M_Make_Call (plus parameters) tells Northern's Norstar phone system to have telephone set number 21 dial a phone number. Northern's Norstar and other open phone systems (those that can be commanded by an external computer which you and I can program) all have their own command sets. Each command set is made up of function calls with funny words like M_Make_Call. Typically those function calls work in C, a common software language. A function call will reach into the specialized driver that controls the phone system (an exact analogy is the driver that drives a laser printer) and get the phone system to do something. A programmer must use these function calls if he/she wants to control the phone system from software. Exactly how M_Make_Call works is typically not revealed to the programmer. That keeps the manufacturer's technology proprietary and secret. It also saves the programmer the time and expense of writing the driver.

COMMDESK BANKER A communications software package offered by MCI International that provides all the capabilities of COMMDesk, plus a security feature essential for financial transactions.

COMMDesk MANAGER An MCI definition. A communications software package designed to run on an IBM PC/XT/AT or compatible that gives the user full access to all MCI International and MCI communications services.

COMMERCENET A nonprofit group that works to accelerate the application of electronic commerce on the Internet. www.commerce.net/information/about.html

COMMERCIAL BUILDING TELECOMMUNICATIONS WIRING STANDARD In 1985, the Electronic Industries Association undertook the task of developing a standard for commercial and industrial building wiring. Approved and published on July 9, 1991, the EIA/TIA-568 "Commercial Building Telecommunications Wiring Standard" defines a generic wiring system which will support a multiproduct, multivendor environment and which will have a useful life of over 10 years. The EIA/TIA standard is based on star topology in which each workstation is connected to a telecommunications closet situated within 90 meters of the work area. Backbone wiring between the communications closets and the main cross-connect is also organized in a star topology. However, direct connections between closets are allowed to accommodate bus and ring configurations. Distances between closets and the main cross-connect are dependent on backbone cable types and applications. Each workstation is to be provided with a minimum of two communications outlets (which may be on the same faceplate). One outlet is supported by a four-pair, 100-ohm ushielded twisted-pair (UTP) cable. The other may be supported by (a) an additional four-pair UTP cable, (b) a two-pair, 150 ohm shielded twisted pair (STP) cable or (c) a two-fiber 62.5 /125 micron fiber optic cable. For more on cabling and cabling components, see CATEGORY OF PERFORMANCE.

COMMERCIAL INTERNET The part of the Internet provided by commercial services. Allows business usage of the Internet without violating the appropriate usage clause of the National Science Foundation NETwork (NSFNET), who actually runs the Internet.

COMMERCIAL INTERNET EXCHANGE ASSOCIATION This is a nonprofit trade association for public data internetworking service providers. www.cix.org/cixhome.html

COMMITTED INFORMATION RATE CIR. When a customer buys a shared service like frame relay, he commits to a certain minimum data transmission rate he will use. The monthly bill a customer will receive will include two elements — usage and a charge for the committed rate. In the early days of frame relay when few people were using the service, customers were opting for a low committed information, thus keeping their bills low, but knowing that they could always get their transmissions through — because there were few other people on the service. As the service got more popular, many customers found they had to hike their committed information rate if they wanted to get their information through. For a more technical explanation, see CIR.

COMMON AUDIBLE The same as Common Bell. Ringer wiring is such that ringing occurs on more than one CO or PBX line.

COMMON BATTERY A battery (or several batteries) that acts as a central source of energy for many pieces of equipment. In many telecommunications applications, a common battery provides 48 volts of power to a central office switch and to all its phones.

COMMON BATTERY SIGNALING A system in which the signaling power of a telephone is supplied by the battery at the servicing switchboard. Switchboards may be manual or automatic, and "talking power" may be supplied by common or local battery.

COMMON BELL A bell or ringer which sounds when any of the lines terminating on that phone rings. A term harking back to 1A2 key system days.

COMMON BUSINESS LINE CBL. An option with 800 Service that has been replaced by 800 Business Line.

COMMON CARRIER A company that furnishes communications services to the general public. It is typically licensed by a state or federal government agency. A common carrier cannot refuse to carry you, your information or your freight as long as you conform to the rules and regulations as filed with the state or federal authorities. See OTHER COMMON CARRIER.

COMMON CARRIER BUREAU A department of the Federal Communications Commission responsible for recommending and implementing regulatory policies on interstate and international common carrier (voice, video, data) activities.

COMMON CHANNEL INTEROFFICE SIGNALING CCIS. A way of transmitting all signaling information for a group of trunks by encoding that information and transmitting it over a separate channel using time-division digital methods. By transmitting that signaling information over a separate channel, CCIS saves huge long distance bandwidth, which in the past was used to switch calls across the country only to find a busy signal and then come all the way back again to signal the calling party a busy. For the biggest explanation of common channel signaling, see SIGNALING SYSTEM 7. See also MTP, SCCP, ISUP, ISDN and TCAP.

COMMON CHANNEL SIGNALING This is a Bellcore definition: A network architecture which uses Signaling System 7 (SS7) protocol for the exchange of information between telecommunications nodes and networks on an out-of-band basis. It performs three major functions: 1. It allows the exchange of signaling information for interoffice circuit connections. 2. It allows the exchange of additional information services and features, e.g. CLASS, database query/response, etc. 3. It provides improved operations procedures for network management and administration of the telecommunications network. For the biggest explanation of common channel signaling, see SIGNALING SYSTEM 7. See also ISDN, ISUP, MTP, SCCP, STP and TCAP.

COMMON CHANNEL TRANSIT EXCHANGE An intermediate exchange where networking of common channel signaling systems occurs.

COMMON CONTROL An arrangement in which items of control equipment in a switching system are shared. They are associated with a given call only during the periods required to accomplish the control functions. All crossbar and electronic switching systems have common control.

COMMON CONTROL SWITCHING ARRANGEMENT CCSA. An AT&T offering for very big companies. Those big companies can create their own private networks and dial anywhere on them by dialing a standard seven digit number, similar to a local phone number. The corporate subscriber rents private, dedicated lines and then shares central office switches. CCSA uses special CCSA software at the central office.

COMMON COSTS Costs of the provision of some group of services that cannot be directly attributed to any one of those services.

COMMON EQUIPMENT In telephone systems Common Equipment are items that are used by several or all phones for processing calls. On a key system, the device that permits a light on any instrument to flash on and off may be Common Equipment when used to control all lights on all instruments.

COMMON INTERMEDIATE FORMAT A videophone ISDN standard which is part of the ITU-T's H.261. It produces a color image of 352 by 288 pixels. The format uses two B channels, with voice taking 32 kbps and the rest for video.

COMMON MAIL CALLS New APIs (Application Programming Interfaces) from Microsoft which allow you to move information around your various mail services — the ones on your LAN, on your wireless pager, etc.

COMMON MODE The potential or voltage that exists between neutral and ground. Electronic equipment requires this to be as close to 0 volts as possible or not to exceed 1/2 volt.

COMMON MODE INTERFERENCE 1. Interference that appears between signal leads, or the terminals of a measuring circuit and ground. 2. A form of coherent interference that affects two or more elements of a network in a similar manner (i.e., highly coupled) as distinct from locally generated noise or interference that is statistically independent between pairs of network elements.

COMMON MODE REJECTION RATIO CMRR. The ratio of the common mode interference voltage at the input of a circuit to the corresponding interference voltage at the output.

COMMON MODE VOLTAGE 1. The voltage common to both input terminals of a device. 2. In a differential amplifier, the unwanted part of the voltage between each input connection point and ground that is added to the voltage of each original signal.

COMMON RETURN A return path that is common to two or more circuits and that serves to return currents to their source or to ground.

COMMON RETURN OFFSET The dc common return potential difference of a line.

COMMON TRUNK In telephone systems having a grading arrangement, a trunk accessible to all groups of the grading.

COMMON USER CIRCUIT A circuit designated to furnish a communication service to a number of users.

COMMON USER NETWORK A system of circuits or channels allocated to furnish communication paths between switching centers to provide communication service on a common basis to all connected stations or subscribers.

COMMONALITY 1. A quality that applies to material or systems: (a) possessing like and interchangeable characteristics enabling each to be utilized, or operated and maintained by personnel trained on the others without additional specialized training; (b) having interchangeable repair parts and/or components; (c) applying to consumable items interchangeably equivalent without adjustment. 2. A term applied to equipment or systems that have the quality of one entity possessing like and interchangeable parts with another equipment or system entity.

COMMUNICATING APPLICATIONS A General Magic term. An application whose design presupposes the user's desire to send and receive messages. For a Personal Intelligent Communicator to be effective, it needs to be equipped with a suite of communicating applications. All Magic Cap applications are built to communicate.

COMMUNICATING APPLICATIONS PLATFORM A General Magic term. The Cap in Magic Cap. Software on which Personal Intelligent Communicators are based. It is designed to make it easy for developers to create communicating applications and services. Magic Cap can run on dedicated devices as well as other computer operating systems.

COMMUNICATING OBJECTS A term created in the fall of 1992 by Mitel's VP Tony Bawcutt for a new Mitel division which specializes in making PC printed cards for and software drivers and developer tools for those cards. Those cards are designed to be the building blocks of what Mitel calls multimedia applications — but what are more properly called PC-based voice and call processing telecom developer building blocks. One of the first cards Mitel introduced was an ISDN S-access card which converts PCs into ISDN telephones, also called voice and data workstations.

COMMUNICATING WORD PROCESSOR A dedicated word processor that includes software for sending word processed files over phone lines. Communicating word processors have now largely been replaced by PCs (Personal Computers) running word processing programs and asynchronous communications software programs.

COMMUNICATION CHANNEL A two-way path for transmitting voice and/or data signals. See also CIRCUIT.

COMMUNICATION CONTROLLER Another name for a Front End Processor, a specialized computer which was common in 3270 data communications networks. The FEP acted as a data communications "traffic cop," removing the communications traffic routing and controlling burden from the mainframe computer which lay behind the FEP. In short, the FEP designates a device placed between the network and an input/output channel of a processing system (i.e. the computer).

COMMUNICATION SERVER A dedicated, standalone system that manages communications activities for other computers.

COMMUNICATION WORKERS OF AMERICA CWA. A national union of telephone industry employees, currently very worried about its future membership growth given the phone industry's propensity to let its surplus workers go.

COMMUNICATIONS ACT OF 1934 Federal legislation which established national telecommunications goals and created the Federal Communications Commission to regulate all interstate and international communications. See COMMUNICATIONS ACT RE-WRITE.

COMMUNICATIONS ACT RE-WRITE A plan to re-write the Communications Act of 1934 to bring telecommunications regulation into the twentieth century. The basic idea is to "de-regulate" the telecommunications industry, which means remove restrictions on local Bell operating companies and regulated cable TV companies. It's taking a long time, since no one wants restrictions removed from potential competitors, making those potential competitors actual competitors. Problems include — Should the local phone Bell operating companies be allowed into long distance?

COMMUNICATIONS ADAPTER Device attached to an IBM System 3X computer or an IBM PC that allows communications over RS-232 lines.

COMMUNICATIONS CONTROL CHARACTER A character intended to control or help transmission over data networks. There are ten control characters specified in ASCII which form the basis for character-oriented communications control procedures.

COMMUNICATIONS PROTOCOL Specifications which define hardware and software requirements for that type of communications. In short, the format governing the communication and the transfer of data between two or more devices.

COMMUNICATIONS SATELLITE A satellite circling the earth, usually at a distance of about 22,000 miles, with electronic equipment for relaying signals received from the earth back to other points on the earth. See GEOSTATIONARY SATELLITE.

COMMUNICATIONS SERVER Also called an asynchronous server or asynchronous gateway. A communications server is a type of gateway that translates the packetized signals of a LAN to asynchronous signals, usually used on telephone lines or on direct connections to DEC and other minicomputers and mainframes. It handles different asynchronous protocols and allows nodes on a LAN to share modems or host connections. Usually one machine on a LAN will act as a gateway, sharing its serial ports or an RS-232 connection to a minicomputer. All devices on the LAN can use this machine to get to the modems and the minicomputer.

COMMUNICATIONS SETTINGS Settings that specify how information is transferred from your computer to a device (usually a printer or modem).

COMMUNICATIONS SYSTEM ENGINEERING The translation of user requirements for the exchange of information into cost-effective technical solutions of equipment and subsystems.

COMMUNICATIONS TOOLBOX An extension of he Apple Macintosh operating system that provides protocol conversion and the drivers needed for communications tasks.

COMMUNICATIONS ZONE A military term: Rear part of theater of operations (behind but contiguous to the combat zone), which contains the lines of communications, establishments for supply and evacuation, and other agencies required for the immediate support and maintenance of the field forces.

COMMUNICATOR A British term. An alternative, and probably more meaningful, name for a telebusiness agent. Or is called in North America — an agent.

COMMUNITY ANTENNA TELEVISION CATV. Signals from distant TV stations are picked up by a large antenna, typically located on a hill, then amplified and piped all over the community below on coaxial cable.

COMMUNITY OF INTEREST A grouping of telephone users that call each other with a high degree of frequency. Often several Communities of Interest exist within an organization. This phenomenon can influence design for service when new switches are planned.

COMMUTATOR A device used on a dynamo to reverse the connection periodically in order to cause the current flow in one direction, i.e., to produce direct current.

COMPACT DISC A standard medium for storage of digital audio data, accessible with a laser-based reader. CDs are 12 centimeters (about 4 3/4") in diameter. CDs are faster and more accurate than magnetic tape for audio. Faster, because even though data is generally written on a CD contiguously within each track, the tracks themselves are directly accessible. This means the tracks can be accessed and played back in any order. More accurate, because data is recorded directly into binary code; mag tape requires data to be translated into analog form. Also, extraneous noise (tape hiss) associated with mag tape is absent from CDs. See CD-ROM.

COMPACT DISC INTERACTIVE A compact disc format, developed by Philips and Sony, which provides audio, digital data, still graphics and limited motion video. See CD-I.

CompactPCI See PICMG.

COMPANDER See COMPANDING.

COMPANDING The word is a contraction of the words "compressing" and "expanding." Companding is the process of compressing the amplitude range of a signal for economical transmission and then expanding them back to their original form at the receiving end.

COMPARTMENTATION A military/government term: A method employed to segregate information of different desired accessibilities from each other. It may be used for communications security purposes.

COMPATIBLE A widely misused word. In the computer world, two computers are said to be compatible when they will produce the identical result if they run identical programs. Another meaning is whether equipment — peripherals and components — can be used interchangeably with each other, from one computer to another. Compatibility used to be regarded as a useful trait in 1A2 key telephones. But then the electronics revolution came along and now there are no compatible electronic telephones from different manufacturers. This means you can't take an electronic Mitel PBX phone, example, and have it work behind a Northern Telecom PBX. And a Northern Telecom PBX phone won't work behind an AT&T PBX. The major compatibility in our industry is at the lowest common denominator — the tip and ring analog phone.

COMPATIBLE SIDEBAND TRANSMISSION That method of independent sideband transmission wherein the carrier is deliberately reinserted at a lower level after its normal suppression to permit reception by conventional AM receivers. The normal method of transmitting compatible SSB (AME) is the emission of the carrier plus the upper sideband.

COMPELLED SIGNALING A signaling method in which the transmission of each signal in the forward direction is inhibited until an acknowledgement of the satisfactory receipt of the previous signal has been sent back from the receiver terminal.

COMPETITIVE LONG DISTANCE COALITION A Washington, D.C. lobbying group.

COMPILATION The translation of programs written in a language understandable to programmers into instructions understandable to the computer. Think of programmers writing in every language but Greek and computers understanding only Greek. In this case, Greek is called machine language. The other languages (the programmer languages) are called things like COBOL, FORTRAN, Pascal, dBASE. A compiler is a special program that translates from all these other languages into machine language.

COMPILER A program that takes the source code a programmer has written and translates it into object code the computer can understand. A computer program used to convert symbols meaningful to a human into codes meaningful to a computer. For example, a compiler takes instructions written in a "higher" level language such as BASIC, COBOL or ALGOL and converts them into machine code which can be read and acted upon by a computer. Compilers converts large sections of code at one time, compared to an interpreter which translates commands one at a time.

COMPLEMENTARY METAL OXIDE SEMICONDUCTOR CMOS. A method of building chips which produces a logic circuit family which uses very little power.

COMPLEMENTARY NETWORK SERVICE CNS. CNSs are basic services associated with end user's lines that make it easier for ESPs to offer them enhanced services. Some examples of CNSs include Call Forwarding Busy/Don't Answer, Three Way Calling, and Virtual Dial Tone. See OPEN NETWORK ARCHITECTURE.

COMPLETE DOCUMENT RECOGNITION The ability to perform recognition on documents, retaining as much information as possible about the features and formatting of the original, and including the ability to capture images as well as text.

COMPLETED CALL Careful with this one. In telephone dialect, a Completed Call is one that has been switched to its destination and conversation has begun but has not yet ended.

COMPLETION RATIO The proportion of the number of attempted calls to the number of completed calls.

COMPLIMENTARY NETWORK SERVICES CNS. The means for an enhanced-service provider's customer to connect to the network and to the enhanced service provider. Complimentary network services usually consist of the customer's local service (e.g.,business or residence line) and several associated service options, e.g., call-forwarding service.

COMPONENT SOFTWARE Component software is software constructed from reusable components. It was popularized by Microsoft Visual Basic and its successful custom control architecture. This architecture allows third party software components to "plug" into and extend the Visual Basic development environment. Hundreds of third party components, or custom controls, exist — for everything from accessing a mainframe database to programming a computer telephony board. Component-based software development is a productive way to build software. System developers benefit from being able to tailor their development environment for a specific need. Consider the development of an IVR system that allows callers to access their account balance stored on an IBM mainframe. To build this system, Visual Basic developers extend their development environment with a custom control for telephony and another that provides access to an IBM mainframe. There's no need to learn a new and proprietary language for telephony development. Plus, every control is accessed through a common interface of actions, properties, and events.

COMPONENT VIDEO Transmission and recording of color television that stores separate channels of red, green and blue.

COMPOSITE Output of a multiplexer that includes all data from the multiplexed channels. Contrast with AGGREGATE.

COMPOSITE LINK The datastream composed of all the input channels and control and signaling information in a multiplexed circuit. The Composite Link Speed is the transmission speed of the circuit.

COMPOSITE MATERIALS Composite materials consist of two or more components. They make it possible to combine the best properties of different materials; for example, the compression strength and low price of concrete with the tensile strength of reinforcing rods. Composite materials include: Reinforced concrete, fiber-reinforced plastic, fiber-reinforced metals, plywood, chipboard and ceramics. The composites mainly considered for antennas are fiber-reinforced plastics. They combine the low weight and protective properties of plastics with the stiffness and strength of fiber.

COMPOSITE SIGNALING A direct current signaling system that separates the signals from the voice band by filters. Two pairs (a quad) provide talking paths and full-duplex signaling for three channels. Also called CX Signaling.

COMPOSITE VIDEO A television signal where the chrominance signal is a sine wave that is modulated onto the luminance signal which acts as a subcarrier. This is used in NTSC and PAL TV systems. Composite video is the visual wave form representation used in color television. Composite video is analog and must be converted to digital to be used in multimedia computing. See also DIGITAL VIDEO.

COMPOSITED CIRCUIT A circuit that can be used simultaneously for telephony and dc telegraphy, or signaling; separation between the two being accomplished by frequency discrimination.

COMPOUND A term used to designate an insulating or jacketing material made by mixing two or more ingredients.

COMPOUND DOCUMENT The simple explanation: A compound document contains information created by using more than one application. It is a document often composed of a variety of data types and formats. Each data type is linked to the application that created it. A compound document might include audio, video, images, text, and graphics. Compound documents first became possible to the world of PCs with the introduction of Windows 3.1, which included OLE (Object Linking and Embedding). OLE allows you to write a letter in your favorite Windows word processor, embed a small voice icon in your document, send your letter to someone else, have them open your letter, place their mouse on the voice icon and hear whatever comments you recorded. To make this possible, both you (the creator) and your recipient would need access to programs that could read both the text and the voice. Ideally, you would both be on a LAN (Local Area Network) and would both get access to the identical applications software, resident, presumably, on the LAN's file server. See COMPOUND MAILBOX.

COMPOUND DOCUMENT MAIL See COMPOUND DOCUMENT.

COMPOUND MAILBOX A mailbox for mail from all sources — fax, voice mail, e-mail, pager, etc. See COMPOUND DOCUMENT.

COMPRESSED VIDEO Television signals transmitted with much less than the usual bit rate. Full standard coding of broadcast quality television typically requires 45 to 90 megabits per second. Compressed video includes signals from 3 mb/s down to 56 kb/s. The lower bit rates typically involve some compromise in picture quality, particularly when there's rapid motion on the screen.

COMPRESSION Reducing the representation of the information, but not the information itself. Reducing the bandwidth or number of bits needed to encode information or encode a signal, typically by eliminating long strings of identical bits or bits that do not change in successive sampling intervals (e.g., video frames). Compression saves transmission time or capacity. It also saves storage space on storage devices such as hard disks, tape drives and floppy disks

COMPRESSION ALGORITHM The arithmetic formulae which convert a signal into smaller bandwidth or fewer bits.

COMPRESSOR See COMPANDING.

COMPROMISE EQUALIZER Equalizer set for best overall operation for a given range of line conditions. This is often fixed but may be manually adjustable.

(next page)

COMPSURF COMPrehensive SURFace Analysis. A Novell program that checks the surface of a hard disk, marks off sections that are lousy and therefore shouldn't be written to, and then low level formats the disk. The program is slow, but thorough and rigorous. No hard disk should ever be used on a file server on a Novell local area network without being subjected to this wonderful program. Don't believe Novell when it says that you don't need to subject new disks to COMP-SURF. You should submit ALL disks.

COMPUCALL Northern Telecom DMS central office link to computer interface. An open architecture specification. Northern Telecom spells it as CompuCALL. According to Northern Telecom's own words, CompuCALL employs the Switch Computer Application Interface (SCAI) open architecture standard to connect the central office with customers' general-purpose business computers. CompuCALL consists of:

● The CompuCALL base software (NTXJ59AA) in the Northern Telecom DMS-100 switch, or the Meridian Automatic Call Distribution (ACD) Server, that sends and receives SCAI messages; and

● The CompuCALL transport mechanism that physically links the switch to the computer or other external processor and carries the SCAI message.

Northern Telecom also supplies the Meridian ACD CompuCALL Options (NTXJ39AA) and other applications software which rely on the CompuCALL base. Computers and software vendors provide application programming interface

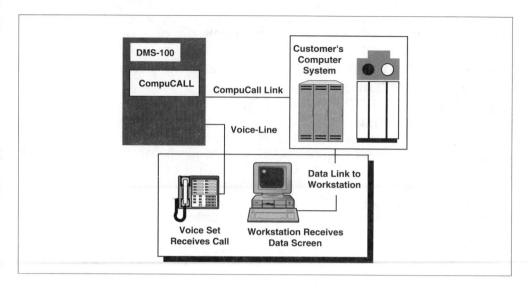

(API) software as well as business application software. The API, which resides in the business computer, converts SCAI messages into information that can be used by computer-based business application software.

The first applications of CompuCALL integrate computer databases with voice telephony:

● CompuCALL Coordinated Voice and Data provides an agent a screen of information about a caller concurrently with receipt of a call.

● CompuCALL Voice Processing Integration uses Interactive Voice Response (IVR) systems and Voice Response Units (VRU) to obtain additional information about callers and direct them to the appropriate agent.

● CompuCALL Third-Party Call Control lets the customer's computer place outgoing calls.

Successful implementation of CompuCALL requires interaction with application software on a business computer. CompuCALL consists of:

●The CompuCALL base software residing in the Northern Telecom DMS-100 central office switch that sends and receives SCAI messages; and

● The CompuCALL transport mechanism that physically links the switch to the computer or other external processor and carries the SCAI message.

Computer and software vendors provide application programming interface (API) software as well as business application software. The API, which resides in the business computer, converts SCAI messages into information that can be used by computer-based business application software. CompuCALL is based on the seven-layer protocol defined by the International Telegraph and Telephone Consultative Committee's (CCITT) Open System Interconnection (OSI) reference model. The product is transport independent. With BCS33, CompuCALL is scheduled to be available for Verifications Office (VO) on X.25. See also OPEN APPLICATION INTERFACE.

COMPUNICATIONS A recent creation meaning the combination of telephones, computers, television and data systems.

COMPUSERVE An on-line, dial-up service — one of the largest worldwide. CompuServe has everything from electronic mail to manufacturer-sponsored forums where you can download files for updated drivers, etc. CompuServe is one of the hardest on line services to find your way around. See the following definitions.

COMPUSERVE ELECTRONIC MAIL You can send electronic mail to CompuServe addresses. Here's the formula: All CompuServe addresses are either of the form 7xxxx,xxx or 1xxxxx,xxx. (where each "x" signifies a digit from 0 to 7). There can be from 2 to 4 digits following the comma. To send mail to such an address from the Internet, change the comma to a period and attach "@CompuServe.com" as is shown in the following example:

74906.1610@compuserve.com or 100906.1610@compuserve.com

COMPUSERVE B+ FILE TRANSFER This file transfer protocol is used by the CompuServe information service and no one else. Recovery of interrupted transfers is supported. In CompuServe B+, the host initiates the transfer. In contrast, in XMODEM, the receiver initiates the transfer, i.e. tells the distant computer to begin sending the file.

COMPUSERVE MAIL HUB A facility of CompuServe which enables users on a local area network operating Novell Message Handling Service (MHS) software to exchange electronic messages with other MHS users, CompuServe Mail subscribers and users of other E-mail services that can be reached via a CompuServe gateway.

COMPUTER This is a definition straight from AT&T Bell Laboratories. "An electronic device that accepts and processes information mathematically according to previous instructions. It provides the result of this processing via visual displays, printed summaries or in an audible form.

COMPUTER AIDED DIALING A newer (and allegedly less offensive) term for predictive dialing. See also PREDICTIVE DIALING.

COMPUTER AIDED PROFESSIONAL PUBLISHING CAP. The computerization of professional publishing (as opposed to desktop operations), including true color representation of the layout on the workstation screen.

COMPUTER AND BUSINESS EQUIPMENT MANUFACTURERS ASSOCIATION CBEMA. Association active before Congress and the FCC promoting the interests of the competitive terminal, computer and peripheral equipment industries.

COMPUTER AND COMMUNICATIONS INDUSTRY ASSOCIATION CCIA. Organization of data processing and communications companies which promotes their interests before Congress and the FCC.

COMPUTER INQUIRY A series of ongoing FCC proceedings examining the distinctions between communications and information processing to determine which services are subject to common carrier regulation. The FCC decision in 1980 resulting from the second inquiry was to limit common carrier regulation to basic services. Enhanced services and customer premises equipment are not to be regulated. This meant the Bell operating companies had to set up separate subsidiaries if they were to offer non-regulated services.

Computer Inquiry III, adopted by the FCC in May, 1986, removed the structural separation requirement between basic and enhanced services for the BOCs and for AT&T. CI III replaced that requirement with "nonstructural safeguards." This action resulted in the imposition of such concepts as "comparably efficient interconnection" (CEI) and Open Network Architecture (ONA). The FCC's jurisdiction regarding Computer Inquiry I, II and III has now been usurped by Judge Greene, who insists on fairly tight control over the non-basic telephone company activities of the Bell operating companies. Sometimes he gives dispensations (waivers). Sometimes he doesn't. His word these days is final law on what the Bell operating companies can and can't do.

COMPUTER SUPPORT TELEPHONY See CST.

COMPUTER TELEPHONY A term coined by Harry Newton to describe the industry that concerns itself with applying computer intelligence to telecommunications devices, especially switches and phones. Computer Telephony has two basic goals: to please customers and to enhance corporate productivity. Computer Telephony covers six broad segments:

1. Messaging.

Voice, fax and electronic mail, fax blasters, fax servers and fax routers, paging and unified messaging (also called integrated messaging) and Internet Web-vectored phone, fax and video messaging.

2. Real-time Connectivity.

Inbound and outbound call handling, "predictive" and "preview" dialing, automated attendants, LAN / screen-based call routing, one number calling / "follow me" numbers, video, audio and text-based conferencing, "PBX in a PC," collaborative computing.

3. Transaction Processing and Information Access via the Phone.

Interactive voice response, audiotex, customer access to enterprise data, "giving data a voice," fax on demand and shopping on the World Wide Web.

4. Adding Intelligence (and thus value) to Phone Calls.

Screen pops of customer records coincident with inbound and outbound phone calls, mirrored Web page "pops," smart agents, skills-based call routing, virtual (geographically distributed) call centers, computer telephony groupware, intelligent help desks and "AIN" network-based computer telephony services.

5. Core Technologies.

Voice recognition, text-to-speech, digital signal processing, applications generators (of all varieties — GUI to forms-based to script-based), VoiceView, DSVD, computer-based fax routing, USB (Universal Serial Bus), GeoPort, video and audio compression, call progress, dial pulse recognition, caller ID and ANI, digital network interfaces (T-1, E-1, ISDN BRI and PRI, SS7, frame relay and ATM), voice modems, client-server telephony, logical modem interfaces, multi-PC telephony synchronization and coordination software, the communicating PC, the Internet, the Web and the "Intranet."

6. New Core Standards.

The ITU-T's T.120 (document conferencing) and H.320 (video conferencing), Microsoft's TAPI — an integral part of Windows 95 and NT, Novell's TSAPI — a phone switch control NLM running under NetWare. Intel's USB and InstantON. Natural MicroSystems / Mitel's MVIP and H-MVIP. Dialogic has SCSA. And the industry has ECTF.

That's today. But what really excites is the potential. It's huge. Despite the above, phone calls today are dumb, seriously bereft of common sense. Few phones have "backspace erase." 75% of business calls end in voice mail! Often in voice mail jail. Every call not completed is an irritated customer and a lost sale. Computer telephony addresses the waste. Computer telephony adds intelligence to the making and receiving of phone calls. Bingo, happier customers and more completed transactions.

The best news: We now have the technology, the resources, the computer power, the new standards and the muscle to back our hype. We also have many new players who are, thankfully, not burdened by the assumptions of yesteryear's telecommunications industry. We also have legions of developers and systems and integrators who are grabbing these computer telephony tools and are cranking out hundreds of customer-pleasing, productivity-enhancing solutions for your business. Computer Telephony delivers. And fortunately, industry now wants it.

Once a year, typically in March, industry leaders meet at a trade show called Computer Telephony Conference and Exposition. There is a monthly magazine called Computer Telephony Magazine. For more, call 1-800-999-0345 or 212-691-8215. See also TELEPHONY, TELEPHONY SERVICES and WINDOWS TELEPHONY.

COMPUTER-LIKE TRANSPORT An AT&T term for the carrying of digital information with the potential for acting on that information at any network node as appropriate.

COMPUTERNAME The name by which the lan identifies a server or a workstation in lan Manager terminology. Each computername must be unique on the network.

COMSAT The COMmunications SATellite corporation was created by Congress as the exclusive provider to the U.S. of satellite channels for international communications. COMSAT is also the U.S. representative to Intelsat and Inmarsat, two international groups responsible for satellite and maritime communications. Comsat is now being merged with Continental Telephone, also known as Contel.

COMSPEC COMmand SPECification. A configuration command that tells MS-DOS where to find the program that interprets what is typed at the prompt. Except in unusual circumstances, that program is COMMAND.COM. COMSPEC is typically used when you have the program COMMAND.COM somewhere other than in the root directory of your C: drive (if you have a hard disk machine) or your A: drive if you have a floppy system. Let's say you want to tell your computer to find COMMAND.COM on your D: drive, the command in your AUTOEXEC.BAT program would be:

SET COMSPEC=D:\COMMAND.COM

COMSTAR A domestic communications satellite system from Comsat.

CONCATENATION Joining several fibers together end-to-end.

CONCENTRATION A fundamental concept to telephony. Communications from a number of phones are sent out on a smaller number of outgoing lines. The theory is that, since not all the phones are being used at any one time, fewer trunks than phones are needed. Some phone system designs assume that only 5% of the phones will be in use at any one time. Some phone systems design assume 10%. In some phone-intensive industries, you can't make any assumptions about concentration. You have to assume one line per phone. No concentration. TELECONNECT Magazine is around one phone per line. We are very phone intensive. See CONCENTRATION RATIO.

CONCENTRATION RATIO The ratio between lines and trunks in a concentrated carrier system or line concentrator.

CONCENTRATOR 1. This telecommunications device allows a number of circuits (typically slow speed ones) to be connected to a smaller number of lines for transmission under the assumption that not all of the larger group of lines will be used at the same time. The concentrator allows a shared transmission medium to accommodate more data sources than there are channels currently available within the transmission medium. A concentrator's job is to save money on transmission. 2. Some LANs use concentrators, or access units, that allow network devices to be interconnected through a central point. The wiring is star, also called home run. Attaching devices through a central concentrator typically simplifies the maintenance of the LAN. A concentrator is used when connecting a LAN over the "normal" twisted wires in a building which were put there originally to carry voice and which now have to be used because — for one reason or another — it's not possible to connect the LAN using its normal bus coaxial cable connection.

CONCENTRICITY In a wire or cable, the measurement of the location of the center of the conductor with respect to the geometric center of the circular insulation.

CONCENTRICITY ERROR The amount by which a fiber's core is not centered in its cladding. The distance between the center of the two concentric circles specifying the cladding diameter and the center of the two concentric circles specifying the core diameter.

CONCERT A basket of international telecommunications services offered by British Telecom and MCI.

CONCERT VNS Concert VNS is a worldwide, flexible virtual private voice and data network that offers customers a consistent feature set available in multiple countries. The network combines the geographic reach of both MCI's Vnet and BT's International Virtual Network (IVN) physical networks and is connected to public networks around the world. Concert VNS provides a comprehensive set of virtual network capabilities for international voice and data applications.

CONCERT NETWORK MANAGEMENT SYSTEM British Telecom operating environment.

CONCURRENCY The shared use of resources by multiple interactive users or applications at the same time. Concurrency often means that a company need only buy as many licenses to a program as it has people using the program at one time — concurrent users, in other words. See SOFTWARE METERING.

CONCURRENCY CONTROL A feature that allows multiple users to execute database transactions simultaneously without interfering with each other.

CONCURRENT SITE LICENSE Companies that buy software for multiple computers typically buy one copy of the program and a license to reproduce it up to a certain number of times. This is called a site license, though it may apply to its use throughout an organization. Site licenses vary. Some require that a copy be bought for each potential user — the only purpose being to indicate the volume discount and keep tabs. Others allow for a copy to be placed on a network server but limit the number of users who can gain simultaneous access. This is called a Concurrent Site License. And many network administrators prefer this concurrent license, since it gives them greater control. For example, if the software is customized, it need be customized only once, namely on the server.

CONDENSER A device for storing up electrical energy and consisting of two or more conducting surfaces or electrodes separated by an insulating medium called a dialectic.

CONDENSER ANTENNA An antenna consisting of two capacity areas.

CONDENSER MICROPHONE Microphone which operates through changes in capacitance caused by vibrations of its conductive diaphragm.

CONDITIONS Busy. Voice Mail. Out of service. All the situations that a phone line is likely to find itself in.

CONDITIONED CIRCUIT A circuit that has conditioning equipment to obtain the desired characteristics for voice or data transmission. See CONDITIONING.

CONDITIONED LOOP A loop that has conditioning equipment to obtain the desired line characteristics for voice or data transmission. See CONDITIONING.

CONDITIONING Electrical treatment of transmission lines to improve their performance for specific uses such as data transmission. The "tuning" or addition of equipment to improve the transmission characteristics of a leased voice-grade line so that it meets the specifications for higher-speed data transmission. Voice-grade lines often have too much "noise" on them. By altering the equipment at both ends of the line, this noise on the line can be overcome. This allows transmission of data, which is much more sensitive to noise than voice.

Here is another definition of conditioning: A procedure used to make circuit transmission impairments lie within certain acceptable limits which are specified in a tariff (typically used on telephone lines leased for data transmission to improve transmission speed and quality). Usually done with special equipment or routing.

CONDOFIBER A shared tenancy cable or shared ownership facility such as a transatlantic fiber cable. Multiple vendors such as Sprint, MCI and AT&T may all own a group of fibers with responsibility for maintaining their own operation while at the same time paying an overall "association" fee for the common maintenance of the overall cable.

CONDUCTANCE The opposite of resistance; a measure of the ability of a conductor to carry an electrical charge. Conductance is a ratio of the current flow to the potential difference causing the current flow. The unit of conductance is Mho (a reversed spelling of Ohm).

CONDUCTING MATERIALS Substances which offer relatively little resistance to the passage of an electric current.

CONDUCTIVITY A term used to describe the ability of a material to carry an electrical charge. The opposite of specific resistance. Usually expressed as a percentage of copper conductivity - copper being one hundred percent. Conductivity is expressed for a standard configuration of conductor.

CONDUCTOR Any substance, usually a wire or cable, that can carry (i.e. offer a relatively small opposition to the passage of) an electrical current.

CONDUIT A pipe, usually metal but often plastic, that runs either from floor to floor or along a floor or ceiling to protect cables. A conduit protects the cable and prevents burning cable from spreading flames or smoke. Many fire codes in large cities thus require that cable be placed in metal conduit. In the riser subsystem when riser closets are not aligned, conduit is used to protect cable as well as to provide the means for pulling cable from floor to floor. In the horizontal wiring subsystem, conduit may be used between a riser or satellite closet and an information outlet in an office or other room. Conduit is also used for in-conduit campus distribution, where it is run underground between buildings and intermediate manholes and encased in concrete. Multiduct, clay tile conduit may also be used.

CONDUIT RUN The path taken by a conduit or group of conduits.

CONFEREE Participant in a conference call who is not the call controller. This definition courtesy Hayes. According to Hayes, a "controller" is the person who sets up the conference call.

CONFERENCE BRIDGE A telecommunications facility or service which permits callers from several diverse locations to be connected together for a conference call. The conference bridge contains electronics for amplifying and balancing the conference call so everyone can hear each other and speak to each other. The conference call's progress is monitored through the bridge in order to produce a high quality voice conference and to maintain decent quality as people enter or leave the conference.

CONFERENCE CALL Connecting three or more people into one phone conversation. You used to have to place conference calls through an AT&T operator (you still can). But now you can also organize conference calls with most modern phone systems or a conference bridge. If conferencing is important to you, make sure your conferencing device has amplification and balancing. If not, it will simply electrically join the various conversations together and people at either end won't be able to hear each other. There are different types of conference devices you can buy, including special teleconferencing devices that sit on conference tables and perform the function of a speakerphone, albeit a lot better. There are also dial-in devices called conference bridges. But, however, you use these devices, they will requires lines (and/or trunks). If you install one inside your phone system, be careful have the extra spare extensions. For a conference of 10 people, you'll typically need 10 extensions connected to your conference bridge. See CONFERENCE BRIDGE.

CONFERENCE, MEET-ME A conference call in which each of the people wishing to join the conference simply dials a special "Meet-Me" Conference phone number, which automatically connects them into the conference. It is a feature of some PBXs and also some special Conferencing Equipment. See CONFERENCE BRIDGE.

CONFERENCING Several parties can be added to a phone conversation through Conferencing.

CONFIDENCER A noise-cancelling microphone for use on a telephone in noisy places. A confidencer is not an easy device to use.

CONFIDENTIAL RECEPTION The ability to receive a facsimile transmission directly into memory which can be printed out or viewed at a later time.

CONFIDENTIAL TRANSMISSION A facsimile message that is sent confidentially into memory or a private mailbox, to be retrieved by the receiver at a later time. It's usually retrieved by using a confidential passcode or password.

CONFIG.SYS A file of commands used to set up a PC. MS-DOS reads it each time it starts. Config.sys is where you put commands for device drivers for a mouse, a RAM drive, instructions on where to put DOS, how much memory to set for your cache, etc. Other configuration parameters like how many open files are allowed, how many buffers, how many drives, etc. are also put in this file. See also AUTOEXEC.BAT.

CONFIGURATION The hardware and software arrangements that define a computer or telecommunications system and thus determine what the system will do and how well it will do it. This information can be entered in the CMOS and EEPROM setup programs.

CONFIGURATION DATABASES Rolm/IBM words for those databases which represent unique user specifications relating to system and phone features. These databases can be entered on-site and are not part of the generic software which runs the phone system.

CONFIGURATION FILE An unformatted ASCII file that stores initialization information for an application.

CONFIGURATION MANAGER 1. A SCSA system service which manages configuration information and controls system startup.

2. An Intel Plug'n Play term. A driver, such as the ISA Configuration Utility, that configures devices and informs other device drivers of the resource requirements of all devices installed in a computer system. The Windows 95 Resource Kit defined configuration manager as the central component of a Plug and Play system that drives the process of locating devices, setting up their nodes in the hardware tree, and running the resource allocation process. Each of the three phases of configuration management-boot time (BIOS), real mode, and protected mode-has its own configuration manager.

CONFIGURATION MANAGEMENT One of five categories of network management defined by the ISO (International Standards Organization). Configuration management is the process of adding, deleting and modifying connections, addresses and topologies within a network.

CONFIGURATION REGISTRY A database repository for information about a computer's configuration.

CONFORMANCE TEST A test performed by an independent body to determine if a particular piece of equipment or system satisfies the criteria of a particular standard, sometimes a contract to buy the equipment.

CONFIRMING DESIGN LAYOUT REPORT DATE CDLRD. The date a common carrier accepts the facility designed proposed by the Telco.

CONFORMING END OFFICE Central office with the ability to provide originating and terminating feature group D local access and transport area access service.

CONGESTION CONTROL The process whereby packets are discarded to clear buffer congestion in a packet-switched network.

CONGESTION MANAGEMENT The ability of a network to effectively deal with heavy traffic volumes; solutions include traffic scheduling and enabling output ports to control the traffic flow. See BECN.

CONNECT TIME Measure of computer and telecommunications system usage. The interval during which the user was on-line for a session.

CONNECTED 1. On line. 2. A voice recognition term for words spoken clearly in succession without pauses. For recognition to occur, words or utterances must be separated by at least 50 milliseconds (1/20th of a second). Generally refers to digit recognition and sometimes used to describe fast discrete recognition.

CONNECTED TIME The length of time a path between two objects is active.

CONNECTED USER A Windows NT term. A user accessing a computer or a resource across the network.

CONNECTING ARRANGEMENT The manner in which the facilities of a common carrier (phone company) and the customer are interconnected.

CONNECTING BLOCK A plastic block containing metal wiring terminals to establish connections. from one group of wires to another. Usually each wire can be connected to several other wires in a bus or common arrangement. A 66-type block is the most common type of connecting block. It was invented by Western Electric. Northern Telecom has one called a Bix block. There are others. These two are probably the most common. A connecting block is also called a terminal block, a punch-down block, a quick-connect block, a cross-connect block. A connecting block will include insulation displacement connections (IDC). In other words, with a connecting block, you don't have to remove the plastic shielding from around your wire conductor before you "punch it down."

CONNECTION 1. A path between telephones that allows the transmission of speech and other signals. 2. An electrical continuity of circuit between two wires or two units, in a piece of apparatus. 3. An SCSA term which means a TDM data path between two Resources or two Groups. It connects the inputs and outputs of the two Resources, and may be unidirectional (simplex) if either of the Resources has only an input or an output. Otherwise it is bi-directional (dual simplex). It usually has a bandwidth that is a multiple of a DS0 (64kbit) channel. Inter-group connections are made between the Primary Resource of each Resource Group.

CONNECTION ORIENTED The model of interconnection in which communication proceeds through three well-defined phases: connection establishment, information transfer, connection release. Examples include X.25, Internet TCP and OSI TP4 and ordinary telephone calls. See CONNECTION SERVICE.

CONNECTION ORIENTED OPERATION A communications protocol in which a logical connection is established between communicating devices. Connection-oriented service is also referred to as virtual-circuit service.

CONNECTION ORIENTED TRANSMISSION Data transmission technique involving setting up connection before transmission and disconnecting it afterward. A type of service in which information always traverses the same pre-established path or link between two points. See CONNECTIONLESS SERVICE.

CONNECTION SERVICE A circuit-switching service whereby a connection is switched into place at the beginning of a session and held in place until the session is completed. Also referred to as circuit switching. The circuit switched in place may be real or virtual. See CIRCUIT SWITCHING.

CONNECTIONLESS MODE TRANSMISSION In packet data transmission, a mode of operation in which each packet is encoded with a header containing destination address sufficient to permit the independent delivery of the packet without the aid of additional instruments. See also CLOUD, CONNECTIONLESS NETWORK and CONNECTIONLESS SERVICE.

CONNECTIONLESS NETWORK A type of communications network in which no logical connection (i.e. no leased line or dialed-up channel) is required between sending and receiving stations. Each data unit (datagram) is sent and addressed independently. IEEE 802 LAN standards specify connectionless networks. Connectionless networks are becoming more common in broadband city networks now increasingly offered by phone companies.

CONNECTIONLESS SERVICE A networking mode in which individual data packets in a network (local or long distance) traveling from one point to another are directed from one intermediate node to the next until they reach their ultimate destination. Because packets may take different routes, they must be reassembled at their destination. The receipt of a transmission is typically acknowledged from the ultimate destination to the point of origin. A connectionless packet is frequently called a datagram. A connectionless service is inherently unreliable in the sense that the service provider usually cannot provide assurance against the loss, error insertion, misdelivery, duplication, or out-of-sequence delivery of a connectionless packet. Connectionless networks may be better than connection-oriented ones for obtaining management information over a failing network because a device doesn't have the additional burden of maintaining a network connection.

CONNECTIONLESS TRANSMISSION Data transmission without prior establishment of a connection.

CONNECTIONS PER CIRCUIT HOUR CCH. A unit of traffic measurement; the number of connections established at a switching point per hour.

CONNECTIVITY Property of a network that allows dissimilar devices to communicate with each other.

CONNECTOR A device that electrically connects wires or fibers in cable to equipment, or other wires or fibers. Wire and optical connectors most often join transmission media to equipment (host computers and terminal devices) or cross connects. A Connector at the end of a telephone cable or wire is used to join that cable to another cable with a matching Connector or to some other telecommunications device. Residential telephones use the REJ-11C connector. Computer terminals with an RS-232-C interface, use the DB-25 connector. The RS-232-C standard is actually the electrical method of using the pins on a DB-25. See RS-232-C.

CONS Connection Oriented Network Service. See CONNECTION SERVICE.

CONSENT DECREE 1982 The agreement which divested the Bell Operating Companies from AT&T. It took effect at midnight on December 31, 1983.

CONSERVATION OF RADIANCE A basic principle stating that no passive optical system can increase the quantity L/n^2, where L is the radiance of a beam and n is the local refractive index. Formerly called conservation of brightness, or the brightness theorem.

CONSOLE 1. A large telephone which a PBX attendant uses to answer incoming calls and transfer them around the organization. Before you buy a PBX for your company, make sure your operator has checked out its console. Some are very difficult to use. Some are easy. Some operators hate some consoles. Some consoles hate some operators. You can measure the efficiency of consoles by comparing keystrokes to do simple jobs and comparing them — e.g. answer an incoming line, dial an extension and transfer the call. How many keystrokes does your PBX take? 2. The device which allows communications between a computer operator and a computer. 3. The console is the Novell NetWare name for the monitor and keyboard of the file server. Here you can view and control the file server or router activity. At the console, you can enter commands to control disk drives, send messages, set the file server or router clock, shut down the file server, and view file server information. NetWare commands you can enter only from the console (for example, MONITOR) are called console commands. Keep your file server locked up and away from prying eyes. It's clearly not just a case of changing passwords and getting in and mucking around. There have been examples of thieves simply removing the file server's hard disk, putting it in their briefcase and walking off with it.

CONSOLELESS OPERATION Some PBXs can work without a console. Some must have a console. It's good to check. Consoles are expensive. If you don't want one — because your company is small — you don't want to be forced to buy one, only to have it sit idly by.

CONSOLIDATED CARRIER Carriers that provide connection both as interexchange carriers as well as international carriers.

CONSTANT BIT RATE CBR. A data service where the bits are conveyed regularly in time (following a timing source or clock just as members of a marching band follow the beat of the drummer). Voice and video traffic has to be transported at constant bit rate because they are sensitive to variable delay and, as such, have to be transported without any interruptions in the flow of data.

CONSTANT CARRIER Physical line specification selection indicating full duplex line in bisync network.

CONSTRUCTION ZONE The building of the new information infrastructure by telecommunications and cable companies.

CONSULT To seek another's endorsement of a decision you've already made.

CONSULTANT See CONSULT and CONSULTANT LIAISON PROGRAMS.

CONSULTANT LIAISON PROGRAMS Large users often use communications consultants to help them choose systems and long distance phone lines. In recognition of the important role consultants play, many suppliers have consultant liaison programs. Such programs typically consist of a toll-free number and somebody on the other end to answer technical and pricing questions, a three-ring containing information on all the company's products and services, occasional seminars and, for those extra-privileged consultants, trips to all expense paid trips to exotic places and "something" else. With MCI that "something else" is a dial-up, toll-free, bulletin board. Dial it up with your PC, you can download MCI's latest prices and services. It's truly splendid as most of the paperwork others issue is obsolete the moment it's issued.

CONSULTATION See CONSULTATION HOLD.

CONSULTATION HOLD PBX feature which allows an extension to place a call on hold while speaking with another call. The idea is "consulting with" someone while you have someone else on the phone.

CONTACT A strip or piece of metal which makes an electrical contact when some electromechanical device like a relay or a magnet operates. Contacts are often plated with precious metal to prevent them from oxidizing (i.e. rusting) and thus messing up the switch.

CONTACT GATEWAY A Rockwell ACD term. A hardware/software package that acts as a gateway to integrate various ACD, voice response, host computer and live agent processes.

CONTACT HISTORY A log of all the contacts, either by phone or letter, made with a prospect or customer. This is an important factor in building up a marketing database which can be used to accurately target prospects.

CONTACT IMAGE SENSOR Uses a flat bar of light-emitting diode that directly touches the original. It eliminates the step of having the diodes move through the lens, which causes poorer resolution. This method is a more sophisticated than the charged-coupled device scanning method.

CONTACT MANAGEMENT A business has customers and prospects. In computerese, they're called "contacts." Software to "manage" your customers and prospects is called contact management software. It has three elements: First, a screen or two of information about that contact (address, phone number, notes about your conversations, etc.) Second, the ability to print lists, and mailers, etc. And third, often a tie-in with your phone system to let your computer dial your clients and fax them stuff. With many newer phone systems, you have one extra benefit — namely when your phone rings, your contact management software will receive the calling phone number and pop up the screen or two about your contact. This way you'll be a little prepared before you answer the phone. See also ANI and CLID.

CONTACT REGION The section of the jack wire inside the plug opening as shown in Subpart F of FCC rule 6B, figures 6B.500 (a) (3) and 6B.500 (b) (3).

CONTENDED ACCESS In local area networking technology it's the shared access method that allows stations to use the medium on a first-come, first-served basis.

CONTENDING PORT A programmable port type which can initiate a connection only to a preprogrammed port or group of ports.

CONTENT In today's information rich and hyped society, "carriage" is the new name for transmission. And "content" is the new name for what we carry. Content is a more than just phone calls, of course. It's movies, music, games, on-line books, information, etc. See also CONTENT SUPPLIER.

CONTENT PROCESSING Voice processing is the broad term made up of two narrower terms — call processing and content processing. Call processing consists of physically moving the call around. Think of call processing as switching. Content consists of actually doing something to the call's content, like digitizing it and storing it on a hard disk, or editing it, or recognizing it (voice recognition) for some purpose (e.g. using it as input into a computer program.

CONTENT SUPPLIER Content is a new fancy name for what telecommunications facilities carry. It includes movies, music, games, on-line books, information, etc. Content suppliers are thus movie studios, publishers, and music companies.

CONTENTION Contention occurs when several phones are vying for access to a line and only one of them can get it at one time. Some method is usually established for selecting the winner (first in, first out, campon, etc.) and accommodating the loser(s) (.e.g. giving them a busy tone). When you cannot get an outside line from your extension you have been in contention and lost.

CONTEXT DEPENDENT SOFT KEYS Many telephones now have an LCD screen. Sometimes such screens have unmarked keys underneath them and/or at their side. What these keys do depends on the "labels" appearing on the screen. They are called "context dependent" because what those keys do depends on where the call is at that time. The first context dependent soft keys were on the Mitel SuperSet 4 phones. When the handset was resting on the phone, only three of the six context sensitive keys had meaning. One said "Program," one said "Msg" and one said "Redial." When you picked the phone up, three buttons would now be alive. One would say "Page," one would say "Redial" and one would say "Hangup." If the phone rang and you picked it up, one button would now say "transf/conf" (meaning transfer/conference. When another phone was ringing. one button would say "Pickup," letting you push that button and answer someone else's phone. And so on. The neatest implementation of context sensitive keys was probably on the Telenova (now no longer manufactured). At one point when you were in voice mail, this phone's six buttons looked exactly like a cassette recorder —- record, play, fast forward, fast reverse, etc. It was brilliant. No one has ever made using voice mail so easy.

CONTEXT SENSITIVE A term from the computer industry which means that "Help" is only a keystroke away. Hit F1 and Help information will flash on the screen. That information will be relevant to what you're doing now, i.e. that help is within the context of what's going on right this moment. See also CONTEXT DEPENDENT SOFT KEYS.

CONTEXT SWITCH The technique with which an Intel 80x86 microprocessor handles multitasking is called a context switch. The CPU performs a context switch when it transfers control from one task to another. In the process, it saves the processor state (including registers) of one task, then loads the values for the task that is taking control. Context switching is the kind of multitasking that is done in standard mode Windows, where the CPU switches from one task to another, rather than allocating time to each task in turn, as in timeslicing.

CONTIGUOUS PORT Ports occurring in unbroken numeric sequence.

CONTIGUOUS SLOTTING This term refers to the process of selecting individual DS-0 circuits, within a DS-1 circuit or DS-3 circuit, which are adjacent to one another. Due to the timing difference which can result when non-adjacent channels are selected, contiguously slotted channels are preferable when the end equipment is designed to multiplex the individual low-speed channels into a single, higher speed connection.

CONTIGUOUS UNITED STATES The area within the boundaries of the District of Columbia and the 48 contiguous states as well as the offshore areas outside the boundaries of the coastal states of the 48 contiguous states, (including artificial islands, anchored vessels and fixed structures erected in such offshore areas for the purpose of exploring for, developing, removing and transporting resources therefrom) to the extent that such areas appertain to and are subject to the jurisdiction and control of the United States within the meaning of the Outer Continental Shelf Land Act, 43 U.S.C. Section 1331, et seq.

CONTINENTAL TELECOM INC. CONTEL. A telephone company made up of more than 600 small phone companies. In 1990 it merged with GTE in a tax-free swap of shares. Contel was formed and grown by Charles Wohlstetter, an ex-stockbroker, who became comfortable in the process of growing Contel. In late 1990, Contel merged with GTE, which is a euphemism for GTE buying Contel.

CONTINUITY An uninterrupted electrical path.

CONTINUITY CHECK A check to determine whether electrical current flows continuously throughout the length of a single wire on individual wires in a cable.

CONTINUITY CHECK TONE CCT. A single frequency of 2000 Hz which is transmitted by the sending exchange and looped back by the receiving exchange. Reception of the returned indicates availability of the channel. See ITU-T Recommendation.271.

CONTINUOUS A word used in voice recognition to mean a type of recognition that requires no pause between utterances.

CONTINUOUS DTMF This is a feature of some phones (especially cellular phones) that sends touchtone sounds for as long as the key is held down, allowing access to services such as voice mail and answering machines that need long-duration tones. Some phones automatically have continuous DTMF; some don't. It's worth checking. Continuous DTMF makes a lot more sense.

CONTINUOUS INFORMATION ENVIRONMENT A term for the world we live in — in which information (text, voice, video, images, etc.) is flowing at us continuously. And our job is, somehow, to manage the information. The idea is to use the new computer telephony terms to manage the information.

CONTINUOUS WAVES A series of wave or cycle of current all of which have a constant or unvarying amplitude.

CONTINUOUSLY VARIABLE Capable of having one of an infinite number of values, differing from each other by an arbitrarily small amount. Usually used to describe analog signals or analog transmission.

CONTRACT For the purposes developing applications in the telecommunications industry, there are two types of contracts: Active and Passive. An active contract is one you must sign. A passive contract is the type of contract you find in a software package. By opening the shrink wrapped package, you are committing yourself to the terms of the contract inside the package — the terms of which mostly consist of not duplicating the software in an authorized way.

CONTROL CABLE A multiconductor cable made for operation in control or signal circuits.

CONTROL CHARACTER A non-printing ASCII character which controls the flow of communications or a device. Control characters are entered from computer terminal keyboards by holding down the Control key (marked CTRL on most keyboards) while the letter is pressed. To ring a bell at remote telex terminal, an operator could hold down the CTRL key, and tap the "G" key, since Control-G is the BELL character. Most computers display Control as the "^" character in front of the designated letter. For example, ^M is the Carriage Return character.

CONTROL CIRCUIT X.21 interface circuit used to send control information from DTE to DCE.

CONTROL EQUIPMENT 1. The central "brains" of a telephone system. That part which controls the signaling and switching to the attached telephones. Known as the KSU (or key service unit) in a key system. 2. Equipment used to transmit orders from an alarm center to remote site to enable you to do things by remote control.

CONTROL FIELD Field in frame containing control information.

CONTROL HEAD ROAM LIGHTS Indicates that the cellular phone is outside the "home" system.

CONTROL OF ELECTROMAGNETIC RADIATION 1. Measures taken to minimize electromagnetic radiation emanating from a system or component, or to minimize electromagnetic interference. Such measures are taken for purposes of security and/or the reduction of interference, especially on ships and aircraft.

2. A national operational plan to minimize the use of electromagnetic radiation in the United States and its possessions and the Panama Canal Zone in the event of attack of imminent threat thereof, as an aid to the navigation of hostile aircraft, guided missiles, or other devices.

CONTROL OF FLOW LANGUAGE Programming-like constructs (IF, ELSE, WHILE, GOTO, and so on) provided by Transact-SQL so that the user can control the flow of execution of SQL Server queries, stored procedures, and triggers. This definition from Microsoft SQL server.

CONTROL PANEL The control panel on the Apple Macintosh is for general hardware and software settings. Icons allow a user to customize the system or application, or select a particular service, such as a specific printer, set the sound level, the date and time and choose an Ethernet connection through the network control panel.

CONTROL POINT A program that manages an APPN network node and its resources, enabling communications to other control points in the network.

CONTROL SEGMENT A worldwide network of Global Positioning System monitoring and control installations that ensure the accuracy of satellite positions and their clocks.

CONTROL SIGNAL 1. In the public network, control signals are used for auxiliary functions in both customer loop signaling and interoffice trunk signaling. Control signals are used in the customer loop for Coin Collect and Coin Return and Party Identification. Control signals used in interoffice trunk signaling include Start Dial (Wink or Delay Dial) signals, Keypulse (KP) signals or Start Pulse (ST) signals. 2. In modem communications, control signals are modem interface signals used to announce, start, stop or modify a function. Here's a table showing common RS-232-C and ITU-T V.24 control signals

Pin	Control Signal	From	To
4	Request-To-Send (RTS)	DTE	DCE
5	Clear-To-Send (CTS)	DCE	DTE
6	Data Set Ready (DSR)	DCE	DTE
8	Carrier Detect (CD)	DCE	DTE
20	Data Terminal Ready (DTR)	DTE	DCE
22	Ring Indicator (RI)	DCE	DTE

CONTROL STATION On a multiaccess link, a station that is in charge of such functions as selection and polling.

CONTROL TIER An AT&T term for the tier within the Universal Information Services network node that provides the transport network's connection control function.

CONTROL UNIT An architectural component of a processor chip which orchestrates processor activity and handles timing to make sure the processor doesn't overlap functions.

CONTROL PACKAGE NETWORK A Rolm/IBM term for a multinode network used by the processors in one CBX node to communicate with the processors in other nodes. CPN-1 is used with RolmBus 74. CPN-2 is used with Rolmbus 295. Formerly called HUB.

CONTROLLED ENVIRONMENT VAULT CEV. It is a low maintenance, water-tight concrete or fiberglass container typically buried in the ground which provides permanent housing for remote switches, remote line concentrators, pair gain and fiber transmission systems. Because it is buried, it can often be installed in utility easements or other places where local building laws may be a problem. This below ground room that houses electronic and/or optical equipment is under controlled temperature and humidity conditions.

CONTROLLER 1. In the truest sense, a device which controls the operation of another piece of equipment. In its more common data communications sense, a device between a host and terminals that relays information between them. It administers their communication. Controllers may be housed in the host, can be stand-alone, or can be located in a file server. Typically one controller will be connected to several terminals. The most common controller is the IBM Cluster Controller for their 370 family of mainframes. In an automated radio, a controller is a device that commands the radio transmitter and receiver, and that performs processes, such as automatic link establishment, channel scanning and selection, link quality analysis, polling, sounding, message store and forward, address protection, and anti-spoofing. 2. Participant in a conference call who sets up the conference call.

CONTROLLER CARD Also called a hard disk/diskette drive controller. It's an add-in card which controls how data is written to and retrieved from your PC's various floppy and hard drives. Controller cards come in various flavors, including MFN and SCSI. Controller cards are the devices used to format hard drives.

Controller cards are not hard drive specific (except within categories). Controller cards will format many drives. But once you have a hard drive that has been formatted by that one controller card, it tends to prefer talking to that controller card forever. If you switch your hard disk to another machine, switch the controller card along with it. If you switch your hard disk to another machine, but not the controller card, then format the hard disk. That's not a "100% Do It Or Else You'll Be Disappointed" rule. But just a "Play It Safe and Switch Them" rule.

CONTURING In digital facsimile, density step lines in received copy resulting from analog-to-digital conversion when the original image has observable gray shadings between the smallest density steps of the digital system.

CONUS A military term for CONtiguous United States (lower 48 states). See CONTIGUOUS UNITED STATES.

CONVECTION COOLING Design techniques used in switching system construction to permit safe heat dissipation from the equipment without the need for cooling fans.

CONVECTOR The device which covers the steam heating radiator in buildings and typically sits underneath a window. Also called a weathermaster.

CONVECTOR AREA An area allocated for heat circulation and distribution. Convector areas, typically built into a wall, can be used as a satellite location only if a more suitable area is unavailable.

CONVERGENCE 1. A measure of the clarity of a color monitor. A measure of how closely the red, green and blue guns in a color monitor track each other when drawing a color image. The other measures are focus and dot pitch. 2. A LAN term. The point at which all the internetworking devices share a common understanding of the routing topology. The slower the convergence time, the slower the recovery from link failure. 3. The word to describe a trend, now that most media can be represented digitally, for the traditional distinctions between industries to blur and for companies from consumer electronics, computer and telecommunications industries to form alliances, partnerships and other relationships, as well as to raid each others markets.

CONVERSATION PATH The route from originating port to terminating port for a two-way call. A conversation thus typically requires two ports on most PBXs.

CONVERSATION TIME The time spent on a conversation from the time the person at the other end picks up to the time you or him hang up. Conversation time plus dialing, searching and ringing time equal the time your circuit will be used during a call.

CONVERSATIONAL MODE TELEX An MCI International product providing real time exchange between Telex terminals or other compatible devices that allows instantaneous, two-way conversations in writing.

CONVERTER 1. A vacuum tube which combines the functions of oscillator and mixed tube. 2. A device for changing AC to DC and vice versa. An ancient radio term. 3. An adapter, such as one that allows a modular phone to be plugged into a 4-hole jack.

4. A British term. A repeater that also converts from one media type to another, such as from fibre (British spelling) to copper. Often called a media adaptor.

CONVOLUTIONAL CODE Error protection code encoding data bits in a continuous stream. An error-correction code in which each m-bit information symbol to be encoded is transformed into an n-bit symbol (n>m) where the transformation is a function of the last k information symbols, and k is referred to as the constraint length of the code. Convolutional codes are often used to improve the performance of radio and satellite links.

COOPERATIVE PROCESSING Mainframe and intelligent workstations dividing application code between them.

COPLAND Apple's code name for a flashy new operating system — the one designed to make people forget about Windows 95. I found mention of Copland about two weeks before Windows 95 was due to be released by Microsoft, August 24, 1995.

COPOLYMER Compound resulting from the polymerization of two different monomers.

COPROCESSOR 1. An additional processor which takes care of specific tasks, the objective being to reduce the load on the main CPU. Many IBM PCs and IBM clones have the capacity to install a coprocessor chip which does only arithmetic functions. This significantly speeds up your computer if you do a lot of calculations. See MATH COPROCESSOR.

COPW Customer Owned Premises Wire. You own the telephone wiring in your office.

COPY A nice new telephone system programming feature. We found it on Northern Telecom's Norstar phone. With this button, certain programmed settings can be copied from one line to another, or from one telephone to another. Line programmable settings that can be copied on the Norstar are Line Data, Restrictions, Overrides, and Night Service. Telephone settings that can be copied are Line Access, Restrictions, Overrides, and Permissions.

COPYRIGHT A copyright protects the original author of a story, software program, song movie, piece of sculpture, or other original work from direct copying. Copying may be inferred where alleged copyist had access to the copyrighted work. The copyright notice (the @ symbol, or the word "Copyright", the year of creation, and the name of the copyright owner) should be provided on each copy of the work. Copyrights may also be registered with the Library of Congress, but this is not necessary in all cases. Copyright protects the expression of an idea, not the idea itself. (In appropriate cases, patents can be used to protect the idea.) Where the idea is so simple that there is only one way to express it, the idea and its expression may merge, preventing copyrightability. This logic was used successfully in defense of several suits involving "clean room" reverse engineering of microcode: A first group hacked out the code, and prepared a complete functional specification defining the function of each instruction. A second group then wrote new code implementing these functions. Since there had been no copying, there could be no copyright infringement; the fact that both versions of the code for some instructions were identical merely showed that the idea and expression had merged. There are only so many ways to code an ADD instruction, after all. See INTELLECTUAL PROPERTY, PATENT and TRADE SECRET.

CORD A small, flexible insulated wire.

CORD BOARD The earliest manual PBX. Usually an elegant wooden device consisting of lots of cords with plugs on them. These cords sat horizontally sticking up, like missiles in a silo. Each cord corresponded to an extension. Whenever the phone rang, the cord board attendant would answer it. Each incoming line was a vertical hole. When the operator had figured for whom the call was, he/she would simply plug the cord corresponding to the desired extension into the hole corresponding to the incoming trunk. The operator would reverse the process if the internal user wanted to make an external call. Either the operator would dial the call first, or simply plug in the user's extension and thus allow the user to dial the call directly. The tip of the plug and the circular ring of the plug gave the term "tip and ring" to telephony. In electronics, it's known as positive and negative. See CORD CIRCUIT.

CORD CIRCUIT A switchboard circuit, terminated in two plug-ended cords, used to establish connections manually between user lines or between trunks and user lines. A number of cord circuits are furnished as part of the manual switchboard position equipment. The cords may be referred to as front cord and rear cord or trunk cord and station cord. In modern cordless switchboards, the cord circuit is switch operated. See CORD BOARD.

CORD LAMP The lamp associated with a cord circuit that indicates supervisory conditions for the respective part of the connection. See CORD BOARD.

CORDBOARD See CORD BOARD.

CORDLESS TELEPHONE A telephone with no cord between handset and base. Each piece contains a radio transmitter, receiver, and antenna. The handset contains a rechargeable battery; the base must be plugged into an AC outlet. Depending on product design, radio frequency, environmental conditions, and national law, range between handset and base can be 10 feet to several miles. Cordless phones were once all analog. Now a breed of digital ones is out. They work much better in electrically noisy environments — like the typical office.

CORDLESS SWITCHBOARD A telephone switchboard in which manually operated keys are used to make connections. See CORD BOARD.

CORE The central glass element of a fiber optic cable through which the light is transmitted (typically 8-12 microns in diameter for single mode fiber and 50-100 microns in diameter for multimode fiber). This light conducting portion of the fiber is defined by the high refraction index region. The core is normally in the center of the fiber, bounded by the cladding material.

CORE GATEWAY The primary routers in the Internet. Historically,one of a set of gateways (routers) operated by the Internet Network Operations Center at BBN. The core gateway system formed a central part of Internet routing in that all groups would advertise paths to their networks from a core gateway, using the Exterior Gateway Protocol (EGP).

CORE NON-CIRCULARITY The percent that the shape of the core's cross section deviates from a circle. Sometimes referred to as core ovality.

CORE SIZE Primary description of a fiber. Stated in microns. Does not include cladding. Determines end surface area which accepts and transmits light.

CORNER REFLECTOR 1. A device, normally consisting of three metallic surfaces or screens perpendicular to one another, designed to act as a radar target or marker. 2. In radar interpretation, an object that, by means of multiple reflections from smooth surfaces, produces a radar return of greater magnitude than might be expected from the physical size of the object. 3. A reflected electromagnetic wave to its point of origin. Such reflectors are often used as radar targets. 4. Passive optical mirror, that consists of three mutually perpendicular flat, intersecting reflecting surfaces, which returns an incident light beam in the opposite direction. 5. A reflector consisting of two mutually intersecting conducting flat surfaces.

CORPORATE ACCOUNT SERVICE An MCI specific service involving a single, unified reporting system for multiple business that the customer owns, franchises, manages, or directs.

CORPORATE ID NUMBER The MCI term for the number which identifies a customer on a corporate level. (Not all MCI customers have a corporate ID number.)

CORPORATE NETWORK Also called an internetwork or a wide area network. A network of networks (the mother of all networks) that connects most or all of a corporation's voice, data, and video resources using various methods, including the phone system, LANs, private data networks, leased telecommunications lines, and public data networks. Connections between networks are made with bridges and routers.

Corporate networks come in many shapes and sizes. Often, they will consist of networks within the same building or facility. Here, networks are combined using bridges and routers. Corporate networks may also span great distances. Such internetworks require different types of connections than single-facility internetworks, though the fundamentals are similar. Internetworks that connect remote facilities usually rely on some type of public or leased data communications network provided by the phone company or a data network service company. Bridges and routers are still required to connect networks to the long-distance data service, whether it's an X.25 packet switched network, a T-1 line, or even a regular phone line. See also BRIDGE and ROUTER.

CORPORATION FOR OPEN SYSTEMS INTERNATIONAL COS. A not-for-profit consortium based in Fairfax, VA that helps resolve open systems issues, both technically and businesswise. It helps organize ISDN Solutions '94, video teleconferencing, open set top boxes, cooperative routers and SONET issues.

CORRELATION The AMA (Automatic Message Accounting) function that permits the association of AMA data generated at the same network system or at physically separate network systems. There are three levels of correlation that affect Advanced Intelligent Network Release 1: record level, service level, and customer level. Definition from Bellcore in reference to Advanced Intelligent Network.

CORRIDOR OPTIONAL CALLING PLAN New York Telephone offers a discounted way for subscribers in the 212 and 718 area codes to call five northern New Jersey counties — Bergen, Essex, Hudson, Passaic and Union. See CORRIDOR SERVICE.

CORRIDOR SERVICE A term that Bell Atlantic and Nynex are using for calls to and from the New York City area to and from Northern New Jersey, or between Philadelphia and Southern New Jersey.

CORROSION The destruction of the surface of a metal by chemical reaction.

COS 1. See CLASS OF SERVICE. 2. Compatible for Open Systems. 3. Corporation for Open Systems international. A Federal Government blessed organization which aims towards standardizing OSI and ISDN. COS members includes everyone from end-users to manufacturers. COS deals with private and public networking issues.

COSINE Cooperation for Open Systems Interconnection Networking in Europe. A program sponsored by the European Commission aimed at using OSI to tie together European research networks.

COSNAME Identifies class of service SNA.

COST OF SERVICE PRICING A procedure, rationale or methodology for pricing services strictly on the basis of the cost to provide those services.

COT 1. Continuity Check Message. The second of the ISUP call set-up messages. Indicates success or failure of continuity check if one is needed. See ISUP and COMMON CHANNEL SIGNALING. 2. Central Office Terminal

COTS COnnection Transport Service.

COUCH COMMANDO A couch potato who insists on taking charge of what he and the rest of the couch potatoes are watching on the TV.

COUCH POTATO A person who spends their life sitting on a couch surfing TV channels with remote control TV device. See MOUSE POTATO.

COULOMB The quantity of electricity transferred by a current of one ampere in one second. One unit of quantity in measuring electricity.

COUNTER-ROTATING RING An arrangement whereby two signal paths, whose direction opposite to each other, exists in a ring topology.

COUNTERPOISE A system of electrical conductors used to complete the antenna system in place of the usual ground connection.

COUNTRY CODE 1. The one, two or three digit number that, in the world numbering plan, identifies each country or integrated numbering plan in the world. In short, the one, two or three digits that precede the national number in an international phone call. This code is assigned in and taken from Recommendation E.163 (Numbering Plan for International Service) adopted by the ITU-T. A list of the country codes can be found in Section 1.8 of the Local Exchange Routing Guide (LERG). 2. In international record carrier transmissions, the country code is a two or three alpha or numeric abbreviation of the country name following the geographical place name.

COUPLED MODES 1. In fiber optics, a condition wherein energy is transferred among modes. The energy share of each mode does not differ after the equilibrium length has been reached 2. In microwave transmission, a condition where energy is transferred from the fundamental mode to higher order modes. Energy transferred to coupled modes is undesirable in usual microwave transmission in a waveguide. The frequency is kept low enough so that propagation in the waveguide is only in the fundamental mode.

COUPLING Any means by which energy is transferred from one conductive or dielectric medium (e.g., optical waveguide) to another, including fortuitous occurrences. Types of electrical coupling include capacitive (electrostatic) coupling, inductive coupling, and conductive (hard wire) coupling. Coupling may occur between optical fibers unless specific action is taken to prevent it. Coupling between fibers is very effectively prevented by the polymer overcoat, which also prevents the propagation of cladding modes, and provides some degree of physical protection.

COUPLING LOSS The power loss suffered when coupling light from one optical device to another.

COUPON From Britain: A tear-off slip to encourage response to advertisements or to a promotion on packaging. The information is keyed into a telebusiness system which automatically handles the follow-up. This may be a phone call, acknowledgement letter, brochure, distribution of lead to a distributor and so on.

COURIER DISPATCH The Courier Dispatch service offered by MCI International allows customers to generate and send high-priority messages from their own Telex terminals to any destination in the Continental U.S. and Hawaii.

COVERAGE The percent of completeness with which a metal braid covers the underlying surface.

COVERAGE AREA The geographic area served by a cellular system; that is, the area in which service is available to users of the system. Once the mobile telephone number has traveled outside the coverage area, the mobile telephone will show "NO SERVICE."

COW Cellsite On Wheels. A trailer with antenna and transmitting/receiving hardware used to provide temporary service in emergencies, special events, remote testing and repair, or until a normal tower can be erected. Comes with climate control, diesel generator, and self-supporting wind-resistant 84' antenna mast. Both full-size COWs and Mini-COWs are available.

COW INTERFACE Character-Oriented Windows Interface. An SAA-compatible user interface for OS/2 applications.

CP Connection Point in Northern Telecom parlance.

CP/M Control Program for Microcomputers. An erstwhile popular operating system for primarily 8-bit microcomputer systems based on the family of Intel 8080 family of microprocessor chips. CP/M system was originally written by Gary Kidall a programmer and consultant who later formed a company called Intergalatic Digital Research (later just Digital Research). Sadly, that company never upgraded CP/M to 16-bit machines. Thus it left the way open for Bill Gates and the company he formed, Microsoft, to create MS-DOS, which, in its initial form, bore a remarkable resemblance to CP/M.

CPC 1. Calling Party Control. 2. Calling Party Connected.

CPE Customer Provided Equipment, or Customer Premise Equipment. Originally it referred to equipment on the customer's premises which had been bought from a vendor who was not the local phone company. Now it simply refers to telephone equipment — key systems, PBXs, answering machines, etc. — which reside on the customer's premises. "Premises" might be anything from an office to a factory to a home. GTE once used CPE to refer to "Company Provided Equipment." It doesn't any longer.

CPI Computer to PBX Interface. This proprietary hardware/software interface provides direct connectivity between a PBX's switching network and a host computer to allow switched access between the host computer and data terminal equipment connected with the PBX. The interface is based on the North American Standard T-Carrier specification (24 multiplexed 64 kbps channels operating at a combined speed of 1,544 Mbps). Developed by Northern Telecom, Inc. this interface uses in-band signaling and provides bidirectional data transmission at speeds up to 56 Kbps synchronous per channel. See OPEN APPLICATION INTERFACE.

CPI-C IBM SAA Common Programming Interface-Communication between SNA and OSI environments.

CPM 1. Customer Premise Management. 2. Critical Path Method. See also CP/M.

CPN Computer PBX Network.

CPNI Customer Proprietary Network Information. Information which is available to a telephone company by virtue of the telephone company's basic service customer relationship. This information may include the quantity, location, type and amount of use of local telephone service subscribed to, and information contained on telephone company bills. This is the definition of CPNI that the independent voice mail and live telephone answering industry uses.

CPODA Compression Priority Demand Assignment. Another protocol for converting voice into data bits. See also PCM.

CPS Characters per second, or cycles per second. In asynchronous communications, there are typically ten bits per characters — 8 bits for the character and one stop and one start bit.

CPU The Central Processing Unit. The computing part of a computer. The "brain" of the computer. It manipulates data and processes instructions coming from software or a human operator. See CENTRAL PROCESSING UNIT.

CR 1. Carriage Return. The key on a computer called Carriage Return or sometimes "ENTER." Touching this key usually signals the computer that the entry has been completed and is now ready for processing by the computer. See CARRIAGE RETURN. 2. Critical (alarm status). Indicates a failure affecting more than 96 customers. An AT&T definition. 3. Call Reference.

CRACKER A person who "cracks" computer and telephone systems by gaining access to passwords, or by "cracking" the copy protection of computer software. A cracker usually does illegal acts. A Cracker is a "Hacker" whose hacks are beyond the bounds of propriety, and usually beyond the law. The term "cracker" is said to derive from the word "safecracker." See HACKER.

CRAFT Cooperative Research Action For Technology.

CRAFT TERMINAL A PCS wireless term. A craft terminal is a device built specifically to provide a man-machine interface that is otherwise not available. The interface is customized to provide a view into a particular device's operation such as a proprietary switch or BSS, which is a Base Station Sub-system charged with managing radio frequency resources and radio frequency transmission for a group of BTSs, which is a Base Transceiver Station, used to transmit radio frequency over the air.

CRAFTSPERSON In the phone industry, a craftsperson has two distinct meanings. First, it is the person who toils to instal phones, repair outside plant, fix problems inside central offices. This person typically carries tools and dresses in jeans. Second, craftspeople are at the bottom of the management hierarchy in most phone companies. They typically belong to a union. Craftspeople are not "in management." See LEVEL.

CRASH The complete failure of a hardware device or a software operation. Usually used to mean a "fatal" crash in which the device or software must be started from a "power up" condition. See BOOT.

CRC Cyclic Redundancy Check. A process used to check the integrity of a block of data. A CRC character is generated at the transmission end. Its value depends on the hexadecimal value of the number of ones in the data block. The transmitting device calculates the value and appends it to the data block. The receiving end makes a similar calculation and compares its results with the added character. If there is a difference, the recipient requests retransmission. CRC is a common method of establishing that data was correctly received in data communications. See CRC CHARACTER and CYCLIC REDUNDANCY CHECK.

CRC CHARACTER A character used to check the integrity of a block of data. The character is generated at the transmission end. Its value depends on the hexadecimal value of the number of ones in the data block. And it is added to the data block. The receiving end makes a similar calculation and compares its results with the added character. If there's a difference, there's been a mistake in transmission. So, please, re-send the data.

CRD Contention Resolution Device.

CREAM SKIMMING Selecting only the most profitable markets or services to sell into. Choosing the cream of the market. An erstwhile popular economic theory to deny new entrants into the telephone industry.

CREDENTIALS A way of establishing, via a trusted third party, that you are who you claim to be.

CREDFACS Conduit, Risers, Equipment space, Ducts and FACilitieS. Collective term for pathway elements used in communications cabling.

CREDIT CARD PHONE A pay telephone that accepts credit cards with magnetic strips on them instead of coins.

CRITICAL ANGLE The smallest angle at which a ray will be totally reflected within a fiber.

CRITICAL MESS An unstable stage in a software project's life when any single change or bug fix can result in two or more new bugs. Continued development at this stage leads to an exponential increase in the number of bugs.

CRITICAL TECHNICAL LOAD That part of the total technical power load required for synchronous communications and automatic switching equipment.

CROSS ASSEMBLER An assembler that can run symbolic-language on one type of computer and produce machine-language output for another type of computer.

CROSS BORDER DIGITAL DATA SERVICE CDDS. An MCI International digital, private-line service that provides customers with service that provides customers with 56 kbps dedicated terrestrial channels between the U.S. and Canada.

CROSS BORDER TERRESTRIAL DIGITAL DATA SERVICE CTDDS. An MCI International point-to-point dedicated, leased channel service enabling customers to transmit traffic between the U.S. and Canada over digital terrestrial facilities at a transmission speed of 1.544 Mbps.

CROSS CONNECT Distribution system equipment used to terminate and administer communication circuits. In a wire cross connect, jumper wires or patch cords are used to make circuit connections. In an optical cross connect, fiber patch cords are used. The cross connect is located in an equipment room, riser closet, or satellite closet.

CROSS CONNECT FIELD Wire terminations grouped to provide cross connect capability. The groups are identified by color-coded sections of backboards mounted on the wall in equipment rooms, riser closets, or satellite closets, or by designation strips placed on the wiring block or unit. The color coding identifies the type of circuit that terminates at the field.

CROSS CONNECTION Cross-connection is the connection of one wire to another usually by anchoring each wire to a connecting block and then placing a third wire between them so that an electrical connection is made.

CROSS COUPLING The coupling of a signal from one channel, circuit, or conductor to another, where it becomes an undesired signal. See COUPLING.

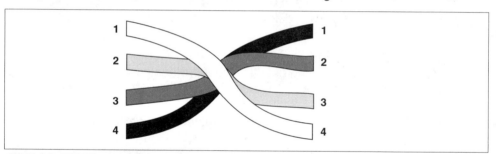

CROSS EXTENSION CABLE When you make an REJ-11 extension cable, the wiring crosses over. Conductor 1 becomes 4. Conductor 2 becomes 3. Conductor 3 becomes 2. And conductor 4 becomes one. Next time you have an REJ-11 extension cable in your hand, hold the REJ-11s next to each other and compare them. You'll notice the cross-over of the conductors.

CROSS PLAN TERMINATION The conversion of ten-digit telephone numbers to seven digits, or vice versa.

CROSS POLARIZATION The relationship between two radio waves where one is polarized vertically and the other horizontally.

CROSS SUBSIDIZATION Supporting one area of a business from revenues generated by another area. Local phone companies in the U.S. have long argued that their ability to compete

CROSS WYE A cable used at the host system, or network interface equipment that changes pin/signal assignment in order to conform to a given wiring standard (USOC, AT&T PDS, DEC MMJ, etc).

CROSSBAR A switching system that uses a centrally-controlled matrix switching network of electromechanical switches which worked with magnets and which connected horizontal and vertical paths to establish a path through the network. Crossbar is known for its reliability but is now largely obsolete because it takes up a lot of space and isn't programmable.

CROSSBAR TANDEM A 2-wire common-control switching system with a space-division network used as local tandem, toll tandem, and CAMA switching. While originally designed to switch trunks, some systems have been locally modified to accept loop-start or ground-start lines.

CROSSCOMM A networking company specializing in token ring internetworking and enterprise-wide networks. Located in Marlboro, MA.

CROSSED PINNING Configuration that allows two DTE devices or two DCE devices to communicate. See also CROSSOVER CABLE.

CROSSLINK An X.25 link connecting two XTX NCs on the same level.

CROSSOVER CABLE Another word for NULL MODEM CABLE. A cable used to join two computers together. Usually conductors 2 and 3 are reversed in an RS-232 serial connection.

CROSSPOINT A single element in an array of elements that comprise a switch. It is a set of physical or logical contacts that operate together to extend the speech and signal channels in a switching network.

CROSSPOLARIZED OPERATION The use of two transmitters operating on the same frequency, with one transmitter-receiver pair being vertically polarized and the other pair horizontally polarized (orthogonal polarization).

CROSSPOSTING Crossposting is putting one copy of an electronic file up on the Internet in such a way that it can be viewed from any of several newsgroups (discussion areas). Today's Internet software lets readers avoid seeing a widely crossposted article more than once. They see it in the first group they find it. Crossposting is frowned upon in the Internet when it becomes excessive and off-topic. Crossposting is a less serious offense than spamming, which is seriously frowned upon. See SPAMMING.

CROSSTALK Crosstalk occurs when you can hear someone you did not call talking on your telephone line to another person you did not call. You may also only hear half the other conversation. Just one person speaking. There are several technical causes for crosstalk. They relate to wire placement, shielding and transmission techniques. CROSSTALK is also the name of once popular telecommunications software program for 8- and 16-bit microcomputers.

CROSSTALK ATTENUATION The extent to which a communications system resists crosstalk.

CRT Cathode Ray Tube. The glass display device found in television sets and video computer terminals. See CATHODE RAY TUBE.

CRTC Canadian Radio Television and Telecommunications Commission. Canada's federal telecom regulator. It's based in Ottawa.

CRYPTANALYSIS 1. The steps and operations performed in converting encrypted messages into plain text without initial knowledge of the key employed in the encryption. 2. The study of encrypted texts. The steps or processes involved in converting encrypted text into plain text without initial knowledge of the key employed in the encryption.

CRYPTO A term used to describe encrypted information. The use of encryption on data communications circuits lessens the chance that the information will be successfully copied by eavesdroppers.

CRYPTOCHANNEL A complete system of crypto-communications between two or more holders. The basic unit for naval cryptographic communication. It includes: (a) the cryptographic aids prescribed; (b) the holders thereof; (c) the indicators or other means of identification; (d) the area or areas in which effective; (e) the special purpose, if any, for which provided; and (f) pertinent notes as to distribution, usage, etc. A cryptochannel is analogous to a radio circuit.

CRYPTOGRAPHY The process of concealing the contents of a message from all except those who know the key. Cryptography is unregulated in the United States. See CLIPPER CHIP.

CRYSTAL MICROPHONE A microphone, the diaphragm of which is attached to a piezo-electric crystal, which generates electrical currents when torque is applied, due to the vibration of the diaphragm. The earliest form of microphone, now obsolete. See also CONDENSER and ELECTRET MICROPHONE.

CS Convergence Sublayer. The upper portion of BISDN Layer 3.

CS-1 Capability Set 1. Term used by ITU-T to refer to their initial set of Advanced Intelligent Network (AIN) standards. Contains 18 trigger detection points. Bellcore (Bell Communications Research) plans to adopt the CS-1 terminology for its own AIN.

CSA 1. Callpath Services Architecture — IBM's computer host to PBX interface. It links computer and telephone systems. See also CALLBRIDGE and OPEN APPLICATION INTERFACE. 2. Canadian Standards Association — a non-profit, independent organization which operates a listing service for electrical and electronic materials and equipment. It is the body that establishes telephone equipment (and other) standards for use in Canada. The Canadian counterpart of the Underwriters Laboratories.

CSA T-528 Canadian equivalent of EIA-606 standard, harmonized.

CSA T-529 Canadian equivalent of EIA-568 standard, harmonized.

CSA T-530 Canadian equivalent of EIA-569 standard, harmonized. defined. Also has Rcv Clock, and both Xmit Clocks for synchronous systems. For use with modems, the lack of Ring Indicate is a drawback.

CSC 1. Customer Service Center 2. Customer Service Consultant 3. Customer Service Coordinator 4. Customer Support Center 5. Customer Support Consultant.

CSDC Circuit Switched Digital Capability. AT&T defines it as a technique for making end-to-end digital connections. Customers can place telephone calls normally, then use the same private connection to transmit high-speed data. CSDC is a circuit-switched, 56-kbps, full-duplex data service that provides high-speed data communications over regular telephone lines.

CSFI IBM Communications Subsystem For Interconnection: networking software.

CSI 1. Called Subscriber Identification. This is an identifier whose coding format contains a number, usually a phone number from the remote terminal used in fax. 2. Capability Set I. A set of service-independent building blocks for the creation of IN services developed by the European Telecommunications Standards Institute and the ITU-T.

CSMA Carrier Sense Multiple Access. In local area networking, CSMA is a way of getting onto the LAN. Before starting to transmit, personal computers on the LAN "listen" to make sure no other PC is transmitting. Once the PC figures out that no other PC is transmitting, it sends a packet and then frees the line for other PCs to transmit. With CSMA, though stations do not transmit until the medium is clear, collisions still occur. Two alternative versions (CSMA/CA and CSMA/CD) attempt to reduce both the number of collisions and the severity of their impact. See CSMA/CA and CSMA/CD.

CSMA/CA Carrier Sense Multiple Access (CSMA) with Collision Avoidance. In local area networking, CSMA technique that combines slotted time-division multiplexing (TDM) with carrier sense multiple access/collision detection (CSMA/C) to avoid having collisions occur a second time. CSMA/CA works best if the time allocated is short compared to packet length and if the number of stations (these days PCs) is small. See CARRIER SENSE MULTIPLE ACCESS/COLLISION AVOIDANCE and CSMA.

CSMA/CD Carrier Sense Multiple Access with Collision Detection. In local area networking technology, CSMA technique that also listens while transmitting to detect collisions.

CSMA/CD is a leading control technique for getting onto and off a local area network. All devices attached to the network listen for transmissions in progress (i.e. carrier sense) before starting to transmit (multiple access). If two or more begin transmitting at the same time and their transmissions crash into each other, each backs off (collision detection) for a different amount of time (determined by an algorithm) before again attempting to transmit.

If you didn't understand the above definition, try this one: CSMA/CD: Abbreviation for Carrier Sense Multiple Access with Collision Detection, a method of having multiple workstations access a transmission medium (multiple access) by listening until no signals are detected (carrier sense), then transmitting and checking to see if more than one signal is present (collision detection). Each workstation attempts to transmit when they "believe" the network to be free. If there is a collision, each workstation attempts to retransmit after a preset delay, which is different for each workstation. It is one of the most popular access methods for PC-based LANs. Think of it as entering a highway from an access road, except that you can crash and still try again. Or think of it as two polite people who start to talk at the same time. Each politely backs off and waits a random amount of time before starting to speak again. Ethernet-based LANs use CSMA/CD. See Ethernet and IEEE 802.3.

CSMDR Centralized Station Message Detail Recording.

CSO Central Services Organization; an Internet service that makes it easy to find user names and addresses.

CSR 1. Customer Station Rearrangement (as in Centrex). 2. Customer Service

Representative. A customer care agent that provides direct customer support. 3. Customer Service Record. Computer printout that details the fixed monthly charges billed by your local telephone company. The CSR is composed of computer codes called USOCs, which in turn correspond to a particular tariffed service. USOCs tell the telephone company's billing system what tariff rate should be billed for a particular service. In order to ensure your telephone bill is correct you must request and review this document. No telecom manager should be without this important document.

CST Computer Supported Telephony, a term coined by Siemens. Here is an explanation from Dr. Peter Pawlita of Siemens. "More people communicate by telephone than by any other means. The reason is simple: The telephone bridges any distance, saves travel time and can be used spontaneously and is universally available. Unfortunately telephone usage is often associated with annoying delays and frayed nerves resulting from such things as time wasted in finding a number, dialing errors, and the absence of the dialed party. Added to this the person to whom you are speaking does not have the knowledge you require, or has to spend a long time looking or documents. What could be more obvious, therefore, than to turn these problems over to the computer — to implement Computer Supported Telephony (CST). CST denotes the functional connection of a computer system to a PBX at the application level. CST applications can automatically initiate calls, receive incoming calls, and provide "just-in-time" business data, documents and notes on the screen. All this makes telephony more convenient, time-saving, efficient and largely error-free."

CSTA Computer Supported Telephony Application. A standard from the European Computer Manufacturers Association (ECMA) for linking computers to telephone systems. Basic CSTA is a set of API call agreed upon by the ECMA. See also CST and OPEN APPLICATION INTERFACE.

CSTP Customer Specific Term Plan. See CUSTOMER SPECIFIC TERM PLAN.

CSU 1. Channel Service Unit. Also called a Channel Service Unit/Data Service Unit or CSU/DSU because it contains a built-in DSU device. A device to terminate a digital channel on a customer's premises. It performs certain line coding, line-conditioning and equalization functions, and responds to loopback commands sent from the central office. A CSU sits between the digital line coming in from the central office and devices such as channel banks or data communications devices. A Channel Service Unit is found on every digital link and allows the transfer of data at a range greater than 56 Kbps. A 56 Kbps circuit would need a 56 Kbps DSU on both ends to transfer data from one end to the other. A CSU looks like your basic "modem," except it can pass data at rates much greater and does not permit dial-up functions (unless it has an asynch dial-backup feature).

2. Channel Sharing Unit. Line bridging device that allows several inputs to share one output. CSUs exist to handle any input/output combination of sync or asynch terminals, computer ports, or modems and thus these units are variously called modem sharing units, digital bridges, port sharing units, digital sharing devices, modem contention units, multiple access units, control signal activated electronic switches or data-activated electronic switches.

CSU/DSU See CSU.

CSUA Canadian Satellite Users Association. Trade association of satellite users.

CT Cordless Telephone.

CT-2 Interim Standard for the Telepoint service favored by UK Memorandum of Understanding with other network operators.

CT1 Cordless Telephony Generation 1. A new type of low-cost public cordless telephone system getting popular in Europe. You carry a cheap handset. You go to within several hundred yards of a local antenna and you make your phone call. You can't receive calls as you can on a cellular radio. You can't make calls unless you're close to the antenna. The service helps overcome the serious lack of street-side coin and public phones in Europe. CT1 is the analog version of the interface specification. See CT2 and CT2+.

CT2 Cordless Telephony Generation 2, interface specification for digital technology, currently in use in the U.K. for telepoint (payphone) applications. Think of telepoint phones as cellular phones but using micro-cells. By having smaller cells than normal cellular cells, CT2 phones can be smaller, cheaper and lighter. The first generation of these phones didn't do well, since they weren't smaller and lighter; there weren't many micro-cells and you couldn't receive an incoming call. See CT1.

CT2+ An expansion of the CT2 interface specification that would extend network capabilities and allow backwards compatibility with CT2 handsets. See CT1 and CT2.

CT3 Ericsson's proprietary cordless phone system.

CTA Competitive Telecommunications Association. Trade association of alternate long distance carriers (resellers) in Canada.

CTCA Canadian Telecommunications Consultants Association. Professional organization of telecommunications consultants.

CTD Continuity Tone Detector.

CTE 1. Channel Translation Equipment. 2. Coefficient of thermal expansion.

CTI Computer Telephone Integration. A term for connecting a computer (single workstation or file server on a local area network) to a telephone switch (e.g. a PBX or an ACD) and have the computer issue the switch commands to move calls around. The classic application for CTI is in call centers. Picture this: A call comes in. That call carries some form of caller ID — either ANI or Class Caller ID. The switch "hears" the calling number, strips it off, sends it to the computer. The computer does a lookup, sends back the switch instructions on what to do with the call. The switch follows orders. It might send the call to a specialized agent or maybe just to the agent the caller dealt with last time. There are emerging standards for CTI. See also TSAPI and WINDOWS TELEPHONY.

CTIA 1. Cellular Telecommunications Industry Association. Washington, D.C.-based industry association. 2. Computer Technology Industry Association, a Lombard, Illinois trade association.

CTIP Computer Telephony Interface Products. Adapters that allow telephones to work with computers. An example is the Konnexx connector, which fits between the handset and the phone, allows a connection to a PC modem or fax machine.

This definition contributed by Larry Kettler of San Diego.

CTS 1. Clear To Send. Pin 5 on the 25-conductor RS-232-C interface or an RS-232-C signal used in the exchange of data between the computer and a serial device. 2. Communication Transport System. CTS is The Siemon Company's proprietary structured wiring system. It consists of the methodology and the connecting hardware products to plan, design, and implement the communications wiring infrastructure for commercial buildings (for more information see the company's CTS Design Workbook and CTS Training Videotape). The Siemon Company is based in Watertown, CT. 3. Conformance Testing Services.

CTTS Coax To The Curb. An approach that provisions a multiline remote terminal to deliver voice and data to concentrated residential applications.

CTTU Centralized Trunk Test Unit. An operational support system providing centralized trunk maintenance through a data link on a switch.

CTX Centrex.

CUA Common User Access.

CUCKOO-CLOCK Telecom slang for some 6- and 10-button models of AT&T 1A2 wall phones shaped vaguely like traditional cuckoo-clocks. These were probably the first multi-line phones to come with handsets that plugged into the base with Trimline-style 5-pin plugs, before the current modular connectors were adopted. Often seen in hospitals on TV shows.

CUG Closed User Group. Selected collection of terminal users that do not accept calls from sources not in their group and also often restricted from sending messages outside the group.

CURIE POINT The temperature at which certain elements (usually so-called "rare earth" elements) relax their resistance to magnetic changes. In a magneto-optic disk drive the surface to be marked is heated briefly by a laser light to its Curie point. Magnetism is then applied in the proper polarity to make the spot a "1" or a "0." It cools, and is locked in that position, until it re-heated and changed again. This is how magneto-optic drives can be erasable.

CURRENT A measure of how much electricity passes a point on a wire in a given time frame. Current is measured in amperes, or amps. The abbreviation for current is I. See OHM'S LAW.

CURRENT CARRYING CAPACITY The maximum current an insulated conductor can safely carry without exceeding its insulation and jacket temperature limitations.

CURRENT LOOP Transmission technique that recognizes current flows, rather than voltage levels. It has traditionally been used in teletypewriter networks incorporating batteries as the transmission power source. In this serial transmission system, a pair of wires connecting the receiving and sending devices transmit binary 0 (zero) when no current flows and a binary 1 (one) when current is flowing.

CURSOR A symbol on a screen indicating where the next character may be typed. Cursors may be solid, blinking, underlines, etc. Many programs, computers and phone systems allow you to reprogram the cursor to what you like. One author of this dictionary, Harry Newton, likes a non-blinking solid block, which came standard with his original CP/M version of WordStar, but doesn't any longer.

CURSOR SUBMARINING A liquid crystal display on a computer laptop screen doesn't write to screen very fast. When you move a cursor across your screen or move your mouse quickly across the screen, the cursor disappears. This phenomenon is known as cursor submarining. Cute.

CURVES AND ARCS A computer imaging term. Paint packages handle curves and arcs in a variety of ways. Examples include spline curves, where-in you specify a series of points and the package draws a curve that smoothly approaches those points, and "three point" curves, in which the first two points anchor the ends of the curve and third selects the apex.

CUSEEME An Internet videoconferencing system that enables up to eight users to see and hear each other on their computer screens. Pronounced "See You, See me."

CUSTOM CALLING A group of special services available from the central office switching system which the telco can offer its subscribers without the need for any special terminal equipment on their premises. Basic custom calling features now available include call waiting, 3-way calling, abbreviated dialing (speed calling), call forwarding, series completing (busy or no answer) and wake up or reminder service.

CUSTOM ISDN A version of ISDN BRI (Basic Rate Interface) provided off an AT&T 5ESS central office. It actually offers more features and is easier to install than a National ISDN-1 BRI line. We are all awaiting the specifications on National ISDN-2, which is meant to be "standard." Meantime, Custom ISDN is the most popular, most versatile and most understood ISDN service in North America. See ISDN.

CUSTOM LOCAL AREA SIGNALING SERVICES CLASS. A generic term (like WATS) describing several enhanced local service offerings such as incoming-call identification, call trace, call blocking, automatic return of the most recent incoming call, call redial, and selective forwarding and programming to permit distinctive ringing for incoming calls. See CLASS.

CUSTOMER CARE CENTER A term created by Alex Szlam, the president of Melita International, Norcross, GA to describe a telephone call center with three basic elements: First, the database technology and the marketing savvy to fill that database with individual customer preference information. Second, the ability to intelligently handle inbound phone calls. Third, the ability to intelligently make outbound calls. See also CUSTOMER SENSITIVITY KNOWLEDGE BASE.

CUSTOMER CONTROL An AT&T term for the ability for an end user to monitor, choose, modify, redesign and/or program the type of service received from a network.

CUSTOMER INFORMATION MANGER CIM. An MCI definition. A component of the NCS which supports the creation and maintenance of customer databases for Vnet customers. Customers have remote access to and control over their portion of the NCS database via a terminal at the customer's location.

CUSTOMER NETWORK MANAGEMENT CNM. An ATM term. CNM allows users of ATM public networks to monitor and manage their portion of the carrier's circuits. Thus far, the ATM forum has agreed that the CNM interface will give users the ability to monitor physical ports, virtual paths, usuage parameters, and quality of service parameters.

CUSTOMER PREMISES EQUIPMENT CPE. Terminal equipment — telephones, key systems, PBXs, modems, video conferencing devices, etc. — connected to the telephone network and residing on the customer's premises.

CUSTOMER PROPRIETARY NETWORK INFORMATION CPNI. Information which is available to a telephone company by virtue of the telephone company's basic service customer relationship. This information may include the quantity, location, type and amount of use of local telephone service subscribed to, and information contained on telephone company bills. This is the definition of CPNI that the independent voice mail and live telephone answering industry uses.

CUSTOMER PROVIDED LOOP The customer assumes responsibility for ordering, coordinating, maintaining, and billing for the local loop.

CUSTOMER PROVIDED TERMINAL EQUIPMENT Or just Customer Provided Equipment (CPE). Terminal equipment connected to the telephone network which is owned by the user or leased from a supplier other than the local telephone operating company.

CUSTOMER SENSITIVITY KNOWLEDGE BASE A term created by Alex Szlam of Melita International, Norcross, GA to describe a complex database that would keep track of your customers' preferences. Such database would be updated almost automatically based on every contact you had with the customer. The database would probably be object-oriented since the idea is define customer preferences based on individual preferences, not on a statistical analysis of conglomerate preferences such as those typically gleaned from existing character databases.

CUSTOMER SERVICE CENTER CSC. MCI organization responsible for installing, verifying, and maintaining MCI customers and customer service.

CUSTOMER SERVICE RECORD CSR. Computer printout that details the fixed monthly charges billed by your local telephone company. The CSR is composed of computer codes called USOCs, which in turn correspond to a particular tariffed service. USOCs tell the telephone company's billing system what tariff rate should be billed for a particular service. In order to ensure your telephone bill is correct you must request and review this document. No telecom manager should be without this important document.

CUSTOMER SERVICE UNIT CSU. A device that provides an accessing arrangement at a user location to either switched or point-to-point, digital circuits. A CSU provides local loop equalization, transient protection, isolation, and central office loop-back testing capability. See also CSU/DSU.

CUSTOMER SPECIFIC TERM PLAN A Customer Specific Term Plan is an option offered by AT&T on the purchase of its 800 services whereby customers can earn additional discounts by committing to a multi year contract. This also is one of two plans used by aggregators to resell 800 services. The other is the Revenue Volume Pricing Plan.

CUT To transfer a service from one facility to another.

CUT BACK TECHNIQUE A technique for measuring optical fiber attenuation or distortion by performing two transmission measurements. One is at the output end of the full length of the fiber. The other is within 1 to 3 meters of the input end.

Without disturbing the source-to-fiber coupling, access to the short length output is accomplished by "cutting back" the test fiber.

CUT DOWN A method of securing a wire to a wiring terminal. The insulated wire is placed in the terminal groove and pushed down with a special tool. As the wire is seated, the terminal cuts through the insulation to make an electrical connection, and the tool's spring-loaded blade trims the wire flush with the terminal. Also called punch down.

CUT THROUGH 1. Cut-through is a voice processing term. It's what stops voice prompt playback when a key is pressed. Some of the speech recognition solutions also add cut-through that will stop voice prompt playback as soon as you start talking. Only voice cards that support continuous speech recognition are able to provide cut-through. Cut-though can be a problem in some cases. Imagine yourself at the airport trying to make a call using a speech recognition system. At the start of a new prompt, the airport public address system blares out a last boarding call for a flight. If cut-through is active, it would stop playing the prompt and wait on your response. Now what do you do? 2. The act of connecting one circuit to another, or a phone to a circuit. This is when a user dials the access code for the circuit and is immediately "cut through" to the tie line. The user controls the call. It is a tie line operation.

CUT THROUGH RESISTANCE A measure of an insulation's ability to withstand penetration by sharp edges.

CUTOFF ATTENUATOR A waveguide of adjustable length that varies the attenuation of signals passing through the waveguide.

CUTOFF FREQUENCY 1. The frequency above which, or below which, the output current in a circuit, such as a line or a filter, is reduced to a specified level. 2. The frequency below which a radio wave fails to penetrate a layer of the ionosphere at the angle of incidence required for transmission between two specified points by reflection from the layer.

CUTOFF MODE The highest order mode that will propagate in a given waveguide at a given frequency.

CUTOVER The physical changing of lines from one phone system to another, or the installation of a new system. It's usually done over the weekend, accompanied by heavy praying that everything will go right. There are two types of cutovers — flash cuts and parallel cuts. Parallel cuts occur when the old phone system is left functioning and the new one, central switching equipment and phones, is installed around it. This means that for some weeks there are two sets of phones, two sets of wires, two switches, two sets of phone lines, etc. The parallel cut is a far more reliable method of cutting over a new switch. But it's also more expensive.

A "flash cut" occurs in a flash. On Friday, everyone is using the old switch. When everyone comes to work on Monday, the old switch and its phones have disappeared. In its place, there's a brand new system. Sometimes it works. More often than not, there are remaining nagging problems. With any Cutover, it's a good idea to set up a Complaint or Cutover Number. Thus, if anyone's having trouble with their phone, they can call this number and get their problems taken care of. How well these problems are taken care of will determine how well the cutover went and how well the employees perceive the new switch is working. Perception, not reality, is what's at stake here.

CV Old Bell-Speak for single-line phone. It stands for Combined Voice. In old Bell-Speak it meant that the two parts of the phone that dealt with voices were combined into one unit (the handset). Before this, there were phones like the HH (Hand-Held) where there was a piece you spoke into and another piece you put to your ear. From CV, you get CVW (CV Wall phone) and later on, KV (Key Voice) and KVW (Key Wall phone). Later on all this crept into the USOC codes — the Universal Service Order Code numbering systems the local Bell operating phone companies used to identify products and services. See USOC.

CVD Chemical Vapor Deposition.

CVF Compressed Volume File. A Microsoft term which refers to a file on a compressed disk. The term was first introduced in MS-DOS 6.0, which first had double-your-disk-space technology. That technology was later removed when Stac Electronics, originator of Stacker disk doubling technology, took Microsoft to court and won.

CVSD Continuously Variable Slope Delta modulation. A method for coding analog voice signals into digital signals that uses 16,000 to 64,000 bps bandwidth, depending on the sampling rate.

CVP 1. Certified Vertical Partner. 2. A British term: Co-operative Voice Processing, gives the caller the ability to move seamlessly between an Interactive Voice Processing device and a live agent.

CW 1. Call Waiting (as in Custom Calling Service). 2. Continuous Wave.

CWA Communications Workers of America. A national union of telephone industry employees, currently very worried about its future membership growth given the phone industry's propensity to let its surplus workers go.

CXR Carrier.

CX SIGNALING A direct current (DC) signaling system that separates the signal from the voice band by filters. Also called Composite Signaling.

CYBARIAN A person who makes a living doing online research and information retrieval (comes from cyberspace librarian). Also known as a data surfer or a super searcher.

CYBER Five letters which can, seemingly, be attached to a word and made into a noun or a verb. The first Cyber word was Cyberspace, a term coined by science fiction writer William Gibson in his 1984 fantasy novel "Neuromancer" to describe the "world" of connected computers and the society that gathers around them. The idea of Cyberspace is that this world of computer networks can be explored with the proper addresses and codes. People who use the system for hours on end are said to be lost in cyberspace. Today, many people say that world has arrived in the form of the Internet. And, so with projections that there will be 100 million users of the Internet by the year 2000, the word Cyber has become popular. There's "The Cyberbrary of Congress" (books Congress has on on-line). According to William Safire writing in the New York Times Magazine of December 11, 1994, "cyber is the hot combining form of our time. If you don't have cyber-phobia, you are a cyberpiliac." The US News & World Report labels its election night on-line forum a cybercast. The Washington Post wrote that "battlefield valor belongs not to the brawny soldier but to the astrophysics major who invented smart bombs," somebody who's called a cyberwonk.

CYBERBUSINESS A company that does most of its business on the Internet is called a Cyberbusiness.

CYBERIA Electronic stuff for the cyberpeople. An advertisement in the November 12, 1995 issue of the New York Times (Sunday) Magazine showed Cyberia covering everything from modern chairs to laptop computers, to cellular phones to an Apple Newton PDA.

CYBERNETICS A term invented in 1948 by Norbert Wiener, the automation genius, who declared "We have decided to call the entire field of control and communications theory, whether in the machine or the animal, by the same term Cybernetics."

CYBERPUNK A work coined by a book called "Cyberpunk: Outlaws and Hackers on the Computer Frontier" by Katie HaFner and John Markoff. The book defines Cyberpunk as what you and I know as a computer hacker — a person who manages to get into other people's computer systems. He does this usually through telephone lines. In most cases, hackers see themselves as harmless electronic joyriders. But they occasionally steal data, inject viruses and misleading information and disrupt legitimate business and research. Sometimes they get caught.

CYBERSEX Adult-oriented computer games, images and chat lines. A place where people can discuss their sex lives and wanton desires with total strangers in online (over phone line) forums, even falling in love without having ever met face to face.

CYBERSKATING Browsing the Internet. See CYBERSPACE.

CYBERSPACE A term coined by science fiction writer William Gibson in his fantasy novel Neuromancer to describe the "world" of connected computers and the society that gathers around them. The idea of Cyberspace is that this world of computer networks can be explored with the proper addresses and codes. People who use the system for hours on end are said to be lost in cyberspace. Today, many people say that world has arrived in the form of Internet. John Perry Barlow, a rock-'n'-roll lyricist turned computer activist, defined cyberspace in Time magazine as "that place you are in when you are talking on the phone." Thus by Barlow's definition, just about everybody has already been to cyberspace. I prefer Gibson's definition.

CYCLE One complete sequence of an event or activity. Often refers to electrical phenomena. One electrical cycle is a complete sine wave. (A complete set of one positive and one negative alternation of current.) In the battery business, a cycle is the process of one complete battery discharge and recharge. See CYCLE LIFE.

CYCLE LIFE In the battery business, cycle life is the useful life of a rechargeable battery, expressed as the total number of discharges and recharges.

CYCLE MANAGER EXTRACTION An MCI system which selects processable calls from Distribution and forwards them to the appropriate MCI Reference System for billing.

CYCLE POOLS Where dial-up call records are stored in MCI's Revenue System until extracted for billing.

CYCLE SLIP A discontinuity in the measured carrier beat phase resulting from a temporary loss-of-lock in the carrier tracking loop of a Global Positioning System receiver.

CYCLE TIME The time to complete a cycle. In microcomputers, it's the time between successive RAM read or write operations.

CYCLIC DISTORTION In telegraphy, distortion that is neither characteristic, bias, nor fortuitous, and which in general has a periodic character. Its causes are, for example, irregularities in the duration of contact time of the brushes of a transmitter distributor or interference by distributing alternating currents.

CYCLIC REDUNDANCY CHECK CRC. A check performed on data to see if an error has occurred in the transmitting, reading or writing of the data. A CRC is performed by reading the data, calculating the CRC character and comparing its value to the CRC character already present in the data. If they are equal, the new data is presumed to be the same as the old data. Otherwise, it's wrong. Re-send the data. A CRC character is figured by treating a block of data as a string of bits that are equal to a binary number. Then we divide that number by another predetermined binary number and append the remainder from the division to the data. We call that appended number the CRC character.

CYLINDER A hard disk drive contains a number of platters, which are divided into tracks. A cylinder is a collection of all corresponding tracks on all sides of the platters in a disk drive. Think of a hard disk consisting of dozens of concentric cylinders, each of slightly different diameters. These distinct concentric storage areas on the hard disk roughly correspond to the tracks on a floppy diskette. Generally, the more cylinders a hard disk has, the greater its storage capacity.

CYPRESS A Rolm/IBM desktop device which combines a data terminal, a digital phone and several time management software features.

D CHANNEL In an ISDN interface, the "D" channel (the Data channel) is used to carry control signals and customer call data in a packet switched mode. In the BRI (Basic Rate Interface, i.e. the lowest ISDN service) the "D" channel operates at 16,000 bits per second, part of which will carry setup, teardown, ANI and other characteristics of the call. 9,600 bps will be free for a separate conversation by the user. In the PRI (Primary Rate Interface, i.e. ISDN equivalent of T-1), the "D" channel runs at 64,000 bits per second. The D channel provides the signaling information for each of the 23 voice channels (referred to as "B channels"). The actual data which travels on the D channel is much like that of a common serial port. Bytes are loaded from the network and shifted out to the customer site in a serial bit stream. The customer site of course responds with its serial bit stream, too. An example of a data packet sent from the network to indicate a new call has the following components:

Customer Site ID:

   Type of Channel Required (Usually a B channel)

   Call Handle (Not unlike a file handle)

   ANI and DNIS information

   Channel Number Requested

   A Request for a Response

This packet is responded to by the customer site with a format similar to:

   Network ID

   Channel Type is OK

   Call Handle

The packets change as the state of the call changes, and finally ends with one side or the other sending a disconnect notice. The important concept here is the fact the information on the D channel could actually be anything — any kind of serial data. It could just as well be sports scores! So with that in mind, consider the Channel Number Requested packet above. This is the networks' selected channel for the customer site to use. Normally, this number is between 1 and 23, but could be a higher number if needed. This is what NFAS is all about. NFAS (Non Facility Associated signaling, pronounced N-FAST without the T) allows a D channel to carry call information regarding channels which may not even exist in the same PBX or PC system. See also ISDN and DS-0.

D CONDITIONING A type of conditioning which controls harmonic distortion and signal-to-noise ratio so that they lie within specified limits.

D LINK Diagonal Link. A SS7 signaling link used to connect STP pairs that perform work at different functional levels. These links are arranged in sets of four (called quads).

D REGION That portion of the ionosphere existing approximately 50 to 90 kilometers above the surface of the Earth. Attenuation of radio waves, caused by ionospheric free-electron density generated by cosmic rays from the sun, is pronounced during daylight hours.

D TYPE The standard connector used for RS-232-C, RS-423 and RS-422 communications. D-type connectors are typically seen in nine, 15 and 25 pin configurations.

D-AMPS Digital Advanced Mobile Phone Service. A term for digital cellular radio in North America. In Europe, it's called GSM and in Japan PDC.

D-BANK Another name for channel bank. A device that multiplexes groups of 24 channels of digitized voice input at 64 Kbps into T-1 aggregate outputs of 1,544 Mbps.

D-BIT Also called DBIT. The delivery confirmation bit in an X.25 packet used to indicate whether or not the DTE wishes to receive an end-to-end acknowledgment of delivery. In short, a bit in the X.25 packet header that assures data integrity between the TPAD and the HPAD.

D-INSIDE WIRE Direct-Inside Wire. Made of 24-gauge, annealed-copper conductors with color-added PVC, which allows it to be pulled in conduit without the aid of lubricants. Generally used in the horizontal subsystem.

D/A Digital to Analog conversion.

D/A CONVERTER Digital to Analog converter. A device which converts digital pulses, i.e. data, into analog signals so that the signal can be used by analog device such as amplifier, speaker, phone, or meter.

D/I Drop and Insert. See BIT STUFFING and BIT ROBBING.

D1, D1D, D2, D3, D4 and D5 T-1 framing formats developed for channel banks. All formats contain a framing bit in every 193rd bit position. The Superframe (introduced in D2 channel banks) is made up of 12 193-bit frames, with the 193rd bit sequence being repeated every 12 frames. D2 framing also introduced robbed bit signaling, where the eighth bit in frames 6 and 12 were "robbed" for signaling information (like dial pulses). D1D was introduced after D2 to allow backwards compatibility of Superframe concepts to D1 banks.

D2-MAC One of two European formats for analog HDTV.

D3 FORMAT 24 data channels on one standard (North American standard) T1/D3 span line. Each data channel is 8-bits wide and has a bandwidth of 8KHz. See also DS-1.

D3/D4 Refers to compliance with AT&T TR (Technical Reference) 62411 definitions for coding, supervision and alarm support. D3/D4 compatibility ensures support of digital PBXs, M24 services, Megacom services and Mode 3 D3/D4 channel banks at a DS-1 level.

D4 In T-1 digital transmission technology, D4 is the fourth-generation channel bank. A channel bank is the interface between the T-1 carrier system and a analog premises device such as an analog PBX (private branch exchange).

D4 CHANNELIZATION Refers to compliance with AT&T TR (Technical

Reference) 62411 in regards to the DSI frame layout (the sequential assignment of channels and time slot numbers within the DSI).

D4 FRAMING First read T-1 FRAMING. The most popular framing format in the T1 environment is D-4 framing. The name stems from the way framing is performed in the D-series of channel banks from AT&T. There are 12 separate 193-bit frames in a super-frame. The D-4 framing bit is used to identify both the channel and the signaling frame. In voice communications, signaling is an important function that is simulated and carried by all the equipment in the transmission path. In D-4 framing, signaling for voice channels is carried "in-band" by every channel, along with the encoded voice. "Robbed-bit-signaling" is a technique used in D-4 channel banks to convey signaling information. With this technique, the eighth bit (least significant bit) of each of the 24 8-bit time slots is "robbed" every sixth frame to convey voice related signaling information (on-hook, off-hook, etc.) for each voice channel. See also EXTENDED SUPER-FRAME FORMAT.

DA 1. Doesn't answer, as in "The phone rang DA." 2. Directory Assistance. 3. Demand Assignment. 4. Discontinued Availability. Meaning a circuit that was once available is now no longer. 5. Destination Address, a field in FDDI, Ethernet and Token Ring packets which identifies the unique MAC (Media Access Control, the lower part of ISO layer two) address of the recipient. 6. Desk Accessory. Standard desk accessories on the Apple Macintosh include a calculator, alarm clock and the chooser. Desk accessories are available to the user regardless of the application currently in use, networked or non-networked. Desk accessories are installed in the Apple menu and accessed from there.

DAA Data Access Arrangement. A device required before the FCC registration program if a customer was going to hook up CPE (Customer Provided Equipment), usually modems and other data equipment, to the telephone network. Today, equipment is FCC registered (under Part 68) meaning that the device itself is approved for connection to the phone network. DAAs can still be found in old DP (data processing) installations.

DAB Dynamically Allocable Bandwidth.

DAC Digital to Analog Converter. A device which converts digital pulses, i.e. data, into analog signals so that the signal can be used by analog device such as amplifier, speaker, phone, or meter.

DACC Digital Access Cross-Connect.

DACD Digital Automatic Call Distributor. New York Telephone's name for its central office provided ACD.

DAC Digital-to-analog converter. A chip that converts the binary numbers that represent particular colors to analog red, green and blue signals that a color monitor displays.

DACOMNET A packet-switched network in South Korea.

DACS Digital Access and Cross-connect System. A digital switching device for routing and switching T-1 lines, and DS-0 portions of lines, among multiple T-1 ports. It performs all the functions of a normal "switch," except connections are typically set up in advance of the call, not together with the call, as in most, normal low bandwidth communications systems (e.g. voice- band voice and data). A DACS is in essence a manual T-1 switch.

DACS/CCR Digital Access Crosscontrol System/Customer Controlled Reconfiguration is a feature of AT&T Accunet T1.5 service. DACS/CCR allows Accunet subscribers to redirect T-1 trunk or DS-0 data traffic over the public network from a terminal on their own premises.

DAEMON An agent program which continuously operates on a UNIX server and provides resources to client systems on the network. Daemon is a background process used for handling low-level operating system tasks.

DAF Destination Address Field.

DAISY CHAIN A method of connecting devices in a series. The computer's signals are passed through the chain from one device to the next. Jack 1 is connected to jack 2, which is connected to jack 3 and so on. The last jack in the chain is not connected to jack 1. A SCSI adapter is a daisy chain. It can support a daisy chain of up to seven devices. Intel's Universal Serial Bus also is a daisy chain.

DAISY WHEEL PRINTER A printer that prints its characters on paper using a rotating wheel with "fingers." Mounted on the fingers are the various characters. The wheel rotates, bringing the character in line with the paper, then a hammer strikes the character against the ribbon, forming an image on the paper. Daisy wheel printers are typically used for "letter quality" correspondence and are popular for word processing. Their letters are crisp and attractive. But the speed of printing is slow because of the time it takes to rotate the wheel into place. These days, more and more of what used to be printed by daisy wheel printers is now printed by laser and inkjet printers which print faster, more quietly and do a nicer job.

DAL Dedicated Access Line. A private tie line from you to your long distance or local phone company. The line may be analog or digital, e.g. a T-1 circuit.

DAMA Demand Assigned Multiple Access. A way of sharing a channel's capacity by assigning capacity on demand to an idle channel or an unused time slot.

DAMPED WAVE A wave consisting of a series of oscillations or cycles of current gradually decreasing amplitude.

DAMPING 1. The decreasing of the amplitude of oscillations caused by resistance in the circuit. 2 The progressive diminution with time of certain quantities characteristic of a phenomenon. 3. The progressive decay with time in the amplitude of the free oscillations in a circuit. 4. More generally, decreasing some dimension of a phenomenon, such as its power.

DAP Directory Access Protocol. The protocol used between a Directory User Agent (DUA) and Directory System Agent (DSA) in an X.500 directory system.

DAP INFORMATION DISTRIBUTOR DID. An MCI definition. Software which directs the distribution of network information from the Operational Data Integrator to the Data Access Points.

DARK CURRENT The external current that, under specified biasing conditions, flows in a photosensitive detector when there is no incident radiation.

DARK FIBER Unused fiber through which no light is transmitted or installed fiber optic cable not carrying a signal. Sometimes dark fiber is sold by a carrier without the (usually) accompanying transmission service. It's "dark" because it's sold without light communications transmission. The customer is expected to put his own electronics and signals on the fiber and make it light.

DARPA Defense Advanced Research Projects Agency. Formerly called ARPA, it is a US government agency that funded research and experimentation with the ARPANET and later the Internet. The group within DARPA responsible for the ARPANET is ISTO (Information Systems Techniques Office), formerly IPTO (Information Processing Techniques Office). See also DARPA INTERNET.

DARPA INTERNET World's largest internetwork, linking together thousands of networks around world. Sponsored by U.S. Defense Advanced Research Projects Agency.

DASD Direct Access Storage Device. Any on-line data storage device. Usually refers to a magnetic disk drive, because optical drives and tape are considered too slow to be direct access devices. Pronounced DAZ-dee. The term is said to have been invented by IBM.

DASS Direct Access Secondary Storage. Same as near-line: storage on pretty-fast storage devices (e.g., rewritable optical) that are less expensive than hard drives but faster than off-line devices.

DASS1 digital Access Signaling. A British term. The original British Telecom (BT) ISDN signalling developed for both single line and multi-line Integrated Digital Access but used in the BT ISDN pilot service for single line IDA only.

DASS2 A British Term. A message-based signalling system following the ISO-based model developed by British Telecom to provide multi-line IDA interconnection to the BT network.

DAT Digital Audio Tape used to identify a type of digital tape recorder and player as well as the tape cassette. DAT tape machines record music that is much crisper, and free of the hisses and pops that mar traditional analog recordings. The drawback with DAT tape machines is they require considerable tape to store music digitally. In a DAT machine, the music is recorded by sampling the music 48,000 each second. Each of those samples is represented by a number that is written as a 16-digit string of zeros and ones. There are two such signals, once for each stereo channel, meaning that storing a single second of music requires about 1.5 million bits. On top of that, extra bits are added to allow the system to mathematically correct errors and help the machine automatically find a particular song on the tape. All together, according to Andrew Pollack writing in the New York Times, a single second of music on a digital audio tape requires 2.8 million bits. But compression techniques are cutting down the amount of information required to be recorded.

DATA This is AT&T Bell Labs' definition: "A representation of facts, concepts or instructions in a formalized manner, suitable for communication, interpretation or processing." Typically anything other than voice.

DATA ABSTRACTION A term in object-oriented programming. An object is sometimes referred to as an instance of an abstract data type or class. Abstract data types are constructed using the built-in data types supported by the underlying programming language, such as integer and date. The common characteristics (both attributes and methods) of a group of similar objects are collected to create a new data type or class. Not only is this a natural way to think about the problem domain, it is a very efficient way to write programs. Instead of individually describing several dozen instances, the programmer describes the class once. Once identified, each instance is complete with the exception of its instance variables. The instance variables are associated with each instance, i.e., each object; methods exist only with the classes. See OBJECT ORIENTED PROGRAMMING.

DATA ACCESS ARRANGEMENT DAA. Equipment that allows you to attach your data equipment to the nation's phone system. At one stage, DAAs were required by FCC "law." Now, their limited functions are built into directly attached devices, such as terminals, computers, etc.

DATA ACCESS POINT DAP. MCI computer that holds the number translation and call-routing information for 800 and Vnet services. These computers respond to inquiries from MCI switches on how to handle these calls.

DATA ARRANGEMENT In the public switched telephone networks, a single item or group of items present at the customer side of the purposes, including all equipment that may affect the characteristics of the interface.

DATA ATTRIBUTE A characteristic of a data element such as length, value, or method of representation.

DATA BANK A collection of data in one place. The data is not necessarily logically related, nor is it necessarily consistently maintained. See DATABASE.

DATA BASE See DATABASE, which is our preferred spelling.

DATA BASE ADMINISTRATOR DBA. A computer at MCI that maintains the master file of Vnet translation information. The master file is created when a customer begins service and can be changed at anytime through CIM. The updated copies of the database are downloaded each night to the DAPs.

DATA BASE LOOKUP A software program which allows telephone users to find information on someone calling via the LCD window on their phone. This information comes to the user via CLID (Calling Line IDentification) or ANI (Automatic Number Identification). See also CLASS.

DATA BUBBLE A new organization within BellSouth to provide high-speed digital services. No one seems to know why it's called "Data Bubble," except that someone inside BellSouth clearly thinks the term is cute.

DATA BURST Burst transmission.

DATA BUS A bus transmits and receives data signals throughout the computer or telephone system. See BUS.

DATA CIRCUIT TERMINATING EQUIPMENT See DATA COMMUNICATIONS EQUIPMENT and DCE.

DATA CIRCUIT TRANSPARENCY The capability of a circuit to transmit all data without changing its content or structure.

DATA COMMUNICATIONS The transfer of data between points. This includes all manual and machine operations necessary for this transfer. In short, the movement of encoded information by means of electrical transmission systems. See DATA COMMUNICATIONS EQUIPMENT.

DATA COMMUNICATIONS CHANNEL A three-byte, 192 kbps portion of the

SONET signal that contains alarm, surveillance and performance information. It can be used for internally or externally generated messages, or for manufacturer specific messages.

DATA COMMUNICATIONS EQUIPMENT DCE. A definition of an interface standard between computers and printers. A device typically comes configured as a DCE or DTE. See DCE and DTE. Which way it comes determines how you connect it to another device.

DATA COMPRESSION Reducing the size of a file of data by eliminating unnecessary information, such as blanks and redundant data. The idea of reducing the size is to save money on transmission or to save money on storing the data. The file or program which has been compressed is useless in its compressed form and must be "decompressed," i.e. brought back to normal before use. One method of data compression replaces a string of repeated characters by a character count. Another method uses fewer bits to represent the characters that occur more frequently. See also COMPRESSION.

Here's another definition, courtesy the US Department of Commerce: 1. The process of reducing (a) bandwidth, (b) cost, and (c) time for the generation, transmission, and storage of data by employing techniques designed to remove data redundancy. 2. The use of techniques such as null suppression, bit mapping, and pattern substitution for purposes of reducing the amount of space required for storage of textual files and data records. Some data compaction methods employ fixed tolerance bands, variable tolerance bands, slope-keypoints, sample changes, curve patterns, curve fitting, floating- point coding, variable precision coding, frequency analysis, and probability analysis. Simply squeezing noncompacted data into a smaller space, e.g., by transferring data on punched cards onto magnetic tape, is not considered data compression. See DATA COMPRESSION TABLE.

DATA COMPRESSION PROTOCOLS All current high-speed dial-up modems also support data compression protocols. This means the sending modem will compress the data on-the-fly (as it transmits) and the receiving modem will decompress the data (as it receives it) to its original form. There are two standards for data compression protocols, MNP-5 and ITU-T V.42 bis. Some modems also use proprietary data compression protocols. A modem cannot support data compression without using an error control protocol, although it is possible to have a modem that only supports an error control protocol but not any data compression protocol. A MNP-5 modem requires MNP-4 error control protocol and a V.42 bis modem requires V.42 error control protocol. Note that although V.42 include MNP-4, V.42 bis does not include MNP-5. However, virtually all high-speed modems that support ITU-T V.42 bis also incorporate MNP-5. The maximum compression ratio that a MNP-5 modem can achieve is 2:1. That is to say, a 9,600 bps MNP-5 modem can transfer data up to 19,200 bps. The maximum compression ratio for a V.42 bis modem is 4:1. That is why all those V.32 (9,600 bps) modem manufacturers claim that their modems provide throughput up to 38,400 bps.

Are MNP-5 and V.42 bis useful? Don't be fooled by the claim. It is extremely rare, if ever, that you will be able to transfer files at 38,400 or 57,600 bps. In fact, V.42 bis and MNP-5 are not very useful when you are downloading files from online services. Why? How well the modem compression works depends on what kind of files are being transferred. In general, you will be able to achieve twice the speed for transferring a standard text file (like the one you are reading right now). V.42 bis and MNP-5 modem cannot compress a file which is already compressed by software. In the case of MNP-5, it will even try to compress a precompressed file and actually expand it, thus slow down the file transfer! The above information courtesy modem expert, Patrick Chen.

DATA COMPRESSION TABLE A term from US Robotics, makers of fine modems. A data compression table is a table of values assigned for each character during a call under data compression. Default values in the table are continually altered and built during each call. The longer the table, the more efficient the throughput gained.

DATA COMPRESSORS Also called compactors. These devices take over where high speed modems and statistical multiplexers leave off. They save phone lines by a doubling of data throughput by further compressing async or sync data streams.

DATA CONCENTRATOR A device which permits the use of a transmission media by a number of data sources greater than the number of channels currently available for transmission.

DATA CONTAMINATION Data corruption.

DATA CONTROL BLOCK A data block usually at the beginning of a file containing descriptive information about the file.

DATA CONVERSION Converting data from one format to another. Conversion typically falls into three basic categories. 1. To convert to a form usable by the equipment you have, e.g. you convert some data from tape to disk (because you don't have a tape drive). Or you may convert from one method of encoding data to another, say from EBCDIC to ASCII, because you don't have software which can understand IBM's EBCDIC method of coding. 3. Or you may convert from one format to another, e.g. from the dBASE method of encoding databases to the Paradox method, or from WordStar to WordPerfect. There are many service bureaus whose job is to convert computer data from one form to another and there are now many programs out to do the conversion. Our favorite programs are Word-for-Word for converting word processing formats and Data Junction for converting database formats. See also DATA COMPRESSION.

DATA COUNTRY CODE A 3-digit numerical country identifier that is part of the 14-digit network terminal number plan. This prescribed numerical designation further constitutes a segment of the overall 14-digit X.121 numbering plan for a ITU-T X.25 network.

DATA DIALTONE Networking as widespread as the telephone. The Internet is widely thought to contain the beginnings of Data Dialtone. See INTERNET, METCALFE's LAW, and WORLD WIDE WEB.

DATA DICTIONARY 1. A part of a database management system that provides a centralized meaning, relationship to other data, origin, usage, and format. 2. An inventory that describes, defines, and lists all of the data elements that are stored in a database.

DATA DIRECTORY An inventory that specifies the source, location, ownership, usage, and destination of all of the data elements that are stored in a database.

DATA ELEMENT A basic unit of information having a unique meaning and sub-categories (data items) of distinct units or values. Examples of data elements are military personnel grade, sex, race, geographic location, and military unit.

DATA ENCRYPTION STANDARD DES. A cryptographic algorithm for the protection of unclassified computer data issued as Federal Information Processing Standard Publication. The DES, which was promulgated by the National Institute of Standards and Technology (NIST)--formerly the National Bureau of Standards (NBS)--is intended for public and Government use.

DATA ENTRY Using an I/O device (input/output device), such as a keyboard on a terminal, to enter data into a computer.

DATA FILE A database typically contains multiple files of information. Each file contains multiple records. Each record is made up of one or more fields. Each field contains one or more bytes of data. The terms file, record and field find their roots in manual office filing systems.

DATA FILL One name for the specifications your ISDN phone lines. Ask for your ISDN Data Fill. It will give you useful information, such as how your lines are set up -- voice, data, data/voice, etc.

DATA FRAME An SCSA term. A set of time slots which are grouped together for synchronization purposes. The number of time slots in each frame depends on the SCbus or SCxbus Data Bus data rate. Each frame has a fixed period of 125us. Frames are delineated by the timing signal FSYNC.

DATA GRADE CIRCUIT A circuit which is suitable for transmitting data. High speed data needs better quality phone lines than normal dial-up phone circuits. You can acquire such circuits from many telephone companies. To upgrade voice phone lines to high-speed data circuits, you must sometimes "condition" the phone line. See CONDITIONING.

DATA GROUP A number of data lines providing access to the same resource.

DATA HUNT GROUP An AT&T Merlin term. A group of analog or digital data stations that share a common extension number. Calls are connected in a round-robin fashion to the first available data station in the group.

DATA INTEGRITY The concept of data being protected so that it retains its original meaning and value and is not messed up. Data integrity is also a performance measure based on the rate of undetected errors. A measure of how consistent and accurate computer data is. In data transmission, error correcting protocols, such a LAP-M, MNP and X-modem — provide methods of ensuring that data arrives at the destination in its full integrity. This is done in many ways, including retransmitting messed-up blocks.

Data integrity can be threatened by hardware problems, power failures and disk crashes, but most often by application software. In a database system, data integrity can be threatened if two users are allowed to update the same item or record of data at the same time. Record locking, where only a single user at a time is allowed access to a given data record, is a method of insuring data integrity.

DATA LINE INTERFACE The point at which a data line is connected to a telephone system.

DATA LINE MONITOR A measuring device that bridges a data line and looks at how clean the data is, whether the addressing is accurate, the protocol, etc.

Being only a monitor, it does not in any way affect the information traveling on the line. See DATA MONITOR.

DATA LINE PRIVACY Prohibits activities which would insert tones on a data station line used by a facsimile machine, a computer terminal or some other device sensitive to extraneous noise.

DATA LINK A term used to describe the communications link used for data transmission from a source to a destination. In short, a phone line for data transmission. Or, A fiber optic transmitter, cable, and receiver that transmits digital data between two points.

DATA LINK CONTROL DLC. Characters used in data communications that control transmission by performing various error checking and housekeeping functions -- connect, initiate, terminate, etc.

DATA LINK ESCAPE The first control character of two-character sequence used exclusively to provide supplementary line-control signals.

DATA LINK LAYER The second layer of the Open Systems Interconnection data communications model of the International Standards Organization. It puts messages together and coordinates their flow. Also used to refer to a connection between two computers over a phone line. See OSI MODEL.

DATA MESSAGE A message included in the GPS (Global Positioning System) signal which reports the satellite's location, clock corrections and health. Included is rough information on the other satellites in the constellation.

DATA MONITOR A device used to look at a bit stream as it travels on a circuit. It will show the user what is going down both sides of a data channel. It will show what the user at his terminal is typing, and what the computer is responding with. Extremely useful for troubleshooting data communications problems. Also called a Data Scope.

DATA MULTIPLEXER A device allowing several data sources to simultaneously use a common transmission medium while guaranteeing each source its own independent channel. See MULTIPLEXER.

DATA NETWORK IDENTIFICATION CODE DNIC. In the ITU-T International X.121 format, the first four digits of the 14-digit international data number; the set of digits that may comprise the three digits of the data country code (DCC) and the 1-digit network code (which is called the "network digit"). See DNIC.

DATA NUMBERING PLAN AREA DNPA. In the U.S. implementation of the ITU-T X.25 network, the first three digits of a network terminal number (NTN). The 10-digit NTN is the specified addressing information for an end-point terminal in an X.25 network.

DATA OBJECT An individually addressable unit of information, specified by a data template and its content, that can persist independently of the invocation of a service.

DATA OVER VOICE A device that takes a voice grade line and multiplexes it so it can carry a voice and a data signal. Typically the data is carried in analog form. Thus, to put data on this type of circuit, you need a modem. It is called Data Over Voice, because the data streams (transmission and reception) travel at a higher frequency than the voice conversations using a technique called frequency division multiplexing (FDM).

DATA PACKET SIGNALING All telephone switches use the same three general types of signals: + Event Signaling initiates an event, such as ringing. + Call Progress Signaling denotes the progress (or state) of a call, such as a busy tone, a ringback tone, or an error tone. + Data Packet Signaling communicates certain information about a call, for example, the identify of the calling extension, or the identity of the extension being called.

DATA PACKET SWITCH System-common equipment that electronically distributes information among data terminal equipment connected to a data transmission network. The switch distributes information by means of information packets addressed to specific terminal devices.

DATA PBX A PBX for switching lots of low-speed asynchronous data. A switch that allows a user on an attached circuit to select from among other circuits, usually one at a time and on a contention basis, for the purpose of establishing a through connection. Distinguished from a PBX in that only digital transmissions, and not analog voice, is supported. Like a telecommunications PBX that makes and breaks phone connections, a data PBX makes and breaks connections between computers and peripherals. In response to dynamic demand, it establishes communications paths between devices attached to its input/output ports by receiving, transmitting and processing electrical signals. Usually, data PBXs work off PCs' serial ports rather than through cable attached to a network interface card. For that reason, they are restricted to serial speeds, topping out at about 19.2K bits per second. For switching lots of low-speed asynchronous data, a data PBX (also called a line selector) can be better than a LAN. Total throughput can actually be higher. See also LINE SELECTOR.

DATA PHASE A phase of a data call during which data signals may be transferred between DTEs that are interconnected via the network.

DATA PORT Point of access to a computer that uses trunks or lines for transmitting or receiving data.

DATA PROTECTION A means of ensuring that data on the network is safe. Novell's NetWare protects data primarily by maintaining duplicate file directories and by redirecting data from bad blocks to reliable blocks on the NetWare server's hard disk. A hard disk's Directory Entry Table (DET) and File Allocation Table (FAT) contain address information that tells the operating system where data can be stored or retrieved from. If the blocks containing these tables are damaged, some or all of the data may be irretrievable. NetWare reduces the possibility of losing this information by maintaining duplicate copies of the DET and FAT on separate areas of the disk. If one of the blocks in the original tables is damaged, the operating system switches to the duplicate tables to get the location data it needs. Data protection within standard NetWare also involves such features as read-after-write verification, Hot Fix, and disk mirroring or duplexing. See DISK MIRRORING and HOT FIX.

DATA RATE The measurement of how quickly data is transmitted. Expressed in bps (bits-per-second).

DATA RECORD See DATA FILE and DATABASE MANAGEMENT SYSTEM.

DATA SCRAMBLER A device used in digital transmission systems to convert an input digital signal into a pseudo random sequence free from long runs of marks, spaces, or other simple repetitive patterns.

DATA SCOPE See DATA MONITOR.

DATA SECURE LINE A single tip and ring line off the PBX which is protected against any tones (like call waiting) or break-ins that would otherwise mess up any ongoing data transmission call.

DATA SECURITY The protection of data from unauthorized (accidental or intentional) modification, destruction, disclosure, or delay.

DATA SEGMENT A pre-defined set of data elements ordered sequentially within a set, beginning and ending with unique segment identifies and terminators. Data segments combine to form a message. Their relation to the message is specified by a Data Segment Requirement Designator and a Data Segment Sequence. Data Segment is an EDI (Electronic Data Interchange) term.

DATA SEGMENT REQUIREMENT DESIGNATOR An EDI (Electronic Data Interchange) requirement designator determines that if and when the data segment will occur in a message: - MANDATORY. The segment must appear in the message. - CONDITIONAL. The segment will occur in the message depending on agreement conditions. The relevant conditions must be given as part of the message definition. - OPTIONAL. The segment may or may not occur.

DATA SEGMENT SEQUENCE In Electronic Data Interchanges, each data segment has a specific place within a message. The data segment sequence determines exactly where a segment will occur in a message: - HEADING AREA. A segment occurring in this area refers to the entire message. - DETAIL AREA. A segment occurring here is detail information only will override any similar specification in the header area. - SUMMARY AREA. Only segments containing total or control information may occur in this area (e.g., invoice total, etc.)

DATA SERVICE UNIT DSU. Device designed to connect a DTE (Data Terminal Equipment like a PC or a LAN) to a digital phone line to allow fully-digital communications. A DSU is sort of the digital equivalent of a modem. In more technical terms, a DSU is a type of short haul, synchronous data line driver, normally installed at a user location that connects a user's synchronous equipment over a 4-wire circuit to a serving dial-central-office. This service can be for a point-to-point or multipoint operation in a digital data network. DSUs are typically used for leased lines. For switched digital services, you need a CSU/DSU also called a DSU/CSU. See CSU/DSU and DSU/CSU.

DATA SET In AT&T jargon, a data set is a modem, i.e. a device which performs the modulation/demodulation and control functions necessary to provide compatibility between business machines which work in digital (on-off) signals and voice telephone lines. In IBM jargon however, a data set is a collection of data, usually in a file on a disk. See also MODEM.

DATA SET READY One of the control signals on a standard RS-232-C connector. It indicates whether the data communications equipment is connected and ready to start handshaking control signals so that transmission can start. See RS-232-C and the Appendix.

DATA SHEETS What Business Communications Review calls its statistical and descriptive material comparing PBXs. BCR includes these data sheets in its excellent BCR Manual of PBXs. This manual is the most extensive write-up of larger (more than 200 line) PBXs in the world. It is available from Telecom Library on 1-800-LIBRARY.

DATA SIGNALING RATE The total of the number of bits per second in the transmission path of a data transmission system. A measurement of how quickly data is transmitted, expressed in bps, bits-per-second.

DATA SINK Part of a terminal in which data is received from a data link.

DATA SOURCE The originating device in a data communications link.

DATA STREAM 1. Collection of characters and data bits transmitted through a channel. 2. An SCSA term. A continuous flow of call processing data.

DATA SURFER A person who makes a living doing online research and information retrieval. Also known as a Cybarian (comes from librarian) or a super searcher.

DATA SYNCHRONIZATION The process of keeping database data timely and relevant by sending and receiving information between laptops, between desktops in the field and between bigger computers at headquarters. See also SYNCHRONIZATION and REPLICATION.

DATA SWITCHING EXCHANGE DSE. The equipment installed at a single location to perform switching functions such as circuit switching, message switching, and packet switching.

DATA TERMINAL EQUIPMENT DTE. A definition of hardware specifications that provides for data communications. There are two basic specs your hardware can conform to, DTE (Data Terminal Equipment) or DCE (Data Communications Equipment). See DCE and DTE.

DATA TERMINAL READY One of the control signals on a standard RS-232-C connector. It indicates if the data terminal equipment is present, connected and ready and has had handshaking signals verified. See RS-232-C and the Appendix.

DATA TRANSFER RATE The average number of bits, characters, or blocks per unit time passing in a data transmission system.

DATA TRANSFER REQUEST SIGNAL A call control signal transmitted by a DCE to a DTE to indicate that a distant DTE wants to exchange data.

DATA TRANSFER TIME The time that elapses between the initial offering of a unit of user data to a network by transmitting data terminal equipment and the complete delivery of that unit to receiving data terminal equipment.

DATA TYPING When converting a database from one format to another, several conversion programs will convert the data to a common format before converting it to the final version. During the conversion process a program may check through the data in the database to determine what it is and arbitrarily make one field numeric, one field character, one field memo, etc.

DATA WAREHOUSE A database warehouse consolidates information from many departments within a company. This data can either be accessed quickly by users or put on an OLAP server for more thorough analysis. Data warehouses often use OLAP servers. OLAP stands for On Line Analytical Processing, also called a multidimensional database. According to PC Week, these databases can slice and dice reams of data to produce meaningful results that go far beyond what can be produced using the traditional two-dimensional query and report tools that work with most relational databases. OLAP data servers are best suited to work with data warehouses.

DATABASE A collection of data structured and organized in a disciplined fashion so that access is possible quickly to information of interest. There are many ways of organizing databases. Most corporate databases are not one single, huge file. They are multiple databases related to each other by some common thread, e.g. an employee identification number. Databases are made up of two elements, a record and a field. A record is one complete entry in a database, e.g. Gerry Friesen, 12 West 21 Street, New York, NY 10010, 212-691-8215. A field would be the street address field, namely 12 West 21 Street.

Databases are stored on computers in different ways. Some are comma delineated. They differentiate between their fields with commas -- like Gerry's record above. A more common way of storing databases is with fixed length records. Here, all the fields and all the records are of the same length. The computer finds fields by index and by counting. For example, Gerry's first name might occupy the first 15 characters. Gerry's last name might be the next 20 characters, etc. Where Gerry's names are too short to fill the full 15 or 20 characters, their fields are "padded" with specially-chosen characters which the computer recognizes as padded characters to be ignored. The most important thing to remember about databases is that all the common database programs, like dBASE, Paradox, Rbase, etc. don't automatically make backups of their files like word processing programs do. Therefore, before you muck with a database file -- sort it, index it, restructure it, etc. Please make sure you make a backup of the main database file.

DATABASE MANAGEMENT SYSTEM DBMS. Computer software used to create, store, retrieve, change, manipulate, sort, format and print the information in a database. Database management systems are probably the fastest growing part of the computer industry. Increasingly, databases are being organized so they can be accessible from places remote to the computer they're kept on. The "classic" database management system is probably an airline reservation system.

DATABASE OBJECT One of the components of a database: a table, view, index, procedure, trigger, column, default, or rule.

DATABASE SERVER A specialized computer that doles out database data to PCs on a LAN the way a file server doles out files. Where a traditional DBMS runs both a database application and the DBMS program on each PC on the LAN, a database server splits up the two processes. The application you wrote with your DBMS runs on your local PC, while the DBMS program runs on the database server computer. With a regular file server setup, all the database data has to be downloaded over the LAN to your PC, so that the DBMS can pick out what information your application wants. With a database server, the server itself does the picking, sending only the data you need over the network to your PC. So a database server means vastly less network traffic in a multi-user database system. It also provides for better data integrity since one computer handles all the record and file locking. See SERVER.

DATAGRAM A transmission method in which sections of a message are transmitted in scattered order and the correct order is re-established by the receiving workstation. Used on packet-switching networks. The Dow Jones Handbook of Telecommunications defines it as, "A single unacknowledged packet of information that is sent over a network as an individual packet without regard to previous or subsequent packets." Here's another definition I found. A finite-length packet with sufficient information to be independently routed from source to destination. In packet switching, a self-contained packet, independent of other packets, that carriers information sufficient for routing from the originating data terminal equipment to the destination data terminal equipment, without relying on earlier exchanges between the equipment and the network. Unlike virtual call service, there are no call establishment or clearing procedures, and the network does not generally provide protection against loss, duplication, or misdelivery. Datagram transmission typically does not involve end-to-end session establishment and may or may not entail delivery confirmation acknowledgment. A datagram is the basic unit of information passed across the Internet. It contains a source and destination address along with data. Large messages are broken down into a sequence of IP datagrams. See CONNECTIONLESS MODE TRANSMISSION.

DATAGRAM PACKET NETWORK The type of packet-switched network in which each packet is individually routed. This may result in a loss of sequence within a message because of alternate routing, or a loss of portions of a message because of packet elimination for congestion control. See DATAGRAM.

DATAKIT VCS The Datakit VCS is an AT&T packet switch that can switch over 44,000 packets per second and support up to 3,500 simultaneous virtual circuits. According to AT&T, the Datakit VCS is a digital virtual circuit switch with an architecture that combines the advantages of LANs, PBXs, data circuits and X.25 packet switches.

DATAP The programmer and system house in Atlanta which provides several long distance carriers with value-added services -- what Sprint calls its SCADA system manufacturer.

DATAPAK A packet-switched network run in Denmark, Sweden, Finland and Norway and operated by their respective governments.

DATAPATH A name that's becoming generic for a data service that provides digital, full-duplex data transmission at speeds of 300 bps through 19.2 Bps asynchronous and 1,200 through 64 Kbps synchronous. Datapath has built in auto-baud and hand-shaking protocols.

DATAPHONE A service mark of AT&T for various data hardware products such as modems and printers and services. See also DDS.

DATASPAN DataSPAN is generally characterized as a "fast packet" service and is based on frame relay standards recommended by the International Consultative Committee for Telephone & Telegraph (CCITT)(now called the ITU-T) and the American National Standards Institute (ANSI). Northern Telecom has introduced DataSPAN as a new DMS SuperNode value-added, data communications service that is targeted toward connecting high-speed Local Area Networks. Northern Telecom asserts that DataSPAN's rapid and efficient data transport assures reliable delivery and substantial performance improvement over current LAN interconnect solutions. DataSpan switching and transmission delay is less than 3 ms per node; X.25 switching and transmission delay can be up to 50 ms per node. Using Frame Relay, wide-area packet switching can be accomplished with the same level of performance that is traditionally limited to complex, dedicated private-line networks. DataSPAN is accessed through standard DS-0 or DS-1 links.

DATE AND TIME STAMP Many voice mail systems will append the date and time of receipt of voice messages for their users/subscribers.

DATEL SERVICES An MCI International service that carries data for medium-volume users. This service provides two-way data and voice transmission for simplex, half-duplex, and full duplex operations.

DATEX P An Austrian packet-switched network in Austria and Germany and run by their respective governments.

DATING FORMAT The format employed to express the time of an event. The time of an event on the UTC time scale is given in the following sequence; hour, day, month, year; e.g., 0917 UT, 30 August 1997. The hour is designated by the 24-hour system. UTC stands for Coordinated Universal Time, believe it or not.

DAUGHTERBOARD First there is the motherboard. That's the main circuit board of a computer system. The motherboard contains edge connectors or sockets so other PC (printed circuit) boards can be plugged into it. Those PC boards are called Fatherboards. Some fatherboards have pins on them into which you can plug smaller boards. Those boards are called Daughterboards. In a voice processing system, you might have a Fatherboard to do faxing. And you might have a range of Daughterboards, which allow you to connect different types of phone connections. Different boards exist for standard analog tip and ring, digital switched 56, etc. See also MOTHERBOARD.

DAUGHTERCARD Same as DAUGHTERBOARD.

DAVIC Digital Audio/Video Council

DAY-OF-WEEK FACTORS A call center term. A historical pattern consisting of seven factors, one for each day of the week, that defines the typical distribution of call arrival throughout the week. Each factor measures how far call volume on that day deviates from the average daily call volume. This is a historical pattern.

DB Should really be written as dB. Decibel. A unit of measure of signal strength, usually the relation between a transmitted signal and a standard signal source. Therefore, 6 dB of loss would mean that there is 6 dB difference between what arrives down a communications circuit and what was transmitted by a standard signal generator. See DECIBEL for a better explanation.

DB LOSS BUDGET Should be written as dB. dB Loss Budget is the amount of light available to overcome the attenuation in the optical link and still maintain specifications.

DB-9 This is the standard nine-pin RS-232-C serial port on the IBM AT and most laptop computers. The term DB-9 is used to describe both the male and female plug. So be careful when you order. See also the Appendix in this Dictionary for more information on the pinning of RS-232-C plugs.

DB-15 A standardized connector with 15 pins. It can be used Ethernet transceivers. It can also be used for connecting VGA monitors.

DB-25 The standard 25-pin connector used for RS-232-C serial data communications. In a DB-25 there are 25-pins, with 13 pins in one row and 12 in the other row. DB-25 is used to describe both the male and female plug. So be careful when you order. See also the Appendix in this Dictionary for more information on the pinning of RS-232-C plugs.

DB2 IBM's relational database system that runs on System 370-compatible mainframes under the MVS operating system.

DBA 1. Dynamic Bandwidth Allocation. 2. Database administrator. The individual in the organization with the responsibility for the design and control of databases.

DBIT Also called D-BIT. The delivery confirmation bit in an X.25 packet that is used to indicate whether or not the DTE wishes to receive an end-to-end acknowledgment of delivery. In short, a bit in the X.25 packet header that assures data integrity between the TPAD and the HPAD.

DBM Decibels below 1mW. This should be written as dBm. Output power of a signal referenced to an input signal of 1mW (Milliwatt). Similarly, dBm0 refers to output power, expressed in dBm, with no input signal. (O dBM = 1 milliwatt and -30 dBm = 0.001 milliwatt). See DECIBEL.

DBMS Database management system. A computer program that manages data by providing the services of centralized control, data independence, and complex physical structures. Advantages include efficient access, integrity, recovery, concurrency control, privacy, and security. A DBMS enables users to perform a variety of operations on data, including retrieving, appending, editing, updating, and generating reports.

DBRN A ratio expressed in DeciBels above Reference Noise.

DBS Direct Broadcast Satellite.

DBT Deutsche Bundespost Telecom.

DBU Decibels below 1uW.

DC Direct Current. The flow of free electrons in one direction within an electrical conductor, such as a wire. DC also stands for Delayed Call.

DC SIGNALING A collection of ways of transmitting communications signals using direct current -- the type of current produced by a dry cell household "D" cell battery. DC signaling is only used on cable. It's an out-of-band signal.

DCA 1. Defense Communication Agency. US government agency responsible for installation of Defense Data Networks, including the ARPANET and MILNET, and PSNs. The DCA writes contracts for operation of the DDN (Defense Data Network) and pays for network services. 2. Document Content Architecture. The IBM approach to storing documents as two types of document group: draft documents and final form documents. For presentation, the draft document is transformed into a final document through an office system.

DCC 1. Data Communications Channel. Channels contained within section and line overhead used as embedded operations channels to communicate to each network element. An AT&T SONET term. 2. Digital Compact Cassette. A digital version of the familiar analog audio cassette. A DCC recorder can play and record both analog and digital cassettes. But the digital ones will sound a lot better.

DCD 1. Data Carrier Detect. Signal from the DCE (modem or printer) to the DTE (typically your PC), indicating it (the modem) is receiving a carrier signal from the DCE (modem) at the other end of the telephone circuit. 2. Dynamically Configurable Device. A dynamically configurable device is a fancy name for a Plug and Play device, so-called because you don't have to reboot the system after installing one.

DCE Data Communications Equipment. In the RS-232-C "standard" developed by the Electronic Industries Association, there are DCE devices (typically modems or printers) and DTE (Data Terminal Equipment) devices, which are typically personal computers or data terminals. The main difference between a DCE and DTE is the wiring of pins two and three. But there is, of course, no standardization. When wiring one RS-232-C device to another, it's good to know which device is wired as a DCE and which as a DTE. But it's actually best to go straight to the wiring diagram in the appendix of the device's instruction manual. Then you compare the wiring diagram of the device you want to connect and build yourself a cable that takes into account the peculiar (i.e. strange) vagaries of the engineers who designed each product. In short, with an RS-232-C connection, the modem is usually regarded as DCE, while the user device (terminal or computer) is DTE. In a X.25 connection, the network access and packet switching node is viewed as the DCE. DCE devices typically transmit on pin 3 and receive on pin 2. DTE (Data Terminal Equipment) devices typically transmit on pin 2 and receive on pin 3. See also the Appendix.

DCH D-Channel Handler.

DCM Digital Circuit Multiplication. A means of increasing the effective capacity of primary rate and higher level PCM hierarchies, based upon speech coding at 64 Kbit/s. Also a Digital Carrier Module.

DCP Digital Communications Protocol.

DCP TELEPHONE A digital voice telephone of the AT&T model 7400 series, operated with the Digital Communications Protocol (DCP) used in System 75/85 digital PBXs.

DCS 1. Distributed Communications system. See DISTRIBUTED SWITCHING. 2. Digital Crossconnect System. A device for switching and rearranging private line voice, private line analog data and T-1 lines. A DCS performs all the functions of a normal "switch," except that connections are typically set up in advance of when the circuits are to be switched -- not together with the call. You make those "connections" by calling an attendant who makes them manually, or dialing in on a computer terminal -- one similar to an airline agent's. See also NETWORK RECONFIGURATION SERVICE. 3. Digital Cellular System. 4. Digital Communications System. 5. DCS. A packet-switched network implemented in Belgium and opeated by the Belgian government.

DCS 1800 Digital Cellular System at 1800 MHz. A GSM (Global System for Mobile Communications) standard for cellular mobile telephony established by ETSI (European Telecommunications Standards Institute) for operation at 1800 MHz.

DCT 1. Digital Carrier Termination. 2. Discrete Cosine Transform. A form of coding used in most of the current image compression systems for bit rate reduction.

DCTI Desktop Computer Telephone Integration. Basically, providing a way for your computer to control your telephone set.

DCV Digital compressed video

DDA Domain Defined Attribute. A way of adding additional information to the address of your electronic mail in order to avoid confusion between people of the same or similar name.

DDB Digital Data Bank.

DDC Direct Department Calling.

DDCMP Digital Data Communications Message Protocol. A byte-oriented, link-layer protocol from Digital Equipment Corp., used to transmit messages between stations over a communications line. DDCMP supports half- or full-duplex modes, and either point-to-point or multipoint lines in a DNA (Digital Network Architecture) network.

DDD Direct Distance Dialing. The "brand name" the Bell System used to call its Message Toll Telephone Network. It used the words "Direct Distance Dialing" to convince the public to dial their own long distance calls directly without the help of an operator.

DDE See DYNAMIC DATA EXCHANGE

DDEML Dynamic Data Exchange Management Library. A feature of Microsoft Windows.

DDI Direct Dialing Inward. A British term. It is a service where a call made to a DDI number arrives direct, without the intervention of an organisation's operator, at an extension or, if routed via an ACD, a group of extensions. A specific DDI number is assigned to each campaign. When an agent answers a call made to one of these DDI numbers, the relevant script and screen are instantly displayed, so the agent can give an appropriate response.

DDM Distributed Data Management Architecture. An IBM SNA LU 6.2 transaction providing users with facilities to locate and access data in the network. It involves two structures: DDM Source, and DDM Target. The DDM Source works with a transaction application to retrieve distributed data and transmits commands to the DDM Target program on another system where the data that has been requested is stored. The DDM Target interprets the DDM commands, retrieves the data and sends it back to the DDM Source that originated the request.

DDN Defense Data Network. A network that provides long haul and area data communications and interconnectivity for DoD systems, and supports the DoD suite of protocols (especially TCP and IP). All equipment attached to the DDN by military subscribers must incorporate, or be compatible with, the DoD Internet and transport protocols. DDN was split off from ARPANET to handle U.S. military needs. It is also called MILNET.

DDP Distributed Data Processing. See DISTRIBUTED SWITCHING.

DDS 1. Dataphone Digital Service, also called Digital Data System. DDS is private line digital service, typically with data rates at 2,400; 4,800; 9,600 and 56,000 bits per second. DDS is offered on an inter-LATA basis by AT&T and on an intra-LATA basis by the Bell operating companies. AT&T has now incorporated it into their Accunet family of offerings. But, by the time your read this, they may have a new name for the service, like Accunet. 2. Digital Data Storage. A DAT format for storing data. It is sequential -- all data that is recorded to the tape falls after the previous block of data.

DDSD Delay Dial Start Dial. A start-stop protocol for dialing into a switch.

DE Discard Eligible. The frame relay standard specifies that data sent across a virtual connect in excess of that connection's Committed Information Rate (CIR) will be marked by the network as being eligible for discard in the event of network congestion. DE data is the first to be discarded by the network when congestion occurs, thus providing protection for data sent within the parameters of the CIR. It is the responsibility of the intelligent end equipment and/or protocol to recognize the discard and respond by resending the information.

DE FACTO Used to describe standards. Reflecting current or actual practice, but not having approval or sanction by any official standards-setting organization. usually created by an individual manufacturer or developer - hence, often used as a synonym for proprietary. The Hayes At auto-dial modem command language is an example of a de facto standard. Very often, de facto standards form the basis for de jure standards (Ethernet was the basis of Institute of Electrical and Electronic Engineers or IEEE standard 802.3). Contrast with DE JURE.

DE FOREST, LEE Lee de Forest invented the vacuum tube in 1907. Until the invention of the transistor after World War II, all radio, long distance telephony and complicated electronics, including electronic computers, were derived from de Forest's invention.

DE JURE Used to describe standards approved or sanctioned by an official standards setting organization. ITU-T Recommendation X.25 for packet data networks is an example of a de jure standard. Contrast with DE FACTO.

DEAD SECTOR In facsimile, the elapsed time between the end of scanning of one line and the start of scanning of the following line.

DEAD SPOT A cellular radio term. It denotes an area within a cell where service is not available. A dead spot is usually caused by hilly terrain which blocks the signal to or from the cell tower. It can also occur in tunnels and indoor parking garages. Excessive foliage or electronic interference can also cause dead spots. If you encounter a dead spot, tell your cellular radio supplier. They often will do something.

DEAD TREE EDITION The paper version of a publication available in both paper and electronic forms. If you are reading my dictionary on paper, you are reading the dead tree edition.

DEADLINE During the Civil War, captured troops were placed in a field. They were told they could move wherever they wanted in the field except beyond a line that was drawn around the field. If they did, they would be shot. Thus the origin of the word deadline.

DEADLOCK See DEADLY EMBRACE.

DEADLY EMBRACE Stalemate that occurs when two elements in a process are each waiting for the other to respond. For example, in a network, if one user is working on file A and needs file B to continue, but another user is working on file B and needs file A to continue, each one waits for the other. Both are temporarily locked out. The software must be able to deal with this.

DEALER Dealer is simply a person who sells equipment -- hardware or software -- made by someone else. That dealer may be a distributor of Novell LAN software. Or that dealer may be in the secondary telecom equipment business, i.e. a company that buys and sells secondary market telephone equipment. Generally in the secondary equipment business, a dealer takes ownership of the equipment (see BROKER). He tests and refurbishes it before remarketing. An authorized dealer has a contract with the manufacturer to buy equipment at a preset price. He also has the added support of a manufacturer's warranty. An independent dealer has no formal agreement with the manufacturer. He uses a variety of sources to obtain equipment and his warranty is backed only by the company's internal resources.

DEALER BOARD British term meaning "trading turret."

DEALING ROOM British term meaning "trading room."

DEBBIE WARREN A remarkable woman of great stamina, great perseverance and great tolerance. How do we know this? Anyone married to Stuart desperately needs these character traits. Favorite pastimes: Rachael and Jennifer.

DEBIT CARD The term telephone "debit card" covers three categories of a new type of telephone calling card, variously called "calling card" and "prepaid telephone card." The definitions are in flux. Here's the best shot at debit card: A telephone debit card is a piece of credit-card size plastic with some technology on it or embedded into which represents the value of the money remaining on the debit card. Such money can be used to make phone calls. The technology on the card is most typically an integrated circuit, a magnetic strip, bar codes which can be read by an optical reader. See BREAKAGE, CALLING CARD and PREPAID TELEPHONE CARD.

DEBUG A MS-DOS program to examine or alter memory, load and look at sectors of data from disk and create simple assembly-language programs. MS-DOS DEBUG.COM lets you write some small programs. You can use DEBUG to correct problems in some programs.

DEC Digital Equipment Corporation. A leading manufacturer of minicomputers. The Unix operating system, developed at Bell Labs, runs on DEC computers. DEC, with its headquarters in Massachusetts and having sold so many computers to Western Electric for inclusion in central office switches and toll switches, is sometimes referred to as "Eastern Electric." Kenneth H. Olsen founded DEC in 1957 with three employees in 8,500 square feet of leased space in a corner of an old woolen mill.

DEC LAT A proprietary data communications protocol developed by DEC.

DECags DEC ASAI Gateway Services. Two-directional link to AT&T's Definity. See also OPEN APPLICATION INTERFACE.

DECIBEL dB. A unit for measuring the power of a sound or the strength of a signal. It is expressed as the ratio of two values. Here is an explanation from James Harry Green's excellent book The Dow Jones-Irwin Handbook of Telecommunications. (Get a copy from Telecom Library 1-800-LIBRARY.) Mr. Green writes, "The power in telecommunications circuits is so low that it is normally measured in milliwatts. However, the milliwatt is not a convenient way to express differences in power level between circuits. Voice frequency circuits are designed around the human ear, which has a logarithmic response to changes in power. (Likewise, the human eye has a logarithmic response to changes in light.) Therefore in telephony, the decibel, which is a logarithmic rather than a linear measurement, is used as a measure of relative power between circuits or transmission level points. A change in level of 1 dB is barely perceptible under ideal conditions...Increases or reductions of 3 dB result in doubling or halving the power in a circuit. This ratio is handy to remember when evaluating power differences.

The corresponding figure for doubling or halving voltage is 6 dB. See DB.

DECIDE A deadly computer virus.

DECIMAL Our normal numbering system. It is to the base 10.

DECISION CIRCUIT A circuit that measures the probable value of a signal element and makes an output signal decision based on the value of the input signal and a predetermined criterion or criteria.

DECISION INSTANT In the reception of a digital signal, the instant at which a decision is made by a receiving device as to the probable value of a signal condition.

DECISION SUPPORT SYSTEMS DSS. Computerized systems for transforming data into useful information, such as statistical models or predictions of trends, which is used by management in the decision-making process. There are several aspects of the best decision support systems: First, they are connected to mainframe databases. Second, they are accessible by executives from their desktops. Third, there are usually lots of programs for producing graphs, charts and writing simple reports, i.e. for the executives to extract and portray information in forms that are most useful to them.

DECNET DEC's proprietary Ethernet LAN that works across all of the company's machines, endowed with a peer-to-peer methodology. See DEC.

DECODER A device that converts information from one form to another -- typically from analog to digital and vice versa. See DECODING.

DECODING Changing a digital signal into analog form or into another type of digital signal. The opposite of Encoding. See also MODEM. Decoding and coding should not be confused with deciphering and ciphering. See DES.

DECOLLIMATION In optics, that effect wherein a beam of parallel light rays is caused to diverge or converge from parallelism. Any of a large number of factors may cause this effect, e.g., refractive index inhomogeneities, occlusions, scattering, deflection, diffraction, reflection, refraction.

DECOLUMNIZATION The process of reformatting multi-column documents into a signal column. Generally, when you are processing a document for use in a word processing program, a single column of text is preferable to multiple columns.

DECOMPRESSION Decompression is the process of expanding a compressed image or file so it can be viewed, printed, faxed or otherwise processed.

DECRYPT To convert encrypted text into its equivalent plain text by means of a cryptosystem. This does not include solution by cryptanalysis. The term decrypt covers the meanings of decipher and decode.

DECT Digital European Cordless Telecommunications. An interface specification under development and governing pan-European digital mobile telephony of the future. Based on advanced TDMA technology, DECT covers cordless PBXs, telepoint and residential cordless telephony. DECT frequency is 1800-1900 MHz.

DEDICATED ACCESS A connection between a phone or phone system (like a PBX) and an IntereXchange Carrier (IXC) through a dedicated line. All calls over the line are automatically routed to a particular IXC.

DEDICATED BYPASS A connection between a phone or phone system (like a PBX) and an IntereXchange Carrier (IXC) through a dedicated line that is not provided by the dominant local provider of local phone service. For example, I live in New York. I might order a leased T-1 to MCI. If that line is not provided by Nynex, it is "dedicated bypass." Such bypass circuits are often cheaper and better quality than what the dominant local carrier can provide.

DEDICATED ARRAY PROCESSOR A microprocessor on a hardware-based RAID array that controls the execution of RAID array-specific functions, such as rebuilding. See RAID.

DEDICATED ATTENDANT LINK Assures that there will always be an intercom link available for your attendant or receptionist or operator to announce incoming calls.

DEDICATED CHANNEL OR CIRCUIT A channel leased from a common carrier by an end user used exclusively by that end user. The channel is available for use 24 hours a day, seven days a week, 52 weeks of the year, assuming it works that efficiently.

DEDICATED CIRCUIT A circuit designated for exclusive use by specified users. See also DEDICATED CHANNEL.

DEDICATED FEATURE BUTTONS The imprinted feature buttons on a telephone: Conf or Conference, Drop, HFAI (Hands Free Answerer on Intercom), Hold, Mute or Microphone, Speaker or Speakerphone, Transfer, Message, and Recall.

DEDICATED LINE Another name for a private leased line or dedicated channel. A dedicated line provides the ability to have constant transmission path from point A to point B. A dedicated line may be leased or owned. It may be assigned a single purpose, such as monitoring a distant building. It may be part of a network, with the ability for many to dial into it. It may be a tie-line between your offices or it may be a line to a long distance carrier. In this case, you do not have to dial a local connection number or put in an authorization code. A WATS line is in effect a Dedicated Line to AT&T or whomever you purchased WATS from.

DEDICATED MACHINE A computer designed to run only one program or do one thing. This machine cannot easily be re-programmed to do another task, as, for example, a general-purpose machine can. A general-purpose machine, however, can be dedicated to running only one task if programmed to do so.

DEDICATED MODE When a file server or router on a local area network is set up to work only as a file server or router, it runs in dedicated mode.

DEDICATED SERVER A computer on a network that performs specialized network tasks, such as storing files. The word "dedicated" means that the computer is used exclusively as a server. It is not used as a workstation, which means no one is sitting in front of it, using it. A dedicated server sits all alone, attached to its network, working happily all by itself.

DEDICATED SERVICE A communication network devoted to a single purpose or group of users, e.g., AUTOVON, FTS. It may also be a subset of a larger network; e.g., AUTOVON, FTS.

DEDICATED TRUNK A trunk which bypasses the Attendant Console and rings through to a particular phone, hunt group or distribution group.

DEEP SPACE Space at distances from the Earth approximately equal to or greater than the distance between the Earth and the Moon.

DEEP UV Printed circuits are made by optical lithography, by shining light through a negative, or mask. In the beginning, it was visible light, but lately it's been made with more precise ultraviolet light, which can print lines as thin as 0.15 micron wide. They call this light "deep uv" and it is ultraviolet light emitted by an excimer or pulsing laser.

DEFACTO STANDARDS Standards, widely accepted and used, but lacking formal approval by a recognized standards organization. The Hayes AT command set, MS-DOS, Windows, TCP/IP etc. are defacto standards.

DEFAULT The default is a factory-set hardware of software setting or configuration. It is the preset value that the program or equipment comes with. It will work with default values in the absence of any other command from the user. For example, communications software programs, such as Crosstalk, Blast, etc., have as their default settings 300 baud, 8 bit, one stop bit, no parity. If you want to run at 1,200 baud, you have to change that "default" setting.

DEFAULT CARRIER Generic name given to the long distance carrier which will carry the traffic of customers who haven't pre subscribed to a long distance carrier.

DEFENSE DATA NETWORK DDN. The Department of Defense integrated packet switching network capable of worldwide multilevel secure and non-secure data transmission.

DEFERRED PROCESSING Performing operations as a group or batch, all at once. Using batch mode, you can quickly prescan your documents, capturing just the image of each page, then perform recognition on these images later, freeing your computer for interactive work.

DEFINITION A figure of merit for image quality. For video-type displays, it is normally expressed in terms of the smallest resolvable element of the reproduced received image.

DEGAUSS To demagnetize. To degauss a magnetic tape means to erase it. See DEGAUSSER.

DEGAUSSER Device to demagnetize color picture tube for color purity.

DEGRADATION In communications, that condition in which one or more of the established performance parameters fall outside predetermined limits, resulting in a lower quality of service.

DEGRADED SERVICE STATE The condition wherein degradation prevails in a communication link. For some applications e.g., automatic switching to a non degraded standby link, degradation must persist for a specified period of time before a degraded service state is considered to exist.

DEGREE OF COHERENCE A measure of the coherence of a light source.

DEGREE OF ISOCHRONOUS DISTORTION In data transmission, the ratio of (a) the absolute value of the maximum measured difference between the actual and the theoretical intervals separating any two significant instants of modulation (or demodulation) to (b) the unit interval. These instants are not necessarily consecutive. The degree of isochronous distortion is usually expressed as a percentage. The result of the measurement should be completed by an indication of the period, usually limited, of the observation.

DEGREE OF START-STOP DISTORTION 1. In asynchronous data transmission, the ratio of (a) the absolute value of the maximum measured difference between the actual and theoretical intervals separating any significant instant of modulation (or demodulation) from the significant instant of the start element immediately preceding it to (b) the unit interval. 2. The highest absolute value of individual distortion affecting the significant instants of a start-stop modulation. The degree of distortion of a start-stop modulation (or demodulation) is usually expressed as a percentage.

DEINSTALLATION A term used in the secondary telecom equipment business. The shutoff and disconnect of machine power and the disassembly of a PBX switch to prepare for its removal from a switch room facility. A properly executed deinstallation will include all necessary parts for the reassembly, operation, maintenance and acceptance of the switch and any of its components at the next location.

DEJITTERIZER A device for reducing jitter in a digital signal, consisting essentially of an elastic buffer into which the signal is written and from which it is read at a rate determined by the average rate of the incoming signal. Such a device is largely ineffective in dealing with low-frequency impairments such as waiting-time jitter.

DELAY The wait time between two events, such as the time from when a signal is sent to the time it is received. There are all sorts of reasons for delays, such as propagation delays, satellite delays, etc.

DELAY, ABSOLUTE The time elapsed between transmission of a signal and reception of the same signal.

DELAY ANNOUNCEMENTS These are pre-recorded announcements to incoming callers that they are being delayed and being placed in an ACD queue. Sample: "Please wait. All our agents are permanently busy. You are being placed on Eternity Hold. Don't go away or you'll never be allowed back." Some announcements are giving callers sales pitches and some idea of how long they'll have to stay on line until someone helps them.

DELAYED DELIVERY Hold a message for delivery later. Just as the words say.

DELAYED DELIVERY FACILITY A facility that employs storage within the data network whereby data destination for delivery to one or more addresses may be held for subsequent delivery at a later time.

DELAY DISTORTION The difference, expressed in time, for signals of different frequencies to pass through a phone line.

DELAY ENCODING A method of encoding binary data to form a two-level signal. A binary zero caused no change of signal level unless it is followed by another zero, in which case a transition takes place at the end of the first bit period. A binary "1" causes a transition from one level to the other in the middle of the bit period. Used primarily for encoding of radio signals since the spectrum of the encoding of signal contains less low frequency energy than an NRZ signal and less high frequency energy than a biphase signal.

DELAY EQUALIZER A corrective piece of electronic circuitry designed to make communications circuit delays constant over a desired frequency range. A delay equalizer is a device that adds a delay to analog signals, which will travel through a medium faster than other frequencies used to transmit portions of the same data. The objective is to create a medium that transfers the information on all the used frequencies in the same time over the same distance, thus eliminating transmission delay distortion.

DELAY LINE A transmission line, or equivalent device, designed to introduce delay.

DELAY MODULATION A modulation scheme that uses different forms of delay in a signal element. Frequently used in radio, microwave and fiberoptic systems.

DELAYED RING TRANSFER An optional KTU facility that provides for automatic transfer to the ringing signal from a principal telephone set to the attendant telephone station after an adjustable number of rings.

DELAYED TRANSMISSION A fax machine feature that allows a document to be transmitted automatically at a specific time.

DELAYED SENDING A feature of fax machines which allows the machine to be programmed to send its transmissions at a later time -- to take advantage of lower phone rates, for example.

DELIMITER A special word or character that allows a computer to recognize the beginning or end of a portion of a program or segment of data.

DELIVERED BLOCK A successfully transferred block.

DELIVERED OVERHEAD BIT A bit transferred to a destination user, but having its primary functional effect within the telecommunication system.

DELIVERED OVERHEAD BLOCK A successfully transferred block that contains no user information bits.

DELIVERY CONFIRMATION Information returned to the originator indicating that a given unit of information has been delivered to the intended addresses.

DELIVERY ENVELOPE An X.400 term.

DELNI Digital Ethernet Local Network Interconnect

DELPHI FORECASTING One of the silliest methods of forecasting the future. Namely, to ask a bunch of alleged experts (often academic eggheads) what they think might happen and then averaging out their opinions, sort of.

DELTA CHANNEL In T-carrier/ISDN communications, a delta channel/"D channel" contains signaling and status information.

DELTA FRAME Also called Difference Frame. Contains only the pixels different from the preceding Key Frame. Delta frames reduce the overall size of the video clip to be stored on disk or transmitted on phone lines.

DELTA MODULATION A method for converting analog voice to digital form for transmission. It is the second most common method of digitizing voice after Pulse Code Modulation, PCM. Sampling is done in all conversion of analog voice to digital signals. The method of sampling is what distinguishes the various methods of digitization (Delta vs.' PCM, etc.). In delta modulation, the voice signal is scanned 32,000 times a second, and a reading is taken to see if the latest value is greater or less than it was at the previous scan. If it's greater, a "1" is sent. If it's smaller, a "0" is sent.

Delta modulation's sampling rate of 32,000 times a second is four times faster than PCM. But Delta records its samples as a zero (0) or a one (1), while PCM takes an 8-bit sample. Thus PCM encodes voice into 64,000 bits per second, while Delta codes it into 32,000. Because delta has fewer bits, it could theoretically produce a poorer representation of the voice. In actual fact, the human ear can't hear the difference between a PCM and a Delta encoded voice conversation.

Delta modulation has much to recommend it, especially its use of fewer bits. Unfortunately no two delta modulation schemes are compatible with each other. So to get one delta-mod digital PBX to speak to another, you have to convert the voice signals back to analog. With AT&T making T-1 a de facto digital encoding scheme, PCM has become the de facto standard for digitally encoding voice. And although there are three types of PCM in general use, they can be made compatible on direct digital basis (i.e. without having to go back to analog voice). One problem with PCM is that American manufacturers typically put twenty four 64,000 bit per second voice conversations on a channel and call it T-1. The Europeans put 30 conversations on their equivalent transmission path. Thus, you can't directly interface the American and the European systems. But there are "black boxes" available...(In this business, there are always black boxes available.)

DELTA SIGMA MODULATION A variant of delta modulation in which the integral of the input signal is encoded rather than the signal itself. A normal delta modulation encoder by an integrating network. See DELTA MODULATION.

DELURKING Coming out of online "lurking mode," usually motivated by an irresistible need to flame about something. "I just had to delurk and add my two cents to that conversation about a woman's right to abortion."

DELUXE QUEUING A feature that allows incoming calls from phone users, tie trunks and attendants to be placed in a queue when all routes for completing a particular call are busy. The queue can be either a Ringback Queue (RBQ)-- the user hangs up and is called back when a trunk becomes available -- or an Off-Hook Queue (OHQ) -- the user waits off-hook and is connected to the next available trunk. Deluxe Queuing is a term used mainly by AT&T. Most modern PBXs have this feature. Most have simpler names, however.

DEMAND ASSIGNED MULTIPLE ACCESS See DAMA.

DEMAND ASSIGNMENT A technique where users share a communications channel. A user needing to communicate with another user on the network activates the required circuit. Upon completion of the call, the circuit is deactivated and the capacity is available for other users.

DEMAND FACTOR The ratio of the maximum demand on a power system to the total connected load of the system.

DEMAND LOAD In general, the total power required by a facility. The demand load is the sum of the operational load (including any tactical load) and non operational demand loads. It is determined by applying the proper demand factor to each of the connected loads and a diversity factor to the sum total.

DEMAND PAGING The common implementation in a PC of virtual memory, where pages of data are read into memory from storage in response to page faults.

DEMAND PRIORITY Access method providing support for time sensitive applications such as video and multimedia as part of the proposed 100BaseVG standard offering 100Mbit/s over voice grade UTP (Unshielded Twisted Pair) cable. By managing and allocating access to the network centrally, at a hub rather than from individual workstations, sufficient bandwidth for the particular application is guaranteed on demand. Users, say its proponents, can be assured of reliable, continuous transmission of information.

DEMAND PUBLISHING The production of just the number of printed documents you need at the present time, as in "just in time." In short, the immediate production of printed documents which have been created and stored electronically.

DEMAND SERVICE In ISDN applications, a telecommunications service that establishes an immediate communication path in response to a user request made through user-network signaling.

DEMARC or DEMARK (Pronounced D-Mark.) The demarcation point between the wiring that comes in from your local telephone company and the wiring you install to hook up your telephone system -- your CPE (Customer Provided Equipment) wiring. A Demarc might be anything as simple as an RJ-11C jack (one trunk) or an RJ-14C (two trunks) or an RJ-21X (up to 25 trunks) or a 66-block. A 66-block is a punchdown block on one side of which the telephone company may punch down its trunks and on the other, you may punch down your connections into your phone system. On a 66 block, there are little metal clips called "bridging clips" between you and the phone company. Lifting these clips off cuts your equipment from the phone company's trunks. This way you can quickly see whose fault it is. Often it's yours. But, if you think it's theirs and they come and find it's yours, they'll bill you. See DEMARCATION POINT or DEMARCATION STRIP.

DEMARCATION POINT The point of a demarcation and/or interconnection between telephone company communications facilities and terminal equipment, protective apparatus, or wiring at a subscriber's premises. Carrier-installed facilities at or constituting the demarcation point consist of a wire or a jack conforming to Subpart F of Part 68 of the FCC Rules.

DEMARCATION STRIP The terminal strip or block (typically a 66 block) which is the physical interface between the phone company's lines and the lines going directly to your own phone system. See also DEMARC.

DEMKO Denmark Elektriske MaterielKOntrol (Denmark Testing Laboratory).

DEMOCRATICALLY SYNCHRONIZED NETWORK A mutually synchronized network in which all clocks in the network are of equal status and exert equal amounts of control on the others.

DEMODULATION The process of retrieving an electrical signal from a carrier signal or wave. The reverse of modulation. See MODEM.

DEMULTIPLEX DEMUX. To separate two or more signals previously combined by compatible multiplexing equipment.

DEMULTIPLEXER A device that pulls several streams of data out of a bigger, fatter or faster stream of data.

DEMULTIPLEXING A process applied to a multiplex signal for recovering signals combined within it and for restoring the distinct individual channels of the signals.

DEMUX Jargon for demultiplexer.

DENet The Danish Ethernet Network which consists of many Ethernet networks in universities connected together by bridges.

DENIAL OF SERVICE The removal of a LAN service from a user, usually for malicious purposes.

DENIS THE LITTLE The 6th century monk who decided that history should be split between B.C. and A.D.

DENSITY 1. The number of bits (or bytes) in a defined length on a magnetic medium. Density describes the amount of data that can be stored. 2. The number of circuits that can be packed into an integrated circuit.n 3. In a facsimile system, a measure of the light transmission or reflection properties of an area, expressed by the logarithm of the ratio of incident to transmitted or reflected light flux.

DENWA Japanese for telephone.

DEPARTURE ANGLE The angle between the axis of the main lobe of an antenna pattern and the horizontal plane at the transmitting antenna.

DEPERSONALIZATION In 1879 a flu epidemic in Lowell, MA make it likely that all four of the telephone operators would get sick simultaneously. To help substitute operators, management numbered each of the exchange's two hundred plus customers. No problem. The customers accepted the change easily.

DEPLANING Getting off a plane. See DETRAINING.

DEPOLARIZATION 1. In electromagnetic wave propagation, that condition wherein a polarized transmission being transmitted through a nonhomogeneous medium has its polarization reduced or randomized by the effects of the medium being traversed. 2. Prevention of polarization in an electric cell or battery.

DEPOPULATE A technique to reduce the traffic load on a switch by removing devices from the shelf or cabinet. Depopulating reduces the effective device capacity of a switch but can increase switching capacity. This is a ploy used to give older PBX systems traffic capacity nearer true ACD systems.

DEPRESSED CLADDING FIBER An optical fiber construction, usually single mode, that has double cladding, the outer cladding having an index of refraction intermediate between the core and the inner cladding.

DEREGULATION The removal of regulatory authority to control certain activities of telephone companies. An attempt by federal authorities to make the telephone industry more competitive. Deregulation is meant to benefit the consumer. Sometimes it does. Sometimes it doesn't. Often, it's a scapegoat for whatever subsequently goes wrong.

DERIVATION EQUIPMENT Produces narrow band facilities from a wider band facility. Such equipment can, for instance, derive telegraph grade lines from the unused portion of a voice circuit.

DES Data Encryption Standard. An algorithm for encrypting (coding) data designed by the National Bureau of Standards so it is impossible for anyone without the decryption key to get the data back in unscrambled form. The DES standard enciphers and deciphers data using a 64-bit key specified in the Federal Information Processing Standard Publication 46, dated January 15, 1977. DES is not the most advanced system in computer security and there are possible problems with its use. Proprietary encryption schemes are also available. Some of these are more modern and more secure. The quality of your data security is typically a function of how much money you spend. See CLIPPER CHIP and NSA.

DESCENDERS Those parts (or tails) of the letters p, y, j and g which descend below the base line. This type style is much easier to read than one in which the tails rest on the base line. Watch out for true (i.e. real) descenders when you're buying a system. Most have them these days, but many telephone screens don't. Careful.

DESCRAMBLER A device which corrects a signal (often video) that has been intentionally distorted to prevent unauthorized viewing. Used with satellite TV systems. See DES.

DESI STRIP A slang term for Designation Strip, the small printed piece of paper or card that slides into or attaches onto a telephone and tells you which button answers which line or which button does what in the way of features or intercom.

DESIGN LAYOUT REPORT DLR. A record containing the technical information that describes the facilities and terminations provided by a local telephone company to a long distance telephone company. The technical information is needed by the long distance carrier to design the overall service and includes such items as cable makeup (gauge, loading, length, etc.), carrier channel bank type and system mileage, signaling termination compatibility, etc. The DLR is sent to the designated Carrier representative via the local Telephone Company's Engineering Department.

DESIGNATION STRIP Also called Desi Strip. A designation Strip is the small printed piece of paper that slides into or attaches onto a telephone and tells you which button answers which line or which button does what in the way of features or intercom.

DESKEWING An imaging term. Adjusting -- straightening -- an image in software to compensate for a crooked scan.

DESKTOP The computer's working environment. The screen layout, the menu bar, and the program icons associated with the machine's operating environment. Apple's Macintosh (introduced on January 24, 1984) really started the idea that the computer's screen was a desktop. With the introduction of Windows, IBM PCs and clones now also have desktops.

DESKTOP COLLABORATION Using ISDN lines or analog lines with high speed lines, you can link your desktop computers so teleworkers, suppliers and clients can share documents and work together no matter where they are.

DESKTOP CONNECTION AT&T's code name for hardware which includes an AT&T serial port adapter, DSS cable and a 9 to 25 pin connector and some software to make it work. The new name for desktop connection is PassageWay. It attaches to the back of the AT&T phone. The cable connects the adapter to your PC's serial port. In AT&T's words, the AT&T PassageWay integrates telephone functions with a Microsoft Windows 3.1 or greater application, facilitating outdialing using the Hayes Command Set used by modems, linking caller identification to PC business applications, and paving the way to an open interface between the PC software and the telephone. As a development platform, AT&T PassageWay offers an application layer access to features of the telephone including receiving information on visual/audible alerts and telephone displays, activating button presses, turning the speakerphone on or off, adjusting the volume of the telephone and dialing, including some call state progress. In addition, operating with Windows provides a unique way of accessing and sharing information between applications that co-reside on a PC. Windows provides a Graphic User Interface

(GUI) that allows software packages to be easily developed. Windows also offers the Dynamic Data Exchange (DDE) interface between co-resident applications that is a standard for sharing information on DOS PCs. AT&T PassageWay also passes information using Microsoft's DDE standard. See also AT&T APPLICATIONS PARTNER.

DESKTOP METAPHOR A desktop metaphor is the conceptual way a workstation screen area is used to emulate a user's physical desktop through graphic icon images. The icon maps directly to its real life function. For example, a trash can icon will allow a user to "throw out" a document. Gives an application a "user friendly" feel. Desktop metaphors are consistent throughout all Windows and windows-like applications, like Sparc's OPEN LOOK.

DESKTOP PATTERN A Windows 3.1 term. A design that appears across the desktop. You can use Control Panel to create your own pattern or choose a pattern provided by Windows.

DESKTOP VIDEO Communications that rely either on video phones or personal computers offering a video window.

DESKTOP VIDEOCONFERENCING By combining ISDN technology and individual PCs, people can meet "face-to-face" without leaving their offices. It's a way to reduce costly and time-consuming travel, maybe.

DESPUN ANTENNA Of a rotating communications satellite, an antenna, the direction of whose main beam with respect to the satellite is continually adjusted so that it illuminates a given area on the surface of the Earth, i.e., the footprint does not move.

DESTINATION ADDRESS That part of a message which indicates for whom the message is intended. Usually a collection of characters or bits. Just like putting a destination address on an envelope. On a token ring network this is a 48-bit sequence that uniquely defines the physical name of the computer to which a LAN data packet is being sent. The IEEE assures that in the world of LANs no two devices have the same physical address. It does so by assigning certain numbers to vendors of token ring adapters, the devices that connect computers to a token ring network.

DESTINATION ADDRESS FILTERING A feature of bridges that allows only those messages intended for the extended LAN to be forwarded.

DESTINATION CODE See DESTINATION FIELD.

DESTINATION DOCUMENT The document into which an object is linked or embedded via OLE. The destination document is sometimes also called the container document.

DESTINATION FIELD The field in a message header that contains the network address of the individual for whom the message is meant and who will (with luck and good management) receive the message.

DESTINATION NODE Those system nodes which receive messages over the control packet network from the source or transmitting node.

DESTINATION POINT CODE DPC. The part of a routing label that identifies where the SS7 signaling message should be sent.

DESTINATION SERVICE ACCESS POINT DSAP. The logical address of the specific service entity to which data must be delivered when it arrives at its destination. This information may be built into the data field of an IEEE 802.3 transmission frame.

DESTUFFING The controlled deletion of stuffing bits from a stuffed digital signal, to recover the original signal.

DETECTOR 1. In a radio receiver, a circuit or device that recovers the signal of interest from the modulated wave. 2. In an optical communications receiver, a device that converts the received optical signal to another form. Currently, this conversion is from optical to electrical power; however, optical-to-optical techniques are under development.

DETEM An opto-electronic transducer that combines the function of an optical detector and emitter in a single device or module. Do not confuse with DTERM, a name for one of NEC's telephones that work on its NEAX 2000 and 2400 PBXs.

DETOUR Difficulty in gaining access to the information highway. Often involves a Highway Construction Supervisor solving your access problem.

DETRAINING Getting off a train. An absolutely ghastly word invented by the railroad industry to keep them on a par with new, awful language invented by the airline industry. See also DEPLANING.

DETECTOR A device which converts or rectifies high frequency oscillations into a pulsating direct current or which translates radio frequency power into a form suitable for the operation of an indicator. This is most frequently a vacuum tube, less commonly a crystal. Coherers and delicate chemical rectifiers were used in former years.

DETENT TUNER "Click" type of TV tuner.

DEVICE CONTENTION 1. Occurs when more than one application is trying to use the same device, such as a modem or printer. Some of the newer operating systems do a better job handling handling device contention. 2. The way Windows 95 allocates access to peripheral devices, such as a modem or a printer, when more than one application is trying to use the same device.

DEVICE CONTROL A multimedia definition. Device control enables you to control different media devices over the network through software. The media devices include VCRs, laser disc players, video cameras, CD players, and so on. Control capabilities are available on the workstation through a graphical user interface. They are similar to the controls on the device itself, such as play, record, reverse, eject, and fast forward. Device control is important because it enables you to control video and audio remotely -- without requiring physical access.

DEVICE DRIVER 1. A special type of software (which may or may not be embedded in firmware) that controls devices attached to the computer, such as a printer, a scanner, a voice card, a diskette drive, a CD-ROM, a hard disk, monitor or mouse. Device drivers are typically loaded low into the memory of PCs in the MS-DOS CONFIG.SYS command, or they're loaded high using the Devicehigh command. A device driver is software that expands an operating system's ability to work with peripherals. A device driver controls the software routines that make the peripherals work. 2. A program that enables a specific piece of hardware (device) to communicate with Windows 95. Although a device may be installed on your computer, Windows 95 cannot recognize the device until you have installed and configured the appropriate driver.

DEVICE ID A Plug and Play term. A code in a device's Plug and Play extension that indicates the type of device it is. The device ID and the vendor ID create a unique identifier for each PnP (Plug N Play) device.

DFA Doped Fiber Amplifier.

DFI Digital Facility Interface. An 5ESS switch circuitry in a DTLU responsible for terminating a single digital facility and generating one PIDB.

DFT Direct Facility Termination. A telephone company trunk that terminates directly on one or more telephones.

DG Directorate General (CEC).

DGPS Differential Global Positioning Service -- a new venture of the US Coast Guard, which it hopes to have ready by 1996. It will use an existing network of radio beacons throughout the US to create a fixed grid of known reference points in order to improve the accuracy of the Defense Department's GPS signal. The Coast Guard hopes to achieve an accuracy of about 10 meters.

DGT Direccion General de Telecommunicaciones (Spanish General Directorate of Telecommunications).

DHCP Dynamic Host Configuration Protocol.

DHRYSTONES Benchmark program for testing the speed of a computer. It tests a general mix of instructions. The results in Dhrystones per second are the number of times the program can be executed in one second. The Dhrystone benchmark program is used as a standard indicating aspects of a computer system's performance in areas other than its floating-point performance, for instance, integer processes per second, enumeration, record and pointer manipulation. Since the program does not use any floating-point operations, performs no I/O, and makes no operating system calls, it is most applicable to measuring the performance of systems programming applications. The program was developed in 1984 and was originally written in Ada, although the C and PASCAL versions became more popular by 1989. See WHETSTONES.

DIA/DCA Document Interchange Architecture/Document Content Architecture. IBM promulgated architectures, part of SNA, for transmission and storage of documents over networks, whether text, data, voice or video. Becoming industry standards by default.

DIAGNOSTIC PROGRAMS Programs run by the computer portion of a PBX to detect faults in the system. Such programs may run automatically at regular intervals or continuously. The goal of diagnostic programs is to detect faults before they become serious and to alert someone -- typically the attendant -- to do fix it. Some diagnostic programs stop running when the switch gets too busy. Some don't. You can dial into some diagnostic programs from afar. And you can't in some. Remote diagnostic programs are probably the greatest boons to improved reliability of telephone systems.

DIAGNOSTICS A term used in the secondary marketplace. Original Equipment's Manufacturer (O.E.M) prescribed test procedure whose successful completion is normally required for maintenance acceptance of a switch, cabinet, or peripheral piece of equipment. Comment: A new maintenance contract will not go into effect until the maintenance company accepts the results of the diagnostics.

DIAL A PRAYER A sarcastic name for the local 611 number run by the local telephone companies as their centralized number for repair.

DIAL-AROUND A method used by callers to purposely bypass a payphone company's local or long distance carrier services. Such methods include calling cards and alternative carrier's collect services, such as 1-800-COLLECT or 1-800-CALL-ATT. Payphone operators receive little or no revenue from such calls.

DIAL BACKUP 1. A network scheme using dial-up phone lines as a replacement for failed leased data lines. In one typical case, two dial-up lines can be used. One dial-up link is used to transmit data and the other to receive data, thus giving us full-duplex data transmission. 2. A security feature that ensures people do not log into modems that they shouldn't have access to. When a connection is requested, the system checks the username presented for validity, then "dials back" the number associated with that username.

DIAL BY NAME You can dial someone by spelling their name out on the touch-tone pad. Typically, the system plays a recorded announcement giving directions for using the Dial by Name feature: the caller then inputs the appropriate digits/letters. When the system recognizes a match, a recorded announcement states the name of the dialed party for confirmation by the caller before automatically completing the call. If the input digits are not uniquely associated with a particular station the system may ask the caller to pick a name from a menu of choices. Dial by name is getting cheaper. Automated attendants are being programmed to have the feature. And you shouldn't buy an auto attendant unless it has this feature.

DIAL CALL PICKUP A phone user on a PBX or hybrid can dial a special code and answer calls ringing on any other phone within his own predefined pickup group.

DIAL DICTATION ACCESS A service feature available with some switching systems that permits dialing a special number to access centralized dictation equipment.

DIAL IN TIE TRUNK A Dial In Tie trunk is a trunk that may be accessed by dialing an access code and then seizing a dedicated transmission path to a distant PBX (or another PBX a short distance away). Once the trunk is seized in the distant PBX, the caller may then use the features of that PBX, depending on the class-of-service and restrictions assigned to the trunk.

DIAL IT 900 SERVICE A special one-way mass calling service that allows prospects, customers and others to reach you from anywhere across the country. In contrast to 800-service, the caller pays the 900 charge, generally one charge for the first minute, with a lesser charge for each additional minute. DIAL-IT 900 Service is a great way to involve your customers and prospects in a promotion! Premium Billing lets you select a rate above standard DIAL-IT 900 rates. The long distance carriers (through their deals with local phone companies) handle the billing. You, the information provider, split the revenues with the long distance provider. International DIAL-IT 900 service is currently available from a growing number of countries.

DIAL LEVEL The selection of stations or services associated with a PBX, based on the first digit(s) dialed.

DIAL PICK-UP PBX feature. A phone on a PBX can answer another ringing phone by dialing a few digits. Also called an access code.

DIAL PULSING A means of signaling consisting of regular momentary interruptions of a direct or alternating current at the sending end in which the number of interruptions corresponds to the value of the digit or character. In short, the old style of rotary dialing. Dial the number "five" and you'll hear five "clicks." See DIAL SPEED, DIAL TRAIN and DTMF.

DIAL PULSE SIGNALING A type of address signaling in which dial pulse is implemented to signal the distant equipment. See DIAL PULSING.

DIAL REPEATING TRUNKS PBX tie trunks used with terminating PBX equipment capable of handling telephone signaling without attendant involvement.

DIAL SERVICE ASSISTANCE DSA. A service feature associated with the switching center equipment to provide operator services, such as information, intercepting, random conferencing, and precedence calling assistance.

DIAL SPEED The number of pulses a rotary dial can send in a given period of time, typically 10 per second. A Hayes modem with a communications package, like Crosstalk, can send 20 pulses per second.

DIAL STRING A Dial String is the sequence of characters sent to a device which can dial a phone number. Such a device might be a modem or a voice processing card. Here are some "digits" in a dial string: ! — flashhook (TAPI standard); & — flashhook (Dialogic); T — use tone dialing; , — pause (typically of half a second to two seconds); W — wait for dial tone.

DIAL STRING/COMMAND STRING A sequence of characters and digits used for dial-in access; ATDT5107861000,,,,,,,,123456, fo xample.

DIAL THROUGH A technique, applicable to access circuits, that permits an outgoing routine call to be dialed by the PBX user after the PBX attendant has established the initial connection.

DIAL TONE The sound you hear when you pick up a telephone. Dial tone is a signal (350 + 440 Hz) from your local telephone company that it is alive and ready to receive the number you dial. If you have a PBX, dial tone will typically be provided by the PBX. Dial tone does not come from God or the telephone instrument on your desk. It comes from the switch to which your phone is connected to.

DIAL TONE DELAY The specific time that transpires between a subscriber's going off-hook and the receipt of dial tone from a servicing telephone central office. It's a measure of the time needed to provide dial tone to customers. Many of the local public service commissions in the United States say that 90% of customers should receive dial tone in fewer than three seconds.

DIAL TONE FIRST COIN SERVICE A type of pay phone service in which dial tone is received when the caller goes off-hook and coins must be inserted only after the call is connected.

DIAL TRAIN The series of pulses or tones sent from the phone that's calling and the switching system it's attached to in order to signify the call's destination.

DIAL UP The use of a dial or push button telephone to create a telephone or data call. Dial-up calls are usually billed by time of day, duration of call and distance traveled. A connection to the Internet, or any network, where a modem and a standard telephone are used to make a connection between computers. See DIAL UP LINE.

DIAL UP LINE A telephone line which is part of the switched nationwide telephone system. Typically a "dial up line" is a standard analog POTS line. These days, ISDN lines are dial up, also. So this definition is changing also.

DIAL UP MODEM A modem that connects to a remote resource for the duration of an individual call.

DIAL UP NETWORKING A Windows 95 definition. It is a service that provides remote networking for telecommuters, mobile workers, and system administrators who monitor and manage servers at multiple branch offices. Users with Dial-Up Networking on a computer running Windows 95 can dial in for remote access to their networks for services such as file and printer sharing, electronic mail, scheduling, and SQL database access.

DIAL ZERO PHONE A telephone on a Northern Telecom Norstar phone system which is assigned to ring when someone dials 0 (zero) from another Norstar telephone.

DIALAN DMS Integrated Access Local Area Network

DIALBACK SECURITY Dialback security is a telecom security feature. If a person calls in wanting remote access, the system asks for a password. Once it receives a correct password, it hangs up on the caller and dials back a predefined remote number, only then giving the caller access. Unless the hacker has you tied up in your living room, it makes things very secure. It can be made even more secure with multiple passwords and features like voice recognition.

DIALED NUMBER IDENTIFICATION SERVICE See DNIS and 800 SERVICE.

DIALED NUMBER RECORDER Also called a Pen Register. An instrument that records telephone dial pulses as inked dashes on paper tape. A touchtone decoder performs the same thing for a touchtone telephone.

DIALING PATTERN Dialing pattern refers to the digits you need to dial to place local, long distance, collect calls, or other phone calls. Dialing patterns will vary due to different types of telephone carrier switching equipment, computer software and the host carrier's credit policies (e.g. automatic roaming versus credit card roaming when using a cellular phone).

DIALING PLAN A description of the dialing arrangements for customer use on a network.

DIALOG BOX A dialog box is a temporary window which prompts you to input information or make selections necessary for a task to continue.

DIALOGIC Dialogic Corporation, Parsippany, NJ, is a leading manufacturer of interactive voice processing equipment, most of it PC-based. They sell equipment through value added resellers, dealers and distributors. Many of their dealers "add value" to the Dialogic components by doing their own specialized software programming, tailoring Dialogic products to particular specialized (and useful) applications. See also AEB. PEB and SCSA.

DIAPHRAGM The thin flexible sheet which vibrates in response to sound waves (as in a microphone) or in response to electrical signals (as in a speaker or the receiver of telephone handset).

DIBIT A group of two bits which can be represented by a single change of modulation of the carrier signal. On phase modulation, one of four phases in four-phase modulation is used to represent 00, 01, 10 or 11.

DICHROIC FILTER An optical filter designed to transmit light selectively according to wavelength (most often, a high-pass or low-pass filter).

DICHROIC MIRROR A mirror designed to reflect light selectively according to wavelength.

DICTATION ACCESS AND CONTROL A telephone system feature which allows a user to dial a dictation machine and use that machine (giving it instructions by push button) as if it were in his office. Typically, the material on that dictation machine is taken off by one or several typists of a centralized pool and word processed into letters, reports, legal briefs, etc. Telephone suppliers usually don't supply the dictation equipment. Newer telephone dictation machinery is, in reality, a specialized application of voice processing equipment. See VOICE PROCESSING.

DICTATION TANK A recording gadget which receives messages dictated through the telephone system. This tank contains tape which can then be transcribed into letters or documents. See DICTATION ACCESS AND CONTROL.

DID Direct Inward Dialing. You can dial inside a company directly without going through the attendant. This feature used to be an exclusive feature of Centrex but it can now be provided by virtually all modern PBXs and some modern hybrids, but you must connect via specially configured DID lines from your local central office. A DID (Direct Inward Dial) trunk is a trunk from the Central office which passes the last two to four digits of the Listed Directory Number to the PBX or hybrid phone system, and the digits may then be used verbatim or modified by phone system programming to be the equivalent of an internal extension. Therefore, an external caller may reach an internal extension by dialing a 7-digit central office number. Notice: DID is different from a DIL (Direct-In-Line) where a standard, both-way central office trunk is programmed to always ring a specific extension or hunt group. DID lines cannot be used for outdial operation, since there is no dialtone offered.

DIEL Advisory committee on telecommunications for DIsabled and Elderly People (UK).

DIELECTRIC A nonconducting or insulating substance which resists passage of electric current, allowing electrostatic induction to act across it, as in the insulating medium between the plates of a condenser. Also an insulating material otherwise used (e.g. a Bakelite panel, or the cambric covering of a wire is a dielectric material). See also SEMICONDUCTOR.

DIELECTRIC ABSORPTION The penetration of a dielectric by the electric strain during a period of time.

DIELECTRIC CONSTANT The ratio of the capacity of a condenser with a given dielectric to the capacity of the same condenser with air as the dielectric.

DIELETRIC LENS A lens made of dieletric material that refracts radio waves in the same material that an optical lens refracts light waves.

DIELECTRIC PROCESS A printing process that uses a specially treated, charge-sensitive paper. Paper is roller-fed past an electrode array where an electrical charge is applied on line-by-line to form a latent image, then passed through a toner. The toner adheres to the charged image and heat fuses the toner to the paper to create the printed document.

DIELECTRIC SHEATH OR CABLE A sheath or cable that contains no electrically conducting materials such as metals. Dielectric cables are sometimes used in areas subject to high lightning or electro-magnetic interference. Synonym for nonmetallic cable.

DIELECTRIC STRENGTH The property of material which resists the passage of an electric current. It is measured in terms of voltage required to break down this resistance (such as volts per mil.).

DIELECTRIC TEST A test in which a voltage higher than the rated voltage is applied for a specified time to determine the adequacy of the insulation under normal conditions.

DIFFERENTIAL MODULATION Modulation in which information is encoded into differences of successive signals. Delta modulation is an example.

DIFFERENTIAL PHASE-SHIFT KEYING DPSK. A modulation technique in which the relative changes of the carrier signal's phase are coded according to the data to be transmitted. See PHASE SHIFT KEYING.

DIFFERENTIAL POSITIONING Precise measurements of the relative positions of two receivers tracking the same GPS (Global Positioning System) signals.

DIFFIE-HELLMAN KEY A technique of changing encryption techniques on the fly. In a landmark 1976 paper, called New Directions in Cryptograph, IEEE Transactions on Information Theory, W. Diffie and M. Hellman describe a method by which a secret key can be exchanged using messages that do not need to be kept secret. This type of "public" key management provides a significant cost advantage by eliminating the need for a courier service. In addition, security can be considerably enhanced by permitting more frequent key changes and eliminating the need for any individual to have access to the key's actual value.

DIFFRACTION The deviation of a wavefront from the path predicted by geometric optics when a wavefront is restricted by an opening or an edge. Diffraction is usually most noticeable for openings of the order of a wavelength.

DIFFRACTION GRATING An array of fine, parallel, equally spaced reflecting or transmitting lines that mutually enhance the effects of diffraction at the edges of each so as to concentrate the diffracted light very close to a few directions depending on the spacing of the lines and the wavelength of the diffracted light.

DIGILINE Southwestern Bell's name for ISDN BRI service.

DIGIPATH A New York and New England Telephone service, Digipath Digital Service provides point-to-point and multi-point full duplex, two-way, private digital data communications at synchronous data rates of 2.4, 4.8, 9.6, 19.2 and 56 Kbps within a New York State Regional Calling Area (RCA).

DIGIPATH OPTION: SECONDARY CHANNEL CAPABILITY An optional feature for New York Telephone's 56 Kbps Digipath service. It allows customers a second channel at 2.6 Kbps, independent of the primary channel. Customers usually use this "extra" channel for diagnosing the line; for running network management over the same line; or to transmit a second, lower speed data stream through the same line.

DIGIREPEATER Digital Repeater

DIGIT Any whole number from 0 to 9.

DIGIT DELETION It's nice to make it easy for people to dial their desired numbers. Part of making it "nice" is to keep their pattern of dialing consistent. The charm of our ten-digit numbering system in North America -- the three digit area code and seven digit local number -- is its consistency, making for easy use and easy remembering. Some corporate networks, however, don't use a common numbering scheme. They might use tie trunks to get to Chicago, and insist on the user dialing 69, instead of the more common 312 area code. They might insist on the user dialing 73 when he wants to go to Los Angeles. But if he wants to reach the LA office, he might dial 235. This can be awfully confusing. So some switches -- central office and PBXs -- have the ability to insert or delete digits. That is, they will recognize the number dialed and change it as it progresses through the network. The user, however, knows nothing of this. He simply dials a normal phone number and listens as his call progresses normally. Digit insertion and digit deletion are components of a PBX feature called common number dialing.

DIGIT INSERTION See DIGIT DELETION.

DIGITAL 1. In displays, the use of digits for direct readout. 2. In telecommunications, in recording or in computing, digital is the use of a binary code to represent information. See PCM (as in Pulse Code Modulation.) Analog signals -- like voice or music -- are encoded digitally by sampling the voice or music analog signal many times a second and assigning a number to each sample. Recording or transmitting information digitally has two major benefits. First, the signal can be reproduced precisely. In a long telecommunications transmission circuit, the signal will progressively lose its strength and progressively pick up distortions, static and other electrical interference "noises."

In analog transmission, the signal, along with all the garbage it picked up, is simply amplified. In digital transmission, the signal is first regenerated. It's put through a little "Yes-No" question. Is this signal a "one" or a "zero?" The signal is reconstructed (i.e. squared off) to what it was identically. Then it is amplified and sent along its way. So digital transmission is much "cleaner" than analog transmission. The second major benefit of digital is that the electronic circuitry to handle digital is getting cheaper and more powerful. It's the stuff of computers. Analog transmission equipment doesn't lend itself to the technical breakthroughs of recent years in digital. See also PCM, as in Pulse Code Modulation.

DIGITAL ACCESS AND CROSS-CONNECT SYSTEM See DACS and DIGITAL CROSS-CONNECT SYSTEM.

DIGITAL AUDIO The storage and processing of audio signals digitally. It usually requires at least 16 bits of linear coding to represent each digital sample.

DIGITAL AUDIO TAPE See DAT.

DIGITAL CELLULAR The state of the art in cellular communications technology. Implementation will result in substantial increases in capacity (up to 15 times that of analog technology). In addition, digital will virtually eliminate three major problems encountered by users of analog cellular: static, loss/interruption of signal when passing between cells (during handoff), and failure to get a connection because of congested relays. Specifications for TDMA digital systems have been developed in North America (D-AMPS), in Europe (GSM) and in Japan (PDC).

DIGITAL CIRCUIT MULTIPLICATION DCM is a variation of analog TASI -- Time Assigned Speech Interpolation. In DCM, speech is encoded digitally and advanced voice band coding algorithms are applied to TASI's old speech interpolation techniques. DCM delivers a four to fivefold increase in the effective capacity of normal pulse code modulation (PCM) T-1 links operating at 1.544 megabits per second. DCM equipment is used on the TAT-8 transatlantic optical fiber submarine cable. Most DCM equipment has three operating elements: a speech activity detector. An assignment mapping and message unit, and a speech reconstitution unit. See February, 1987 issue of Data Communications for more.

DIGITAL COMMAND SIGNAL Signal sent by a fax machine or card when the caller is transmitting, which tells the answerer how to receive the fax. Modem speed, image width, image encoding and page length are all included in this frame.

DIGITAL COMMUNICATIONS MANAGER DCM. An MCI monitoring system that maintains communications through the network with the Site Controllers, the Extended Super-frame Monitoring Units, and the 1/O DXCs. The DCM issues requests for data and collects alarm and performance information, which is processed and stored in real-time for further computation and display.

DIGITAL COMPACT CASSETTE DCC. A digital version of the familiar analog audio cassette. A DCC recorder can play and record both analog and digital cassettes. But the digital ones will sound a lot better.

DIGITAL CONVERGENCE A Microsoft term for getting all the digital devices of the office and the home together working in a seamless architecture. See AT WORK.

DIGITAL CROSS-CONNECT SYSTEM DACS or DCS. A specialized type of high-speed data channel switch. It differs from a normal voice switch, which switches transmission paths in response to dialing instructions. In a digital cross-connect system, you give it separate and specific instructions to connect this line to that. These instructions are given independently of any calls that might flow over the system. This contrasts with a normal voice switching in which switching instructions and conversations go together. Commands to a digital cross-connect system can be given by an operator at a console or can be programmed to switch at certain times. For example, you might want to change the T-1 24-voice conversation circuit to Chicago at 11 A.M. each day to allow for the president's 30 minute video conference call.

DIGITAL ECHO CANCELLER A Digital Echo Canceller is an echo canceller as opposed to an echo suppressor. An echo canceller filters out unwanted echoes among incoming signals, while the echo suppressor shut-offs the entire signal, by using an analog voice switch. The Digital Echo Canceller is one application of a digital transversal filter.

DIGITAL ENVELOPING Digital enveloping is an application in which someone "seals" a message m in such a way that no one other than the intended recipient, say "Bob," can "open" the sealed message. The typical implementation of digital enveloping involves a secret-key algorithm for encrypting the message (i.e., a content-encryption algorithm) and a public-key algorithm for encrypting the secret key (i.e., a key-encryption algorithm)

DIGITAL ETHERNET LOCAL NETWORK INTERCONNECT Delni. The

product offered by Digital Equipment Corp. that allows up to eight active devices to be connected to a single Ethernet transceiver. A similar device is manufactured by many other suppliers under various names. The DELNI can be thought of as "Ethernet in a box."

DIGITAL FACILITIES MANAGEMENT SYSTEM A Northern Telecom software which integrates the maintenance of all types of digital facilities from T-1 to the high-bit fiber. Largely used by telephone companies.

DIGITAL FACSIMILE EQUIPMENT Facsimile equipment that employs digital techniques to encode the image detected by the scanner. The output signal may be either digital or analog. Examples of digital facsimile equipment are ITU-T Group 3, ITU-T Group 4, STANAG 5000 Type I and STANAG 5000 Type II.

DIGITAL FREQUENCY MODULATION The transmission of digital data by frequency modulation of a carrier, as in binary frequency-shift keying.

DIGITAL LAT PROTOCOL The LAT protocol, announced by Digital in the mid '80s, is today one of the industry's most widely used protocols for supporting character terminals over Ethernet networks. See LAT.

DIGITAL LINE PROTECTION Many extensions behind PBXs deliver greater voltage to the desk than do normal tip and ring analog lines. This higher voltage can damage a PCMCIA modem inside a laptop. In fact, it can destroy the modem. Newer PCMCIA cards (now called PC cards) have Digital Line Protection, which protects against that higher voltage -- what one manufacturer called "innovative isolation circuitry."

DIGITAL LOOPBACK A diagnostic feature on a modem, a short haul microwave or some other digital transmission equipment which allows the user to loop a signal back from one part of the system to another to test the circuit or the equipment. Digital loopbacks can be as long or as short as are necessary to isolate the problem. By looping a signal back and measuring it at both ends of the loop (at the beginning and at the end), you can see if the device carried the message cleanly and is thus, operating correctly.

DIGITAL MICROWAVE A microwave system in which the modulation of the radio frequency carrier is digital. The carrier is still a standard microwave radio wave. The digital modulation may be frequency or phase shift, but the control of that modulation is the digital bit stream.

DIGITAL MONITOR Receives discrete binary signals at two levels; one level corresponds to Logic 1 (true) while the other corresponds to Logic O (false). Monitors generally were of this type before VGA models appeared. Digital monitors do not have as wide a range of color choices as analog types; digital EGA monitors, for example, can display just 16 colors out of a palette of 64.

DIGITAL MULTIPLEXER A device for combining digital signals. Usually implemented by interleaving bits, in rotation, from several digital bit streams either with or without the addition of extra framing, control, or error detection bits. In short, equipment that combines by time division multiplexing several signals into a single composite digital signal.

DIGITAL MULTIPLEX HIERARCHY An ordered scheme for the combining of digital signals by the repeated application of digital multiplexing. Digital multiplexing schemes may be implemented in many different configurations depending upon the number of channels desired, the signaling system to be used, and the bit rate allowed by the communication medium. Some currently available multi-plexers have been designated as D1-, DS-, or M-series, all of which operate at T-carrier rates. Extreme care must be exercised when selecting equipment for a specific system to ensure interoperability, because there are incompatibilities among manufacturers' designs (and various nations' standards).

DIGITAL NETWORK A network in which the information is encoded as a series of ones and zeros rather than as a continuously varying wave -- as in traditional analog networks. Digital networks have several major pluses over analog ones. First, they're "cleaner." They have far less noise, static, etc. Second, they're easier to monitor because you can measure them more easily. Third, you can typically pump more digital information down a communications line than you can analog information.

DIGITAL PHASE-LOCKED LOOP A phase-locked loop in which the reference signal, the controlled signal, or the controlling signal, or any combination of these, is in digital form.

DIGITAL PHASE MODULATION The process whereby the instantaneous phase of the modulated wave is shifted between a set of predetermined discrete values in accordance with the significant conditions of the modulating digital signal.

DIGITAL PORT ADAPTER DPA. A device which provides conversion from the RS449/422 interface to the more common interfaces of RS-232-C, v.35, WE-306 and others.

DIGITAL RECORDING A system of recording by conversion of musical infor-mation into a series of pulses that are translated into a binary code intelligible to computer circuits and stored on magnetic tape or magnetic discs. Also called PCM - Pulse Code Modulation.

DIGITAL REFERENCE SIGNAL DRS. A digital reference signal is a sequence of bits that represents a 1004-Hz to 1020-Hz signal.

DIGITAL SELECTIVE CALLING DSC. A synchronous system developed by the International Radio Consultative Committee (CCIR), used to establish contact with a station or group of stations automatically by radio. The operational and technical characteristics of this system are contained in CCIR Recommendation 493.

DIGITAL SIGNAL A discontinuous signal. One whose state consists of discrete elements, representing very specific information. When viewed on an oscillo-scope, a digital signal is "squared." This compares with an analog signal which typically looks more like a sine wave, i.e. curvey. Usually amplitude is represent-ed at discrete time intervals with a digital value.

DIGITAL SIGNAL PROCESSOR A specialized digital microprocessor that performs calculations on digitized signals that were originally analog (e.g. voice) and then sends the results on. There are two main advantages of DSPs -- first, they have powerful mathematical computational abilities, much more than normal computer microprocessors. DSPs need to have heavy mathematical computation skills because manipulating analog signals requires it. For example, DSPs are often called upon to compress video signals. Each sample must be examined and processed. And all done in very little time. The second advantage of a DSP lies in the programmability of digital microprocessors. Just as digital microprocessors have operating systems, so DSPs are now acquiring their very own operating systems. DSPs are used extensively in telecommunications for tasks such as echo cancellation, call progress monitoring, voice processing and for the compression of voice and video signals. They are also used in devices from fetal monitors, to anti-skid brakes, seismic and vibration sensing gadgets, super-sensitive hearing aids, multimedia presentations and low cost desktop fax machines. DSPs are replacing the dedicated chipsets in modems and fax machines with programmable modules -- which, from one minute to another, can become a fax machine, a modem, a teleconferencing device, an answering machine, a voice digitizer and device to store voice on a hard disk, to a proprietary electronic phone. DSPs will do (and are already doing) for the telecom industry what the general purpose microprocessor (e.g. Intel's 80286 or 80386) did for the personal computer industry. DSPs are made by Analog Devices, AT&T, Motorola, NEC and Texas Instruments, among others.

DIGITAL SIGNATURE The network equivalent of signing a message so that you cannot deny that you sent it and that the recipient knows it must have come from you. In short, an electronic signature which cannot be forged. It verifies that the document originated from the individual whose signature is attached to it and that it has not been altered since it was signed.

DIGITAL SPEECH INTERPOLATION DSI. A type of multiplexing. A way of sharing bandwidth among a larger number of users than we really have circuits for. DSI allocates the silent periods in human speech to active users. At least 50% of a voice conversation is always quiet. The technique was originally called TASI (Time Assigned Speech Interpolation). TASI and DSI are lousy for data because they "clip" the first little bit of every new snippet of conversation -- unless you hog the channel the whole time by talking incessantly or transmitting continuously. If you pause, you'll get clipping as the system drops you and then reconnects you. Clipping can ruin the meaning of the beginning of data conversations, unless the header knows that TASI or DSI is coming up or the data transmission is following some reasonable protocol and can resend the data. Unfortunately, this slows transmission. DSI and TASI are somewhat similar techniques to STATISTICAL MULTIPLEXING.

DIGITAL SUBSCRIBER LINE A fancy name for an ISDN BRI channel. Here's AT&T's definition: "A three-channel digital line that links the ISDN customer's terminal to the telephone company switch with four ordinary copper telephone wires. Operated at the Basic Rate Interface (with two 64-kilobit per second circuit switched channels and one 16-kilobit packet switched channel), the DSL can carry both voice and data signals at the same time, in both directions, as well as the signaling date used for call information and customer data. With the introduction of the AT&T 5E5 generic, up to eight different users can be served by a single DSL." See also ISDN.

DIGITAL SWITCHING A connection in which binary encoded information is routed between an input and an output port by means of time division multiplexing rather than by a dedicated circuit.

DIGITAL TO ANALOG CONVERSION A circuit that accepts digital signals and converts them into analog signals. A modem typically has such a circuit. It also has other circuits, such as those doing with signaling. See MODEM.

DIGITAL VIDEO Digital video is video recorded and played digitally, i.e. in on-on bits. Traditional analog video -- the one we have seen in our homes for eons — is recorded and played back in analog format, i.e. in analog wave forms. Why Digital Video? Due to its versatility, digital video has several advantages over analog video. You can edit it, store it, and transmit it easily. Digital video may be taken from analog source -- such as standard over-the-air National Television Systems Committee (NTSC) analog source. Or it me be taken from an analog video camera and a VCR. To convert analog video into digital video typically requires a board inside a PC. Analog video is typically recorded on tape, such as a VCR. Digital video is typically recorded on a hard disk (magnetic or optical) or on a CD-ROM. Two common digital video technologies are Intel's Digital Video Interactive (DVI) and Microsoft's Audio/Video Interleaved (AVI). See ANALOG, DIGITAL VIDEO INTERACTIVE and INDEO VIDEO.

DIGITAL VIDEO INTERACTIVE DVI. A compression and playback technology originally developed by RCA's Sarnoff Research Institute and eventually acquired by Intel Corp. DVI is not a compression technique per se but a brand name for a set of processor chips that Intel is developing to compress video onto disk and to de-compress it for playback in real time at the U.S. standard motion video rate of 30 frames per second. The chip set includes both a pixel processor, which performs most of the decompression and also handles special video effects, and a display processor, which performs the rest of the decompression and produces the video output. DVI's greatest long-term advantage, according to Nick Arnett writing in PC Magazine, is that its microprocessors are programmable, so DVI can be adapted to a variety of compression and decompression schemes.

DIGITAL VOICE CODING Technology by which linear audio (voice) samples are collected and then compressed using an encoding algorithm. Typically used to store voice data for future decoding.

DIGITIZE Converting an analog or continuous signal into a series of ones and zeros, i.e. into a digital format. See DELTA MODULATION and PULSE CODE MODULATION. See also the Appendix.

DIGITIZED VOICE Analog voice signals represented in digital form. There are many ways of digitizing voice. See PULSE CODE MODULATION for the most common.

DIGITIZER 1. A device that converts an analog signal into a digital representation of that signal. Usually implemented by sampling the analog signal at a regular rate and encoding each sample into a numeric representation of the amplitude value of the sample. 2. A device that converts the position of a point on a surface into digital coordinate data.

DIGROUP Two groups of 12 digital channels combined to form one single 24-channel T-1 system.

DIKES A wire-cutter.

DIL Direct-In-Line. A standard, both-way central office trunk is programmed to always ring a specific extension or hunt group within the PBX. This contrasts with Direct Inward Dialing, which allows an external caller to reach an internal extension by dialing a 7-digit central office number. A DID (Direct Inward Dial) trunk is a trunk from the Central office which passes the last two to four digits of the Listed

Directory Number into the PBX, thus allowing the PBX to switch the call to and thus ring the correct extension.

DILUTION OF PRECISION The multiplicative factor that modifies the ranging error. It is caused solely by the geometry between the user and his set of GPS (Global Positioning System) satellites. Known as DOP or GDOP.

DIM Document Image Management. The electronic access to and manipulation of documents stored in image format, accomplished through the use of automated methods such as high-powered graphical workstations, sophisticated database management techniques and networking.

DIMENSION An analog PBX that used PAM techniques, first introduced in the late 1970s by Western Electric (now AT&T Technologies) for AT&T. Now effectively discontinued except for the hotel/motel version. Some claim Archie McGill was responsible for Dimension. Others claim it was Bob Hawke.

DIMMED In Windows, dimmed means unavailable, disabled, or grayed. A dimmed button or command is displayed in light gray instead of black, and it cannot be chosen.

DIMS Document Image Management System.

DIN Deutsche Institut fur Normung (German Institute for Standardization). DIN specifications are issued under the control of the German government. Some are used on a worldwide basis to specify, for example, the dimensions of cable connectors, often called DIN connectors. See also VME.

DINA Distributed Intelligence Network Architecture.

DIOCES Distributed Interoperable and Operable Computing Environments and Systems.

DIODE This wonderful explanation comes from George Gilder's book Microcosm: "Named from the Greek words meaning two roads, an ordinary diode is one of the simplest and most useful of tools. It is a tiny block of silicon made positive on one side and negative on the other. At each end it has a terminal or electrode (route for electrons). In the middle of the silicon block, the positive side meets the negative side in an electrically complex zone called a positive-negative, or p-n, junction. Because a diode is positive on one side and negative on the other, it normally conducts current only in one direction. Thus diodes play an indispensable role as rectifiers. That is, they can take alternating current (AC) from your wall and convert it into direct current (DC) to run your computer.

"In this role, diodes demonstrate a prime law of electrons. Negatively charged, electrons flow only toward a positive voltage. They cannot flow back against the grain. Like water pressure, which impels current only in the direction of the pressure, voltage impels electrical current only in the direction of the voltage. To attempt to run current against a voltage is a little like attaching a gushing hose to a running faucet.

"It had long been known, however, that if you apply a strong enough voltage against the grain of a diode, the p-n wall or junction will burst. Under this contrary pressure, or reverse bias, the diode will eventually suffer what is called avalanche breakdown. Negative electrons will overcome the p-n barrier by brute force of numbers and flood "uphill" from the positive side to the negative side. In erasable programmable read-only memories (EPROMs), this effect is used in programming computer chips used to store permanent software, such as the Microsoft operating system in your personal computer (MS-DOS). Avalanche breakdown is also used in Zener diodes to provide a stable source of voltage unaffected by changes in current."

DIODE MATRIX RINGING A method of connecting a common audible line to a system so that all stations do not ring on all lines. See also MATRIX RINGING.

DIODEA A semiconductor device which allows electricity to pass through it in only one direction, restricting flow the other way.

DIP 1. See DIP SWITCH. 2. Document Image Processing. A term for converting paperwork into electronic images manipulable by a computer. Components of include input via scanner, storage on optical media and output via video display terminal, printer, fax, micrographics, etc.

DIP SWITCH Dual In-Line Package. A teeny tiny switch usually attached to a printed circuit board. It may peek through an opening in a piece of equipment. It may not. It usually requires a ball point pen or small screwdriver to change. There are only two settings -- on or off. Or 1 or 0. But printed circuit boards often have many DIP switches. They're used to configure the board in a semipermanent way. The DIP switches are similar to integrated circuit chips which have two rows (dual) of pins in a row (in-line) that fit into holes on a printed circuit board. If something doesn't work when you first install it, check the dip switches first. Then check the cable connecting it to something else.

DIPLEXER A device that permits parallel feeding of one antenna from two transmitters at the same or different frequencies without the transmitters interfering with each other. Diplexers couple transmitter and receiver to the same antenna for use in mobile communications.

DIPOLE Antenna fed from the center. Name often applied to "rabbit ear" antenna.

DIRECT BOND An electrical connection using continuous metal-to-metal contact between the things being joined.

DIRECT BROADCAST SATELLITE DBS. A satellite transmitting TV programs which can be received by small and somewhat inexpensive dish antennas often installed in back yards or on the roofs of houses. Direct broadcast satellites have generated more interest in Europe, which suffers from a lack of TV programs (good and bad), than in the U.S. which has plenty. The back yard satellite antennas you see in America are not receiving signals from Direct Broadcast Satellites. They are receiving them from satellites designed to transmit and receive from large, commercial dishes.

DIRECT CONNECT A term describing a customer hooking directly into a long-distance telephone company's switching office, bypassing the local phone company. Such "direct connect" could be via a leased copper pair, a specially-run copper pair, a fiber optic or a private microwave system. See DIRECT ELECTRICAL CONNECTION, which is different. See DIRECT CONNECT MODEM.

DIRECT CONNECT MODEM A modem connected to telephone lines using a modular plug or wired directly to the outside phone line. It thus transfers electrical signals directly to the phone network without any intermediary protective device. Direct connect modems must be certified by the FCC. Direct connect modems are more much reliable and more accurate than acoustically coupled modems. Virtually all modems these days are directly connected. One day pay phones will even come with RJ-11 jacks into which you can plug the modem of your portable laptop computer.

DIRECT CONNECTION Connection of terminal equipment to the telephone network by means other than acoustic and/or inductive coupling.

DIRECT CONTROL SWITCHING The switching path is set up directly through the network by dial pulses without the use of central control. The telex network is an example of direct control switching. A step by step central office also uses direct control switching.

DIRECT CURRENT DC. A flow of electricity always in the same direction. Contrast with alternate current (AC).

DIRECT CURRENT SIGNALING DX. A method whereby the signaling circuit E & M leads use the same cable pair as the voice circuit and no filter is required to separate the control signals from the voice transmission.

DIRECT DEPARTMENT CALLING DDC. A telephone service that routes incoming calls on a specific trunk or group of trunks to specific phones or groups of phones.

DIRECT DISTANCE DIALING DDD. A telephone service which lets a user dial long distance calls directly to telephones outside the user's local service area without operator assistance.

DIRECT ELECTRICAL CONNECTION A metallic connection between two things. The normal electrical way of connecting two things. This dumb definition is included in this dictionary because there was a time back in the early 1970s and before, when you couldn't (i.e. weren't allowed to) directly electrically connect your own phone or phone system to the nation's phone network. Those were the "good old days" when they (the Bell System) were trying to convince the world that electrically connecting anyone else's phones could harm the network. They never did prove this, and so today we have direct electrical connection of FCC-certified phone equipment. It's certified so it won't cause any harm to the network. See PART 68.

DIRECT IN LINE See DIL.

DIRECT IN TERMINATION Incoming calls on a PBX may be programmed to route directly to pre selected telephones without the attendant intervening. DIT features may be assigned to trunk circuits on a day, night or full time basis. Direct In Termination is slightly different from DIRECT INWARD DIALING, though how different depends on whose PBX you're using.

DIRECT INTERLATA CONNECTING TRUNK GROUPS Those trunk groups used for switched LATA access that interconnect Interexchange Carriers (IXCs) used to connect that Point of Presence (POPs) directly with the Bell Operating Company (BOC) end office switching system.

DIRECT INWARD DIALING DID. The ability for a caller outside a company to call an internal extension without having to pass through an operator or attendant. In large PBX systems, the dialed digits are passed down the line from the CO (central office). The PBX then completes the call. Direct Inward Dialing is often proposed as Centrex's major feature. See also DIRECT INWARD SYSTEM ACCESS (DISA) for another approach to DID.

DIRECT INWARD SYSTEM ACCESS DISA. This feature of a telephone system allows an outside caller to dial directly into the telephone system and to access all the system's features and facilities. DISA is typically used for making long distance calls from home using the company's less expensive long distance lines, like WATS or tie lines. It's also used for leaving dictation for the typing pool. With DISA, you can dial individual extensions without the aid (or hindrance) of an operator. To use DISA, one must punch in from your touchtone phone a short string of numbers as a password code.

The problem with DISA is that "phone phreakers" (i.e. unauthorized people) often acquire that number or figure it out and run up expensive long distance phone calls. It's best to restrict DISA to trusted people and check the numbers called and bills generated. Changing the password code from time to time can help prevent this. DISA is acquiring a whole new life. It's becoming something called AUTO-MATED ATTENDANT. An additional piece of equipment, called an automated attendant, is placed next to the phone system. You dial a special phone number (as you do with DISA). You're answered by a recording that says "Dial the extension you want." In DISA, the response is typically just a tone. An automated attendant is designed to save on operators and speed up outside people getting to talk to your inside people. Automated attendant is being suggested as a lower cost alternative to Centrex.

The following is excerpted from a document Northern Telecom sent to its PBX users. Read it. It's well-done:

PBX features that are vulnerable to unauthorized access include call forwarding, call prompting and call processing features. But the most common ways hackers enter a company's PBX is through Direct Inward System Access (DISA) and voice mail systems. They often search a company's trash for directories or call detail reports that contain 800 numbers and codes. They have also posed as systems administrators and conned employees into telling them PBX authorization codes. More "sophisticated" hackers use personal computers and modems to break into databases containing customer records showing phone numbers and voice mail access codes, or simply dial 800 numbers with the help of sequential number generators and computers until they find one code that gives access to a phone system. Once these thieves have the numbers and codes, they can call into the PBX and place calls out to other locations. In many cases, the PBX is only the first point of entry for such criminals. They can also use the PBX to access the company's data system. Call-sell operators can even hide their activities from law enforcement officials by using "PBX-looping" - using one PBX to place calls out through another switch in another state.

To minimize the vulnerability of the Meridian 1 system to unauthorized access through DISA, the following safeguards are suggested:

1) Assign restricted Class of Service, TGAR and NCOS to the DISA DN. 2) Require users to enter a security code upon reaching the DISA DN. 3) In addition to a security code, require users to enter an authorization code. The calling privileges provided will be associated with the specific authorization code. 4) Use Call Detail Recording (CDR) to identify calling activity associated with individual authorization codes. As a further precaution, you may choose to limit printed copies of these records. 5) Change security codes frequently. 6) Limit access to administration of authorization codes to a few, carefully selected employees.

DIRECT LINE TERMINATIONS The term refers to central office/PBX lines which terminate directly on telephones, and are generally common to all instruments within the system. In a square configuration on a Key Telephone System, these lines must appear at the same button location on each phone.

DIRECT MEMORY ACCESS DMA is a technique in which on adapter bypasses a computer's CPU, and handles the transfer of data between itself and the system's memory directly.

DIRECT OUTWARD DIALING DOD. The ability to dial directly from an extension without having to go through an operator or attendant. In PBX and hybrid phone systems, you dial 9, listen for a dial tone, and then dial the number you want to reach. In some phone systems, you don't have to listen for the second dial tone. You can dial straight through. All phone systems now have DOD. The older ones didn't, especially cordboard PBXs. Some Club Meds and lots of cheap hotels (especially the ones Harry -- the editor -- stays in) do not have DOD.

DIRECT STATION SELECT DSS. A piece of key system equipment usually attached to an operator's phone set. When the operator needs to call a particular extension he/she simply touches the corresponding button on the Direct Station Select equipment. Typically DSS equipment/feature is part of a Busy Lamp Field (BLF), which shows with lights what's happening at each extension. Is it busy? Is it on hold? Is it ringing? See BUSY LAMP FIELD.

DIRECT STATION SELECT INTERCOM DSS. An interoffice caller can punch one button on his or her phone and dial his desired person, instead of dialing the full intercom number. Direct station select is like having an auto dial or speed dial button for everyone in the office. DSS saves time, but adds more buttons to the phone -- one button for each extension the user wants to dial.

DIRECT TERMINATION OVERFLOW DTO. An optional MCI Vnet and 800 Service feature, which allows a call to "overflow" to shared lines for completion by the local telephone company if the dedicated line is busy.

DIRECT TRUNK A trunk between two class 5 central offices.

DIRECT TRUNK ACCESS A PBX feature. By dialing some digits, the attendant can directly access any specific trunk. You'd do this if you want to check the trunk for problems, etc.

DIRECT TRUNK SELECT Permits you, the user, the attendant, or an attached computer telephony system to access an individual outgoing trunk instead of one chosen by the PBX from a group of trunks. You may want to grab a special trunk to get access to a specially conditioned data line, for example. Direct trunk select is particularly important in testing computer telephony systems and facilities as it is usually the best method to use to address specific ports on a VRU (Voice Response Unit) or switching system.

DIRECTED CALL PICKUP An extension user on a phone system user can answer calls -- ringing or holding -- on any other phone by dialing a unique answer code. If the call has already been answered by the called phone, the user who dials the answer code will join the connection in conference. Some tones will alert the conversing parties to the intrusion.

DIRECTIONAL ANTENNA An antenna which impels electrical waves with more energy in one direction than in another, or which receives electrical waves more readily from one direction than from another.

DIRECTIONAL COUPLER 1. A device put in a microwave system's waveguide to couple a transmitter and receiver to the same antenna.

2. A transmission coupling device for separately sampling (through a known coupling loss) either the forward (incident) or the backward (reflected) wave in a transmission line. A directional coupler may be used to sample either a forward or backward wave in a transmission line. A unidirectional coupler has available terminals or connections for sampling only one direction of transmission; a bidirectional coupler has available terminals for sampling both directions. For optical fiber applications.

DIRECTORIES Are places within a hard disk volume where you can store files or subdirectories. The term subdirectory is relative. A directory is a subdirectory only in relation to the directory above it. To a directory below it, the same directory is a parent directory.

DIRECTORY 1. A list of all the files on a floppy diskette or hard disk. A directory may also contain other information such as the size of the files and the amount of free space remaining. 2. Also a telephone directory.

DIRECTORY ASSISTANCE DA. Formerly known as "Information", but changed because they were getting too many stupid questions. DA is provided by the local telephone company. It allows the subscriber to call for phone numbers. In most states, the local phone company charges for this service, or will begin to very shortly. AT&T and MCI charge for long distance directory assistance. Most local phone companies will give you the person's address as well as his phone number if you ask for it.

DIRECTORY CACHING A method of decreasing the time it takes to find a file's location on a PC's disk. The FAT (File Allocation Table) and directory entry table are written into the file server's memory. The area holding all directory entries is called the directory cache. The file server can find a file's address (from directory cache) and the file data (from the file cache) much faster than retrieving the information from disk.

DIRECTORY INFORMATION BASE DIB. Made up of information about objects. The collective information held in the directory. An X.500 term.

DIRECTORY INFORMATION TREE DIT. Information that outlines the structure of an X.500 directory.

DIRECTORY NAME As defined in the X.500 Recommendations, the Directory Name is an ITU term for the name of a directory entry. For example, used to retrieve an O/R (Originator/Recipient) Name for message submission.

DIRECTORY NUMBER 1. The full complement of digits associated with the name of a subscriber in a telephone directory. This is a very long way of saying the obvious, namely your phone number. 2. A unique phone number which is automatically assigned to each telephone or Data Terminal during System Startup. The DN, also referred to as an intercom number, is often used to identify a telephone when settings are assigned during programming.

DIRECTORY PACKAGE The process of adding, deleting and moving people attached to PBX or Centrex phones is more than simply programming in new extensions. Or should be. First, there are the changes necessary for the call accounting system. Second, there are changes necessary for "The Corporate Phone Directory". In the past, the directory bore little relation to the telephone system and it was often months, and sometimes years behind the actual phone system. Now some phone systems are incorporating various Directory Software Packages into the PBXs.

Some features included in these systems are the ability to dial someone by name -- both for the attendant and for the individual phone user, i.e. dial HARRY, or HAR, instead of 3245. Some also include the ability to interface to the call accounting system. So that who's in what corporate department corresponds to which department's bill. There's also that important thing called a Telephone Directory. It would be useful if you could hook a laser printer to the telephone system and tell it to print, in neat, photo-ready columns, an alphabetical (by last name), departmental or any other sorted telephone directory. Some of the newer PBXs have "directory package" features which include some or all of the above. Most users find today's necessity of at least three different systems to be a pain in the behind. Rightly so. The three different systems are CDR, phone directory and extension dialing in the PBX. The three are often out of synch.

DIRECTORY REPLICATION A Windows NT term. The copying of a master set of directories from a server (called an export server) to specified servers or workstations (called an import computers) in the same or other domains. Replication simplifies the task of maintaining identical sets of directories and files on multiple computers, because only a single master copy of the data must be maintained. Files are replicated when they are added to an exported directory and every time a change is saved to the file.

DIRECTORY REPLICATOR SERVICE A Windows NT term. Replicates directories, and the files in those directories, between computers. See DIRECTORY REPLICATION.

DIRECTORY SERVICE 1. A simple term for the information service which the telephone company runs on 411 or 555-1212. 2. A computer networking term. The facility within networking software that provides information on resource available on the network, including files, users, printers, data sources, applications, and so on. The directory service provides users with access to resources and information on extended networks.

DIRECTORY SERVICES A service that provides information about network objects. DNS (Domain name System) provides node address information. An X.500 Directory service provides any appropriate information an enterprise wishes to include in the X.500 directory itself.

DIRECTORY SYNCHRONIZATION The reconciliation of user directories from two electronic mail post offices. Many gateways and messaging switches have software to automate reconciliating these directories.

DIRECTORY TREE A list of directories. A directory tree looks like an organizational chart and shows how your directories and subdirectories are related. Our favorite program that shows the directory tree in your hard disk is called CTREE. You can pick it up from many electronic bulletin boards for free, including from TELECONNECT Magazine's on 212-989-4675.

DIRECTTALK DirectTalk is IBM's family of voice processing products, introduced in 1991. According to IBM, its new CallPath DirectTalk product line lets business automate routine operations and also provide callers with easy access to many kinds of information over the telephone. There are two versions of DirectTalk: DirectTalk/2 which requires OS/2 Version 2, and runs on any OS/2 certified Microchannel (MCA) or Industry Standard Architecture (ISA) bus personal computer; DirectTalk/6000 which requires AIX and runs on any IBM RISC System/6000. DirectTalk has features, including:

Application Developers tools and aids, 3270 and 5250 terminal emulation support, Voice recognition, Text to speech, Telecommunications Devices for the Deaf (TDD), Analog/T1/E1 support, Dynamic invocation of multiple applications, Voice messaging, Integrated Voice mail support (DirectTalk/6000 only), and integration with CallPath CallCoordinator. DirectTalk/2 ranges from 2 to 48 voice ports with voice storage capacity in excess of 100 hours. DirectTalk/6000 ranges from 12 to 96 voice port with voice storage capacity over 144,000 hours. See also CALLPATH SERVICES ARCHITECTURE.

DIRTBAGS Digitally Initiated Resale of Telecommunications Bypass Applications by Scumbags. A term created by Ron Adams of Marylhurst College in Washington. There is some confusion between another definition — Digitally Initiated Reorigination of Telecommunications Bypass Access Generated by Scumbags. It is ascribed to Karen Corcoran of MCI's Atlanta office to describe as a group the various hackers, phreakers, and others who invade our networks and/or steal long distance service.

DIRTY POWER Dirty power typically refers to alternating current that is not a perfect sine wave and not perfectly 120 volt. There are all sorts of ways electricity can be made "dirty." It can be affected by spikes. Spikes are transient impulses (sometimes called glitches) of relatively high amplitude but very short duration. Spikes so short that a very high-speed oscilloscope is needed to observe them can often cause problems. Many spikes can occur in a fraction of a cycle.

Power can also be affected by sags and surges. Sags and surges are rapid changes in the amplitude of an AC voltage. These are generally caused by abrupt changes in the load on a power source or circuit (such as when an air conditioner starts up), and can range from a fraction of a cycle to several complete cycles. Power can also be delivered consistently beyond its rating. In New York Con Edison guarantees 120 volts plus or minus 10%. Any level below 108 volts or above 132 volts Con Edison would consider dirty power. These are called low or high average variations. And they occur when the average voltage is above or below a desired level for significant periods of time, usually measured in seconds, minutes or longer.

Other kinds of dirty power include: Blackouts or brownouts. They occur when the power is switched off or lost completely (blackout), or when the voltage feeding a load is deliberately or inadvertently reduced significantly for a sustained period (brownout). Common mode noise is a small (+1V-2V) signal that appears between a neutral line and ground (earth) where there should be no signal. High/low frequency variations occur when the instantaneous frequency of an AC power source differs from its normal frequency, e.g., 60 Hz, by 0.5 Hz or more. Phase angle variations can be observed in three-phase systems whenever the phase relationships vary from their normal 120-degrees.

DIS Draft International Standard. As specified by ISO, a development step representing near final status on a specification. Once a specification has reached DIS status, companies are encouraged to develop actual products based on it.

DISA 1. Direct Inward System Access. DISA is a way of dialing into a phone system. It's been the major way crooks have dialed into PBXs and stolen toll calls. See DIRECT INWARD SYSTEM ACCESS. 2. Data Interchange Standards Association, Inc. DISA is the Secretariat and administrative arm of the Accredited Standards Committee (ASC) X12 which has responsibility for developing Electronic Data Interchange (EDI) standards. DISA OnLine is an electronic messaging and information system designed for use by DISA's member constituency. www.disa.org

DISABLE You figured this one. It means to prevent a hardware device from working. Unplugging it is the easiest way. It also refers to a tone or other signal which you send over a phone line to disable the equipment at the other end.

DISASTER RECOVERY

DISC An older method of spelling DISK, as in Floppy DISK. Disc (spelled with a C) is now more commonly used to refer to optical storage devices, like CD (Compact Discs) and MO (Magneto Optical) discs. See also MS-DOS.

DISCHARGE BLOCK A protective device through which unwanted voltages discharge to ground.

DISCO TECH Slang expression for a technician who only handles disconnections.

DISCONNECT 1. The breaking or release of a circuit connecting two telephones or data devices. 2. The occasional April Fools issue of TELECONNECT Magazine, New York City. Sometimes funny. Sometimes not.

DISCONNECT FRAME Indicates in a fax call that the call is done. The sending fax machine sends the disconnect frame before hanging it. It does not wait for a response.

DISCONNECT SIGNAL The signal sent from one end to indicate to the other to shut down the connection.

DISCONNECT SUPERVISION The change in electrical state from off-hook to on-hook. This indicates that the transmission connection is no longer needed.

DISCONNECT SWITCH In a power system, a switch used for closing, opening, or changing the connections in a circuit or system or for purposes of isolation. It has no interrupting rating and is intended to be operated only after the circuit has been opened by some other means, such as by a circuit breaker or variable transformer.

DISCONTINUITY An interruption or drop out of the optical signal.

DISCO TECH Slang expression for a technician who only handles disconnections.

DISCOUNTED PAYBACK PERIOD The number of years in which a stream of cash flows, discounted at an organization's cost of money, repays an initial investment.

DISCOUNTING The process of computing the present worth of a future cash flow by reducing it by a factor equivalent to the organization's cost of money (or some other measure of the value of money as measured by an interest rate) and the time until the cash flow occurs.

DISCRETE In voice recognition, refers to an isolated word. A discrete word is preceded and followed by silence, hence isolated in speech. Discrete words need to be separated by about half a second of silence when spoken to a discrete recognizer.

DISCRETE COSINE TRANSFORM DCT. A pixel-block based process of formatting video data where it is converted from a three dimensional form to a two dimensional form suitable for further compression. In the process the average luminance of each block or tile is evaluated using the DC coefficient. Used in the ITU-T's Px64 videoconferencing compression standard and in the ISO/ITU-T's MPEG and JPEG image compression recommendations.

DISCRETE MULTI-TONE See DMT.

DISCRETIONARY PREVIEW DIALING A single button dialing technique where the agent initiates a call with a single key stroke. Often used in association with a CRT tied to a database. Upon hitting a single button the system selects the phone number field from the screen and dials the number. Contrast this with Forced Preview Dialing. When the call ends, the computer brings up the next screen and starts dialing the call without the agent helping or hindering.

DISCRIMINATING RINGING See DISTINCTIVE RINGING.

DISCUSSION A method of confirming others in their errors.

DISENGAGEMENT DENIAL Disengagement failure due to excessive delay by the telecommunication system.

DISENGAGEMENT FAILURE Failure of a disengagement attempt to return a communication system to the idle state, for a given user, within a specified maximum disengagement time.

DISH Typically a parabolic microwave antenna -- used for receiving line-of-sight terrestrial signals or signals from satellites.

DISK A piece of plastic or metal upon which a coating has been applied and which can thus, record computer information magnetically. The present convention is that a "disk" with a K refers to magnetic storage, while "disc" with a C refers to optical storage. See also MS-DOS.

DISK ARRAY A disk subsystem combined with management software which controls the operation of the physical disks and presents them as one or more virtual disks to the host computer.

DISK CACHE On a PC, a disk cache is the part of RAM that is set aside to temporarily hold data read from disk. A disk cache doesn't have to hold an entire file, as a RAM disk does, but can hold parts of running application software or parts of a data file. Disk-caching software manages the process of swapping data to and from the disk cache. See DISK CACHING.

DISK CACHING A technique used to speed up processing. Each time your application retrieves data from the disk, a special program, called a disk caching program, stores data read from the disk in an area of RAM. When the application next requests more data, some of it may already be in RAM, thereby dramatically speeding the retrieval of data. See DISK CACHE and CACHING.

DISK CONTROLLER A hardware device that controls how data is written to and retrieved from the disk drive. The disk controller sends signals to the disk drive's logic board to regulate the movement of the head as it reads data from or writes data from or writes data to the disk.

DISK DANCERS Teenagers who uses the AOL disks given away in magazines and via direct mail to hop from one free account to another.

DISK DRIVE A device containing motors, electronics and other gadgetry for storing (writing) and retrieving (reading) data on a disk. See DISK DUPLEXING, DISK MIRRORING, DISK OPERATING SYSTEM and other definitions below starting with the work "Disk." See also IDE and ENHANCED IDE.

DISK DRIVE PERFORMANCE Three basic things affect your perception of the speed of your hard disk drive: 1. The disk transfer rate —the speed at which data can be read from or written to the drive's media. This speed is governed mainly by drive mechanics — especially rotational speed, latency and seek time. 2. The controller transfer rate — the speed at which the drive's controller electronics can move data across the interface. This is governed by the design of the drive controller. 3. The host transfer rate — the speed at which the computer can transfer data across the interface. This is a matter of both CPU and bus speeds as well as the hardware that provides the bridge between the host bus and the disk interface.

DISK DUPLEXING A method of failsafe protection, used on file servers on local area networks. Disk duplexing involves copying data onto two duplicate hard disks, each using a separate controllers and a separate disk channel. Disk duplexing protects data against the failure of a hard disk or of the hard disk channel between the disk and the file server. The hard disk "channel" includes the disk controller and interface cable. If any component on one channel fails, the other channel continues to operate normally. (You hope.) The operating system sends a warning message to the workstations to indicate the failure. It's a good idea then to fix the problem fast. See also DISK MIRRORING.

DISK MIRRORING A technique for protecting the information on your hard disk. Disk mirroring writes data simultaneously to two identical hard disks using the same hard disk controller. Here's how it works: You have a special hard disk controller card. That's the card which organizes getting information into and off your hard disk. When you come to write information to your hard disk, your hard disk controller writes first to the first hard disk, called the primary hard disk. The controller retains that information in its memory and then writes it to the second hard disk. This causes a 50% degradation in performance since it now takes twice as long to write to the disk. When the controller comes to read, it reads only from the primary disk. Thus there is no performance degradation in reading. Mirroring is designed to protect against mechanical problems with one of your hard disks. If one of the hard disks break, the other one will take over instantly. You will get a warning message. You will be told to repair the broken disk and you will be told to designate the other disk now as your primary disk (it may already be). That primary disk will now become your bootable disk, the one you boot your computer from. Mirroring does not protect against viruses, or corrupt data or losing data. Any idiocy you can perform on one hard disk you can now happily perform on two. Mirroring does not protect you against a lightning strike which could knock out both your hard disks. Mirroring does not protect against the loss of a controller card since you're only using one. Another protection technique called disk duplexing uses two separate controllers to drive two separate hard disks. See also DISK DUPLEXING.

DISK OPERATING SYSTEM See DOS.

DISK PACK A series of disks mounted horizontally and arranged as a single unit. A disk pack contains more space for storing and retrieving information than one single disk.

DISK SECTOR Magnetic diskettes are typically divided into tracks, each of which contains a number of sectors. A sector typically contains a predetermined amount of data, such as 256 bytes.

DISK SERVER A device equipped with disks and a program that permits users to create and store files on the disks. Each user has access to their own section of the disk. It gives users disk space which they would not normally have at their own personal computers. The disk server is linked to the PCs via a LAN. The next level of sophistication would be a file server, which would allow users to share files.

DISK STRIPING Writing data in stripes across a volume that has been created form areas of free space on from 2 to 32 disks. A Windows NT definition.

DISK SUBSYSTEM A collection of physical disks and the hardware required to connect them to a host computer or network.

DISK/FILE SERVER A mass storage device that can be accessed by several computers, usually through a local area network (LAN).

DISKLESS PC Just what it says: a PC without a disk drive. Used on a LAN, a diskless PC runs by booting DOS from the file server. It does this via a read-only memory chip on its network interface card called a remote boot ROM. Diskless PCs are cheaper than PCs with disks, they're more compact and they offer better security since users can't make off with floppy disks of important and sensitive data or add their own virus-ridden programs to file servers. Diskless PCs appeal primarily to users interested in security. One system of diskless PCs allow the system operator to disable and physically lock the machine's various ports and the computer case itself. Should something go wrong with the machine, the ports can be restored to operating condition by letting the system allow a technician to attach a laptop computer and run diagnostic programs.

DISKLESS WORKSTATION See DISKLESS PC.

DISN Defense Information Systems Network.

DISOSS IBM's Distributed Office Support System.

DISPERSION A term used to describe how an electromagnetic signal is distorted because the various frequency components of that signal have different propagation characteristics. Dispersion is the degree of scattering taking place in the light beam as it travels along the fiber optic. Or the overlapping of a light signal on one wavelength to different wavelengths because of reflected rays and the different refractive index of the core fiber material.

DISPERSION-SHIFTED SINGLE-MODE FIBERS These types of fibers have a different internal configuration. This changes the zero total chromatic dispersion point to 1550nm. This is important because the attenuation at this wavelength is only about half as much as at 1300nm.

DISPLAY The visual presentation of information, usually on a TV-like screen or an array of illuminated digits.

DISPLAY DRIVER A piece of software which translate instructions from the software you are running into thousands of colored dots, or pixels, that appear on your video monitor. A display driver is also called a Video Driver. Symptoms of a video driver giving trouble can range from colors that don't look right, to horizontal flashing lines to simply a black screen. In the Macintosh world, Apple rigidly defined video drivers. Windows, in contrast, is a free-for-all. Windows 3.1 defined the lowest common denominator of displays -- namely 16 colors at 640 x 480 pixels. But most multimedia programs and many games won't run with only 16 colors. They require at least 256 colors.

DISTANCE SENSITIVE PRICING Product pricing based on the distance (airline mileage) between the originating and terminating locations of a call/data transmission.

DISTANCE LEARNING Video and audio technologies into education so students can attend classes in a location distant from where the course is being presented.

DISTANCE VECTOR An approach, or algorithm, used by network equipment in selecting the best available network path by calculating the total distance over which a packet would travel on each alternative route. The shortest distance is usually the most preferred, however, it is possible to consider other factors in the decision as well.

DISTANT LEARNING A Pacific Bell term for students sitting in front of TVs and phones and participating in classes that are being held and delivered elsewhere. In one of PacBell's trials, they used a T-1 signal, so the distant lecturer could see and hear his distant students using full-color video.

DISTINCTIVE DIAL TONES In some phone systems, dial tones sound different. An internal dial tone sounds different to an external dial tone. The logical reason for this is simply to alert the user as to whether he or she is making an intercom or an outside local or long distance call.

DISTINCTIVE RINGING Enables telephone users to distinguish types of incoming calls such as outside calls and inside (intercom) calls by the tone of the ringing.

DISTORT To change some characteristic of a signal during its transmission. See DISTORTION.

DISTORTION 1. The difference in values between two measurements of a signal -- for example, between the transmitted and received signal. "Distortion" typically refers to analog signals. 2. In imaging, distortion is any deformation of the on-screen image. Two common types of distortion are pincushion and barrel.

DISTRIBUTED CAPACITY The capacity in a coil due to the proximity of the turns.

DISTRIBUTED COMMON CONTROL There are two elements of telephone switching: The switching itself and the control of that switching. The earliest step-by-step telephone switches had their "Control" built into them. The dialing information at the beginning of the call physically moved switches. You could say, as a result, that control was distributed throughout the switching system. Then came the 1940s and crossbar exchanges, and the economics pointed to centralizing control. Then came computerized or stored program control (SPC) switches in which large computers were used centrally to perform virtually all the functions of the erstwhile electromechanical senders, registers, markers, etc. -- those things which affect the setting up and tearing down of the call. As computers got smaller and as microprocessors appeared (the so-called computer on a chip), it became economical and efficient to place inexpensive microprocessors in the telephone circuits themselves, in essence getting much of the processing done before it hits the central processing unit. Increasingly, as special microprocessors (so-called "computers on a chip") for telecommunications evolve, we will see more and more of the processing being distributed to further and further away from the central point and closer and closer to the originating telephone instrument. It will be rare in coming years for telephones to come without microprocessors. One day, each phone will have its own switch and the rest of the system will just be one gigantic loop of cable -- not unlike today's local area networks.

DISTRIBUTED COMPUTING ENVIRONMENT DCE. A new idea from Digital Equipment Corporation. Distributed Computing Environment (DCE) is a comprehensive integrated set of services that supports the development, use, and maintenance of distributed applications. Digital's DCE is an implementation of the Open Software Foundation's DCE (OSF DCE). In response to OSF's request for distributed computing technology, Digital submitted for consideration four of Digital's established distributed computing technologies:

Remote Procedure Call (RPC), a joint effort with HP/Apollo; Threads Service, based on Digital DECthreads; Cell Directory Service (CDS), based on the Digital Distributed Name Service (DECdns); Distributed Time Service (DTS), based on the Digital Distributed Time Service (DECdts).

DISTRIBUTED DATA PROCESSING DDP. A data processing arrangement in which the computers are decentralized -- i.e. scattered in various places. Hence, processing occurs in a number of distributed locations and only semi-processed information is communicated on data communications lines from remote points to the central computers. The object of DDP is to save telecommunications charges and to improve network response time.

DISTRIBUTED ENVIRONMENT Refers to a network environment, or topology, in which decision making, file storage and other network functions are not centralized but instead are found through the network. This type of environment is typical for client-server applications and peer-to-peer architectures.

DISTRIBUTED FILE SYSTEM A type of file system in which the file system itself manages and transparently locates pieces of information from remote files and distributes files across a network. It can recognize multiple servers and be accessed independently of where it physically resides on the network.

DISTRIBUTED MANAGEMENT ENVIRONMENT A compilation of technologies now being selected by the Open Software Foundation to create a unified network and systems management framework, as well as applications. Those technologies will complement OSF's own Unix implementation, OSF/1, as well as other operating systems.

DISTRIBUTED MICROPROCESSOR COMMON CONTROL This means that the system employs many individual microprocessors to control system and telephone phone functions. The microprocessors may be located in central processing equipment or in the telephones themselves.

DISTRIBUTED NAME SERVICE A technique for storing network node names so that the information is stored throughout the network (either one LAN or many joined together), and can be requested from, and supplied by, any node.

DISTRIBUTED NETWORK SERVICE Introduced in March 1991, AT&T's Distributed Network Service was designed expressly for the switchless resale community unlike SDN. It allows resellers to purchase large volumes of services and receive progressive discounts on all direct dial domestic and international calls. Resellers may designate any number of locations to participate in the plan with the flexibility of adding locations.

DISTRIBUTED NODES PBX and its "slave" switches which are physically in separate buildings, in separate areas of the campus, in separate parts of the town.

DISTRIBUTED PROCESSING A network of computers such that the processing of information is initiated in local computers, and the resultant data is sent to a central computer for further processing with the data from other local systems. The term also covers computing jobs "farmed out" from a central site to remote processors where faster processing or specialized databases are available. Distributed Processing is often a more efficient use of computer processing power since each CPU can be devoted to a certain task. A LAN is the perfect example of distributed processing. See also DISTRIBUTED DATA PROCESSING.

DISTRIBUTED QUEUE DUAL BUS DQDB. A connectionless packet-switched protocol, normally residing in the Medium-Access Control sublayer of the data link layer. Definition from Bellcore in reference to Advanced Intelligent Network.

DISTRIBUTED SWITCHING When electronics and computers were expensive it made sense to centralize them and run individual lines out for miles to subscribers. Then the economies changed. Electronics and computers became cheaper and running phone lines for miles became very expensive. So switching companies started building small switches which they could put closer to subscribers. Thus, individual local loops would be shorter and the long lines going back to the larger central office would be more efficiently used -- namely by more people. The remote, or distributed switches, are called everything from remote switches to slave switches (because they slave off the main one which is distant). Usually these remote switches are unattended.

DISTRIBUTION Refers to the arrangement of premises wiring runs and their associated hardware required to implement the planned customer premises wiring system extending from the Network Interface Jack to each Communications Outlet.

DISTRIBUTION CABLE Part of the outside cable plant connecting feeder or subfeeder cables to drop wires or buried service wires that connect to the customer's premises. In simpler language, it's the cable from the serving area interface -- a box on a pole, in the ground, etc. -- to the lightning protection at the entrance to the customer's premises. See also FEEDER PLANT and DROP WIRE.

DISTRIBUTION CABLE, INSIDE PLANT Cables usually running horizontally from a closet on a given floor within a building. Distribution cables may be under carpet, simplex, duplex, quad, or higher fiber count cables.

DISTRIBUTION CABLE, OUTSIDE PLANT The cable running from a central office or remote terminal to the side of a subscriber's lot.

DISTRIBUTION FRAME Cables coming in from thousands of subscribers need to connect to the correct ports on a central office. Similarly, cables coming in from many PBX extensions need to connect to the PBX. The cables could be directly wired to the CO or to the PBX. This would be inflexible. It would make future moves and changes a nightmare. So the solution is something called a Distribution Frame. Basically it's a giant wire connecting devices made of metal. There are no electronics in it whatsoever. On one side we punch down the wires coming in from the outside world. On the other side, we punch down the wires coming in from the CO or PBX. Both sides are connected with wire that's called "jumper" wire. By pulling off one end of the jumper wire and moving it to another location we can quickly change phone numbers, add or subtract cabling (one, two or three pairs for normal or electronic phones, etc.). In big central offices, distribution frames can span whole city blocks and the "jumper" wires can be several hundred yards long. Designing distribution frames and their layout in advance is critical, otherwise it becomes a mess and tracing where jumper wires go becomes an enormously time consuming job.

DISTRIBUTION GROUP 1. A group made of phone extensions on a PBX arranged to share the load. In the Rolm PBX, each group is assigned a dummy extension number called a pilot number. 2. A group of telephone extensions on an automatic call distributor (ACD). The ACD answers the incoming calls then checks to see if any agents' phones are free. If none are free, it delivers the caller a message and then puts the caller on hold. Which line the call has come in on may determine which group of agents should handle that call. They would be called a Distribution Group. Once the call is released from hold, it may be sent to a member of that Distribution Group following some pre-determined mathematical formula -- for example, so that everyone's workload is kept constant, or a group of people are kept busy.

DISTRIBUTION SERVICE In ISDN applications, a telecommunications service that allows one-way of information from one point in the network to other points in the network with or without user individual presentation control.

DISTRIBUTION VOLTAGE DROP The voltage drop between any two defined points of interest in a power distribution system.

DISTRIBUTOR A company with a contractual relationship with a manufacturer to buy equipment at a preset price. The manufacturer provides training, advertising and warranty support. Often called an authorized dealer, although a dealer may be one step lower in the distribution chain. A distributor is often used as a generic term for any supplier. Therefore you should clarify whether a distributor is an authorized distributor.

DIT Directory Information Tree. The global tree of entries corresponding to information objects in the OSI X.500 Directory.

DITHERING Dithering is patterning black and white dots to approximate shades of grey on a scanned image.

DIURNAL PHASE SHIFT The phase shift of electromagnetic signals associated with daily changes in the ionosphere. The major changes usually occur during the period of time when sunrise or sunset is present at critical points along the path. Significant phase shifts may occur on paths wherein a reflection area of the path is subject to a large tidal range. In cable systems, significant phase shifts can be occasioned by diurnal temperature variance.

DIVERSITY In microwave communications, the strength of a microwave signal can decrease for many reasons -- heat, rain, fog, etc. This is not good if the objective is to get reliable communications. One solution is to simultaneously send and receive two microwave signals at slightly different frequencies. Since different frequencies respond differently to weather problems, the likelihood is that at least one will get through well. This is called diversity.

DIVERSITY COMBINER A circuit or device for combining two or more signals carrying the same information received via separate paths or channels with the objective or providing a single resultant signal that is superior in quality to any of the contributing signals.

DIVESTITURE On January 8, 1982 AT&T signed a Consent Decree with the U.S. Department of Justice, stipulating that on midnight December 30, 1983, AT&T would divest itself of its 22 telephone operating companies. According to the terms of the Divestiture, those 22 operating Bell telephone companies would be formed into seven regional holding companies of roughly equal size. Terms of the Divestiture placed business restrictions on AT&T and the BOCs. Those restrictions were threefold: The BOCs weren't allowed into long distance, equipment manufacturing, or information services. AT&T wasn't allowed into local telecommunications (i.e. to compete with the BOCs). But it was allowed into computers. The federal Judge overseeing Divestiture, Judge Harold Greene, is slowing the lifting the restrictions against the BOCs being allowed into information services. He has stayed firm on the other two -- equipment manufacturing and long distance.

DIW Type D Inside Wire. Originated as a specific AT&T cable. Now commonly used to describe any 22, 24, or 26 gauge PVC jacketed twisted-pair cable used primarily for inside telephony wiring.

DIX CONNECTORS A local area network connector. DIX connectors on the transceiver local area network cable link it to the network; the male DIX connector plugs into the SpeedLink/PC16 and the female DIX connector attaches to an external transceiver.

DIX ETHERNET The DEC, Intel, Xerox Ethernet standard, also known as Version 1 or Bluebook Ethernet. There are subtle differences between IEEE 802.3 and the DIX Ethernet.

DLC 1. Digital Loop Carrier. 2. See DATA LINK CONTROL. 3. Direct Line Console. An AT&T Merlin term. An answering position used by system operators to answer calls, transfer calls, make calls, set up conference calls, and monitor system operations. Calls can ring on any of the line buttons, and several calls can ring simultaneously (unlike the QCC where calls are sent to a common QCC queue and wait until a QCC is available to receive a call).

DLCI Data Link Connection Identifier. The frame relay virtual circuit number corresponding to a particular destination which is part of the frame relay header and is usually ten bits long.

DLE Data Link Escape. A control character used exclusively to provide supplementary line control signals, control character sequences or DLE sequences. In packet switching, Data Link Escape is a name applied to the Control P non-print character which is used to swap the PAD from the data mode to the command mode in packet switched networks.

DLL 1. Dynamic Link Library. A feature of OS/2 and Windows that allow executable code modules to be loaded on demand and linked at run time. This lets library code be field-updated -- transparent to applications -- and then unloaded when they are no longer needed. Unlike a standard programming library, whose functions are linked into an application when the application's code is compiled, an application that uses DLL links with those DLL functions at runtime. Hence, the term dynamic. 2. Data Link Layer driver. A driver specification developed by DEC primarily to work with DECnet PCSA for DOS. DLL is a shared driver specification, allowing multiple protocol stacks to share a single network interface card.

DLS Data Link Switching. IBM's method for carrying SNA and NetBIOS over TCP/IP operating at the Data Link layer. DLS, now an open Internet spec, can be used with OSPF or PPP.

DLSE Dial Line Service Evaluation.

DLSw DataLink Switching Workgroup. This workgroup has issued a new interoperability standard for integrating SNA and NetBIOS over the TCP/IP protocol. According to Cisco, the new DLSw standard provides interoperability and functionality not currently offered by Informational RFC 1434 or existing DLSw implementations.

DLTU Digital Link Trunk Unit. An AT&T term for a device which provides the interface to digital trunks and lines such as T1, EDSL, and remote line units.

DM Delta Modulation.

DMA Direct Memory Access. A fast method of moving data from a storage device or LAN interface card directly to RAM which speeds processing. In essence, DMA is direct access to memory by a peripheral device that bypasses the CPU.

DMA CHANNEL A channel for direct memory access that does not involve the microprocessor, providing data transfer directly between memory and a disk drive. See DMA.

DMB Digital Multipoint Bridge.

DMI 1. Digital Multiplexed Interface. AT&T's Digital Multiplexed Interface. A PBX to computer interface that divides the T-1 trunk into 23 user channels and one signaling channel. Also used as a T-1 PBX to computer interface. See OPEN APPLICATION INTERFACE. 2. Desktop Management Interface, a protocol independent management interface developed by the DMTF, the Desktop Management Task Force, a group working on improving network printing. Making network printers easier to use -- more standard and easier to use -- requires three basic elements: standardized definitions of printer objects, a protocol for communicating with those objects and an application interface.

DMI-BOS Digital Multiplexed Interface-Bit Oriented Signaling. A form of signaling, which uses the 24th channel of each DSI to carry signaling information, allowing clear channel 64 Kbps functionality.

DMO Digital Modification Order.

DMS Digital Multiplex System. Also the name of a line of digital central office switches from Northern Telecom. There are DMS-10s, DMS-100s, DMS-100Fs and DMS-200s and, by the time you read this, probably more. See also DMS SUPERNODE.

DMS INTEGRATED ACCESS LOCAL AREA NETWORK Shortened to DIALAN. A central office provided local area network offering completely digital, full duplex data transmission at speeds of 300 bps through 19.2 asynchronous and 1,200 bps through 64 kbps synchronous. DIALAN users use existing telephone sets and an Integrated Voice and Data Multiplexer (IVDM) that plugs into a telephone jack.

DMS SUPERNODE The SuperNode is a very flexible central office switch from Northern Telecom which can be configured as a high-capacity local or tandem switch with Common Channel Signaling 7 (CCS7) Service Switching Point (SSP) function, a Signaling Transfer Point (STP), a Service Control Point (SCP), a Digital Network CrossConnect (DNX) system or a network service node with custom programming applications. In 1988, the DMS SuperNode offered twice the capacity of the DMS-100 switch (the older Northern Telecom central office) based on the NT40 processor.

DMS-INODE DMS Integrated STP/SSP Node.

DMT Discrete Multi-Tone. A new technology using digital signal processors to pump more than 6 megabits per second of video, data, image and voice signals over today's existing one pair copper wiring. DMT technology, according to Northern Telecom, provides the following:

● Four "A" channels at 1.5 Mbps. Each "A" channel may carry a "VCR"- quality video signal, or two channels may be merged to carry a "sports"- quality real-time video signal. In the future, all four channels operating together will be able to transport an Extended Definition TV signal with significantly improved quality over anything available today. ("A" channels are asymmetric -- carrying information only from the telephone company to the subscriber's residence. All other channels within ADSL are symmetric or bi-directional.)

● One ISDN "H zero" channel at 384 kbps (kilobits per second). This channel is compatible with Northern Telecom's multi rate ISDN Dialable Wideband Service or equivalent services. This channel could also be used for fast, efficient access to corporate LANs for work-at-home applications, using Northern Telecom's DataSPAN or other frame-relay services.

● One ISDN Basic Rate channel, containing two "B" channels (64 kbps) and one "D" channel (16 kbps). Basic Rate access allows the home user to access the wide range of emerging ISDN services without requiring a dedicated copper pair or the expense of a dedicated NT1 unit at the home. It also permits the extension of Northern Telecom's VISIT personal video conferencing to the home at fractional-T1 rates (Px64).

● One signaling/control channel, operating at 16 kbps giving the home user VCR-type controls over movies and other services provided on the "A" channel including fast-forward, reverse, search, and pause.

● Embedded operations channels for internal system maintenance, audits, and telephone company administration.

● Finally, the home user can place or receive telephone calls over the same copper pair without affecting the digital transmission channels listed above. And since ADSL is passively coupled to the POTS line, the subscriber's POTS capability is unimpaired in the event of a system failure.

DMTE Desktop Management Task Force

DMTF Desktop Management Task Force.

DN Directory Number or subscriber number or telephone number entries. DN is typically the phone number associated with a telephone line. See DIRECTORY NUMBER.

DNA 1. Digital Network Architecture. The framework within which Digital Equipment Corporation (DEC) designs and develops all of its communications products. DNA includes many standards of the OSI Model. Some of these standards will be adopted into ISDN. Acronym also by Network Development Corporation for their network offering. 2. Dynamic Node Access. A high-speed bus invented by Dialogic to join together multiple voice processing PEB-based systems. PEB stands for PCM Expansion Bus. See PEB.

DNAR Directory Number Analysis Reporting.

DNC Dynamic Network Controller.

DNIC Data Network Identification Code. An address to reach a host computer system residing on a different packet switched network than the one you're on. The data equivalent of a telephone number with country code and area code. Typically the DNIC is a four digit number. The first three digits of a DNIC specify a country. The fourth digit specifies a public data network within that country. See also DATA NETWORK IDENTIFICATION CODE.

DNIS Dialed Number Identification Service. DNIS is a feature of 800 and 900 lines that provides the number the caller dialed to reach the attached computer telephony system (manual or automatic). Using DNIS capabilities, one trunk group can be used to serve multiple applications. The DNIS number can be provided in a number of ways, inband or out-of-band, ISDN or via a separate data channel. Generally, a DNIS number will be used to identify to the answering computer telephony system the "application" the caller dialed. For example, a 401K status program may be offered by a service provider to a number of different companies. The employees of each company are provided their own 800 number to call to access their account status. When the computer telephony system sees the incoming DNIS number, it will know to which company the call was directed, and can so answer the phone correctly with a customized "you have reached the 401K line for xyz company. Please enter your personal account code and password..."

Here's another application: You use one 800 phone number for testing your advertisements on TV stations in Phoenix; another number for testing your ads on TV stations in Chicago; and yet another for Milwaukee. The DNIS information can be used in a multitude of ways -- from playing different messages to different people, to routing those people to different operators, to routing those people to the same operators, but flashing different messages on their screens, so the operators answer the phone differently. In Ireland, incoming toll free phone calls from the rest of Europe arrive with DNIS. As a result a phone call arriving from Germany is routed to a computer telephony system playing messages in German. The advantage of DNIS is basically economic: You simply need fewer phone lines. Without DNIS you would need at least one phone line for every different 800 or 900 number you gave out to your callers. Make sure you understand the difference between DNIS and ANI and Caller ID. DNIS tells you the number your caller called. ANI or Caller ID is the number your caller called from. See 800 SERVICE and 900 SERVICE.

DNPA Data Numbering Plan Area. In the U.S. implementation of the ITU-T X.25 network, the first three digits of a network terminal number (NTN). See also DATA NUMBERING PLAN AREA.

DNPIC Directory Number Primary InterLATA Carrier.

DNR 1. Dialed Number Recorder. Also called a Pin Register. An instrument that records telephone dial pulses as inked dashes on paper tape. A touchtone decoder performs the same thing for a touchtone telephone. 2. Dynamic Network Reconfiguration. Allows IBM networks to change addresses without reloading and bringing the network down.

DNS 1. The Domain Naming System is a mechanism used in the Internet for translating names of host computers into addresses. The DNS also allows host computers not directly on the Internet to have registered names in the same style. The DNS is a distributed database system for translating computer names (like ruby.or-a.com) and vice-versa. DNS allows you to use the Internet without remembering long lists of numbers. On TCP/IP networks (like the Internet), the Domain Naming System provides IP address translation for a given computer's domain name. DNS would change a computer name such as harry.newton.com to the machine' actual numeric IP address, which is in the format xxx.xxx.xxx.xxx. The DNS makes it easier to remember where you want to go. 2. See DISTRIBUTED NETWORK SERVICE.

DO A word in a high-level language program which comes before a collection of things to be done, i.e. statements to be executed.

DO-NOT-DISTURB Makes a telephone appear busy to any incoming calls. May be used on intercom-only, by extension line-only or both.

DO-WHILE A programming statement used to perform instructions in a loop while a certain condition exists -- i.e. do something while the variable Y is less than 20.

DOA Dead On Arrival. A term several manufacturers use to refer to equipment which arrives at the customer's premises not working. A person who receives a DOA machine will ask the company for a NPR number -- New Product Return number. This allows them to return the product and have the factory replace it with another new one.

DOC 1. Department of Communications. Canadian government department. 2. See DYNAMIC OVERLOAD CONTROL.

DOC-IT Okidata's name for a combination scanner, printer, copier, fax machine. A truly wonderful machine.

DOCUMENT CAMERA A specialized camera on a long neck that is used for taking pictures of still images -- pictures, graphics, pages of text and objects which can then be sent stand alone or as part of a video conference.

DOCUMENT IMAGE MANAGEMENT DIM. The electronic access to and manipulation of documents stored in image format, accomplished through the use of automated methods such as high-powered graphical workstations, sophisticated database management techniques and networking.

DOCUMENT RECOGNITION The ability to capture all the information on a page (text and images) and perform not only character recognition, but page structure analysis as well.

DOCUMENTATION Written text describing the system, how it works and how to work it. In most cases of high technology products, documentation is awful. Better documentation helps sell equipment and software. Please write your instruction manuals better. Please.

DOCK To insert a portable computer into a base unit. Cold docking means the computer must begin from a power-off state and restart before docking. Hot docking means the computer can be docked while running at full power.

DOCKET Formal FCC/State regulatory commission proceeding, also referred to as a case.

DOCKING STATION Base station for a laptop that includes a power supply, expansion slots, monitor, keyboard connectors, CD-ROM and extra hard disk connectors. A user slides his laptop into a base station and in effect, gets the equivalent of a desktop machine.

DOD Department of Defense.

DOD MASTER CLOCK The U.S. Naval Observatory master clock, which has been designated as the DOD Master Clock to which DoD time and frequency measurements are referenced. This clock is one of two standard time references for the U.S. Government in accordance with Federal Standard 1002; the other standard time reference is the National Institute for Standards and Technology (NIST) master clock.

DOLBY A system of noise/hiss reduction invented by Ray Dolby, widely used in consumer, professional and broadcast audio applications.

DOMAIN The part of a computer network in which the data processing resources are under common control. That's the formal technical definition. But when the Internet came along, the definition got a little looser. On the Internet, most people think of a domain as a place you can visit (with a Web browser) and which you can send e-mail to. "A place you can visit" might be part of a computer -- a subdirectory or two. It might be a single computer or it might be a group of computers masquerading as a single computer. On the Internet, the domain is thus whatever the address is that gets you there. An domain address is computer-telephony.com or teleconnect.com. A domain's address on the Internet is a hierarchical sequence of names (labels) separated by periods (dots), e.g., computer.telephony.com. In fact, the central naming registry on the Internet -- which is called InterNIC -- will only register the word before the .com, the .edu, the .gov and the .mil. In this case, they will register the domain name "telephony.com" or "computertelephony.com." (They are different sub-domains.) What you put in front of your domain name is your concern. Everything that is "something.something.telephony.com" will come to the domain "telephony.com" for resolution (further routing, processing, etc.)

Some people think of a domain as a group of computers on a network that share something in common, such as the job they do, the organization type they belong to, or their location. Top level domains on the Internet (yet another definition of domain) include .COM for commercial organizations; .EDU for educational organizations; .GOV for government organizations, .ORG (miscellaneous organizations, usually non-profit), .NET (network service providers), .INT (international), .AUS for Australia, .NZ for New Zealand, and numerous others specifying foreign countries.

Domain is a term defined differently by various electronic mail vendors. PC Magazine's Frank Derfler defines a domain as referring to a set of hosts on a single LAN that needs only one intermediary post office to move mail from one host to another. A domain may also consist of only one host, depending on its design and implementation. In IBM's SNA, a domain is a host-based systems services control point (SSCP), the physical units (PUs), logical units (LUs), links, link stations and all the affiliated resources that the host (SSCP) can control.

In Microsoft networking, a domain is a collection of computers that share a common domain database and security policy that is stored on a Windows NT Server domain controller. Each domain has a unique name. See also DOMAIN CONTROLLER, DOMAIN NAME, DOMAIN NAMING SYSTEM and WORKGROUP.

DOMAIN CONTROLLER For a Windows NT Server domain, the primary or backup domain controller that authenticates domain logons and maintains the security policy and the master database for a domain.

DOMAIN DEFINED ATTRIBUTE DDA. In X.400 addressing, the DDA is a special field that may be required to assist a receiving E-mail system in delivering a message to the intended recipient. Up to four DDAs are allowed per address, with each DDA address entry made up of two parts, a type and a value. For example, if I were a subscriber to MCI Mail and I wanted to send a message to Harry Newton, this is how I would address it:

TO: Harry Newton EMS: CompuServe / 592-7515 MBX: P=CSMAIL MBX: DDA=ID=70600,2451

If I were a subscriber to CompuServe, the only addressing information I would need would be the number 70600,2451.

DOMAIN NAME In networks using the TCP/IP (Transfer Control Protocol/Internet Protocol), the full domain name consists of a sequence of names (labels) separated by periods (dots), e.g., "pictures.computertelephony.com." See DOMAIN and TCP/IP.

DOMAIN NAME SERVERS Domain Servers are computers on the Internet which contain the the programs and files which make up a domain's name database. Using a name server is much like calling directory assistance; you provide the operator (name server) with a name and it is translated to a telephone number (IP address), which you then use to establish connection with the person (host computer).

the telephone network (Internet) addresses by telephone number (IP address), not really by the person's (domain's) name.

DOMAIN NAMING SYSTEM DNS. in Unix-based networks, of which the Internet is the largest, a domain naming system is the commonly accepted way of giving attached computers names. Domain naming system is sometimes referred to as the BIND (berkeley internet name domain) service in BSD Unix, a static, hierarchical naming service for tcp/ip hosts. A DNS server computer maintains a database for resolving host names and IP addresses, allowing users of computers configured to query the DNS to specify remote computers by host names (in words) rather than IP addresses (which are only numbers). DNS domains should not be confused with Windows NT networking domains, although Windows NT does support and can use the Internet's DNS scheme. See DOMAIN.

DOMESTIC ARC The portion of the geostationary orbit allowing a satellite to return a footprint that almost covers the continental United States.

DOMINANT CARRIER The long distance service provider which dominates a particular market and is subject to tougher regulation than its competitors. An FCC term. Essentially it means AT&T.

DOMSAT Domestic Communications Satellite.

DON'T ANSWER RECALL Allows an extension user on a PBX to automatically retry a call by dialing a special digit code.

DONE DEAL A term used in the secondary telecom equipment business. Term used between seller and buyer to signify that a sale has been agreed to and an oral contract is now in effect, binding both parties to the agreed-to-sale as if a written contract has been signed. A written contract submitted later that does not conform to the original oral agreement is not justification for dissolving the original agreement unless both parties agree to the new written contract.

DONGLE A device to prevent copies made of software programs. A dongle is a small device supplied with software that plugs into a computer port. The software interrogates the device's serial number during execution to verify its presence. If it's not there, the software won't work. A dongle is also called a hardware key. See HARDWARE KEY.

DOOR A software program that allows access to files and programs not built into an electronic bulletin board system, thus letting users run them on-line.

DOPPLER AIDING A signal processing strategy that uses a measured doppler shift to help the GPS Global Positioning System) receiver smoothly track the GPS signal. It allows more precise velocity and position measurement.

DOPPLER SHIFT The apparent shift in the frequency of a signal caused by the relative motion of the transmitter and the receiver.

DOS Disk Operating System, as in MS-DOS, which stands for MicroSoft Disk Operating System. A disk operating system is software that organizes how a computer reads, writes and reacts with its disks -- floppy or hard -- and talks to its various input/output devices, including keyboards, screens, serial and parallel ports, printers, modems, etc. Until the introduction of Windows, the most popular operating system for PCs was MS-DOS from Microsoft, Bellevue, WA.

DOT When you want to impress the Internet veterans you meet at parties, say "dot" instead of "period," for example: "My address is john at site dot domain dot com."

DOT ADDRESSABLE GRAPHICS Refers to the mode of operation on a dot matrix printer which allows you to control each element in the dot matrix printhead. With this feature, you may produce complex graphics drawings.

DOT PITCH A measure of the clarity of a color monitor. Dot pitch measures the vertical distance between the centers of like-colored phosphors on your screen. The smaller the distance, the sharper the monitor. Dot pitch is the major determinant in the clarity of an image on screen. And you can't do anything about it. When you buy a monitor, you buy it with a certain dot pitch and you're stuck with that dot pitch. You may be able, however, to do something about improving convergence and focus -- the other measures of the clarity of a color monitor.

DOT ZERO When new software is issued, it often bears the number .0 (i.e. dot zero) as in MS-DOS 5.0. The theory among software gurus is that you should always avoid a "Dot Zero" revision, since it will likely contain bugs and that one should wait for 4.01 or 5.01 etc. This theory has some validity, although MS-DOS 5.0 came out very clean and was not revised until 6.0.

DOTTED QUAD A set of four numbers connected with periods that make up an Internet address; for example, 147.31.254.130.

DOUBLE BUFFERING The use of two buffers rather than one to temporarily hold data being moved to and from an I/O device. Double buffering increases data transfer speed because one buffer can be filled while the other is being emptied.

DOUBLE CAMP-ON INDICATION A PBX feature. A phone attempting to camp on to another phone which is already being "camped on" shall receive a distinctive audible signal and may be denied the ability to camp-on.

DOUBLE CLICK With a Mac and an IBM-compatible PC running Windows, double-clicking carries out an action, such as beginning a new program. Press and release the mouse button twice in rapid succession to double-click. If you don't double click fast enough, it won't work. Some mouse software allow you to assign the left hand button on the mouse to a single click and the right hand button to a double click. This is very useful.

DOUBLE CRUCIBLE METHOD A method of fabricating optical fiber by melting core and clad glasses into two suitably joined concentric crucibles and then drawing a fiber from the combined melted glass.

DOUBLE DENSITY Refers to a diskette which can contain twice the amount of data in the same amount of space as a single-density diskette. For example, a double-density 360k diskette has a 720k storage capacity. These days double density is an obsolete term, since there are now disks that are "double double" density. Most 3 1/2 inch disks will now hold twice 720K -- or 1,440,000 bytes. These are called high density disks. Toshiba has introduced a "double double double" floppy, which will hold 2,880,000 bytes. But it hasn't caught on, yet.

DOUBLE ENDED SYNCHRONIZATION A synchronization control system between two exchanges, in which the phase error signals used to control the clock at one exchange are derived from comparison with the phase of the internal clock at both exchanges.

DOUBLE INTERRUPTED RING Two quick rings followed by a period of silence indicating the arrival of an outside call in some systems.

DOUBLE MODULATION Modulation of a carrier wave of one frequency by a signal wave, this carrier then being used to modulate another carrier wave of different frequency.

DOUBLE POLE A double pole switch is one which opens and closes both sides of the same circuit simultaneously. Most electrical circuits open and close with only one side being broken.

DOUBLE PULL A method for pulling cable into conduit or duct liner that is similar to backfeed pulling except that it eliminates the need to lay the backfeed cable on the ground.

DOUBLE SIDEBAND CARRIER TRANSMISSION That method of transmission in which frequencies produced by the process of amplitude modulation are symmetrically spaced above and below the carrier. The carrier level is reduced for transmission at a fixed level below that which is provided to the modulator. Carrier is usually transmitted at a level suitable for use as a reference by the receiver except in those cases where it is reduced to the minimum practical level (suppressed carrier).

DOUBLEWIDE Two trailer homes stapled together with a modest gabled roof.

DOUBLY CLAD FIBER An optical fiber, usually single mode, that has a core surrounded by an inner cladding of lower refractive index, which is in turn surrounded by an outer cladding, which has a higher refractive index than the inner cladding. This type of construction is often employed in single-mode fibers to reduce bending losses.

DOV Data Over Voice. A technology used primarily with local Centrex services or special customer premises PBXs for transmitting data and voice simultaneously over twisted-pair copper wiring. Typical data rates for Centrex operation are 9.6 Kbps and 19.2 Kbps.

DOVPATH TRANSPORT SERVICE A New York and New England Telephone service which lets you transmit both voice and data simultaneously on one phone line. The data is carried on a higher frequency, i.e. "Over the Voice." Hence the name Data Over Voice, or DOV. DOVPATH lets you transmit up to 19.2 Kbps asynchronous data, which could be fast enough for talking to a distant mainframe computer.

DOWN-CONVERTER A device for performing frequency translation in such a manner that the output frequencies are lower in the spectrum than the input frequencies.

DOWNLINE LOADING A system in which programs are loaded into the memory of a computer system, such as a LAN bridge, router or server, via the same communication line(s) the system normally uses to communicate with the rest of a network. As opposed to systems in which all programs are loaded into the computer from a disk or tape associated with the computer. A PC connected to a LAN may use this type of loading when it is first turned on in the morning to get the information it needs from a file server. Diskless PCs always work this way.

DOWNLINK 1. The part of a transmission link reaching from a satellite to the ground. Some satellite transmission circuits, especially international ones, are priced and billed separately for the uplink and the downlink. This is because their transmissions are provided by different carriers. 2. In packet data communications, a downlink is a link from an NC or PAD to another NC or PAD on a different level. The defining of downlinks and uplinks depends on the network configuration of PADs, their relationships to each other and the direction of data transmission.

DOWNLOAD To receive data from another computer (often called a host computer or host system or just plain host) into your computer. It's also called to RECEIVE. The opposite is UPLOAD or TRANSMIT. You have to be very careful distinguishing between the two. Choosing the "Download" option in some communications programs automatically erases a file of the same name that was meant for transmission. If that happens, stop everything. Grab your file unerase program and use it. Don't wait. If you wait, you may write over your erased file and never get it back. See DOWNLOADED FONTS.

DOWNLOADED FONTS Fonts that you send to a printer either before or during the printing of a document. When you send a font to a printer, it is stored in printer memory until it is needed. Downloaded fonts are one reason for loading lots of RAM memory into your printer.

DOWNSIZING Downsizing is what happens when companies move from large computer systems to smaller systems. There are four major reasons companies downsize from mainframe-based computer to local area network-based computing: 1. They save money. There are several reasons: a. Mainframe computers cost lots each month in maintenance. They require costly maintenance agreements with the supplier, e.g. IBM. Servers are usually bought without maintenance agreements. When they break, the managers or the workers simply replace the broken parts themselves. b. Mainframe computers cost lots to program. There are comparatively few programs available for mainframes, compared to the plethora of off-the-shelf programs available for workstations. c. Servers require a far less costly home to live. You don't need air-conditioning, special buildings with raised floors, etc. 2. Servers today have the power of mainframes 10 years ago. In fact, servers are now beginning to acquire more power than mainframes of ten years ago. And as servers increasingly acquire several processors, they will leap in power beyond what mainframes have. 3. Servers are typically manufactured from off-the-shelf, standard components that are usually available from several manufacturers. As a result, there is constant competition and constant improvement in quality and features. 4. Servers are much more flexible tools to design networks. You can start with one baby network containing one server and several workstations (a.k.a. clients) and confined to one floor of one small building and grow to a huge, complex network containing thousands of workstations, dozens of servers and spanning the globe.

To most people, downsizing is not only swapping out the "big iron" (the mainframe) and bringing in servers and local area networks. It's also a new way of thinking about the way corporations are organized. Downsizing is often accompanied by re-engineering, which is basically re-organizing for a greater focus on the customer - - a focus which means responding faster to customer needs. See SERVERS.

DOWNSTREAM Refers to the relative position of two stations in a local area network ring topology. A station is downstream if it receives a token after the previous station. See also DOWNSTREAM CHANNEL.

DOWNSTREAM CHANNEL The frequency multiplexed band in a CATV channel which distributes signals from the headend to the users. Compare with UPSTREAM CHANNEL, the band of frequencies on a CATV channel reserved for transmission from the user to the CATV company's headend.

DOWNTIME The total time a telephone system is not working due to some software or hardware failure. You know your vendor is about to lie when he begins to answer a question about "downtime."

DP 1. Dial Pulse (as in dialing a phone) or Data Processing. Also called EDP for Electronic Data Processing. Now more commonly called Management

Information Systems -- or MIS. 2. Demarcation Point. The point of a demarcation and/or interconnection between telephone company communications facilities and terminal equipment, protective apparatus, or wiring at a subscriber's premises. Carrier-installed facilities at or constituting the demarcation point consist of a wire or a jack conforming to Subpart F of Part 68 of the FCC Rules.

DPA 1. Digital Port Adapter. A Northern Telecom word. 2. Demand Protocol Architecture. A technique for loading protocol stacks dynamically as they are required. It is associated with adapter cards in workstations and servers. Only the protocol stacks that are required for a particular communications sessions are loaded. Examples of such stacks include TCP/IP, XNS, SPX/IPX and NetBios.

DPCM Differential Pulse Code Modulation

DPLB Digital Private Line Billing.

DPMI An acronym for DOS Protected Mode Interface. DPMI is an industry standard that allows MS-DOS applications to execute code in the protected operating mode of the 80286 or 80386 processor. The DPMI specification is available from Intel Corporation. It is a superset of the VCPI (Virtual Control Program Interface) specification for controlling multiple programs inside a PC, as well as programs that use protected mode.

DPMS Display Power Manager Signaling is a power reduction feature that places a computer monitor in reduced power when the monitor is still on but has been idle for some time.

DPN LANSCOPE A Northern Telecom software package for remote management of local area networks over wide area networks based on Northern's DPN-100 digital data packet networking system. DPN Lanscope provides fault and performance monitoring, resource management, software distribution and usage tracking for geographically dispersed LANs. Network configuration, status, alarms and performance information are presented to a centralized LAN administrator through a graphics interface.

DPNSS Digital Private Network Signaling System. A standard in Britain which enables PBXs from different manufacturers to be tied together with E-1 lines and pass calls transparently between each -- as easily as if the phones were extensions off the same PBX and were simply making intercom calls. The international version of DPNSS is called Q.SIG, but apparently it's not as well developed.

DPBX Digital PBX. Not a common term. Most PBXs these days are digital.

DPN Northern Telecom term for Data Packet Network.

DPP Distributed Processing Peripheral.

DPU Dynamic Path Update. Allows IBM networks to add new network nodes or change backup routing paths while the front-end is still operating.

DPX DataPath loop eXtension.

DQDB Distributed Queue Dual Bus. The metropolitan area network technology that operates by maintaining a queue at each station to determine when the station may access its dual buses. The dual buses provide bidirectional transmission between each station. DQDB is IEEE's standard 802.6 for MANs (Metropolitan Area Networks). Formerly called QPSX (Queued Packet and Synchronous Exchange). DQDB was devised for metropolitan area networks (MAN). It consists of two uni-directional buses connected as an open ring (i.e., each bus is not directly interconnected). It provides for full duplex operation between any two nodes and the bandwidth available provides for signaling speeds in excess of 155 Mbit/s. Each transmission cell or packet consists of a 5-byte header plus 48 bytes of message. The header bytes include bits of control, priority and an error check sequence. See also ATM.

DRAFT PROPOSAL An ISO standards document that has been registered and numbered but not yet approved.

DRAG Dragging is a way of moving an item on the screen using your mouse. To drag a window in Windows 3.1, for example, move the mouse pointer onto a window's title bar, then hold down the mouse button while moving the mouse across your desktop. When you release the mouse button, the window will remain in its new location. Apply this technique to drag any data object, such as icons or list box items.

DRAG AND DROP The "drag and drop" definition defines how objects from one desktop application can be "dragged" out of that application, through clicking on the object with a mouse, across the desktop and "dropped" on another application. Most of the graphics operating systems, like Windows, Apple's Macintosh and Sun Sparc use Drag and Drop.

DRAG LINE A length of rope or string used to pull wire and cable through conduit or inaccessible spaces. Drag lines are often inserted in wall and ceilings during construction to ease future wire installation.

DRAIN WIRE In a cable, an uninsulated wire laid over the component or components and used as a ground connection.

DRAM 1. Dynamic Random Access Memory chip. Pronounced "dee-ram." The readable/writable memory used to store data in PCs. DRAM stores each bit of information in a "cell" composed of a capacitor and a transistor. Because the capacitor in a DRAM cell can hold a charge for only a few milliseconds, DRAM must be continually refreshed to retain its data. In contrast, static RAM, or SRAM, requires no refresh and delivers better performance, but it is more expensive to manufacture. See also EDO RAM, SRAM, MICROPROCESSOR (for a full explanation). See also DYNAMIC RANDOM ACCESS MEMORY. 2. Digital Recorder Announcer Module.

DRAWING In the manufacture of wire, pulling the metal through a die or series of dies in order to reduce the diameter to a specified size.

DRAWING TOOLS A computer imaging term. The means of creating freehand lines or basic geometric shapes. Paint packages often provide an ellipse-drawing function as a variation of the circle (or vice versa) and a square drawing function as a variation of the rectangle. Virtually all packages offer filled geometric figures, the fill item being either a solid color or a pattern.

DRESSING CABLE You "dress" cable by taking multiple cables and joining them together neatly with cable ties. A nicely-dressed, clean installation is a sign of telephony professionalism. It still exists.

DRIFT A slow change in a normally constant signal. The term typically applies to movements in the signal's frequency.

DRIVE ICON A Windows NT term. An icon in a directory window in File Manager that represents a disk drive on your system. Different icons depict floppy disk drives, CD-ROM drives, network drives, etc.

DRIVE MAPPINGS A Novell NetWare term. Drive mappings provide direct access to particular locations in the directory structure. They are a "shorthand" method for accessing directories on a disk. Instead of typing in the complete path name of a directory that you want to access, you can simply enter a drive letter that has been assigned to that directory. NetWare recognizes two types of drives (physical drives and logical drives) and three types of drive mappings (local, network, and search drive mappings).

DRIVE TYPE A number representing a standard configuration of physical parameters (cylinders, heads and sectors) of a particular type of hard disk drive. You need to know your drive's drive type otherwise the bios of your machine will not recognize your drive on boot up and your PC will not work. Normally this information of your drive's type resides in memory kept alive by a small lithium battery. However, should the lithium battery die, your PC will "forget" which drive it has and it will ask you. If you don't know, you're in big trouble. Your PC simply won't work. My recommendation: write the drive type on two labels -- one to stick on the drive and the other to stick on the bottom of your machine. This way you'll be able to find it easily. You will usually find the drive type's number on paperwork sent originally with your machine.

DRIVEBAR A Windows NT term. Allows you to change drives by selecting one of the drive icons.

DRIVER A driver (which is always software) provides instructions for reformatting or interpreting software commands for transfer to and from peripheral devices and the central processor unit (CPU). Many printed circuit boards which you drop into a PC require a software driver in order for the other parts of the computer and the software you're running to work correctly. In other words, the driver is a software module that "drives" the data out of a specific hardware port. The port in question will usually have another device connected, such as a printer or modem, and the driver will be organized in software (i.e. configured) to communicate with the device.

DROP 1. A wire or cable from a pole or cable terminal to a building. 2. That portion of a device that looks toward the internal station facilities, e.g., toward an AUTOVON 4-wire switch, toward a switchboard,or toward switching center. 3. The central office side of test jacks. 4. To delete, intentionally or unintentionally, part of a signal for some reason, e.g., dropping bits.

DROP AND INSERT That process wherein a part of the information carried in a transmission system is demodulated (dropped) at an intermediate point and different information is entered (inserted) for subsequent transmission.

DROP CABLE 1. The outside wire pair which connects your house or office to the transmission line coming from the phone company's central office. See also DROP WIRE, which is different. 2. In local area networks, a cable that connects perpendicularly to the main network cable or bus, and attaches to the DTE equipment.

DROP CHANNEL OPERATION A type of operation where one or more channels of a multichannel system are terminated (dropped) at any intermediate point between the end terminals of the system.

DROP LOOP The segment of wire from the nearest telephone pole to your home or business.

DROP OUTS Drop outs are one major cause of errors in data communications circuits. The technical definition is that the signal level drops more than 12 dB (decibels) for more than 4 milliseconds. It means some of your data will not arrive. A four millisecond drop out in a transmission at 2,400 bits per second will lose about ten bits. A "drop out" is similar to a person's voice fades away in a telephone conversation. To correct the problem of drop out,we will ask the person (or computer) at the other end to repeat what they just said. "Huh?" This is called retransmission of data. In telephony, drop outs are defined as incidents when signal level unexpectedly drops at least 12 dB for more than 4 milliseconds. (Bell standard allows no more than two drop outs per 15 minute period.)

DROP REPEATER A repeater that is provided with the necessary equipment for local termination (dropping) of one or more channels of a multichannel system.

DROP SET All parts needed to complete connection from the drop (wall plate, coupling, MOD-MOD) to the terminal equipment. This would typically include a modular line cord and interface adapter.

DROP-SHIPMENT Equipment shipped to a buyer from a location separate from the seller's premise. If this third location is a different company, then this third-party supplier bills the seller and the seller bills the buyer. This saves time, but the seller loses control over the equipment's condition.

DROP SIDE Defines all cabling and connectors from the terminal equipment to the patch panel or punch down block designated for terminal equipment at the distribution frame.

DROP WIRE Wires going from your phone company to the 66 Block or protector in your building. See also DISTRIBUTION CABLE.

DROPOUT A short period of time during which a transmission service looses the ability to transmit data. Bell System specifications define a dropout as any such loss which lasts for more than four milliseconds. See DROP OUTS for a longer explanation.

DROPPED CALL A call in which the radio link between the cellular customer and the cell site is broken. Dropped calls can happen often, and for many reasons, including terrain, equipment problems, atmospheric interference, and traveling out of range. In short, a dropped call is a call terminated by other than the calling or called party.

DRU 1. DACS Remote Unit. 2. Digital Remote Unit. An NEC term. It's a multiplexer used to distribute NEC Dterm digital telephones and analog sets throughout the user's communications network, whether that network is local or geographically dispersed. The multiplexing technology used is North American Standard T1 and European Standard E1.

DRUM FACTOR In facsimile systems, the ratio of drum length to drum diameter. Where drums are not used, it is the ratio of the equivalent dimensions.

DRUM SPEED The angular speed of the facsimile transmitter or recorder drum, measured in revolutions per minute.

DRUNKEN SWEDE A way of describing the sound of a computer doing text-to-speech conversion. "Why, he sounds like a drunken Swede." This great definition from Stuart Segal of Phone Base Systems, Inc. in Vienna, VA. Says Stuart, "Our people think that a drunken Swede has recorded this message." It is possible to have a computer generate speech that doesn't sound like a drunken Swede if you throw sufficient horsepower (MIPS and memory) at it. Throwing sufficient horsepower, however, has been expensive, until recently. Drunken Swedes are going to get less and less common as horsepower gets cheaper and cheaper.

DRY CELL A type of primary cell in which the electrolyte is in the form of a paste rather than that of a liquid.

DRY CIRCUIT A circuit over which voice signals are transmitted and which carries no direct current.

DRY CONTACT A dry contact refers to a circuit with an energy level such that a spark is not created in a mechanical relay or switch contracts when the circuit is opened. As a result, no cleaning of the contacts takes place (sparking vaporizes contact materials thereby continually exposing fresh contact material). Sometimes general purpose contacts are gold-flashed so the relay or switch can be used on dry circuits; when used on higher energy circuits the gold coating is destroyed, but no damage is done except that the contact should not be used to carry dry circuit signal levels again. A dry contact might operate a relay which might turn something of higher power on or off. For example, a low voltage signal in a key system might cause a dry contact to close, thus causing much higher voltage to flow to a bell, a klaxon, a strobe light. And, yes, there is a "wet" contact. The term "mercury-wetted relay" refers to a relay or switch in which the movable contact of the device makes contact with a pool of mercury. In fact, before solid-state devices, this was a common technology for switching dry circuits.

DRY ELECTROLYTIC CONDENSER An electrolytic condenser in which the electrolyte is in the form of a paste or jelly rather than that of a liquid.

DRY LOOP POWERING Refers to local (not span) powering, and a transmission medium other than copper wire (microwave/fiber optic).

DRY T-1 A T-1 line with an unpowered interface. A T-1 line with a power is called "Wet."

DRY TWISTED PAIR A normal telephone twisted pair without loading coils. It carries only data, not data and voice.

DS Danske Standardiseringsrad (Danish Standards Institution).

DS- A hierarchy of digital signal speeds used to classify capacities of lines and trunks. The fundamental speed level is DS-0 (64-kilobits per second) and the highest is DS-4 (about 274 million bits per second. Here are the definitions: DS-1, DS-1C, DS-2, DS-3, DS-4. They correspond to 1.544, 3.152, 6.312, 44.736, and 274.176 Mbps. DS-1 is also called T-1.

DS-0 Digital Service, level 0. It is 64,000 bps, the worldwide standard speed for digitizing one voice conversation using pulse code modulation (PCM). There are 24 DS-0 channels in a DS-1.

DS-1 Digital Service, level 1. It is 1.544 Mbps in North America, 2.048 Mbps elsewhere. Why there's no consistency is one of those wonderful, unanswered, questions. The 1.544 standard is an old Bell System standard. The 2.048 standard is a ITU-T standard. Standard for 1.544 Mbps is 24 voice conversations each encoded at 64 Kbps. Standard for 2.048 megabits is 30 conversations.

DS-1C Digital Service, level 1C. It is 3.152 Mbps in North America and is carried on T-1.

DS-2 Digital Service, level 2. It is 6.312 Mbps in North America and is carried on T-2.

DS-3 Digital Service, level 3. Equivalent of 28 T-1 channels, and operating at 44.736 Mbps. Also called T-3.

DS-4 Digital Signal, level 4. 274,176,000 bits per second. 168 T1s. 168 DS1s. 4032 standard voice channels.

DSO Digital Signal, level Zero. Pronounced "D-S Zero." DS0 is 64,000 bits per second. It is equal to one voice conversation digitized under PCM. Twenty-four DS0s (24x64 Kbps) equal one DS1, which is T-1 or 1.544 million bits per second. See DS-0.

DSO-A Refers to a process where a subrate signal (2.4, 4.8, or 9.6 Kbps) is repeated 20, 10 or 5 times, respectively to make a 64 Kbps DS-0 channel.

DSO-B Refers to a process performed by a subrate multiplexer where twenty 2.4 Kbps, ten 4.8 Kbps, or five 9.6 Kbps signals are bundled into one 64 Kbps DS-0 channel.

DS1 Digital Signal, level One. A 1.544 Mbps digital signal carried on a T-1 transmission facility. See DS-1.

DS2 Digital Signal, level Two. 6,312,000 bits per second. Four T1s. Four DS1s. 96 standard voice channels.

DS3 Digital Signal, level Three. 44,736,000 bits per second. 28 T1s. 28 DS1s. 672 standard voice channels.

DS4 Digital Signal, level Four. 274,176,000 bits per second. 168 T1s. 168 DS1s. 4032 standard voice channels.

DSA 1. Distributed Systems Architecture, the network architecture developed by Honeywell. 2. Directory System Agent. The software that provides the X.500 Directory Service for a portion of the directory information base. Generally, each DSA is responsible for the directory information for a single organization or organizational unit.

DSAP Destination Service Access Point. The logical address of the specific service entity to which data must be delivered when it arrives at its destination. This information may be built into the data field of an IEEE 802.3 transmission frame.

DSAT Digital Supervisory Audio Tones. A supervisory signaling scheme used in NAMPS -- a new form of digital cellular radial called Narrow-band Advanced Mobile Phone service. See also NAMP.

DSC Digital Selecting Calling. A synchronous system developed by the International Radio Consultative Committee (CCIR), used to establish contact with a station or group of stations automatically by radio. The operational and technical characteristics of this system are contained in CCIR Recommendation 493.

DSDC Direct Service Dialing Capability. Network services provided by local switches interacting with remote data bases via CCIS.

DSE Data Switching Equipment.

DSI Digital Speed Interpolation. A technique for squeezing more voice conversations onto a line. DSI digitizes speech so it can be cut into slices, such that no bits are transmitted when no one is speaking. As soon as speech begins, bits flow again. See DIGITAL SPEECH INTERPOLATION.

DSL See DIGITAL SUBSCRIBER LINE.

DSN 1. Distributed Systems Network, the network architecture developed by Hewlett-Packard. 2. Double Shelf Network.

DSOB An AT&T Digital Data Service standard that specifies a means of multiplexing several subrate data channels within one DSO. Five 9.6, ten 4.8 or 20 2.4 kbps subrate channels may be multiplexed within one DSO.

DSP 1. Display System Protocol 2. Digital Signal Processor. A Digital Signal Processor is a specialized computer chip designed to perform speedy and complex operations on digitized waveforms. Useful in processing sound and video. See DIGITAL SIGNAL PROCESSOR for a much better explanation.

DSP MODULE An internal module of the National Sensor Conductor NS32FX16 processor that handles vector operations on complex variables, enhancing DSP performance of the device.

DSPRM Microsoft's DSP Resource Manager (DSPRM) is a new layer of code scheduled to be part of the new Chicago operating system. DSPRM is the layer below TAPI and should make the addition of DSP resources to desktop machines far easier and be a boon to computer telephony applications. Microsoft has even gone so far as to specify a recommended hardware platform. When Chicago (Windows 4.0) ships, computer telephony should be the next killer application.

DSR Data Set Ready. This signal is on pin 6 of the RS-232-C connector. It means the modem (which some telephone companies call a "data set") is ready to send data from the terminal. Some modems use Data Set Ready. Some don't. Modems that are snooty enough to give you the DSR signal, are obnoxious enough to not work until they receive the DTR (Data Terminal Ready) signal from the terminal on pin 20. By bridging pins 6 and 20 on the connector at the modem, you can usually get it to work. If it doesn't, bridge in pin 8 (carrier detect) as well.

DSS Direct Station Select. A piece of key telephone equipment usually attached to an operator's phone set. When the operator needs to call a particular extension he/she simply touches the corresponding button on the Direct Station Select equipment. Typically DSS equipment/feature is part of a Busy Lamp Field (BLF), which shows with lights what's happening at each extension. Is it busy? Is it on hold? Is it ringing?

DSS is also Decision Support Systems. Computerized systems for transforming data into useful information, such as statistical models or predictions of trends, usually in a graphical format, which is used by management in the decision-making process. See DECISION SUPPORT SYSTEMS.

DSRR Digital Short Range Radio.

DSTN Double Super Twisted Nematic. A display technology which uses two layers of crystal to correct distortions caused by the first layer and so improve readability.

DSU Digital Service Unit, also called Data Service Unit. Converts RS-232-C or other terminal interface to DSX-1 interface. See DATA SERVICE UNIT.

DSU/CSU The devices used to access digital data channels channels are called DSU/CSUs (Data Service Unit/Channel Service Units). At the customer's end of the telephone connection, these devices perform much the same function for digital circuits that modems provide for analog connections. For example, DSU/CSUs take data from terminals and computers, encode it, and transmit it down the link. At the receive end, another DSU/CSU equalizes the received signal, filters it, and decodes it for interpretation by the end-user.

DSVD Digital Simultaneous Voice and Data. Technology in a modem that allows you to send and receive voice and data on the same "conversation" on one analog phone line. DSVD is a concept being pushed by several manufacturers who want the concept to fly so they can sell equipment. But, as of writing (January, 1996) there are international DSVD standards. Here are some words from a press release issued by Rockwell in Fall, 1995: Rockwell Telecommunications has announced Digital Simultaneous Voice and Data (DSVD) chipsets -- enabling PC users to exchange voice and data over a single, standard phone line. The chipsets are compliant with the recently announced DSVD Protocol Specification, a market-based standard developed by PC and modem industry leaders. Announced by Rockwell, with support from Intel Corporation, Creative Labs, Hayes Microcomputer and U.S. Robotics, the DSVD specification was developed for modems to eliminate the need for two separate phone lines when using collaborative PC-based applications such as personal conferencing, technical support and multi-user computer games.

"The primary goal of creating a standard DSVD specification is to establish broad interoperability," said Armando Geday, business director for Rockwell Modem Systems. "All modems compliant with this specification will communicate with one another. It is Rockwell's intent to aggressively deploy DSVD functionality by providing modem OEMs with complete, lowest-system-cost solutions." What Can You Do With DSVD?

Have you ever promised someone on the telephone that you'd fax a document to them, then forget to send it? Have you ever traveled cross-country or halfway around the world to make a presentation? Have you considered expensive video conferencing hardware and applications as a way to communicate? Ever been frustrated waiting online, hoping to get some technical support?

When you need to work on a project, spreadsheet or presentation with someone from another location, a DSVD modem lets you do it without leaving your office or requiring costly video conferencing equipment. Both parties can simultaneously collaborate on a shared document, each viewing and discussing the additions and modifications made. This can slash time and money previously wasted exchanging faxes and relying on overnight express mail deliveries. Computer and software demonstrations can be easily conducted through a DSVD modem. This is a great way to highlight or test market new features and get immediate customer feedback. For the computer company, DSVD means fewer support follow-up calls and lower telephone bills. With a DSVD modem, you will be able to dial your favorite online catalog showrooms, browse the aisles, ask a salesperson a question or two, then place an order. Unlike other online "malls", with DSVD the human interface is still intact. While you're interactively shopping you can talk with salespeople or even other shoppers, just like the real mall.

DSX Digital System Cross-connect frame. A bay or panel to which T-1 lines and DS1 circuit packs are wired and that permits cross-connections by patch cords and plugs. A DSX panel is used in small office applications where only a few digital trunks are installed. See also DACS.

DSX-1 Digital Signal Cross-connect Level 1. The set of parameters for cross connecting DS-1 lines.

DSX-3 The designation for the DS3 point of interface (cross-connect).

DTC 1. Digital Trunk Controller. 2. Digital Transmit Command.

DTE 1. Data Terminal Equipment. In the RS-232-C standard specification, the RS-232-C is connected between the DCE (Data Communications Equipment) and a DTE. The main difference between a DCE and a DTE is that pins two and three are reversed. See also DCE and the Appendix. 2. Defense Technology Enterprise.

DTE-DCE RATE Data terminal equipment/data communications equipment rate. A designation for the maximum rate at which a modem and a PC can exchange information, expressed in kilobits per second (kbps). For maximum performance, a modem must support a DTE-DCE rate in excess of its maximum theoretical throughput.

DTERM A line of proprietary electronic phones made by NEC for use with its PBXs. The Dterm terminal derives its intelligence from its own microprocessor, which detects events and accepts direction from the PBX.

DTLU Digital Trunk and Line Unit. Provides system access for T1-carrier lines used for inter office trunks or remote switching module umbilicals.

DTMF Dual Tone Multi Frequency. A fancy term describing push button or Touchtone dialing. (Touchtone is a not registered trademark of AT&T, though until 1984 it was.) In DTMF, when you touch a button on a push button pad, it makes a tone, actually a combination of two tones, one high frequency and one low frequency. Thus the name Dual Tone Multi Frequency. In U.S. telephony, there are actually two types of "tone" signaling, one used on normal business or home push button/touchtone phones, and one used for signaling within the telephone network itself. When you go into a central office, look for the test board. There you'll see what looks like a standard touchtone pad. Next to the pad there'll be a small toggle switch that allows you to choose the sounds the touchtone pad will make -- either normal touchtone dialing (DTMF) or the network version (MF).

The eight possible tones that comprise the DTMF signaling system were specially selected to easily pass through the telephone network without attenuation and with minimum interaction with each other. Since these tones fall within the frequency range of the human voice, additional considerations were added to prevent the human voice from inadvertently imitating or "falsing" DTMF signaling digits. One way this was done to break the tones into two groups, a high frequency group and a low frequency group. A valid DTMF tone has only one tone in each group. Here is a table of the DTMF digits with their respective frequencies. One Hertz (abbreviated Hz.) is one cycle per second of frequency.

Digit	Low frequency	High frequency
1	697 Hz.	1209 Hz.
2	697	1336
3	697	1477
4	770	1209
5	770	1336
6	770	1477
7	852	1209
8	852	1336
9	852	1477
0	941	1336
*	941	1209
#	941	1477

There are four other digits defined in the DTMF system and usable for specialized applications that cannot be generated by standard telephones They are:

A	697 Hz.	1633 Hz.
B	770	1633
C	852	1633
D	941	1633

Normal telephones (yours and mine) have 12 buttons, thus 12 combinations. Government Autovon (Automatic Voice Network) telephones have 16 combinations, the extra four (those above) being used for "precedence," which in Federal government parlance is a designation assigned to a phone call by the caller to indicate to communications personnel the relative urgency (therefore the order of handling) of the call and to the called person the order in which the message is to be noted. See also LONG TONES and the four following definitions.

DTMF AUTOMATIC ROUTING This is a term relating to a fax server operating on a Novell file server. In this system, the fax software assigns a four-digit number to each user. A fax sender dials the fax line, and after the fax server answers, it sends a special auto routing request signal. The sender dials the four-digit number for the correct user, and the fax is automatically sent to the user's workstation on the LAN.

DTMF CUT-THROUGH The capability of a voice response system to receive DTMF tones while the voice synthesizer is delivering information, i.e. during speech playback. This capability of DTMF cut-through saves the user waiting until the machine has played the whole message (which typically is a menu with options). The user can simply touchtone his response anytime during the message -- when he first hears his selection number, when the message first starts, etc. When the voice processor hears the touchtoned selection (i.e. the DTMF cut-through), it stops speaking and jumps to the chosen selection. For example, the machine starts to say, "If you know the person you're calling, touchtone his extension in now." But before you hear the "If you know" you push button in 230, which you know is Joe's extension. Bingo, the message stops and Joe's extension starts ringing. DTMF Cut-Through is also known as touchtone type-ahead.

DTMF REGISTER A printed circuit card in a switch that converts the DTMF signals coming from the phone into signals which can be used by the switch's stored program control, central computer to do its switching, etc.

DTMF TO DIAL PULSE CONVERSION A PBX feature. DTMF (push button) phones are very popular. But sometimes you install a PBX with push button phones in an area which doesn't have a central office which will respond to push button tones. It's old. In this case, anyone dialing on a push button phone will find that the PBX converts that dialing to rotary pulsing when the PBX accesses a trunk which can't handle push button dialing. All this doesn't speed up the time the call takes to get through. It just speeds up the user's dialing and makes him or her feel she is dealing with a more modern phone system.

DTP DeskTop Publishing.

DTR Data Terminal Ready. A control signal sent from the DTE to the DCE that indicates that the DTE is powered on and ready to communicate. DTR can also be used for hardware flow control.

DTS Digital Termination Systems. Microwave based transmission technology designed for bypass functions for short-hop, line-of-sight applications. It never converts to analog. Is useful in high-volume, pure-data applications in urban settings where line costs are high. It requires FCC license and is referred to formally by FCC as Digital Electronic Message Service, or DEMS.

DTSR Dial Tone Speed Recording.

DTU Digital Test Unit.

DTX Battery-saving feature on a cellular phone that cuts back the output power when you stop speaking.

DU Fiber Optic Connector developed by Nippon Electric Group.

DUA Directory User Agent. The software that accesses the X.500 Directory Service on behalf of the directory user. The directory user may be a person or another software element.

DUAL Distributed Update Algorithm. A routing algorithm that provides fast rerouting (convergence) with minimal consumption of resources.

DUAL ATTACHMENT CONCENTRATOR A concentrator that offers two connections to the FDDI network capable of accommodating the FDDI dual ring, and additional ports for connection of other FDDI devices.

DUAL ATTACHMENT STATION A device used in local area networks to allow access to two separate cable systems at the same time, providing protection against cable failure or damage.

DUAL CABLE A two-cable system in broadband LANs in which coaxial cable provides two physical paths for transmission, one for transmit and one for receive, instead of dividing the capacity of a single cable.

DUAL COAT An optical fiber coating structure consisting of a soft inner coating and a hard outer coating.

DUAL FIBER CABLE A type of optical fiber cable that has two single-fiber cables enclosed in an extruded overjacket of polyvinyl chloride with a rip cord for peeling back the overjacket to access the fibers.

DUAL HEADSET Also known as an integrated headset. A special type of headset for the blind. One jack plugs into a telephone and another jack plugs into a telephone and another jack plugs into a specially configured PC. This PC provides voice synthesized output. The dual headset allows a visually impaired TSR (Telephone Sales Representative) hands-free capability. Example: The Social Security Administration has numerous blind TSRs handling incoming public calls. Dual headsets allow these blind TSRs to perform their duties with no deterioration in public service. This definition provided by Matt Gottlieb, telecommunications specialist for the Social Security Administration.

DUAL HOMING 1. The process of using two geographically diverse frame relay port connections, each with its own set of virtual circuits, to support a network location running critical business applications which cannot afford network down time. 2. A method of cabling FDDI concentrators and stations that permits a alternative path to the dual ring. Can be used in a tree or dual ring of trees topology.

DUAL LINE REGISTRATION The ability to have two cellular telephone numbers in a single cellular telephone. This allows the user to have service on two cellular systems without "roaming" in a second city (and paying higher toll charges) or to have one number on the wireline and one number on the non-wireline system. This assures the cellular user of backup. I know a salesman who lives in Los Angeles, but spends much of his week serving customers in Phoenix. He has a cellular phone with Los Angeles number and a Phoenix number.

DUAL LINE SERVICE Telephone service where two pairs of wires are connected to the premises. One or both could be in service.

DUAL MODE Dual mode is the cellular industry's term for a cellular phone which will work for both analog and digital cellular phone systems. The cellular phone industry is going digital. Today's analog phones won't work on tomorrow's digital systems. But some phones -- dual mode -- will work on both. You need to buy them over today's analog phones. You also need to be careful that the digital mode which you get in your dual mode cellular phone will work with the digital technology of your local carrier. That's not as standard, as yet, as today's analog technology, which works universally in North America.

DUAL NAM Allows a cellular phone user to have two phone numbers with the same or separate carriers. Very useful for someone who spends half his life in one place and half in another. For example, a friend of mine lives in LA, but works weekdays in Phoenix. His handheld cellular has phone numbers from LA and Phoenix carriers.

DUAL PROCESSING An SFT II configuration under Novell's NetWare that assigns parts of the operating system to separate processors. Because SFT II is split into two engines (the IOEngine and the MSEngine), it is possible to install each engine on a separate CPU, creating dual processing system. However, unless such a system is extremely busy, the extra CPU will not help network performance. Dual processing improves performance only when the servers are being used at near-maximum capacity.

DUAL TONE MULTI-FREQUENCY DTMF. A way of signaling consisting of a push button or touchtone dial that sends out a sound which consists of two discrete tones, picked up and interpreted by telephone switches — either PBXs or central offices. See DTMF for a bigger explanation.

DUAL RING OF TREES TOPOLOGY An FDDI network topology of concentrators and nodes that cascades from concentrators on a dual ring.

DUCT A pipe, tube or conduit through which cables or wires are passed. Duct space is always at a premium. If you ever install a duct, make sure it's twice the diameter you think you need. If you're lucky, it will last a couple of years. The cost of putting in thicker or extra ducts is peanuts compared to the cost of having to install additional ones later. Digging up places is getting very expensive, despite Ditch Witch, a company that makes the greatest backhoe trenching equipment. And also has the greatest name.

DUCT CYCLE The relationship between the time a device or facility is used and the time it is idle.

DUCT LINER A small diameter pipe or tubing placed inside conventional underground conduit so you can install fiber optic or cables. Its main purpose is to provide a clean, continuous path with known frictional characteristics.

DUCTILE Capable of being drawn out, hammered thin or being flexed or bent without failure.

DUE DATE The date an event is to occur, i.e. an installation, a change or a connection. Some vendors give accurate due dates. Penalty clauses work most effectively in ensuring due dates are met.

DUMB SWITCH A slang word for a telecommunications switch that contains only basic switching software and relies on instructions sent it by an outside computer. Those instructions are typically fed the "dumb" switch through a cable from the computer to one or more RS-232 serial ports which the dumb switch sports. The switch makes no demands on what type of computer it talks to, but simply insists that it be able to feed the computer questions and promptly receive responses in a form that it (the switch) can understand. Plain ASCII is OK. For example, the dumb switch might signal the computer, "A call is coming in on port 23, what do I do now?" The computer might reply "Answer it and transfer it to extension 23." Or it might say "answer it and put it on hold," or "answer it, put it on hold and play it recording number three." In essence, a dumb switch is anything but. It is in reality an empty cage containing whatever network interface cards the user has chosen. Each of these network interface cards is designed to "talk" to one type of telephone line. That line might be a T-1 line. It might be a normal tip and ring loop start line. It might be a tie trunk with E&M signaling. The card may handle one or many lines, but always of the same type. The card knows how to answer a call or pulse out a call on that particular type of line. It has all the telephony smarts. What it lacks is the intelligence of what to do with the calls. That is provided by the outside computer. Well, almost. Most "dumb" switches do contain rudimentary intelligence -- a small computer and some memory. That computer is usually programmed to handle "default" calls -- and to handle calls should the link to the outside computer fail, or the outside computer itself fail. Dumb switches come in flavors all the way from residing in their own cabinet to being printed circuit cards which reside in one or more of the personal computer's slots. Dumb switches are programmed to do "specialized" telecom applications, for example emergency 911, added value 800 services, cellular switching, automatic call distributors, predictive dialers, etc. They can, of course, be programmed to be "normal" PBXs. The question increasingly being asked is "If I want to program a specialized telecom application should I use a dumb switch or should I use an open PBX?" And the answer is "It depends." Depends on what you want to do. Depends on what software is available, etc. See also OAI.

DUMB TERMINAL A computer terminal with no processing or no programming capabilities. Hence, it derives all its power from the computer it is attached to -- typically over a local hardwire or a phone line. A dumb terminal does not employ a data transmission protocol and only sends or receives data one character at a time, sequentially. There are many reasons for "dumb" terminals. They're cheap. They're foolproof. Operators don't have to mess with floppy disks, etc. The require minimal training. Dumb terminals are typically used for simple data entry and data retrieval tasks. Their disadvantage is that everything must come from the central computer -- not only the information (data record) but also the form in which to put it. This has led to the creation of "intelligent" terminals, which have a modicum of capabilities -- such as an inbuilt (with software) form, some smart function keys and perhaps, a modicum of processing power, etc.

DUMMY LOAD A dissipative impedance-matched network, used at the end of a transmission line to absorb all incident power, usually converted to heat.

DUMP To copy the entire contents of something -- memory, a file on a disk, a complete disk -- to a printer or another magnetic storage medium. A dump is often called a "core dump," which is a bigger dump than dump.

DUOBINARY SIGNAL A pseudobinary-coded signal in which a "O" ("zero") bit is represented by a zero-level electric current or voltage; a "1" ("one") bit is represented by a positive-level current or voltage if the quality of "O" bits since the last "1" bit is even. and by a negative-level current or voltage if the quantity of "O" bits since the last "1" bit is odd. Duobinary signals require less bandwidth than NRZ. Duobinary signaling also permits addition of error-checking bits.

DUPLEX 1. Simultaneous two-way transmission in both directions. A data communications term. 2. Two-sided printing.

DUPLEX CIRCUIT A telephone line or circuit used to transmit in both directions at the same time. Also referred to as full duplex as opposed to half duplex which allows transmission in only one direction at one time.

DUPLEX OPERATION The simultaneous transmission and reception of signals in both directions.

DUPLEX SIGNALING DX. A direct current signaling system that transmits signals directly on the cable pair. Duplex signaling is a facility signaling system and range extension technique that used bridge type detection of small dc changes. Duplex signaling is typically used on long metallic trunks.

DUPLEX TRANSMISSION The simultaneous transmission of two series of signals by a single operating communicating device. A data communications term.

DUPLEXER 1. A device which splits a higher speed source data stream into two separate streams for transmission over two data channels. Another duplexer at the other end puts the two slower speed streams back together into one higher-spread stream. 2. A waveguide device designed to allow an antenna to be used both transmission and reception simultaneously.

DUTY CYCLE The ratio of operating time to total elapsed time for a device that operates intermittently. Usually expressed as a percentage.

DV-1 As in Northern Telecom's PBX/computer product called the Meridian DV-1.

DVD Digital Versatile Disk. A specification announced in early December, 1995 by nine companies for a new type of digital videodisk, similar to CD-ROMs but able to store far more music, video or data in a common format. DVDs will be 5 inches in diameter and will be able to store 4.7 gigabytes on each side, equivalent to 133 minutes of motion picture and sound, or enough to hold most feature-length movies. The companies announcing DVD were Philips, Toshiba, Matsushita Electric Industrial, Sony, Time Warner, Pioneer Electronic, the JVC unit of Matsushita, Hitachi and Mitsubish Electric.

DVI Digital Video Interactive. A name for including still and moving video pictures in material shown on a PC's screen. DVI is part of multimedia. DVI is also Intel's old name for its scheme for digitizing and compressing video and audio for storage, editing, playback and integration into PC applications. The name has been replaced on the software side with Indeo video technology, on the retail side with Smart Video Recorder and on the hardware side with i750 Processors. See DIGITAL VIDEO INTERACTIVE.

DVTS Pronounced "Divitz." Stands for Desktop Video conferencing Telecommunications System.

DVORAK KEYBOARD A keyboard, invented mainly by August Dvorak, on which letters and characters are arranged for faster and easier typing than on the standard QWERTY keyboard. The QWERTY keyboard was actually designed to be difficult to use, to slow down typists so they wouldn't jam the old typewriters' mechanisms! In that respect the QWERTY keyboard resembles the present touchtone in that it also was designed to be slow and difficult to use so that it wouldn't confuse the early and slow central offices of the time.

DX SIGNALING A form of DC (direct current) signaling in which the differences in voltage on two pairs of a four-wire trunk indicates the supervision information, i.e. the call's beginning, its end, etc. See DUPLEX SIGNALING.

DXI Data eXchange Interface. A specification developed by the SMDS (Switched Megabit (or Multi-megabit) Data Services) Interest Group to define the interaction between internetworking devices and CSUs/DSUs that are transmitting over an SMDS access line. SMDS is a way for a corporate network to dial up switched data services as fast as 45 megabits per second.

DYE SUBLIMATION a spectacular printing process where exactly measured temperatures control the amount of ink transferred from colored ribbons to paper. Under high temperature and pressures, the ink is not melted, but is transformed directly to gas, which hardens on the paper after passing through a porous coating. Dye sub printers create very nearly continuous tones, making them great for natural images. Because the gas makes "fuzzy" dots, dye sub is not recommended for sharp-edged "computer-y" graphics or type. But it does turn out gorgeous photo-like images.

DYNAMIC Events are constantly changing.

DYNAMIC ANSWER This a term typically used in Automatic Call Distributors. The ability to dynamically assign the number of ring cycles (interrupt, more or less) to the queue period when agents are unavailable. The implication of being able to assign this number allows return supervision to the calling in person to be delayed and thus not allow billing on 800 INWATS lines to begin. This is a money saving feature. But it can cost you some customers if they get bored waiting for your phones to pick up.

DYNAMIC BACKUP A backup made while the database is active.

DYNAMIC BANDWIDTH ALLOCATION The capability of subdividing large, high-capacity network transmission resources among multiple applications almost instantaneously, and providing each application with only that share of the bandwidth that the application needs at that moment. Dynamic bandwidth allocation is a feature available on certain high-end T-1 multiplexers that allows the total bit rate of the multiplexer's circuits to exceed the bandwidth of the network trunk. This works because the multiplexer only assigns channels on the network trunk to circuits that are transmitting.

DYNAMIC BEAM FOCUSING When you have a curved cathode ray tube, the distance between the gun which shoots the electrons and all the parts of the screen are equal. When you have a flat screen, the distance varies slightly. Some beams have to travel further. When some have to travel not so far, Dynamic beam focusing, a term I first heard used by NEC, focuses each electron to the precise distance it must travel, thus ensuring edge-to-edge clarity on the screen.

DYNAMIC CAPACITY ALLOCATION The process of determining and changing the amount of shared communications capacity assigned to nodes in the network based on current need.

DYNAMIC CONFIGURATION REGISTRY A part of Chicago (Windows 4.0) which contains a list of all the various hardware bits and pieces that make up your computer. The dynamic configuration registry is a vital element of what Microsoft calls "Plug and Play," which is the ability to remove and add bits and pieces of hardware while the machine is running and have the machine automatically recognize those hardwares and alert applications accordingly.

DYNAMIC DATA EXCHANGE DDE. A form of InterProcess Communication (IPC) in Microsoft Windows and OS/2. When two or more programs that support DDE are running simultaneously, they can exchange information and commands. In Windows 3.xx this capability is enhanced with Object Linking and Embedding (OLE). See OLE.

DYNAMIC HOST CONFIGURATION PROTOCOL DHCP. A protocol for automatic TCP/IP configuration that provides static and dynamic address allocation and management.

DYNAMIC LINK LIBRARY DLL. An executable code module for Microsoft Windows that can be loaded on demand and linked at run time, and then unloaded when the code is no longer needed.

DYNAMIC LOAD BALANCING A technique where a switching system, particularly multiple connected ACDs, apportion incoming calls (the load) to balance the workload. This is done dynamically in real time.

DYNAMIC LOAD & STRESS TESTING An advanced and accurate form of load testing, dynamic load and stress testing more accurately presents the variety of stimulus of external callers, systems and networks to a computer telephony system. It will test your system using real-world user actions and a realistic call mix and busy hour usage profile. Most modern computer telephony network and systems provide a number of services to their users. Each of those services may stress the system in a different fashion. As the usage patterns of those users is varied and what each user will do can vary significantly, it is critical to load test systems with traffic patterns as dynamically and as close as possible to the way the system will be used in the real world. This definition courtesy of Steve Gladstone, author of the book Testing Computer Telephony Systems, available from 212-691-8215.

DYNAMIC LOUD SPEAKER A loud speaker in which the diaphragm is driven by means of a small "voice coil" suspended in a powerful magnetic field.

DYNAMIC MEMORY The most common form of memory, used for RAM, with an access speed ranging from about 60 to 150 nanoseconds. (A nanosecond is thousandth of a second.) Dynamic memory is an inexpensive but relatively complicated form of semiconductor memory with two states: presence and absence of electrical charge. Dynamic memory requires a continuous electrical current. All data is lost when the power is cut. Frequent saving files to disk helps preserve your data.

DYNAMIC MICROPHONE A microphone, the coil of which is moved in a strong magnetic field by vibrations striking the diaphragm to which it is attached. Electrical currents are thus generated in the moving coil.

DYNAMIC NODE ACCESS A high-speed bus invented by Dialogic to join together multiple voice processing PEB-based systems. PEB stands for PCM Expansion Bus. See PEB.

DYNAMIC OVERLOAD CONTROL DOC. The feature of a switch which uses its translation tables and intelligence to allow the switch to adapt to changes in traffic loads by re-routing and blocking call attempts.

DYNAMIC PORT ALLOCATION In a voice processing system running multiple applications, dynamic port allocation is automatic allocation of ports based on the traffic being used by each application.

DYNAMIC RAM RAM memory that requires data to be refreshed periodically to prevent its loss in memory.

DYNAMIC RANDOM ACCESS MEMORY RAM which requires electronic refresh cycles every few milliseconds to preserve its data. See also RANDOM ACCESS MEMORY.

DYNAMIC RANGE In a transmission system, the ratio of the overload level to the noise level of the system, usually expressed in decibels. The ratio of the specified maximum level of a parameter (e.g., power, voltage, frequency, or floating point number representation) to its minimum detectable or positive value, usually expressed in decibels.

DYNAMIC RESOURCE ALLOCATION The assignment of network capacity to specific users and specific services as required on a moment-to-moment basis.

DYNAMIC STORAGE ALLOCATION The allocation of memory space while a program is running. The memory is released when the program is complete.

DYNAMIC VARIATION A short time variation outside of steady-state conditions in the characteristics of power delivered to communication equipment.

DYNAMICALLY ADAPTIVE ROUTING An algorithm, used for route determination in packet-switched networks that automatically routes traffic around congested, damaged, or destroyed switches and trunks and allows the system to continue to function over the remaining portions of the network.

DYNAMIC ROUTING Routing that adjusts automatically to changes in network topology or traffic.

DYNAMO An electrical machine which generates a direct current.

DYNAMOTOR A direct current machine having two windings on its armature: one acting as a motor, the other as a generator.

E (ECHO) CHANNEL 16 Kbps ISDN basic rate channel echoing contents of DCEs to DTEs. Used in bidding for access to multipoint link.

E & M In telephony, a trunking arrangement that is generally used for two way (either side may initiate actions) switch-to-switch or switch-to-network connections. It also frequently used for computer telephony system to switch connections. See E & M LEADS.

E & M LEADS The pair of wires carrying signals between trunk equipment and a separate signaling equipment unit. The "M" lead transmits a ground or battery conditions to the signaling equipment. The "E" lead receives open or ground signals from the signaling equipment. These leads are also known as Ear and Mouth Leads. The Ear lead typically means to receive and the Mouth lead typically means to transmit. Changes of voltage on these leads convey such information as seizure of circuit, recognition of seizure, release of circuit, dialed digits, etc. In the old days it was the PBX operators who originated trunk calls by asking the long distance carrier for free trunks using their mouth or M lead. If the carrier had a free trunk, the PBX heard about it through its ear or E lead. See also E & M SIGNALING.

E & M SIGNALING In telephony, an arrangement that uses separate leads, called respectively the "E" lead and "M" lead, for signaling and supervisory purposes. The near end signals the far end by applying -48 volts dc (vdc) to the "M" lead, which results in a ground being applied to the far end's "E" lead. When -48 vdc is applied to the far end "M" lead, the near-end "E" lead is grounded. The "E" originally stood for "ear," i.e., when the near-end "E" lead was grounded, the far end was calling and "wanted your ear." The "M" originally stood for "mouth," because when the near-end wanted to call (i.e., speak to) the far end, -48 vdc was applied to that lead.

When a PBX wishes to connect to another PBX directly or to a remote PBX or extension telephone over a leased voice grade line, a channel on T-1, the PBX uses a special line interface which is quite different from that which it uses to interface to the phones it's attached directly to (i.e. with in-building wires). The basic reason for the difference between a normal extension interface and the long distance interface is that the signaling requirements differ — even if the voice signal parameters such as level and two-wire, 4-wire remain the same. When dealing with tie lines or trunks it is costly, inefficient and too slow for a PBX to do what an extension telephone would do, i.e. go off hook, wait for dial tone, dial, wait for ringing to stop, etc. The E&M tie trunk interface device is the closest thing there is to a standard that exists in the PBX, T-1 multiplexer, voice digitizer telco world. But even then it comes in at least five different flavors. E&M signaling is the most common interface signaling method used to interconnect switching signaling systems with transmission signaling systems. See E & M LEADS.

E LINK Extended Link. A SS7 signaling link used to connect a Signaling End Point (SEP) to an STP pair not considered its home STP pair.

E MAIL Electronic Mail.

E MAIL GATEWAY A LAN application that fetches messages from one electronic mail system, translates them to the format of another electronic mail system, and then sends them to the "post office" of that other system. The post office is the public entry point — the place you put mail you want the other system to receive.

E PURSE Electronic purse. An electronic monetary transaction card being proposed by several government agencies.

E-1 The European equivalent of the North American 1.544 Mbps T-1,except that E-1 carries information at the rate of 2.048 megabits per second. This is the rate used by European CEPT carriers to transmit 30 64 Kbps digital channels for voice or data calls, plus a 64 Kbps channel for signaling, and a 64 Kbps channel for framing (synchronization) and maintenance. CEPT stands for the Conference of European Postal and Telecommunication Administrations. Since robbed-bit signaling is not used (as it is for T-1 in North America) all 8 bits per channel are used to code the waveshape sample. See E1, E2, E3, and T-1.

E-2 Interim data signal that carries four multiplexed E-1 signals. Effective data rate is 8.448 Mbps.

E-3 CEPT signal which carries 16 CEPT E-1s and overhead. Effective data rate is 34.368 Mbps.

E-911 SERVICE Enhanced 911 service. Dial 911 in most major cities and you'll be connected with an emergency service run typically by a combination of the local police and local fire departments. 911 service becomes enhanced 911 emergency reporting service when there is a minimum of two special features added to it. E-911 provides ANI (Automatic Number Identification) and ALI (Automatic Location Information) to the 911 operator. Picture: A call comes in. Someone is dying. The 911 operator's screen comes alive as his phone rings. The number calling is on the screen. The caller is dying and needs an ambulance. The operator punches a button or two and his screen immediately indicates the location of the ambulance dispatch center nearest the caller. The operator contacts the dispatch center, another button may dispatch a fax of a map of how to get there to the ambulance and an ambulance gets there in short order and saves a live. (Remember, this is a book, not the real world.)

E-BEND A smooth change in the direction of the axis of a waveguide, throughout which the axis remains in a plane parallel to the direction of electric E-field (transverse) polarization.

E-MAIL Electronic Mail.

E-TDMA Extended Time Division Multiple Access. A proposed, new, standard for cellular. Other standards are TDMA (Time Division Multiple Access), CDMA (Code Division Multiple Access) and NAMPS (Narrow Advanced Mobile Phone Service). Refers to the extended (digital cellular) transmission technology developed by Hughes Network Systems. E-TDMA is alleged to have 15 times the capacity of today's analog cellular phone systems — in other words to allow the simultaneous use of 15 times as many cellular phones as today's analog cellular phone system.

E.164 CCITT recommendation for international telecommunication numbering, especially ISDN, BISDN, and SMDS. An evolution of normal telephone numbers. In short, a scheme to assign numbers to phone lines.

E1 Another name given to the CEPT (Conference of European Postal and Telecommunication Administration) digital telephony format devised by the ITU-T that carries data at the rate of 2.048 Mbps (DS-1 level). Plesiochronous system using TDM to carry 32 64 Kb/s digital channels. E1 is the rate used by European CEPT carriers to transmit 30 64 Kb/s digital channels for voice or data calls, plus a 64 Kb/s channel for signaling, and a 64 Kb/s channel for framing and mainte-nance. Plesiochronous means "almost synchronous." In the network sense, when two networks operate with clocks of sufficiently high quality such that the signals in the two networks are nearly synchronous, the networks are plesiochronous. In the synchronization hierarchy, stratum I clocks are required for plesiochronous operation. See E-1 and T0-1, which is the North American equivalent.

E2 Data signal that carries four multiplexed E-1 signals. Effective data rate is 8.448 Mb/s.

E3 CEPT signal which carries 16 CEPT- Is and overhead. Effective data rate is 34.368 Mb/s.

EA SEE EQUAL ACCESS.

EADAS Engineering and Administrative Data Acquisition System.

EADAS/NWM EADAS NetWork Management.

EARLY PACKET DISCARD EPD. A congestion control technique that selec-tively drops all but the last ATM cell in a Classical IP over ATM packet. When con-gestion occurs, EPD discards cells at the beginning of an IP packet, leaving the rest intact. The last cell is preserved because it alerts the switch and the destina-tion station of the beginning of a new packet. Because IP packets from cells have been discarded receive no acknowledgment from the source. Most vendors expect EPD to be used in conjunction with unspecified bit rate (UBR) service. Switches simply junk UBR cells when congestion occurs, without regard for appli-cation traffic. By discarding ceiling selectively, so that whole IP packets are resent, EPD makes UBR a safer option.

EARLY TOKEN RELEASE This is a method of token passing which allows for two tokens to exist on the network simultaneously. It is used primarily in 16-Mbps token ring LANs. On a regular 4-Mbps token ring LAN, the token is passed on only after the sending computer receives its message back from the destination com-puter. With early token release, the sending computer does not wait for its mes-sage to return before passing the token. This means there are two tokens on the network at the same time. This is done to take advantage of the idle time created on the faster token ring. While the message is moving to its destination and back the sending computer is idle. On the 4-Mbps token ring, this is not much of a prob-lem since most of the time the message is on the ring. On the 16-Mbps token ring less of this idle time is transmission time and more is taken by copying the mes-sage to the token ring card. That is, on the faster ring, there is more of a window for a second token. Early token release is especially helpful when traffic is heavy.

EARN European Academic Research Network. A network using BITNET tech-nology connecting universities and research labs in Europe.

EAROM An acronym for Electrically Alterable Read-Only Memory. A type of ROM chip which can be erased and reprogrammed without having to be removed from the circuit board. An EAROM is reprogrammed electrically faster and more conveniently than an EPROM (Erasable Programmable Read-Only Memory). An EAROM chip does not lose its memory when power is turned off.

EARTH GROUND The connection of an electrical system to earth. This connection is necessary to provide lightning and static protection as well as to establish the zero-voltage reference for the system. See EARTH GROUNDING.

EARTH GROUND CONNECTION The conductor which connects directly to earth ground usually via a water pipe or possibly via a copper rod driven into the earth. This ground is different than the logic ground used in electronic circuits.

EARTH GROUND ELECTRODE The conducting body in contact with the earth. The grounding electrode may be a metallic cold water pipe when used in conjunction with a driven rod, a mat, a grid, etc. Earth should never be used as the sole equipment grounding conductor.

EARTH GROUNDING The purpose of earth grounding is essentially threefold: 1. Lightning protection; 2. Static protection; and 3. Establish a zero voltage reference. See GROUND and GROUNDING.

EARTH STATION The antenna and associated equipment used to receive and/or transmit telecommunications signals via satellite.

EARTHING There are two distinct and unique categories in the broad area called grounding. One is earthing, which is designed to guard against the adverse effects of lightning, assist in the reduction of static and bring a zero-voltage reference to system components in order that logic circuits can communicate from a known reference. The other category of grounding is known as equipment grounding. This is the primary means of protecting personnel from electrocution. According to the Electric Power Research Institute, "electrical wiring and grounding defects are the source of 90% of all equipment failures." Many telephone system installer/contractors have found that checking for and repairing grounding problems can solve many telephone system problems, especially intermittent "no trouble found" problems. As electrical connections age, they loosen, corrode and become subject to thermal stress that can increase the impedance of the ground path or increase the resistance of the connection to earth. Equipment is available to test for proper grounding. One of our favorite devices is made by Ecos Electronics in Oak Park, Il. Before you attach any equipment (computer, telephone, hi-fi set, etc.) to an improperly grounded electrical outlet, you should have the problems corrected. See also GROUND and GROUNDING.

EAS Extended Area Service. A novel name for a larger than normal local telephone calling area. The local phone company extends its subscribers the option of paying less per month for a small calling area and paying extra per individual call outside that area (i.e. the extended area), or paying more per month flat rate but having a larger calling area (i.e. having extended area service).

EASE A voice processing applications generator from Expert Systems, Inc. in Atlanta GA.

EASY Sabre Consumer oriented version of American Airlines' Sabre reservation system, accessible as an option on most on line services (American On line,

CompuServe, Delphi, GEnie, Prodigy, etc). It will give you airline flights and prices, and it will allow you to make reservations.

EASYNET The name of DEC's internal corporate network.

EAX Electronic Automatic eXchange. Term used throughout the non-Bell telephone industry to refer to an electronic central office. Similar to ESS (Electronic Switching System), the term used by AT&T and the Bell operating telephone companies.

EBCDIC (Pronounced Eb-si-dick.) Extended Binary Coded Decimal Interexchange Code. It is the way IBM codes characters, letters and numbers into a digital binary stream for use in its larger computers. EBCDIC codes characters into eight bits. This gives it 256 possible characters, 2 x 2 x 2 x 2 x 2 x 2 x 2 x 2 = 256. See also EXTENDED CHARACTER SET.

EBCDIC is mainly used in IBM mainframes and minicomputers, while ASCII is used in IBM and non-IBM desktop microcomputers. EBCDIC is not compatible with ASCII, meaning that a computer which understands EBCDIC will not understand ASCII. But there are many real-time and non-real time translation programs that will convert text files back and forth. A good program is Word-For-Word from MasterSoft. See ASCII.

EBDI Electronic Business Data Interchange. Term for EDI (Electronic Data Interchange). See EDI.

EBONE European Backbone. A pan-European network backbone service.

EBS 1. Electronic Business Set.

2. Enhanced Business Service (also known as P-Phone) is an analog Centrex offering provided by Northern Telecom. It operates over a single-pair subscriber loop., providing normal full duplex audio conversations and a secondary 8 KHz half-duplex amplitude shift-keyed signal, which is used to transmit signaling information to and from the Northern Telecom-equipped central office.

3. Emergency Broadcast System. Some local radio stations have volunteered their services to be part of a group of radio stations which would broadcast information should there be a public emergency. They operate the EBS under the aegis of the Federal Communications Commission. Such emergency would be a natural disaster, a technological disaster or a war.

EBU European Broadcasting Union

EC European Community. Also known as the Common Market; an organization of 12 nations in Western Europe that has its own institutional structure and decision-making framework. The intent of the organization is to promote trade and reduce barriers. Member nations are Belgium, Denmark, France, Germany, Greece, Ireland, Italy, Luxembourg, the Netherlands, Portugal, Spain and the United Kingdom.

ECCENTRICITY Like concentricity a measure of the center of a conductor's location with respect to the circular cross section of the insulation. Expressed as a percentage of center displacement of one circle within the other.

ECH Enhanced Call Handling. ECH systems are those in which a telephone call is handled "intelligently" b a variety of network, human, computer and telecommunications resources. ECH systems cover those from voice mail, to interactive voice response to computer telephone integration to fax-on-demand to complex telephone networks.

ECHELON The name of a startup company in Palo Alto that is making a micro-processor chip destined for mundane household appliances like toasters, air conditioners, ovens, etc. The idea is that chip will be used by these devices to talk to other devices and thus coordinate their coming on and going off and doing things. The chips are destined to be networked together. Early uses for the chip includes smoke detectors which call you when they detect smoke and wall switches that detect when you come into a room and turn the lights on.

ECHO 1. European Commission Host Organization.

2. Exactly what you expect it to mean. You hear yourself speak. Echoes happen in both voice and data conversation. Echoes are good and bad. In voice, an echo happens when the equipment meant to amplify the voice of the party at one end, picks up the signals from the party at the other end, and amplifies them back to that party. Some echo is acceptable (in fact, almost a necessity) in voice conversations. It's called SIDETONE. When the speaker can hear himself speak through the receiver, sidetone gives the speaker some feeling his conversation is actually going through. But too much (i.e. too loud) echo is unacceptable. There are devices called echo suppressors, which do exactly that.

In low speed or on-line data conversations, an echo is positively vital. An echo in a data conversation is where I send my words to the distant computer which "echoes" them back to me and my screen displays them. This way I can visually check if the distant computer received my words/data accurately. In some software programs there's a command called ECHO or ECHOPLEX. Switch it one way, the distant computer echoes the words to my screen. Switch it the other, the words I'm typing on my keyboard are put on my screen.

There are two basic transmission modes in data communications — full duplex and half duplex. In full duplex, I have simultaneous two-way data flowing. In full duplex, I therefore have the capacity to "echo" back the data I am sending and have it displayed on my screen. But this "echoing" depends on the capability and/or programming of the computer at the other end. All dial-up services — Tymnet, GTE Telenet, MCI Mail, etc. — will echo my data back to me so I can check it.

Some computers, such as the extremely dumb Compugraphic typesetter which typeset the first edition of this book, won't send an echo. In this case, if I want to see the data I am sending, I can change the parameters on my communications software to "half duplex." This way I will see what I am sending, but I will not see what the computer is receiving. Which may be very different. (And with our Compugraphic often is.) Of course, watching characters being echoed across your screen is a very poor method of data transmission and only useful in on-line transmissions. Some form of error-checking protocol is much better.

An echo is also a public discussion group that extends over more than one BBS (bulletin board system) via echomail.

ECHO ATTENUATION In a communications circuit (4- or 2-wire) in which the two directions of transmission can be separated from each other, the attenuation of echo signals that return to the input of the circuit under consideration. Echo attenuation is expressed as the ratio of the transmitted power to the received echo power in decibels. See also ATTENUATION.

ECHO CANCELLER Device that allows for the isolation and filtering of unwanted signal caused by echoes from the main transmitted signal. In data communications networks, echo cancelers are used in the same way as PADS are in the network, but some brands of echo cancelers have the ability of being disabled by a 2100 Hertz tone transmitted by the data device prior to the exchange of the data device's handshaking protocol. If the echo canceler cannot be disabled by the data device, it will block the data call from completing.

ECHO CANCELLATION Technique that allows for the isolation and filtering of unwanted signals caused by echoes from the main transmitted signal. See ECHO CANCELLATION.

ECHO CHECK A technique for verifying data sent to another location by returning the received data (echoing it back) to the sending end.

ECHO MODELING A mathematical process where an echo is conceptually created from an audio waveform and subtracted from that form. The process involves sampling the acoustical properties of a room and guessing what form an echo might take, then removing that information from the audio signal.

ECHO RETURN LOSS ERL. The difference between a frequency signal and the echo on that signal as it reaches its destination.

ECHO SUPPRESSOR Used to reduce the annoying effects of echoes in telephone connections. The worst echoes occur on satellite circuits. An echo suppressor works by turning off transmission in the reverse direction while a person is talking, thus effectively making the circuit one way. An echo suppressor obviously impedes full-duplex data — data flowing both ways simultaneously. Echo suppressors are turned off by the high-pitched tone (typically 2025 Hz) in the answering modem, which it uses to signal it's answered the phone and is ready for a data conversation.

ECHO SUPPRESSOR DISABLER An echo suppressor disabler is a device which causes an echo suppressor to be disabled (i.e. turned off). Echo suppressors are turned off by the high-pitched tone (typically 2025 Hz) in the answering modem, which it uses to signal it's answered the phone and is ready for a data conversation. A disabled echo suppressor stays disabled until the circuit is disconnected and restored to its "ready" connection. Because an echo suppressor hinders full duplex transmission in data communications, it is necessary to disable the echo suppressor.

ECHOMAIL A public message area or conference on a bulletin board system (BBS) that is "echoed" to other systems in a BBS network. EchoMail is organized into different groups, each with a different topic and the term normally references communications on a FidoNet network. Also a term referring to the electronic transfer of messages between bulletin board systems.

ECHOPLEX A way of checking the accuracy of data transmitted whereby the data received are returned to the sender for comparison with the original data. Somewhat time consuming. Used typically in slow speed transmissions. See ECHO.

ECITC European Committee for Information Technology testing and Certification.

ECL Emitter Coupled Logic.

ECM Error Correction Mode. An enhancement to Group 3 fax machines.

Encapsulated data within HDLC frames providing the received with an opportunity to check for, and request retransmission of garbled data. See FACSIMILE and V.17.

ECMA European Computer Manufacturers Association. See also CEPT.

ECOC European Conference on Optical Communication.

ECONOMIC BANDWIDTH An AT&T term for the maximum bandwidth that a physical medium can support without a significant increase in its cost.

ECONOMIST Someone who didn't have the personality to make accountant. God apparently invented economists in order to make weather forecasters look good. See ACCOUNTANT.

ECONOMY OF SCALE As throughput gets bigger, so the per unit cost comes down. This is the argument used by economists to justify monopolies — namely that the per unit costs of one supplier are far lower than having two suppliers. The economy of scale argument is used to justify having only one water company in town. It makes more sense in that industry than in the telephone industry.

It was once used in the telephone industry to justify one combined local phone company/long distance phone company/one supplier of terminal equipment. This argument does not really apply to telephony as technological breakthroughs have brought down the cost of getting into the telephone industry and have allowed smaller, competitive companies to become cost effective. Some large telecommunications monopolies, in fact, are experiencing diseconomies of scale. In this case, their cost of per unit business starts to rise as they get very large. Diseconomies of scale are caused by bloated bureaucracies and inertia in management decision making.

ECONOPATH CALLING PLANS Discount plans for New York City businesses to make calls in their regional calling area. For example, Econopath offers a Manhattan business a discount for calls to the East Suffolk region.

ECP 1. Enhanced Call Processing. An Octel term for an interactive customized menu in its voice mail system which provides levels of call routing. See ENHANCED CALL PROCESSING.

2. Extended Capabilities (Parallel) Port. At the same time, as the Enhanced Parallel Port (EPP) was developed by Intel Corp., Xircom Inc. and Zenith, two companies — Microsoft and Hewlett-Packard Co. — were developing a spec called ECP - the Extended Capabilities Port. This type of port offers about the same high speed, two-way throughput as an EPP port. But it can use DMA and a small buffer to provide smoother performance in a multitasking environment, which is why Microsoft supports ECP over EPP. Both specs were defined by the IEEE 1284 committee last year. Chip sets that support 1284 (and therefore can operate in ECP mode or a new EPP 1284 mode) started appearing in PCs early in 1994. See EPP.

ECPA Electronic Communications Privacy Act.

ECS Energy Communications Services.

ECSA Exchange Carriers Standards Association. See EXCHANGE CARRIERS STANDARDS ASSOCIATION.

ECTUA European Council of Telecommunications Users Association.

ECTF Enterprise Computer Telephony Forum is a California non-profit mutual benefit corporation, formed to focus on the technical challenges of interoperability among Computer Telephony Integration (CTI) products. It was formed in the Spring of 1995. Information on the ECTF is available from The ECT Forum, Foster City, CA 415-578-6852. ectf@sbexpos.com. On July 31, 1995, the Versit companies cooperating in computer telephony integration (Apple, AT&T, IBM, Novell and Siemens) announced that they will bring the results of their CTI development efforts (Versit CTI Encyclopedia including Versit TSAPI) to the ECTF, enabling review and use by the companies represented in this forum. In support of these efforts, the Versit CTI companies are also joining ECTF.

EDA Electronic Design Automation.

EDDA The European Digital Dealers Association. An European association of DEC resellers. EDDA members include VARs, systems integrators, leasing companies and service organizations.

EDDY CURRENT LOSSES Losses in electrical devices using iron, due to the currents set up in it by magnetic action.

EDF Erbium-Doped Fiber.

EDFA Erbium-Doped Fiber Amplifier. A form of fiber optical amplification where the transmitted light signal passes through a section of erbium-doped fiber and is amplified by means of a laser pump diode. EDFA is used in transmitter booster amplifiers, in-line repeating amplifiers, and receiver preamplifiers.

EDGE CONNECTOR A connector made of strips of brass or other conductive metal found at the edge of a printed circuit board. The connector plus into a socket of another circuit board to exchange electronic signals.

EDGE SITE A remote network site. A site at the edge of the network.

EDH Electronic Document Handling.

EDI Electronic Data Interchange. A series of standards which provide computer-to-computer exchange of business documents between different companies' computers over phone lines. These standards allow for the transmission of purchase orders, shipping documents, invoices, invoice payments, etc. between an enterprise and its "trading partners." A trading partner in EDI parlance is a supplier, customer, subsidiary, or any other organization with which an enterprise conducts business. EDI software translates fixed field or "flat" files that are extracted from applications into a standard format and hands off the translated data to communications software for transmission. EDI standards are supported (i.e. have been adopted) by virtually every computer company in the country and increasingly, by every packet switched data communications company. For example, you can use IBM VAN — IBM's Value Added Network for Electronic Data Interchange. The formats used to convert the documents into EDI data are defined by international standards bodies and by specific industry bodies. See also IES.

EDISON BATTERY A type of storage battery in which the elements are nickel and iron and the electrolyte is potassium hydroxide. An old type of battery.

EDISON EFFECT The phenomenon attributed to Edison, that when a filament is incandescent a current will flow between it and another electrode in the tube. In other words, the light bulb.

EDITING Editing is a familiar process of changing the content of files to achieve more effective communication by cutting, pasting, cropping, resizing, or copying. Multimedia editing can be done on all types of media: voice annotations, music, still images, motion video, graphics and text. Tools for editing vary from simple tools for email voice annotations to more sophisticated tools for video manipulation. See also ELECTRONIC MAIL.

EDITOR A software program used to modify programs or files while they are being prepared or after they are (allegedly) complete. An editor is really a very rudimentary word processing program. When you buy MS-DOS, one of the programs you get is a rudimentary editing program called EDLIN. Most programmers, however, now prefer more advanced editors, like ZEdit. This dictionary was written in ZEdit.

EDLIN The MS-DOS line editor that comes with DOS and which you can use to create and edit batch files and other small text files. It's not very good. There are far better editors around, including QEdit.

EDLS Extended Digital Subscriber Line. The ISDN EDSL combines 23 B-channels and one 64-Kbps D-channel on a single line. Also called the Primary Access Rate.

EDMS An imaging term. Engineering Document Management System.

EDO RAM Extended Data-Out Random Access Memory. A form of DRAM (Dynamic Random Access memory) that, according to PC Magazine, speeds accesses to consecutive locations in memory by 1. assuming that the access to next memory will target an address in the same transistor row as the previous one and 2. latching data at the output of the chip so it can be read even as the inputs are being changed for the next memory location. EDO RAM reduces memory access times by an average of 10 percent over with standard DRAM chips and costs only a little more to manufacture. EDO RAM has already replaced DRAM in many computers, and the trend is expected to continue. See also DRAM and EDRAM.

EDP Electronic Data Processing. Also DP, as in Data Processing. Basically, a machine (also called a computer) that receives, stores, operates on, records and outputs data. The word "electronic" was added to Data Processing when the industry moved away from tab cards — the 80 column "do not spindle," etc. — and was able to accept data electronically, instead of electromechanically as with the tab cards. People in the industry used to be called EDPers. Now the term MIS — Management Information System — is more common.

EDRAM Enhanced Dynamic Random Access Memory. A form of DRAM (Dynamic RAM) that boosts performance by placing a small complement of static RAM (SRAM) in each DRAM chip and using the SRAM as a cache. Also known as cached DRAM, or CDRAM.

EDS See 1962.

EDSL See EXTENDED DIGITAL SUBSCRIBER LINE.

EDTV See EXTENDED DEFINITION TV.

EDUTAINMENT The answer to the question "What do you get when you cross educational material with interactive video?" A term coined by "someone who obviously knows nothing about either education or entertainment," says Laura Buddine, president of multimedia games maker Tiger Media. But it is becoming popular in residences and it's typically played on PCs with CD-ROM players.

EE End to End signaling. Punch DTMF are sent through the lines to signal the end of a conversation. A tone code is also used to access long distance carriers, to signal your answering machine, or to access your voice mail.

EEC European Economic Community.

EEHLLAPI Entry Emulator High Level Language Applications Programming Interface. An IBM API subset of HLLAPI.

EEHO Either End Hop Off. In private networks, a switch program that allows a call destined for an off-net location to be placed into the public network at either the closest switch to the origination or the closest switch to the destination. The choice is usually by time of day and is usually done to take advantage of cheaper rates.

EEMA European Electronic Messaging Association.

EEPROM Electronically Erasable Programmable Read Only Memory. A read only memory device which can be erased and reprogrammed. Typically, it is programmed electronically (not electromagnetically) with ultraviolet light. EEPROMs don't lose their memory when you lose power. EEPROM used to be often used in PBXs and were the way manufacturers of older style PBXs upgraded their software. In other words, every time they sent you a software upgrade, they'd send you a bunch of chips. You'd pull out a bunch of chips on one of the main boards in the your PBX. And you'd replace them with the new chips. When you don't have a disk drive (and in the olden days disk drives were very expensive), EEPROMs were the only way to go. EEPROM Setup in a computer allows it to recognize certain system board configurations during initialization. You, the user, can then choose options such as the type of memory chips installed and base memory size without changing jumpers on the system board.

EES Escrow Encryption Standard.

EETDN End-to-End Transit Delay Negotiation.

EF&I Engineer, Furnish and Install.

EFD Event Forwarding Discriminator. A wireless telecommunications term. Software that contains a discriminator that determines if a notification should be forwarded on to a particular destination.

EFFICIENCY FACTOR In data communications, the ratio of the time to transmit a text automatically and at a specified modulation rate, to the time actually required to receive the same text at a specified maximum error rate.

EFOC European Fiber Optics and Communications conference.

EFT Electronic Funds Transfer. The moving of bits of data from one bank to another. Done in place of moving little green pieces of paper, called money.

EFTA European Free Trade Association.

EFTPOS Electronic Funds Transfer Point Of Sale.

EGA Enhanced Graphics Adapter. Second color video interface standard established for IBM PCs. Maximum resolution is 640 x 350 pixels. See MONITOR.

EGO SURFING Scanning the Net, databases, print media, or research papers looking for mentions of your own name.

EGP Exterior Gateway Protocol. An Internet protocol for exchanging routing information between autonomous systems.

EGRESS The exit point. This typically refers to information being sent out of, as opposed to being sent in to a frame relay port connection or other network element.

EHz Exahertz (10 to the 18th power hertz). See also SPECTRUM DESIGNATION OF FREQUENCY.

EI Refers to Europe's 2.048 Mbps (T-1 type) digital carrier system.

EIA Electronic Industries Association. A Washington, D.C. trade organization of manufacturers which sets standards for use of its member companies, conducts educational programs and lobbies in Washington for its members' collective prosperity. In April 1988, a new association called the Telecommunications Industry Association was formed by a merger of the US Telecommunications Suppliers Association (USTSA) and the Electronics Industries Association's Information and Telecommunications Technologies Group (EIA/ITG). See EIA INTERFACE.

EIA-232-D New version of RS-232-C physical layer interface adopted in 1987.

EIA-530 Interface using DB-25 connector, but for higher speeds than EIA-232. Has balanced signals (like EIA-422) except for 3 maintenance signals which are EIA-423. Besides Transmit and Receive data, RTS, CTS, DSR, DTR, and DCD are

EIA-561 EIA-232E interface on DIN-8 connector (like Macs use).

EIA 568 An EIA standard for commercial building wiring. The standard covers four general areas; the medium, the topology of he medium, terminations and connections, and general administration. See EIA/TIA 568 below.

EIA-569 Commercial Building Standard for Telecommunications Pathways & Spaces - EIA/TIA, 1991. Lays out guidelines for sizing telecom closets, equipment rooms, conduit, etc . Every architect doing commercial buildings should have to memorize it. Few have even heard of it!

EIA-574 EIA-232E interface on DE-9 connector. (OK, DE is a bit pedantic. Most call it a DB-9, though you'll never find one in a parts book).

EIA-606 Telecommunications Administration Standard for Commercial Buildings. Guidelines covering design and identification of two- level backbone cabling for individual buildings and for campuses.

EIA INTERFACE A set of signal characteristics (time, duration, voltage and current) set up by the Electronic Industries Association to standardize the transfer of information between different electronic devices, like computers, modems, printers, etc. The most famous EIA interface is the RS-232-C (now called the RS-232-D and shortly to be called the RS-232-E). EIA-232 specifies three things: the functions of the interchange circuits, the electrical characteristics, AND the connector (EIA-232-E includes two different connectors).

In contrast, the ITU-T's V.24 specifies ONLY the interchange circuit FUNCTIONS. V.28 specifies electrical characteristics compatible with EIA-232. ISO 2110 is the internal standard that defines the 25-pole D-shell connector compatible with EIA-232. Following the merger of EIA and the ITG part of EIA, all formed EIA telecommunications standards are now EIA/TIA publications and the standard referred to is now known as EIA/TIE-232-D, edition D, being the most recent. See EIA, EIA/TIA-RS-232-E and RS-232-E.

EIA/TIA-232-E The latest version of the familiar RS-232-C serial data transfer standard for communicating between Data Terminal Equipment (DTE) and Data Circuit Terminating equipment employing serial binary data interchange. (EIA/TIE's exact words.) This standard defines the serial ports on computers, which communicate with such things as external modems, serial printers, data PBXs, etc. You can get your very own copy of the 36-page standard from the EIA Standard Sales Office, 2001 Pennsylvania Avenue, NW, Washington D.C. 20006 202-457-4966. See also the APPENDIX.

EIA/TIA 568 EIA/TIA 568 Commercial Building Wiring Standard. This telecommunications standard in early 1991 was out for industry review under draft specification SP-1907B. Its purpose is to define a generic telecommunications wiring system for commercial buildings that will support a multi-product, multi-vendor environment. It covers topics such as:

.Recognized Media .Topology .Cable Lengths/Performance .Interface Standards .Wiring Practices .Hardware Practices .Administration

EIDE Enhanced IDE. See IDE and ENHANCED IDE.

EIGHT HUNDRED SERVICE 800-Service. A generic and common (and not trademarked) term for AT&T's, MCI's, US Sprint's and the Bell operating companies' IN-WATS service. All these IN-WATS services have "800" as their "area code." Dialing an 800-number is free to the person making the call. The call is billed to the person or company being called.

800 Service works like this: You're somewhere in North America. You dial 1-800 and seven digits. Your local central office sees the "1" and recognizes the call as long distance. It ships that call to a bigger central office (or perhaps processes the call itself). At that central office it's processed, a machine will recognize the 800 "area code" and examine the next three digits. Those three digits will tell which long distance carrier to ship the call to.

Until 800 portability, happened in May, 1993 each 800 provider (local and long distance company) was assigned specific 800 three digit "exchanges." For example, MCI had the exchange 999. AT&T had the exchange 542. If you wanted a phone number beginning with 800-999, then you had to subscribe to MCI 800 service. If you wanted a phone number beginning with 800-542, you had to subscribe to AT&T 800 service. With 800 Portability that is no longer the case.

Here is a history of what the phone industry calls 800 Data Base Access Service. It comes courtesy Bellcore:

• After divestiture (1984), the seven regional telecommunications companies began to provide limited 800 Service on their own as well as in conjunction with interexchange carriers. The regional companies transported 800 calls only within their own calling areas. The 800 number — containing 10 digits in accordance with the North American Numbering Plan (NANP) — was routed onto the long distance carrier's networks.

•The Common Carrier Bureau of the Federal Communications Commission (FCC) endorsed an incremental approach that would ultimately give the seven companies the right to create their own 800 Service architecture and eliminate reliance on the only existing signaling system (AT&T's). That approach involved assigning to 800 service providers one or more special numbers from the NANP. These numbers, known as "NXX codes," allowed carriers (MCI, Sprint, NY Telephone, etc.) to identify their own 800 numbers and offer their customers 800 numbers.

• Bellcore — Bell Communications Research — began to develop a new network architecture that would allow an 800 Service subscriber to change to another carrier without changing their existing 800 number (full number portability), in accordance with a September 1991 FCC order. That order declared that 800 data base service should be implemented by March 1993 (later extended to May, 1993) and that the old NXX plan be eliminated as long as access times met certain FCC standards.

• In September 1991, the FCC endorsed the plan initially set forth by the Bell operating companies, which provided that the administration of the Number Administration and Service Center (NASC) be transferred from Bellcore to an independent third party outside the telecommunications industry. Lockheed Information Management Systems Company (IMS) was selected by competitive bid to succeed Bellcore as NASC administrator.

• How 800 data base service works: The telecommunications network architecture that supports 800 Data Base Access Service is considered "intelligent" because data bases within the network supplement the call processing function performed by network switches. The Service uses a Common Channel Signaling (CCS) network and a collection of computers that accept message queries and provide responses. When a caller dials an 800 number, a Service Switching Point (SSP) recognizes from the digits "8-0-0" that the call requires special treatment and processes that call according to routing instructions it receives from a centralized database. This database, called the Service Control Point (SCP), can store millions of customer records.

• Although each regional company maintains whatever number of SCPs it needs to provide 800 Data Bases Access Service, information about how an 800 call should be handled is entered into the SCP through the off-line Bellcore support system called the Service Management System (SMS). SMS is a national computer system which administers assignment of 800 numbers to 800 service providers. It is located in Kansas City, maintained by Southwestern Bell Telephone Company, and administered by Bellcore with information received from 800 Number Administration and Service Center (NASC). The NASC provides user support and system administration for all 800 Service providers who access the SMS/800."

Because 800 service is essentially a data base lookup service, there are a endless "800 services" you can create. Here are the variables that can be used to influence how an 800 phone call is handled and where an 800 phone call ultimately gets sent:

• The number calling. Virtually all 800 calls in North America (excepting Mexico) now come with the information as to from which number the call came.

• The number being called.

• The time of day, week, month etc.

• The instructions given at that particular moment. A computer might say "Sorry, our phone system is busy. We can't take any more calls in New York. Please send this one and all subsequent ones — until informed otherwise — to our phone system in Kansas City.

Here are a few examples of the services 800 providers have created using the above variables:

• TIME OF DAY ROUTING: Allows you to route incoming calls to alternate, pre-determined locations at specified days of the week and times of the day.

• PERCENTAGE ALLOCATION ROUTING: Allows you to route pre-selected percentages of calls from each Originating Routing Group (ORG) to two or more answering locations. Allocation percentages can be defined for each ORG (typically an area code), for each day type and for each time slot.

• SINGLE NUMBER: The same 800 number is used for intrastate and interstate calling.

• CALL BLOCKAGE: You can block calling areas by state or area code. The caller from a blocked area hears the message: "Your 800 call cannot be completed as dialed. Please check the number and dial again or call 1- 800-XXX-XXXX for assistance." (You may want to block callers from areas which didn't see your special commercial, for example.)

• POINT OF CALL ROUTING: Allows a customer to route calls made to a single 800 number to different terminating locations based on the call's point of origin (state or area code.) You establish Originating Routing Groups (ORGs) and designate a specific answering location for each ORG's call.

• CALL ATTEMPT PROFILE: A special service that allows subscribers to purchase a record of the number of attempts that are made to an 800 number. The attempts are captured at the Network Control Point, and from this data a report is produced for the subscriber.

• ALTERNATE ROUTING: Allows a customer to create alternate routing plans that can be activated by the 800 carrier upon command in the event of an emergency. Several alternate plans can be set up using any features previously subscribed to in the main 800 routing plan. Each alternate plan must specify termination in a location previously set up during the order entry process.

• DIALED NUMBER IDENTIFICATION SERVICE: DNIS. Allows a customer to terminate two or more 800 numbers to a single service group and to receive pulsed digits to identify the specific 800 number called. DNIS is only available on dedicated access lines with four-wire E & M type signaling or a digital interface. The customer's equipment must be configured to process the DNIS digits.

• ANI: The carrier will deliver to you the incoming 800 call plus the phone number of the calling party. See also ANI, COMMON CHANNEL INTEROFFICE SIGNALING and ISDN.

• COMMAND ROUTING: Allows the customer to route calls differently on command at any time his business requires it.

• FOLLOW ME 800: Allows the customer to change his call routing whenever he wants to.

Now to the question of how to complete an 800 call. There are essentially two ways to terminate an 800 call. You can end the call on your normal phone line — business or residence. This is the phone line you use for normal in and out calling. That's called not having a dedicated local loop. Or you can end the call on a dedicated phone line. By "dedicated," we mean there's a leased line between your office and the local office of your 800 provider, local or long distance carrier. There are several ways this dedicated "line" might be installed. It could be part of a T-1 circuit. It could be one circuit on one single copper pair. It could even be a phone number dedicated to your 800 number — a phone number you can't make an outgoing call on.

There is one major problem with 800 lines. They're hard to test. You may have bought an 800 number to cover the country, but you may be unreachable from certain parts of the country for weeks on end and not know it. That's part of the problem of a service which uses multiple databases lookup tables and relies on many exchanges to carry the calls. Many companies — like the airlines — recruit their distant employees to call their 800 number regularly. The only part of your 800 IN-WATS line you can test is your local loop (assuming you have one) from the local central office to your office. If you have a dedicated, leased line, you may have local Plant Test Numbers — standard seven digit numbers. You can call these numbers. If they work, you know that the end parts of your lines are working. One of our WATS lines is 1-800-LIBRARY. When it had a dedicated local phone number, it had a plant test number of 212-206-6870. So we could call this and all the subsequent hunt-on numbers every day first thing. Just to check. And when we go traveling, we call our own numbers. Just to check. Now we don't have any dedicated local phone numbers, we rely on prayer. The most common problem we have with our 800 numbers is at our local central office. Seems that it crashes every so often for very short amounts of time. When it starts up, it's meant to load all the tables to give us the features we're paying for — like hunting. Sadly, it doesn't always do this. We then report the trouble to our local phone company. It's usually fixed within an hour or so. Depends on how busy they are. See also 800 at the front of this dictionary.

EIGRP Enhanced Interior Gateway Routing Protocol. Cisco System's newest version of its proprietary routing algorithm, IGRP.

EIP Early Implementers Program. A term Novell coined to refer to those companies who had early on committed to adopt its Telephony Services architecture. See TELEPHONY SERVICES.

EIR Equipment Identity Register. A database repository used to verify the validity of equipment used in mobile telephone service. Black-listed equipment prevents call completion for a user.

EIRPAC A ITU-T X.25 packet-switched network operating in Ireland under the control of the Irish government.

EISA In a computer a "bus" is an electrical channel for getting information and commands in and around the computer. It is the way the central microprocessor running the computer gets its information and commands to the various peripheral devices or device controllers, such as video controllers, hard disk controllers, etc. The original IBM PC was "balanced" in that the microprocessor matched the speed of the bus that came in the machine. But the microprocessor got faster and more powerful and the bus lagged behind. So there has been much effort to speed the bus up, including EISA, which stands for Extended Industry Standard Architecture. EISA is the independent computer industry's alternate to IBM's Micro-Channel data bus architecture which IBM uses in some of its high end PS/2 line of desktop computers. EISA, like Micro-Channel (also called MCA), is a 32-

bit channel. But, unlike IBM's Micro-Channel, plug-in boards which work inside the XT and AT-series of IBM and IBM clone desktop computers will work within EISA machines. They won't work in Micro-Channel machines. EISA expands the 16-bit ISA (Industry Standard Architecture) to 32-bit. EISA technology is useful in computing environments where multiple high performance peripherals are operating in parallel. The intelligent bus master can share the burden on the main CPU by performing direct data transfers into and out of memory. EISA capabilities are valuable when the system is being used as a server on a local area network or is running a multi-user operating system such as UNIX or OS/2. As of writing, over 200 manufacturers had endorsed EISA. Broader, wider buses than EISA are now available. 64-bit is not uncommon, especially among servers. See LOCAL BUS, PCI and VESA for examples of newer, faster buses.

EITHER END HOP OFF EEHO. In private networks, a switch program that allows a call destined for an off-net location to be placed into the public network at either the closest switch to the origination or the closest switch to the destination. The choice is usually by time of day and is usually done to take advantage of cheaper rates.

EITHER WAY OPERATION Same as half-duplex.

EIU Ethernet Interface Unit

EKTS Electronic Key Telephone System.

ELASTIC BUFFER A variable storage device having adjustable capacity and/or delay, in which a signal can be temporarily stored.

ELASTICITY OF DEMAND The relationship between price and the quantity sold. The theory is the lower the price, the more you'll sell. In telecommunications, this has traditionally been true, though sometimes it has taken time for demand to catch up with dramatic price cuts.

ELECTRIC BANANA Telecom installers' slang for TONE PROBE.

ELECTRIC LOCK A cellular phone feature that provides security by locking a cellular phone so it can't be used by unauthorized persons.

ELECTRICALLY POWERED TELEPHONE A telephone in which the operating power is obtained either from batteries located at the telephone (local battery) or from a telephone central office (common battery).

ELECTRODEPOSITON The deposition of a conductive material from a plating solution by the application of electric current.

ELECTROLUMINESCENCE The direct conversion of electrical energy into light.

ELECTROLYSIS The production of chemical changes by passage of current through an electrolyte.

ELECTROLYTE A chemical solution used in batteries, chemical rectifiers, and certain types of fixed condensers.

ELECTROLYTIC PROCESS A printing process where paper is treated with an electrolyte and a stylus passes the signal current through the paper to produce an image. Paper is roll-fed past the stylus and changes color depending on the intensity of current passing through the stylus.

ELECTROMAGNETIC COMPATIBILITY EMC. The ability of equipment or systems to be used in their intended environment within designed efficiency levels without causing or receiving degradation due to unintentional EMI (Electromagnetic Interference). EMI is reduced by, amongst other things, copper shielding.

ELECTROMAGNETIC EMISSION CONTROL The control of electromagnetic emissions. e.g., radio, radar, and sonar transmissions, for the purpose of preventing or minimizing their use by unintended recipients. A military term. Electromagnetic emission is reduced by, amongst other things, copper shielding.

ELECTROMAGNETIC INTERFACE EMI. interference in signal transmission or reception caused by the radiation of electrical and magnetic fields. That's the easy explanation. Here's a more comprehensive explanation: Any electrical or electromagnetic phenomenon, manmade or natural, either radiated or conducted, that results in unintentional and undesirable responses from, or performance degradation or malfunction of, electronic equipment.

ELECTROMAGNETIC INTERFERENCE See ELECTROMAGNETIC INTERFACE.

ELECTROMAGNETIC LINES OF FORCE The lines of force existing about an electromagnet or a current carrying conductor.

ELECTROMAGNETIC WAVE The electric wave propagated by an electrostatic and magnetic field of varying intensity. Its velocity is 186,300 miles per second.

ELECTROMECHANICAL RINGING The traditional bell or buzzer in a telephone which announces incoming calls.

ELECTRON The smallest known particle of matter assumed to be a particle or charge of negative electricity.

ELECTRON GUN Device in a television picture tube from which electrons are emitted toward screen.

ELECTRON TUBE RECTIFIER A device for rectifying an alternating current by utilizing the flow of electrons between a hot cathode and a relatively cold anode.

ELECTRONIC BLACKBOARD This is a teleconferencing tool. At one end there's a large "whiteboard." Write on this board and electronics behind the board pick up your writing and transmit it over phone lines to a remote TV set. The idea is that remote viewers can hear your voice on the phone and see the presentation on the electronic blackboard. The product has not done well because it is expensive — typically several hundred dollars a month just for rent, plus extra hundreds for transmission costs. In Japan, there are similar boards called OABoards — Office Automation Boards. They do one thing differently — they will print a copy on normal letter-size paper of what's written on the board. This takes about 20 seconds. Some of these Japanese OABoards will also transmit their contents over phone lines. So far, neither the OABoards nor the electronic blackboards have found a sizable market in the United States.

ELECTRONIC BULLETIN BOARD A computer, a modem, a phone line and a piece of software. Load communications software in your computer, dial the distant electronic bulletin board. The system will answer and present you with a menu of options. Typically those options will include leave messages, pick up messages, find out information, fill in a survey and upload and download a file.

ELECTRONIC CALL DISTRIBUTION Another term for Automatic Call Distribution. See AUTOMATIC CALL DISTRIBUTOR.

ELECTRONIC COMMERCE Using electronic information technologies to conduct business between trading partners, not necessarily using EDI (Electronic Data Interchange).

ELECTRONIC CUSTOM TELEPHONE SERVICE Provides deluxe key telephone features and simplified access to certain AT&T Dimension PBX phones.

ELECTRONIC DATA INTERCHANGE EDI. The process whereby standardized forms of documents are transferred between systems often run by different companies. EDI is used for placing orders, etc. The form and format of such documents may be defined by vendor specifications, ITU-T standards, the ANSI X.12 standard, or the United Nations EDIFACT standard. See EDI for a fuller explanation. See the next definition.

ELECTRONIC DATA INTERCHANGE ASSOCIATION EDIA. An organization which works to provide a common platform to communicate global EDI activity, bypassing language conventions and national boundaries.

ELECTRONIC DATA PROCESSING See EDP.

ELECTRONIC FRONTIER FOUNDATION EFF. A foundation established by Mitch Kapor, founder of Lotus, to address social and legal issues arising from the impact on society of the increasingly pervasive use of computers as the means of communication and information distribution.

ELECTRONIC FUNDS TRANSFER EFT. A system which transfers money electronically between accounts or organizations without moving the actual money.

ELECTRONIC IMAGE MAIL The transmission of slow scan TV or facsimile via "Store and Forward." Not a common term.

ELECTRONIC KEY SYSTEM A key telephone system in which the electro-mechanical relays and switches have been replaced by electronic devices — often in the phone and in the central cabinet. The innards of the central cabinet of an electronic key system more resemble a computer than a conventional key system. These days, virtually all key systems are electronic. Production of electro-mechanical key systems (such as 1A2) has been severely curtailed and most manufacturers have ceased making it.

ELECTRONIC LOCK Lets you lock your cellular phone so no one can use it. If you use Electronic Lock, you'll have to punch in some extra digits — like a password — to unlock the lock.

ELECTRONIC MAIL A term which usually means Electronic Text Mail, as opposed to Electronic Voice Mail or Electronic Image Mail. Sometimes electronic mail is written as E-Mail. Sometimes as email. These days electronic mail is everything from simple messages flowing over a local area network from one cubicle to another, to messages flowing across the globe on an X.400 network. Such messages may be simple text messages containing only ASCII or they may be complex messages containing embedded voice messages, spreadsheets and images. See ELECTRONIC TEXT MAIL, ELECTRONIC VOICE MAIL, ELECTRONIC IMAGE MAIL and WINDOWS, WINDOWS TELEPHONY.

ELECTRONIC MAIL GATEWAYS A collection of hardware and software that allows users on an E-mail system to communicate and exchange messages with other mail systems that use a different protocol.

ELECTRONIC MESSAGE REGISTRATION A system to detect and count a phone user's completed local calls and then tell the central office the number of message units used. Also used in hotels.

ELECTRONIC MESSAGING ASSOCIATION EMA. The trade association for electronic messaging and information exchange. EMA is based in Fairfax, VA. EMA was formerly called the Electronic mail Association.

ELECTRONIC ORDER EXCHANGE EOE. Inter-company transactions between buyers and sellers handled electronically via standard data communications protocols. EOE can be employed to send purchase orders, price and product listings and order-related information.

ELECTRONIC PHONE General description for most phones designed after about 1980, where many mechanical and electrical parts are replaced by smaller, lighter, and cheaper electronic parts. Features such as mute, redial and memory became popular with these phones, which range in price from $5 to hundreds of dollars.

ELECTRONIC RECEPTIONIST A fancy name for a voice processing automated attendant, except that in addition to all the normal auto attendant features, it also sends messages to personal PCs on LANs telling the owner who's calling and giving the owner (the called party) the choice of doing something with the call — like answering it or putting it into voice mail.

ELECTRONIC REDLINING A term for disenfranchising people and institutions because of their lack of telecommunications services and apparatus. In December, 1993, Vice President of the United States, Al Gore, told the National Press Club, When it comes to ensuring universal service, our schools are the most impoverished institution in society. Only 14% of our public schools used educational networks in even one classroom last year. Only 22% possess even one modem. Video-on-demand will be a great thing. It will be a far greater thing to demand that our efforts give every child access to the educational riches we have in such abundance. The recent article in the Washington Post on the proposed video communication network in the D.C. area is a wake-up call to all of us concerned about "electronic redlining."

ELECTRONIC RINGER A substitute for the conventional telephone bell, that uses music synthesizer circuitry to generate an attention-getting signal played through a speaker. Typical sounds include warbles, chirps, beeps, squawks, and chimes. The writer of this entry, Michael Marcus, once installed a phone with a chirp sound. A few days later, the customer complained that she had not been receiving any calls, and the birds in her yard were chirping much more than usual.

ELECTRONIC SERIAL NUMBER ESN. A unique ID number of a cellular phone that has been embedded in its circuits by the manufacturer. See ESN.

ELECTRONIC SWEEP Variation in the frequency of a signal over a whole band as a means of checking the response of equipment under the test.

ELECTRONIC SWITCHING SYSTEM A telephone switch which uses electronics or computers to control the switching of calls, their billing and other functions. The term is now vaguely defined, with each manufacturer defining it as something somewhat different. In fact, every telephone switch sold today is electronic. The term originally came about because early telephone switches were entirely electro-mechanical. The switch consisted entirely of a moving switch. Devices like relays physically moved in order to send the call through the exchange and on its way. These things moved in direct response to the digits dialed by the telephone subscriber. These switches contained no "intelligence" — i.e. no ability to deviate from a set number of very simple tasks which could be accomplished by electromechanical relays.

Then someone said: it would be more efficient if the "instruction part" of the process were divorced the switching mechanism. This lead to the creation of the "electronic" switch in which the "brains" of the switch are separated from the switching mechanism itself. Thus the "brains" can do simple things like collect the dialed digits as they are slowly dialed and pulse them out quickly to the switch — as fast as it can handle them. Now, the "brains" are typically a digital computer.

ELECTRONIC TANDEM NETWORK 1. Two or more switching systems operating in parallel as part of providing network services (usually voice) to large users.

2. A telephone company switching device used to connect telephone company toll offices located in the same geographic area.

ELECTRONIC TELEPHONE DIRECTORY SERVICE A PBX feature which stores and produces, on demand, a directory of all extension phone numbers. The directory may include all users in a network. A CRT with keyboard and/or printer is usually required for input and retrieval. In some systems, the CRT or another type of alphanumeric display is part of the Attendant Console. In some systems, the directory may also include names and telephone numbers of frequently called outside people, especially those in the speed calling system. The directory may also be enhanced to include SMDR data such as client codes, account codes and client telephone numbers.

ELECTRONIC TEXT MAIL A "Store and Forward" service for the transmission of textual messages transmitted in machine readable form from a computer terminal or computer system. A message sent from one computer user to another is stored in the recipient's "mailbox" until that person next logs onto the system. The system then can deliver the message. Telex, in which a machine readable form of message transmission takes place, is also considered an Electronic Text Mail medium, albeit a very slow one. For an example of electronic mail, please dial our electronic mail system on 212-989-4675. It's free. Parameters are 300, 1200 or 2400 baud, 8 data bits, one stop bit, and no parity.

ELECTRONIC VOICE MAIL A system which stores messages usually spoken over a telephone. These messages can be retrieved by the intended recipient when that person next calls into the system. Also called Voice Mail, it operates just like a touch-tone controlled answering machine.

ELECTRONIC WARFARE See EW.

ELECTROPHOTOGRAPHIC PRINTING A printing method that uses light to modify electrostatic charges on a photoconductive substrate.

ELECTROSTATIC CHARGE An electric charge at rest.

ELECTROSTATIC DISCHARGE ESD. Discharge of a static charge on a surface or body through a conductive path to ground. Can be damaging to integrated circuits.

ELECTROSTATIC PRINTING A method of printing, very common in photo-copying, in which charges are beamed onto the surface of paper. The charges attract particles of a very fine (typically black powder) which sticks to the charges. The black powder is fused permanently on the paper by great heat. "XEROXing" is electrostatic printing. In xeroxing, the black powder is called toner.

ELEGANT An elegant program is one that is efficiently written to use the smallest possible amount of main memory and the fewest instructions.

ELEVATOR EYES A term used in sexual harassment to mean viewing someone up and down.

ELEVATOR SEEKING Organizes the way data is read from hard disks and logically organizes disk operations as they arrive at the Novell NetWare local area network server for processing. A queue is maintained for each disk driver operating within the server. As disk read and write requests are queued for a specific drive, the operating system sorts incoming requests into a priority based on the drive's current head position. As the disk driver services the queue, subsequent requests are located either in the vicinity of the last request or in the opposite direction. Thus, the drive heads operate in a sweeping fashion, from the outside to the inside of the disk. Elevator seeking improves disk channel performance by significantly reducing disk head thrashing (rapid back-and-forth movements of the disk head) and by minimizing head seek times. Imagine how inefficient an elevator would be if the people using it had to get off the elevator in the order they got on.

ELIU Electrical Line Interface Unit.

ELONGATION The fractional increase in length of a material stressed in tension.

ELOT Hellenic Organization for Standardization (Greece).

ELVIS YEAR The peak year of something's popularity.

EM Element Manager. Software and hardware used to manage and monitor components of a telecommunications network at their lowest level.

EMA Electronic Messaging Association, Arlington, VA. www.ema.org

EMACS A standard Unix text editor preferred by Unix types that beginners tend to hate.

EMAG ETSI MIS Advisory Group.

EMAIL A colloquial term for electronic mail. See EMAIL address.

EMAIL ADDRESS The UUCP or domain-based address by which a user is referred to. My email address is HARRYNEWTON@MCIMAIL.COM.

EMAIL GATEWAY An email gateway is typically a PC on LAN. The PC has one or more modem and/or fax/modem cards. Its job is to send and receive e-mails and/or send and receive faxes for everyone on the LAN. To pick up emails, it might dial once an hour into various mail systems, like MCI Mail, CompuServe, and download all the messages for all the people on the LAN. Once it has those messages, it brings them onto its hard disk and then alerts the recipients that they now have an e-mail. See SERVER.

EMAIL REFLECTOR An Internet electronic mail address which automatically sends you back a reply (i.e. reflects mail to you) if you include certain key words in your message to it. Such key words might be "subscribe" or "lists help."

EMAIL SERVER See EMAIL GATEWAY.

EMBARC Motorola's company which does wireless electronic mail to people carrying laptops and palmtops. Embarc, according to Motorola, stands for Electronic Mail Broadcast to A Roaming Computer. Actually Embarc does more than mail. It also broadcasts snippets of news.

EMBED To insert information (an object) that was created in one document into another document (most often the two documents were created with different applications). The embedded object can be edited directly from within the document. To embed under Windows 3.1, you must be using applications that support object linking and embedding.

EMBEDDED BASE EQUIPMENT All customer-premises equipment that has been provided by the Bell Operating Companies (BOCs) prior to January 1, 1984, that was ordered transferred from the BOCs to AT&T by court order.

EMBEDDED CODE FORMATTING ECF. A NetWare definition. This is something of a programming language, in which faxing commands or other program that automatically generates information, formats it, and faxes it without user intervention.

EMBEDDED CUSTOMER-PREMISES EQUIPMENT Telephone-company-provided premises equipment in use or in inventory of a regulated telephone utility as a December 31, 1982.

EMBEDDED OBJECT A Windows term. An embedded object is information in a document that is a copy of information created in another application. By choosing an embedded object, you can start the application that was used to create it, while remaining in the document you're working in.

EMBEDDED SCSI A hard disk that has a SCSI (Small Computer System Interface) and a hard disk controller built into the hard disk unit. See also SCSI.

EMBEDDED SQL SQL statements embedded within a source program and prepared before the program is executed.

EMBEDDED SYSTEM PROCESSORS National Semiconductor's line of high-performance microprocessors used in dedicated systems, such as fax machines and laser printers.

EMBOSSING A means of marker identification by thermal indentation leaving raised lettering on a cable's sheath material.

EMC ElectroMagnetic Compatibility.

EMERGENCY ACCESS An alarm system built into some PBXs. In an emergency it rings all phones.

EMERGENCY BROADCAST SYSTEM EBS. The EBS is composed of AM, FM, and TV broadcast stations; low-power TV stations; and non-Government industry entities operating on a voluntary, organized basis during emergencies at national, state, or operational (local) area levels.

EMERGENCY DIALING A variation on speed calling to call numbers for police, fire department, ambulance, etc. Typically found as special buttons on an electronic phone.

EMERGENCY HOLD "Emergi-hold" allows a 911 caller's line to be held open in the event that a caller attempts to hang up. This gives the PSAP (Public Service Answering Position) agent full control of the call. It will not be released until the agent finishes the call.

EMERGENCY RINGBACK This feature enables the 911 PSAP (Public Service Answering Position) attendant to signal a caller who has either hung up or left the phone off hook. Emergency Ringback enables the PSAP agent to ring a phone which has been hung up or issue a loud "howling" sound from the customer's phone if it has been left off hook.

EMERGENCY TELEPHONE A single line telephone that becomes active when there is no commercial AC power to the Key Service Unit.

EMI ElectroMagnetic Interference or ElectroMagnetic Interface. Leakage of radiation from a transmission medium due to high-frequency energy. EMI is reduced by copper shielding.

EMI/RFI FILTER A circuit or device containing series inductive (load bearing) and parallel capacitive (non-load bearing) components, which provide a low impedance path for high-frequency noise around a protected circuit.

EMISSION 1. Electromagnetic energy propagated from a source by radiation or conduction. The energy thus propagated may be either desired or undesired and may occur anywhere in the electromagnetic spectrum.

2. Radiation produced, or the production of radiation, by a radio transmitting station. For example, the energy radiated by the local oscillator of a radio receiver would not be an emission but a radiation.

EMISSIVITY Ratio of flux radiated by a substance to the flux radiated by black body at the same temperature. Emissivity is usually a function of wavelength.

EMITTER The source of optical power.

EML Element Management Layer. A layer representing the management and monitoring of components, at their lowest level, in a telecommunications network.

EMM An acronym for Expanded Memory Manager, the software that controls expanded memory on an IBM PC or clone. Drivers written for the 80386 microprocessors usually allow you to use extended memory to simulate expanded memory. See EXPANDED MEMORY.

EMM386.EXE An expanded memory manager that comes with MS-DOS, Windows and Windows for Workgroups. It provides access to upper memory and simulates expanded memory using extended memory. This is useful for MS-DOS based applications that can use expanded memory. EMM386 also makes it possible to load programs and device drives into upper memory blocks (UMBs). Although EMM386 can provide more free conventional memory by loading programs and device drivers into UMBs, this only helps when running MS-DOS applications. Windows and Windows for Workgroups uses extended memory (XMS) to run the Windows operating systems and Windows-based applications. Accessing device drivers and application code from UMBs is slower than accessing the same code directly from conventional memory. To maximize the performance when accessing MS-DOS device drives, Microsoft recommends that EMM386 (or similar third party memory managers) not be used. According to Microsoft, "in addition to possible performance penalties, EMM386.EXE will use about 150K of XMS (extended memory) memory to provide a mappable memory range for the UMA in which to load device drivers." Recommended Microsoft, "If you are not running MS-DOS applications that require more conventional memory than is available after loading the necessary device drives and programs in conventional memory, and you are not using MS-DOS applications that require EMS, you may remove EMM386.EXE from your CONFIG.SYS without adversely affecting your system. See EMS and SMARTDRV.EXE.

EMOTAGS Mock HTML tags (<smile>, <smirk>) used in WWW-related e-mail and newsgroups in place of ASCII emoticons, for example: "<flames> Someone tell that jerk to shut up, I'm sick of his vapid whining! </flame>." Definition from Wired Magazine. See EMOTICON.

EMOTICON From Emotional Icon, one of a growing number of typographical cartoons used on BBSs (Bulletin Board Systems) to portray the mood of the sender, or indicate physical appearance. They are meant to be looked at sideways. Some examples:

:-D writer talks too much

:-# writer's lips are sealed

:-o writer is surprised

:-& writer is tongue-tied

ALL CAPS writer is shouting

:) is a smiley face ;)

is a smile with a wink

;(is a frown with a wink

(:(is very sad

;? is a bad guy

[:0 is a wide-open mouth and a crewcut

(:{>X is bald with a handlebar mustache and bow tie

:-l is Wayne Newton

{8<)# is Michael Marcus, the writer of this entry: balding, glasses, mustache, smiling, beard.

Here's another collection of emoticons which I found on the Internet:

:-)   Smile

:-D   Laughing

:)   Smile

:-}   Grin

:-]   Smirk

:-(Frown

;-)   Wink

:-X   Close-mouthed

8-)   Wide-eyed

:-O   Open-mouthed

:-l   I wear a moustache

:-Q   But I don't inhale

:-o   Oh, no!

<g>   Grin

<ggg> Wide Grin

<g....g> Very wide grin

EMP A large and fast-moving electromagnetic pulse caused by lightning.

EMPHASIS In FM transmission, the intentional alteration of the amplitude-versus-frequency characteristics of the signal to reduce adverse effects of noise in a communication system. The higher frequency signals are emphasized to produce a more equal modulation index for the transmitted frequency spectrum, and therefore a better signal-to-noise ratio for the entire frequency range.

EMS 1. Expanded Memory Specification. Several years ago, three computer companies — Lotus, Intel and Microsoft — jointly developed EMS. This standard defines how an MS-DOS program can access memory beyond 640KB while running under MS-DOS. Applications that conform to EMS (sometimes called LIM-EMS for Lotus/Intel/Microsoft Expanded Memory Specification) can take advantage of the computer's memory beyond 640KB of RAM. LIM-EMS uses a portion of the reserved memory area (between 640KB and 1MB) to access RAM beyond 1MB. Software that supports expanded memory uses this window to pass pages of data to and from expanded RAM as needed. See also EXPANDED MEMORY.

2. Enterprise Messaging Server. A new Microsoft concept which allows users to transparently access the messaging engine from within desktop applications to route messages, share files, or retrieve reference data. According to Microsoft, corporate developers will be able to add capabilities using Visual Basic and access EMS by writing either to the X.400 Application Program Interface Association's (XAPIA's) Common Mail Calls (CMC) or to Microsoft's Messaging API (MAPI). See MAPI.

EMT Electrical Metal Tubing. In many towns you must run your electrical AC wire inside metal tubing. In other towns you can run normal plastic insulated wiring. Theoretically, EMT is a safer fire hazard. What you are allowed to run depends on local laws and regulations. Tip: Dimmers for incandescent lights raise havoc with LAN data. Solution: Put the plastic electrical wires inside EMT (Electrical Metal Tubing) and ground the conduit.

EMULATE To duplicate one system with another. To imitate a computer or computer system by a combination of hardware and software that allows programs written for one computer or terminal to run on another. The most common data terminal is a DEC VT-100. Our communications program, Crosstalk, allows us to "emulate" a DEC-VT100 on our IBM PCs and PC clones.

EMULATION What happens one gadget emulates another. See EMULATE.

EMULATOR A device or computer program which can act as if it is a different device or program, that is Emulate (i.e. pretend to be) another device. Certain computer terminals are necessary in specific systems and a terminal that is not that type may be able to act as if it was. If it can, it is an Emulator. This is not a common term. See also the verb EMULATE.

ENABLE To make something happen. Or, in more complex language, to set various hardware and software parameters so that the central computer will recognize those parameters and start doing what you want.

ENABLER An "enabler" is a strange name for a piece of software

ENABLING SIGNAL A signal that permits the occurrence of an event.

ENCAPSULATED POSTSCRIPT FILE EPS. A file that prints at the highest possible resolution for your printer. An EPS file may print faster than other graphical representations. Some Windows NT and non-Windows NT graphical applications can import EPS files.

ENCAPSULATING BRIDGE A LAN/WAN term. A special bridge type usually associated with backbone/subnetwork architectures. Encapsulating bridges place forwarded packets in a backbone-specific envelope — FDDI, for example - and send them out onto the backbone LAN as broadcast packets. The receiving bridges remove the envelope, check the destination address and, if it is local, send the packet to the destination device.

ENCAPSULATION 1. Encasing a splice or closure in a protective material to make it watertight.

2. In object-oriented programming, the grouping of data and the code that manipulates it into a single entity or object. Encapsulation refers to the hiding of most of the details of the object. Both the attributes (data structure) and the methods (procedures) are hidden. Associated with the object is a set of operations that it can perform. These are not hidden. They constitute a well-defined interface — that aspect of the object that is externally visible. The point of encapsulation is to isolate the internal workings of the object so that, if they must be modified, those changes will also be isolated and not affect any part of the program. See OBJECT-ORIENTED PROGRAMMING.

3. An electronic messaging term. The technique used by layered protocols in which a layer adds header information to the PDU (Protocol Data Unit) form the layer above. As an example, in Internet terminology, a packet would contain a header from the physical layer, followed by a header from the network layer (IP), followed by a header from the transport layer (TCP), followed by the application protocol data.

4. See also ENCAPSULATION BRIDGING.

ENCAPSULATION BRIDGING Method of bringing dissimilar networks where the entire frame from one network is simply enclosed in the header used by the link-layer protocol of the other network.

ENCODING The process of converting data into code or analog voice into a digital signal. See also PCM and ADPCM.

ENCRYPTION The transformation of data into a form unreadable by anyone without a secret decryption key. Its purpose is to ensure privacy by keeping the information hidden from anyone for whom it is not intended. In security, encryption is the ciphering of data by applying an algorithm to plain text to convert it to ciphertext.

END ACCESS END OFFICE EAEO. An end office that provides Feature Group D.

END DELIMITER ED. Sequence of bits used by IEEE 802 MAC to indicate the end of a frame. Used in token bus and ring networks, with nondata bits making ED easy to recognize.

END DISTORTION In start-stop teletypewriter operations, the shifting of the end of all marking pulses except the stop pulse from their proper positions in relation to the beginning of the next pulse. Shifting of the end of the stop pulse would constitute a deviation in character time and rate rather than being an end distortion. Spacing end distortion is the termination of marking pulses before the proper time. Marking end distortion is the continuation of marking pulses past the proper time. Magnitude of the distortion is expressed in percent of a perfect unit pulse length.

END FINISH Surface condition at the optical fiber face.

END INSTRUMENT A communication device that is connected to the terminals of a circuit.

END NODE A node such as a PC that can only send and receive information for its own use. It cannot route and forward information to another node.

END OF FILE EOF. A control character or byte used in data communications that indicates the last character of the last record of a file has been read.

END OF MEDIUM EM. A control character used to denote the end of the used (or useful) portion of a storage medium.

END OF MESSAGE EOM. A control character used in data communications to indicate the end of a message.

END OF SHIFT ROUTING A call center term for a process that calls won't be left in limbo when a shift ends. See also SOURCE/DESTINATION ROUTING, SKILLS-BASED ROUTING and CALENDAR ROUTING.

END OF TEXT MESSAGE ETX. A control character used in data communications to indicate the end of a text message. See ETX.

END OF TRANSMISSION BLOCK A communications control character indicating the end of a block of Bisync data for communication purposes.

END OF TRANSMISSION BLOCK CHARACTER A control character used in data communications to indicate the end of a block where data are divided into blocks for transmission purposes.

END OFFICE A central office to which a telephone subscriber is connected. Frequently referred to as a Class 5 office. The last central office before the subscriber's phone equipment. The central office which actually delivers dial tone to the subscriber.

END TO END LOSS The loss of an installed transmission path. The loss consists of the loss of the transmission cable or fiber, splices and connectors.

END TO END SIGNALING A signaling system capable of generating and transmitting signals directly from the originating station to the terminating end after the connection is established, without disturbing the connection. Touchtone dialing is such a system, allowing the user to send tones to a remote computer for data or other access. See POINT TO POINT.

END USER A highfalutin' term for a user. It's actually the occupant of the premises who uses and pays for the telephone service received and does not resell it to others. Bellcore's definition: A user who uses a loop-start, ground-start, or ISDN access signaling arrangement. Definition from Bellcore is part of its concept of the Advanced Intelligent Network.

ENDURABILITY The property of a system, subsystem, equipment, or process that enables it to continue to function within specified performance limits for an extended period of time, usually months, despite a potentially severe natural or man-made disturbance, e.g., nuclear attack, and a subsequent loss of external logistic or utility support.

ENERGY COMMUNICATIONS EC. A PBX feature which communicates with energy consuming and monitoring devices and perform functions like dimming the lights or turning down the heat in a vacant hotel room. See also ENERGY CONTROL.

ENERGY CONTROL Indicates that phone system has software and hardware necessary to control and regulate the energy consuming devices in a user's facility (heating, ventilating, air conditioning, electrical machinery etc.). The system's processor transmits control signals, over existing telephone wiring where possible, to control units at each power-consuming device. This feature always includes user reconfiguration of the system's control parameters in response to operational and/or environmental changes. At one stage, AT&T and some other telephone equipment manufacturers sold energy control as a integral feature of their phone systems. The idea didn't take off for a lot of reasons.

ENERGY DENSITY A beam's energy per unit area, expressed in joules per square meter. Equivalent to the radiometric term "irradiance."

ENGINEERING ORDERWIRE EOW. A communication path for voice or data, or both, that is provided to facilitate the installation, maintenance, restoral, or deactivation of segments of a communication system by equipment operators, attendants, and controllers.

ENFIA Exchange Network Facilities for Interstate Access. A tariff providing a series of options for connecting long distance carriers with local exchange facilities of the local telephone company.

ENHANCED 800 SERVICES A name MCI uses for a family of 800 services with additional features added to them. It includes time of day and day of week routing.

ENHANCED 911 Enhanced 911 is an advanced form of 911 service. With E-911, the telephone number of the caller is transmitted to the Public Safety Answering Point (PSAP) where it is cross-referenced with an address database to determine the caller's location. That information is then displayed on a video-monitor for the emergency dispatcher to direct public safety personnel responding to the emergency. This enables police, fire departments and ambulances to find callers who cannot orally provide their precise location. See also E-911.

ENHANCED CALL PROCESSING An Octel term for the interactive voice response option in its voice mail system. Here's how Octel defines the term: "Companies and departments that receive a heavy volume of calls can use ECP to create menus that are presented to callers. When the system answers a call, a recorded voice instructs the caller how to use a touch-tone telephone to send call routing instructions to the system. Depending on which option is chosen, ECP's customized call routing feature allows a caller to press a single key to reach a pre-determined extension, a voice messaging mailbox where he can leave a message, an Information Center Mailbox where he can listen to a series of recordings giving frequently requested information or additional levels of ECP menus. ECP menus are easily custom-built by the customer to meet its specific needs. Each menu can offer as many as ten options."

ENHANCED DNIS Enhanced DNIS is a combination of ANI and DNIS delivered before the first ring on a T1 span. The number of digits delivered is configurable on a per span basis.

ENHANCED IDE An improved interface to the IDE hard disk interface. Enhanced IDE allows you to attach hard disks of larger than 528 megabytes (the largest normal IDE will handle) up to a maximum of 8.4 gigabytes. Enhanced IDE has a data transfer rate of between 11 and 13 megabytes per second, compared to the 2 to 3 megabytes per second, which normal IDE drives sport. See IDE.

ENHANCED MODE The Intel 8088 and 8086 microprocessors, used in the earliest PCs, run DOS programs using real mode. Real mode causes problems when you try to run more than one program at a time because nothing prevents a poorly designed program from invading another program's memory space, resulting in a system crash. The Intel 80386 microprocessor introduced several technical improvements. For compatibility, an 80386 can run in real mose, but also offers protected mode. In protected mode, the 80386 can address up to four gigabytes of RAM, far more than you can install in any PC. The chip also can simulate more than one 8086 "machines, are protected from one another, preventing memory conflicts.

Running a DOS program in the protected mode of an 80386 computer requires software to manage the memory. Like a traffic cop, this software — called memory-management — puts DOS programs into their own 640K virtual machines, where they work away without interfering with other programs. The most popular memory-management available for 80386 and 80486 is Windows. In 386 Enhanced mode, Windows takes advantage of the 80386/80486/Pentium's virtual memory capabilities. Virtual memory is a way of extending RAM. Most DOS applications swap program instructions and data back and fourth from disk rather than keep them in memory. See EXPANDED MEMORY and EXTENDED MEMORY.

ENHANCED PARALLEL PORT EPP. A new hardware and software innovation (and now a standard) which allows computers so equipped to send data out their parallel port at twice the speed of present parallel ports. There's no difference in the shape of the plug or the number of conductor. See EPP for a fuller explanation.

ENHANCED PRIVATE SWITCHED COMMUNICATIONS SERVICE EPSCS (pronounced EP-SIS). A private line networking offering from AT&T which provides functions similar to CCSA. Big companies are its customers.

ENHANCED SERIAL INTERFACE ESI. A new, broader serial interface announced by Hayes Microcomputer Products, Norcross, GA, and placed in the public domain. The ESI is an extension of the familiar COM card used in personal computers. ESI includes the definition of I/O, control registers, buffer control, Direct Memory Access (DMA) to the system and interaction with attached modem devices. ESI specification is available from Hayes Customer Service at no charge. Combined with Hayes' announcement of ESI was their announcement of new Enhanced Serial Port hardware products for the IBM microchannel and IBM XT/AT or EISA bus personal computers. According to Hayes, the ESI spec and the supporting ESP hardware provide a "cost-effective" communication coprocessor to manager the flow of data between an external high speed modem and PC. This technology prevents loss of data resulting from buffer overflow errors and provides maximum data throughput for high speed modems. Hayes says that the combination of ESP and ESI will allow through-the-phone modem speeds of up to 38.4 Kbps.

ENHANCED SERIAL PORT See ENHANCED SERIAL INTERFACE.

ENHANCED SERVICE PROVIDER ESP. An ESP is a company that provides enhanced or value-added services to end users. An ESP typically adds value to telephone lines using his own software and hardware. Also called an IP, or Information Provider. An example of an ESP is a public voice mail box provider or a database provider, for example, one giving the latest airline fares. An ESP is an American term, unknown in Europe, where they're most called VANs, or Value Added Networks. See also OPEN NETWORK ARCHITECTURE and INFORMATION PROVIDER.

ENHANCED SERVICES Services offered over transmission facilities which may be provided without filing a tariff. These services usually involve some computer related feature such as formatting data or restructuring the information. Most Bell operating companies (BOCs) are prohibited from offering enhanced services at present. But the restrictions are disappearing.

The FCC defines enhanced services as "services offered over common carrier transmission facilities used in interstate communications, which employ computer processing applications that act on the format, content, code, protocol or similar aspects of the subscriber's transmitted information; provide the subscriber additional, different or restructured information; or involve subscriber interaction with stored information." In other words, an enhanced service is a computer processing application that messes in some way with the information transmitted over the phone lines. Value-Added Networks, Transaction Services, Videotex, Alarm Monitoring and Telemetry, Voice Mail Services and E-Mail are all examples of enhanced services.

ENHANCED SMALL DEVICE INTERFACE An interface which improves the rate of data transfer for hard disk drives and increases the drive's storage capacity.

ENHANCED UNSHIELDED TWISTED PAIR EUTP. UTP (Unshielded Twisted Pair) cables that have enhanced transmission characteristics. Cables that fall under this classification include Category 4 and above.

ENIAC Electronic Numerical Integrator and Computor (spelled with an O). Early computer, built in 1944.

ENQ ENQuiry character.

ENQ/ACK PROTOCOL Hewlett-Packard communications protocol in which the HP3000 computer follows each transmission block with ENQ to determine if the destination terminal is ready to receive more data. The terminal indicates its readiness by responding with ACK.

ENRICHED SERVICES PROVIDERS Those third-party service providers (other than Network Providers) who provide value-added services that are accessed through telecommunications networks.

ENSO ETSI National Standardization Organizations (ETSI).

ENTELEC ENergy TELECommunications and electrical association, the oldest nationwide user group in telecommunications. It is an association of communications managers and engineers in the oil, gas, pipeline and utility industries. ENTELEC played an important role in the early opening of competition in the telecommunications industry, including the famous "Above 890" decision, which allowed private companies to build their own long distance microwave system. The decision was called "Above 890" because electromagnetic waves in the radio frequency spectrum above 890 Megahertz (million cycles per second) and below 20 Gigahertz (billion cycles per second) are typically called microwave. Microwave used to be a common method of transmitting telephone conversations and was used by common carriers as well as by private networks. Now fiber is far more common. Microwave signals only travel in straight lines. In terrestrial microwave systems, a single transmission is typically good for 30 miles, at which point you need another repeater tower. Microwave is the frequency for communicating to and from satellites. ENTELEC was formerly known as the Petroleum Industry Electrical Association.

ENTERPRISE COMPUTING Enterprise means the whole corporation. Enterprise computing refers to the computing applications on which a company's life depends: order entry, accounts receivable, payroll, inventory, etc. It is also known by the phrase "mission critical." See also ENTERPRISE NETWORK.

ENTERPRISE NETWORK The word Enterprise was invented by IBM. It means the whole corporation. An enterprise-wide network is one covering the whole corporation. Local PBXs. Local area networks. Internetworking bridges. Wide area networks, etc, etc. See also CORPORATE NETWORK and ENTERPRISE COMPUTING.

ENTERPRISE NUMBER A service provided by AT&T and the Bell operating companies (a.k.a. the Bell System) years ago which allowed people to make collect calls and have their calls automatically accepted by the company at the other end. It was very expensive. It has largely been replaced with 800 IN-WATS service, which is much more successful.

ENTERPRISE SOLUTION Software that enables individuals and groups (either within an organization or part of a virtual organization beyond one company) to use computers in a networked environment to access information from a wide range of sources, collaborate on projects, and communicate easily with text, graphics, video, or sound.

ENTITY An active element within an OSI layer or sublayer.

ENTITY COORDINATION MANAGEMENT The portion of connection management which controls bypass relays and signals connection management that the medium is available.

ENTRANCE AND EXIT RAMPS The companies who control access to the internet and other networks of the information superhighway, whatever that is.

ENTRANCE FACILITY Point of interconnection between the Network Demarcation Point and/or campus backbone and intra building wiring. The Entrance Facility includes overvoltage protection and connecting hardware for the transition between outdoor and indoor cable.

ENUMERATOR A Windows 95 term. A Plug and Play device driver that detects devices below its own device node, creates unique device IDs, and reports to Configuration Manager during startup. For example, a SCSI adapter provides a SCSI enumerator that detects devices on the SCSI bus.

ENVELOPE 1. The boundary of the family of curves obtained by varying a parameter of a wave.

2. The part of messaging that varies in composition from one transmittal step to another. It identifies the message originator and potential recipients, documents its past, directs its subsequent movement by the MTS (Message Transfer System) and characterizes its content.

ENVELOPE DELAY Circuit characteristics which result in some frequencies arriving ahead of others, even though they were transmitted at the same time.

ENVELOPE DELAY DISTORTION The distortion that results when the rate of change of phase shift with frequency over the bandwidth of interest is not constant. It is usually stated as one-half the difference between the delays of the two frequency extremes of the band of interest.

ENVIRONMENT The place your telephone system's main cabinet and main electronics live. While most PBX vendors will specify the room's characteristics, the ultimate responsibility for the room is yours, the user. Not designing your telephone system's environment correctly is tantamount to jinxing your telephone system from the start.

Here are some things to watch out for (your vendor has a more comprehensive list): 1. Sufficient air conditioning? Telephone systems give off heat. You need some way of getting rid of the heat. If you don't, you will blow some of your phone system's delicate electronic circuitry. 2. Sufficient space? Is there room for technicians to get in and around your telephone system so they can repair it? Will you have room for additional cabinets when you need to grow your phone system? 3. Sufficient and correct power? Will you have sufficient clean commercial AC power? Will you require isolation regulators? Or you will require extensive wet cell batteries? Will you have space? 4. Will you have a solid electrical ground? Can you find somewhere solid to ground your telephone system to — other than the third wire on the AC power, which is not suitable for most telephone systems? Beware of cold water pipes which end in PVC plastic pipes.

ENVIRONMENT VARIABLE A Windows 95 and NT definition. A string consisting of environment information, such as a drive, path, or filename, associated with a symbolic name that can be used by Windows 95 or Windows NT. You use the System option in Control Panel or the set command from the Windows NT command prompt to define environment variables.

ENVOY 1. A palmtop communicator introduced by Motorola in March of 1994.

The device lets its users receive and transmit messages via Ardis, a network owned by Motorola and IBM. Envoy contains software from General Magic.

2. Spectrum Envoy is a DSP-based PC-board used for "telephone management" from a company called Spectrum Signal Processing, Burnaby, BC. Telephone management includes voice mail, contact manager, upgradable fax/modem, business audio, etc.

EO 1. End Office. Typically your own central office.

2. Erasable Optical drive. EO drives act like hard drives yet offer virtually unlimited storage because their cartridges are removable. Each cartridge sports at least 650 MB. Some sport 1 gigabyte.

3. EO was a startup in Mountain View, CA which did wireless data. It made a device called EO Personal Communicator 440 and 880. It uses GO's PenPoint operating system and the Hobbit microprocessor made by AT&T, which is "optimized" for telecommunications. In fall of 1994, AT&T closed EO down and stopped the sale of EO devices. It was too expensive and wasn't selling. An excellent book was written about EO. It is called "Startup; A Silicon Valley Adventure Story." It was written by Jerry Kaplan, one of EO's founders. The book is published by Houghton Mifflin.

EOA End Of Address. A header code.

EOB End Of Block. A control character or code that marks the end of a block of data.

EOE See ELECTRONIC ORDER EXCHANGE.

EOF The abbreviation for End Of File. MS-DOS files and some programs often mark the end of their files with a Ctrl Z — or ASCII 26.

EOM End of Message (indicator).

EOT End of Transmission, End of Tape.

EOTC European Organization for Testing and Certification.

EOW Engineered OrderWire.

EPABX Electronic Private Automatic Branch eXchange. A fancy name for a modern PBX. Other fancy names include CBX, Computerized Branch Exchange.

EPD Early Packet Discard. See EARLY PACKET DISCARD.

EPHEMERIS The predictions of current satellite position that are transmitted to the user in the data message of a GPS (Global Positioning System) satellite message.

EPLANS Engineering, PLanning and ANalysis Systems. Software offered by Western Electric (now called AT&T Technologies) to help operating telephone company people run their business better.

EPOXY A liquid material that solidifies upon heat curing, ultraviolet light curing, or mixing with another material. Epoxy is sometimes used for fastening fibers to other fibers or for fastening fibers to joining hardware.

EPP Enhanced Parallel Port. A new hardware and software innovation (and now a standard) which allows computers so equipped to send data out their parallel port at twice the speed of older parallel ports, i.e. those that came on the original IBM PC. The EPP conforms to the EPP standard developed by the IEEE (Institute of Electrical and Electronics Engineers) 1284 standards committee. The EPP specification transforms a parallel port into an expansion bus that theoretically can handle up to 64 disk drives, tape drives, CD-ROM drives, and other mass-storage devices. EPPs are rapidly gaining acceptance as inexpensive means to connect portable drives to notebook computers. There's no difference in the shape of the ordinary, 25-pin D-connector plug/connector or the number of conductors. The Enhanced Parallel Port (EPP) was developed by Intel Corp., Xircom Inc., Zenith, and other companies that planned to exploit two-way communications to external devices. Many laptops built since mid-1991 have EPP ports. See also ECP.

EPROM Erasable Programmable Read Only Memory. A read only memory device which can be erased and reprogrammed. Typically, it is programmed electronically (not electromagnetically) with ultraviolet light. EPROMS are typically returned to the vendor or factory for reprogramming. An Eprom on a graphics card might contain the default or ROM character set. EPROM chips normally contain UV-permeable quartz windows exposing the chips' internals. See also ROM and EEPROM.

EPS Encapsulated PostScript. A desktop publishing and imaging term.

EPSCS (Pron. Ep-Sis.) Enhanced Private Switched Communications Service. An AT&T offering for large businesses with offices scattered all over the country. This service allows such businesses to rent space on AT&T electronic switches and join that switching capacity to leased lines. EPSCS customers get a network control center in their offices which gives them information on the continuing operation of their network and allows them some limited options for changing their services.

EPSN Enhanced Private Switched Network.

EQ Abbreviation for EQUALIZATION.

EQUAL ACCESS All long distance carriers must be accessible by dialing 1 — and not a string of long dialing codes. This is laid down in Judge Green's Modified Final Judgment (MFJ), which spelled out the terms of the Divestiture of the Bell Operating phone Companies (BOCs) from their parent, AT&T. Under the terms of this Divestiture, all long distance common carriers must have Equal Access for their long distance caller customers. City by city telephone subscribers are being asked to choose their primary carrier who they will reach by dialing 1 before their long distance number. All other carriers (including AT&T, if not chosen as primary) can be reached by dialing a five digit code (10XXX), thus providing Equal Access for all carriers. Not all long distance companies will opt for full equal access since this involves considerable expense to the local phone companies. See also FEATURE GROUP A, B, C and D.

EQUAL ACCESS END OFFICE A central office capable of providing equal access. See also EQUAL ACCESS.

EQUAL GAIN COMBINER A diversity combiner in which the signals on each channel are added together. The channel gains are all equal and can be made to vary equally so that the resultant signal is approximately constant.

EQUALIZATION The process of reducing distortion over transmission paths by putting in compensating devices. The telephone network is equalized by the spacing and operation of amplifiers along the way. In recording, equalization is frequency manipulation to meet the requirements of recording; also the inverse manipulation in playback to achieve uniform or "flat" response. Also called Compensation. See EQUALIZATION CIRCUIT.

EQUALIZATION CIRCUIT A compensation circuit designed into modems to counteract certain distortions introduced by the telephone channel. Two types are used: fixed (compromise) equalizers and those that adapt to channel conditions. U.S. Robotics high speed modems use adaptive equalization.

EQUATORIAL ORBIT An orbit with a zero degree inclination angle, i.e. the orbital plane and the Earths' equatorial plane are coincident.

EQUIPMENT CABINET The metal box which houses relays, circuit boards or other phone apparatus. Usually also contains the power supply, which converts the 120 volt AC current into the low voltage direct current necessary to run the telephone system.

EQUIPMENT COMPATIBILITY One computer system will successfully do the same thing that another computer will do with the same data. There are many levels of "equipment compatibility." The only true compatibility, however, is identical machinery. And identical means "identical" down to the very last chip and very last integrated circuit. We have found that some computers — even those consecutively numbered — do not always perform the same. We have empirically proven this for both IBM and AT&T computers.

EQUIPMENT WIRING SUBSYSTEM The cable and distribution components in an equipment room that interconnect system-common equipment, other associated equipment, and cross connects.

EQUIPPED FOR CAPACITY The maximum number of lines and trunks that can be supported by the available hardware. It is not a totally effective measure of the size of a PBX. See WIRED-FOR-CAPACITY.

EQUIVALENT FOUR-WIRE SYSTEM Transmission using frequency division to get full duplex transmission over only one pair of wires. Normally two pairs are needed for full duplex.

EQUIVALENT NETWORK 1. A network that may replace another network without altering the performance of that portion of the system external to the network.

2. A theoretical representation of an actual network.

EQUIVALENT PCM NOISE Through comparative tests, the amount of thermal noise power on an FDM or wire channel necessary to approximate the same judgment of speech quality created by quantizing noise in a PCM channel.

ERASABLE PROGRAMMABLE READ-ONLY MEMORY See EPROM.

ERASABLE STORAGE A storage device whose contents can be changed, i.e. random access memory, or RAM. Compare with read-only storage.

ERASE HEAD On a magnetic tape recorder — voice or video — this is the "head" which erases the tape by demagnetizing it immediately before a new recording is placed on the tape by the adjacent record head.

ERBIUM A rare earth element that when added to fiber optic cabling could obviate the need for repeaters every 20 miles on undersea cables and expand fiber optic cabling to capacities of trillions of bits a second. See ERBIUM-DOPED FIBER AMPLIFIER.

ERBIUM-DOPED FIBER AMPLIFIER EDFA. Erbium-Doped Fiber Amplifiers have become the dominant method for signal amplification in long-haul lightwave transmission systems. EDFAs differ from the normal method of regenerative or electro-optic repeaters in that light does not have be converted to an electrical signal, amplified, and then converted back to light. Optical amplifiers contain a length of erbium-doped (a rare earth) that provides the gain medium, an energy source or "pump" from a laser source as the correct frequency, and a coupler to couple the pump laser to the doped fiber. Both the signal to be amplified and the pump energy are coupled into the doped fiber section of the transmission system. The pump laser puts the erbium-doped fiber into an excited state where it is able to provide optical gain through emission stimulated by a passing signal photon. One of the most important features, after the fact that EDFAs are amazingly simple, is that they are not frequency dependent, and therefore allow bandwidth upgrades (within limits) without replacing the entire transmission systems. Undersea transmission systems, such as Americas 1, TAT-12/13, and TCP-5 use EDFA technology.

ERECTOR SET TELECOM In North America, there's a children's game of building blocks called Leggo. The game comes with hundreds of small plastic blocks, which can be assembled into all sorts of wonderful designs, from castles to gas stations. In England, Leggo sets are also called Meccano sets. The generic term for Leggo and Mechano sets is erector sets. The term "erector set telecom" is a concept created by Harry Newton as a way of explaining "the new open" telecommunications equipment, namely that you build your own computer telephony system from freely-available, non-proprietary hardware and software components. In short, a telecom industry along the same open hardware and software lines as the PC industry. See COMPUTER TELEPHONY.

ERGONOMICS The science of determining proper relations between mechanical and computerized devices and personal comfort and convenience; e.g., how a telephone handset should be shaped, how a keyboard should be laid out.

ERLANG A measurement of telephone traffic. One Erlang is equal to one full hour of use (e.g. conversation), or 60 x 60 = 3,600 seconds of phone conversation. You convert CCS (hundred call seconds) into Erlangs by multiplying by 100 and then dividing by 3,600 (i.e. dividing by 36). Numerically, traffic on a trunk group, when measured in erlangs, is equal to the average number of trunks in use during the hour in question. Thus, if a group of trunks carries 12.35 erlangs during an hour, a little more than 12 trunks were busy, on the average.

Erlang gets its name from the father of queuing theory, A. K. Erlang, a Danish telephone engineer, who, in 1908, began to study congestion in the telephone service of the Copenhagen Telephone Company. A few years later he arrived at a mathematical approach to assist in designing the size of telephone switches. Central to queuing theory are basic facts of queuing life. First, traffic varies widely. Second, anyone who designs a telephone switch to completely handle all peak traffic will find the switch idle for most of the time. He will also find he's built a very expensive switch. Third, it is possible, with varying degrees of certainty to predict upcoming "busy" periods. See also ERLANG, A.K., ERLANG B, ERLANG C and POISSON.

ERLANG B A probability distribution developed by A.K. Erlang to estimate the number of telephone trunks needed to carry a given amount of traffic. Erlang B assumes that, when a call arriving at random finds all trunks busy, it vanishes (the blocked calls cleared condition). Erlang B is also known as "Lost Calls Cleared." Erlang B is used when traffic is random and there is no queuing. Calls which cannot get through, go away and do not return. This is the primary assumption behind Erlang B. Erlang B is easier to program than Poisson or Erlang C. This convenience is one of its main recommendations. Using Erlang B will produce a phone network with fewer trunks than one using Poisson formulae. See also ERLANG, ERLANG A. K., ERLANG C, and TRAFFIC ENGINEERING.

ERLANG C A formula for designing telephone traffic handling for PBXs and networks. Used when traffic is random and there is queuing. It assumes that all callers will wait indefinitely to get through. Therefore offered traffic (see ERLANG) cannot be bigger than the number of trunks available (if it is, more traffic will come in than goes out, and queue delay will become infinite). Erlang C is not a perfect traffic engineering formula. There are none that are.

ERLANG, A. K. In 1918, A. K. Erlang, a Danish telephone engineer, published his work on blocking in "The Post Office Electrical Engineers' Journal," a British publication. Like E.C. Molina, an AT&T engineer, Erlang assumed a Poisson distribution of calls arriving in a given time. Molina had assumed a constant holding time for all calls, whereas Erlang assumed an exponential distribution for holding times. That means that longer calls occur less frequently than shorter calls. Erlang assumed that blocked calls are immediately cleared and lost and do not return. A formula that Erlang worked out based on these assumptions (Erlang B) is still in use in telephone engineering. See ERLANG, ERLANG B, ERLANG C and POISSON.

ERLANG FORMULA A mathematical way of making predictions about randomly arriving work-load (such as telephone calls) based on known information (such as average call duration). Although traditionally used in telephone traffic engineering (to determine the required number of trunks), Erlang formulas have applications in call center staffing as well. See ERLANG.

ERMES 1. European Radio MEssaging System.

2. One of the communications protocols used between paging towers and the mobile pagers/receivers/beepers themselves. Other protocols are POCSAG, ERMES, FLEX, GOLAY and REFLEX. The same paging tower equipment can transmit messages one moment in GOLAY and the next moment in ERMES, or any of the other protocols.

ERP Effective Radiated Power.

ERROR BURST A sequence of transmitted signals containing one or more errors but regarded as a unit in error in accordance with a predefined measure. Enough consecutive transmitted bits in error to cause a loss of synchronization between sending and receiving stations and to necessitate resynchronization.

ERROR CHECKING AND CORRECTION Error checking is the process of checking a "packet" being transmitted over a network to determine if the package, or the data content within the package, has been damaged. If checked and found wanting, damaged packets are discarded. Error correction is the process of correcting the damage by resending a copy of the original packet. In public frame relay services, the network performs the function of error checking, but not error correction. That function is left to the intelligent end equipment (at the user's site).

ERROR CONTROL Various techniques which check the reliability and accuracy of characters (parity) or blocks of data sent over telecommunications lines. V.42, MNP and HST error control protocols (three common dial-up phone line modem protocols) use error detection (CRC) and retransmission of errored frames (ARQ). See ERROR CONTROL PROTOCOLS.

ERROR CONTROL PROTOCOLS Besides high-speed modulation protocols, all current models of high-speed dial-up modems also support error control and data compression protocols. There are two standards for error control protocols: MNP-4 and V.42. The Microcom Networking Protocol, MNP, was developed by Microcom. MNP 2 to 4 are error correction protocols. V.42 was established by ITU-T. V.42 actually incorporates two error control schemes. V.42 uses LAP-M (Link Access Procedure for Modems) as the primary scheme and includes MNP-4 as the alternate scheme. V.42 and MNP-4 can provide error-free connections. Modems without error control protocols, such as most 2400 bps Hayes-compatible modems, cannot provide error-free data communications. The noise and other phone line anomalies are beyond the capabilities of any standard modem to deliver error-free data. V.42 (and MNP 2-4) copes with phone line impairments by filtering out the line noise and automatically retransmitting corrupted data. The filtering process used by V.42 (and MNP 2-4) is similar to the error correction scheme used by file transfer protocols (such as XMODEM). The two modems use a sophisticated algorithm to make sure that the data received match with the data sent. If there is a discrepancy, the data is re-sent.

What is the difference between error control protocols (such as V.42) and file transfer protocols (such as XMODEM)? For one thing, file transfer protocols provide error detection and correction only during file transfers. File transfer protocols do not provide any error control when you are reading e-mail messages or chatting on line. Even though an error control protocol is "on" all the time, we still need file transfer protocols when two modems establish a reliable link. A modem works with bit streams, timing and tones. It does not understand what a file is. When you download or upload a file, your communications software needs to take care of the details related to the file: the filename, file size, etc. This is handled by the file transfer protocol which does more than error-checking.

The other benefit of V.42 (or MNP 4) is that it can improve throughput. Before sending the data to a remote system, a modem with V.42 (or MNP 4) assembles the data into packets and during that process it is able to reduce the size of the data by stripping out the start and stop bits. A character typically takes up 1 start bit, 8 data bits and 1 stop bit for a total of 10 bits. When two modems establish a reliable link using V.42 or MNP 4, the sending modem strips the start and stop bits (which subtracts 20% of the data) and sends the data to the other end. The receiving modem then reinserts the start and stop bits and passes the data to the computer.

Therefore, even without compressing the data you can expect to see as much as 1150 characters per second on a 9600 bps connection. Although the modem subtracts 20% of the data, the speed increase is less than 20% due to the overhead incurred by the error control protocol.

The above definition with great thanks to modem expert Patrick Chen.

ERROR CORRECTING PROTOCOL A method of transmitting bit streams in a mathematical way such that the receiving computer verifies to the sending computer that all bits have been received properly. SNA and XMODEM protocols, in the mainframe and microcomputer environments respectively, are Error Correcting Protocols. See ERROR CONTROL PROTOCOL.

ERROR CORRECTION CODE In computers, rules of code construction that facilitate reconstruction of part or all of a message received with errors.

ERROR CORRECTION MODE A method of transmitting and receiving data that eliminates errors.

ERROR FREE SECOND A Bellcore definition. An error-free second is, surprise, surprise, a one second time interval of digital signal transmission during which no error occurs. That's it.

ERROR LEVEL A numeric value set by some programs that you can test with the errorlevel option of the "If" batch command. It works as follows. Some programs set the DOS errorlevel to a certain number depending on a certain input or response to an event. Let's say when you type the letter "Y" in response to a question the errorlevel is set to 32. Once this is done, you may condition other events based upon this number using an If command in a batch file. You can say "IF ERRORLEVEL = 32 THEN GOTO END." That way, when you type "Y" you will get whatever is at END. This can be very helpful in batch files and other programs for providing "branching" from one event to another based on certain inputs.

ERROR LOGICAL An error in the binary content of a signal, for example, bit error.

ERROR RATE In data transmission, the ratio of the number of incorrect elements transmitted to the total number of elements transmitted.

ERROR SUSPENSE An MCI definition. An automated process which allows billable MCI calls on switch tapes to be processed for billing, while calls with errors are held in the Error Suspense File (a separate file for each switch).

ERROR TRAPPING In software programming, an exception is an interruption to the normal flow of a program. Common exceptions are division-by-zero, stack overflow, disk full errors and I/O (input/output) problems with a file that isn't open. The quality of a software program depends on how completely it checks for possible errors and deals with them. Code used for trapping errors can be excessive. Some programming languages have error trapping built in. Others don't and you have to program it in.

ERSTWHILE An English word meaning previous. I define this word because I use it in this dictionary and lots of readers have told me they don't know it.

ES Errored-Second.

ES/9000 IBM Enterprise System/9000: mainframe computer family.

ESA Emergency Stand Alone.

ESC The ESC key on the keyboard. Often used to leave (escape) a program. Appears on the upper left of some keyboards on the IBM or compatibles but moves around with IBM's latest keyboard redesign whim. See also ESCAPE.

ESCALATION A formal word for taking your trouble up through the levels of management at the vendor — until you get your problem resolved. Some users have formal Escalation Charts, which detail action to be taken depending on how many hours the problem persists, etc. Escalation sometimes works and sometimes doesn't, depending on the vendor. Usually it does. The rule in telecommunications (and we guess most other industries) is that "the squeaky wheel gets the most attention." Escalation works well with honey, flowers, plants and chocolates.

ESCAPE 1. The button on many computer keyboards which allows you to "escape" the present program. ESCape is the ASCII control character — code 27. It is often used to mark the beginning of a series of characters that represent a command rather than data. So called "ESCAPE" because it escapes from the usual meaning of the ASCII code and allows commands to be interspersed in a file of data, especially for data transmission to peripheral devices such as printers and modems. See ESCAPE SEQUENCE.

2. A means of aborting the task currently in progress.

3. A code used to force a smart modem back to the command state from the on-line state.

ESCAPE GUARD TIME An idle period of time before and after the escape code sent to a smart modem, which distinguishes between data and escapes that are intended as a command to the modem.

ESCAPE SEQUENCE A series of characters, usually beginning with the escape character, that is to be interpreted as a command, not as data. Escape sequences are used with ANSI.SYS to change the color of a screen. They are mostly used to send print commands to printers. The name Escape is due to the fact that it "escapes" from the usual meaning of the ASCII code, letting characters be commands instead of data, yet interspersed with data in a transmission.

ESCROW BUCKET A hopper at the outlet of a coin phone's acceptor/rejector that is tipped electrically to return money through the Coin Return or to send the money to the Cash Box as a collection for a completed call.

ESD Electrostatic Discharge.

ESDI 1. Enhanced Small Device Interface. An interface which improves the rate of data transfer for hard disk drives and increases the drive's storage capacity.

2. Northern Telecom term for Enhanced Serial Data Interface.

ESF Extended Super Frame or Extended Superframe Format. A T-1 format that uses the 193rd bit as a framing bit. ESF provides frame synchronization, cyclic redundancy checking and data link bits. Frames consist of 24 bits instead of the previous standard 12 bits as in the D4 format. The standard allows error information to be stored and retrieved easily, facilitating network performance monitoring and maintenance. Electronic Tandem Network.

ESI See ENHANCED SERIAL INTERFACE.

ESMR Enhanced Specialized Mobile Radio.

ESN 1. Emergency Service Number. An ESN is a "list" of emergency numbers that corresponds to a particular ESZ (Emergency Service Zone). This list has to do with 911 service. Usually this ESN list is unique and contains a listing of the corresponding police, figure and ambulance dispatch centers for the caller's area. This "list" is used for selective routing and one button transfer to secondary PSAPs — Public Safety Answering Positions. The ESN/ESZ concept is especially useful in fringe areas.

2. Electronic Serial Number. Each cellular phone is assigned a unique ESN, which

is automatically transmitted to the base station every time a cellular call is placed. The Mobile Telephone Switching office checks the ESN to make sure it is valid, that the phone has not been reported stolen, that the user's monthly bill has been paid, etc., before permitting the call to go through. At least that's the theory. It doesn't always work this way on calls made from roaming cellular phones. And some cellular phones have been known to have their ESNs tampered with, which tends to mess up the billing mechanisms.

3. Electronic Switched Network.

ESOs European Standardization Organizations.

ESP 1. Enhanced Serial Port. The Hayes Enhanced Serial Port (ESP) adapter, introduced in late 1990, replaces and extends the traditional COM1/COM2 serial port adapter. The ESP combines dual 16550 UARTS with an on-board communications coprocessor. The ESP has two distinct modes of operation to provide both old and new standards in the same package: Compatibility Mode and Enhanced Mode. Each ESP port can be independently operated in either mode. Default modes are configured via DIP switches and can be modified by ESP commands. The MCA-bus version of the ESP uses Programmable Option Selection (POS) rather than DIP switches. See ENHANCED SERIAL INTERFACE.

2. Enhanced Service Provider — a vendor who adds value to telephone lines using his own software and hardware. Also called an IP, or Information Provider. An example of an ESP is a public voice mail box provider or a database provider, say one giving the latest airline fares. An ESP is an American term, unknown in Europe, where they're most called VANs, or Value Added Networks. See also OPEN NETWORK ARCHITECTURE and INFORMATION PROVIDER.

3. EncapSulated Postscript File.

ESPA European Selective Paging Association.

ESPRIT European Strategic Program for Research and development in Information Technology. A $1.7 billion research and development program funded by the European Community.

ESS 1. Electronic Switching System. ESS was originally a designation for the switching equipment in Bell System central offices but has slightly more general use now. In the independent telephone company industry, the abbreviation for the same thing is EAX.

2. European Standardization System.

ESS NO 4 AT&T's large toll telephone switch. It will handle over 100,000 trunks and over 500,000 attempts at making a call each hour. It's large and sophisticated and can probably be configured to be the largest telephone switch in the world.

ESS NO 5 AT&T's Class 5 digital central office. See also END OFFICE.

ESSENTIAL SERVICE 1. A service provided by a telecommunications provider, such as an operating telephone company or a carrier, for delivery of priority dial tone. Generally, only up to 10 percent of the customers may request this type of service.

2. A service that is recommended for use in conjunction with NS/EP (national emergency) telecommunications services.

ESSX ESSX (pronounced essex) is some local phone companies' name for Centrex. See CENTREX.

ESZ Emergency Service Zone. This term is used in conjunction with 911 emergency service. An ESZ is a geographic area that is served by a unique mix of emergency services. Each ESZ has a corresponding ESN (a list of Emergency Service Numbers) which enables 911 service to properly route incoming calls.

ET Exchange Termination. Refers to the central office link with the ISDN user.

ETACS Extended TACS. The cellular technology used in the United Kingdom and other countries. It is developed from the U.S. AMPS technology. See also AMPS, TACS, NTACS and NAMPS.

ETB End of Transmission Block.

ETERNITY HOLD Our own creation for what happens when someone puts you on long-term hold. Governmental agencies, airlines and police departments (especially when you need them) tend to be firm believers in placing their callers on Eternity Hold. A new service adjunct to Eternity Hold is Conference Hold. Here everyone on Eternity Hold can speak to each other. We made this up. It doesn't exist, but we think it would be great if it did.

ETHER The medium which, according to one theory, permeates all space and matter and which transmits all electromagnetic waves.

ETHERNET A local area network used for connecting computers, printers, workstations, terminals, servers, etc., within the same building or campus. Ethernet operates over twisted wire and over coaxial cable at speeds up to 10 Mbps. For LAN interconnection, Ethernet is a physical link and data link protocol reflecting the two lowest layers of the DNA/OSI model. The theoretical limit of Ethernet, measured in 64 byte packets, is 14,800 packets per second (PPS). By comparison, Token Ring is 30,000 and FDDI is 170,000.

Ethernet specifies a CSMA/CD (Carrier Sense Multiple Access with Collision Detection). CSMA/CD is a technique of sharing a common medium (wire, coaxial cable) among several devices. As Byte Magazine explained in its January, 1991 issue, Ethernet is based on the same etiquette that makes for a polite conversation: "Listen before talking." Of course, even when people are trying not to interrupt each other, there are those embarrassing moment when two people accidentally start talking at the same time. This is essentially what happens in Ethernet networks, where such a situation is called a collision. If a node on the network detects a collision, it alerts the other nodes by jamming the network. Then, after a random pause, the sending nodes try again. The messages are called frames (see the diagram).

The first personal computer Ethernet LAN adapter was shipped by 3Com on September 29, 1982 using the first Ethernet silicon from SEEQ Technology. Bob Metcalfe created the original Ethernet specification at Xerox PARC and later went on to found 3Com. In the October 31, 1994 issue of the magazine InfoWorld, Bob Metcalfe explained that Ethernet got its name "when I was writing a memo at the Xerox Palo Alto Research Center on May 22, 1973. Until then I had been calling our proposed multimegabit LAN the Alto Aloha Network. The purpose of the Alto Aloha Network was to connect experimental personal computers called Altos. And it used randomized retransmission ideas from the University of Hawaii's Aloha

AN ETHERNET FRAME					
Preamble	Destination address	Source address	Type	Data up to 1500	Frame check sequence
8 bytes	6 bytes	6 bytes	2 bytes	bytes	4 bytes (contains CRC check)

System packet radio network, circa 1970. The word ether came from lumeniferous ether — the omnipresent passive medium once theorized to carry electromagnetic waves through space, in particular light from the Sun to the Earth. Around the time of Einstein's Theory of Relativity, the light-bearing ether was proven not to exist. So, in naming our LAN's omnipresent passive medium, then a coaxial cable, which would propagate electromagnetic waves, namely data packets, I chose to recycle ether. Hence, Ethernet."

According to Metcafe, "Ethernet has been renamed repeatedly since 1973. In 1976, when Xerox began turning Ethernet into a product at 20Mbps, we called it The Xerox Wire. When Digital, Intel, and Xerox decided in 1979 to make it a LAN standard at 10Mbps, they went back to Ethernet. IEEE tried calling its Ethernet standard 802.3 CSMA/CD — carrier sense multiple access with collision detection. And as the 802.3 standard evolved, it picked up such names as Thick Ethernet (IEEE 10Base-5), Thin Ethernet (10Base-2), Twisted Ethernet (10Base-T), and now Fast Ethernet (100Base-T)."

Ethernet PC cards now come in a couple of basic varieties — for connecting to an Ethernet LAN via coaxial cable or via two twisted pairs of phone wires, called 10Base-T. See also 10Base-T, ETHERNET CONTROLLER, ETHERNET IDENTIFICATION NUMBER, ETHERNET SWITCH, ETHERTALK, THINNET and TOKEN RING.

ETHERNET CONTROLLER The unit that connects a device to the Ethernet cable. An Ethernet controller typically consists of part of the physical layer and much or all of the data link layer and the appropriate electronics.

ETHERNET IDENTIFICATION NUMBER This is a unique, hexadecimal Ethernet number that identifies a device, such as a PC/AT with a SpeedLink/PC16 network interface card installed, on an Ethernet network.

ETHERNET SWITCH A new device that connects local area networks. Here's a definition of the capabilities which an Ethernet switch must have from a company called Kalpana Inc. in Santa Clara CA. "What capabilities must a device have to be an Ethernet Switch? Ethernet switching is being embraced as the next milestone solution for bandwidth-constrained Ethernets. To qualify as an Ethernet Switch, the device must: Be capable of switching packets from one Ethernet segment to another "on-the-fly;" Avoid using slower store-and-forward technologies to route packets from one segment to another; Exhibit very low port-to-port latency (the elapsed time between receiving and transmitting a LAN packet is measured in 10s of microseconds, not 100s); Offer a busless, scaleable architecture that increases network carrying capacity as switched connections are added; Support all higher-level products; Provide the technology for creating a massively parallel system with a tens-of-gigabits per second capacity."

ETHERTALK AppleTalk protocol governing Ethernet local area network transmissions. Also the Apple Computer Ethernet adapter and drivers. Apple's implementation of Ethernet is compliant with IEEE specification 802.3.

ETHERTYPE A two-byte code indicating protocol type in an Ethernet local area network packet.

ETI Electronic Telephone Interface.

ETISALAT Emirates Telecommunications Corporation is the sole provider of telecommunications services throughout the United Arab Emirates. The head office is in Abu Dhabi.

ETM Electronic Ticketing Machine. A machine that looks like a banking Automated Teller Machine (ATM), except that it will dispense airline tickets and possibly, hotel reservations, car rental agreements, etc.

ETN Electronic Tandem Network.

ETS 1. European Telecommunications Standard. A standard defined by the European Telecommunications Standards Institute (ETSI).

2. Electronic Tandem Switching. See ELECTRONIC TANDEM SWITCHING.

ETS 300 211 Metropolitan Area Network (MAN) Principles and Architecture.

ERS 300 212 Metropolitan Area Network (MAN) Media Access Control Layer and Physical Layer Specification.

ETS 300 217 Connectionless Broadband Data Service (CBDS).

ETS SET A Northern Telecom term for an electronic Telephone Set.

ETSI European Telecommunications Standards Institute, is the European counterpart to ANSI, the American National Standards Institute. ETSI is based in Sophia-Antipolis, near Nice, France. ETSI's task is to pave the way for telecommunications integration in the European community as part of the single European market program. ETSI was founded in 1988 as a result of an in initiative of the European Commission. It was established to produce telecommunications standards by democratic means, for users, manufacturers, suppliers, administrations, and PTTs. ETSI's main aim is the unrestricted communication between all the member states by the provision of essential European standards. It is now an independent, self-funding organisation that has progressively merged since 1990, with both CEPT and EBU.

ETX End of Text. Indicates the end of a message. If multiple transmission blocks are contained in a message in Bisynch systems, ETX terminates the last block of the message. ETB is used to terminate preceding blocks. The block check character is sent immediately following ETX. ETX requires a reply indicating the receiving station's status.

EUCL End User Common Line charge. An amount added by your local phone company to your monthly phone charges for the privilege (it seems) of providing you phone service. No one seems to understand the reason for this charge. EUCL is (or was) an FCC idea. And the FCC seems to mandate what the local operating phone companies should charge each subscriber for EUCL each month.

EURESCOM EUropean institute for REsearch and Strategic studies in TeleCOMmunication.

EURO-ISDN The European implementation of ISDN. It differs from North American National ISDN-1 in that Euro-ISDN is very limited in the options it offers. In the United States, ISDN comes with many options, including two call appearances, conference calling, call forwarding variable, call forwarding — busy, call forwarding — no answer, voice mail with indicator, two secondary directory numbers, etc. That makes North American ISDN more full-featured, but much less easy to order. Users, can however, call from the United States to Europe and complete ISDN calls. They can not carry their end-user ISDN equipment from the United States and use it in most places in Europe.

EUROSINET-EUROTOP International ISDN pilot project for travel agents.

EUROTELDEV EUROpean TELecommunications DEVelopment. An organization involved in telecommunications standardization.

EUTELSAT EUropean TELecommunications SATellite organization. Inter-governmental organization that aims to provide and operate a communications satellite for public intra-European international telecommunications services. The segment is also used to meet domestic needs by offering leased capacity, primarily for television. U.K. and France are the largest shareholders, with about 25 member countries in total.

EUTP Enhanced Unshielded Twisted Pair. UTP Cables that have enhanced transmission characteristics. Cables that fall under this classification include Category 4 and above.

EV European Videotelephony.

EVA Economic Value Added. A financial measure of whether you're making more money with your plant, factory, assets, etc. in your present business than you would be if you sold everything and stuck the proceeds in a investment. The common assumption is that you can get a 10% or 11% return. If you earn more than that, you're EVA positive. EVA is a term you hear a lot around AT&T. You can become EVA positive in any ways — writing down the value of your capital is one way. Sacking people works too. And, so does selling more (presumably, at a decent price).

EVEN PARITY In data communications there's something called a PARITY BIT that's used for error checking. The transmitting device adds that parity bit to a data word to make the sum of all the "1" ("one" bits) either odd or even. If the sum is odd, the result is called ODD parity. If it's even, it's called EVEN PARITY. See also PARITY.

EVENT An unsolicited communication from a hardware device to a computer operating system, application, or driver. Events are generally attention-getting messages, allowing a process to know when a task is complete or when an external event occurs.

EVENT CODE A code that an agent in a call center enters at the conclusion of a call. Event codes can trigger a variety of follow-up activities such as an acknowledgement letter, or inclusion in a list for a subsequent campaign.

EVENT DRIVEN A style of programming under which programs wait for messages to be sent to them and react to those messages. See EVENT DRIVEN ALARMS/TRIGERS/TICKLETS.

EVENT DRIVEN ALARMS/TRIGGERS/TICKLERS In a parallel process, an event trigger can be set to move the processing forward when a set of criteria is met (ex. the last piece of documentation is added to the file). Alarms can also be time-driven, as when a folder is automatically routed to exception processing if no action is taken within a specified time frame. This term is often found in workflow management.

EVENT HISTORY A history of the activities that have been carried out on a record, (customer or prospect). For example, phone calls and mailers, offers and so on.

EVENT MASK The set of events that the SLEE (Service Logic Execution Environment) designates the ASC (AIN Switch Capabilities) to report for a particular connection segment, and an indication for each event if the ASC should suspend processing events for that connection segment until the SLEE sends a message back. Definition from Bellcore in reference to its concept of the Advanced Intelligent Network.

EVENT SIGNALING All telephone switches use the same three general types of signals: + Event Signaling initiates an event, such as ringing. + Call Progress Signaling denotes the progress (or state) of a call, such as a busy tone, a ringback tone, or an error tone. + Data Packet Signaling communicates certain information about a call, for example, the identify of the calling extension, or the identity of the extension being called.

EW Electronic Warfare. The military use of radar, electronic counter measures and electronic counter-counter measures to keep an enemy from finding invading forces, on land or in the air. It covers such methods as sending planes equipped with equipment which transmit thousands of signals purporting to be signals that an enemy radar might see on locating an incoming plane. By sending thousands of such signals, the enemy's radar becomes a myriad of "radar" signals, of bright spots. Thus it's impossible for the enemy to read any intelligent information. There are also anti-radiation missiles which home in on and destroy air-defense radar facilities. the only defense against such anti-radiation missiles is to turn off the radar. Electronic warfare also covers such techniques as jamming radio frequencies, anti-jamming. It is not the state of Judge Greene's courtroom or the boardroom at the FCC.

eWORLD Apple Computer's on-line, dial-up information service.

EWOS European Workshop for Open Systems.

EXABYTE An exabyte is equal to 10th the 18th power. An exabyte is equal to 1,000 petabytes. Here are the abbreviations: MHz = Megabyte (10 to the 6th power) GHz = Gigabyte (10 to the 9th power) THz = Terabyte (10 to the 12th power) PHz = Petabyte (10 to the 15th power) EHz = Exabyte (10 to the 18th power)

EXALTED CARRIER RECEPTION A method of receiving either amplitude- or phase-modulated signals in which the carrier is separated from the sidebands, filtered and amplified, and then combined with the sidebands again at a higher level prior to demodulation.

EXCA Exchangeable Card Architecture. ExCA is a hardware and software architectural implementation of PCMCIA 2.0 from Intel that allows card interoperability and exchangeability from system to system, regardless of manufacturer. See PCMCIA.

EXCEPTION 1. In telecom, when something happens that's "unusual," it's an exception. The key is to define what's "unusual." For example, you might define that every phone call of longer than 15 minutes is an "exception." Now you have defined an "exception," the question is how to use that information. You might ask the phone system to print out each "exception" call on a printer next to your desk immediately after the call is over. Or you might ask the machine to print "Exceptions" reports at the end of the month listing all the calls over 15 minutes. These reports might be by perpetrator. Or in chronological order, or order of phone number called, etc. In short, any event you define by certain strict parameters can be an "exception." Management reports printed in full are almost useless because they contain so much information, so much paper. Management reports which list only previously-defined "exceptions" are more useful. They show you where to focus your attention so as to improve you or your company's performance.

2. In software programming, an exception is an interruption to the normal flow of a program. Common exceptions are division-by-zero, stack overflow, disk full errors and I/O (input/output) problems with a file that isn't open. The quality of a software program depends on how completely it checks for possible errors and deals with them. Code used for trapping errors can be excessive. Some programming languages have error trapping built in. Others don't and you have to program it in.

EXCEPTION CONDITION In data transmission, the condition assumed by a device when it receives a command that it cannot execute.

EXCEPTION REPORTS Reports generated by "exceptions," often detailing extra long calls or indications of bad circuits. See EXCEPTION.

EXCESS INSERTION LOSS In a optical fiber coupler, the optical loss associated with that portion of the light which does not emerge from the operational ports of the device.

EXCESSIVE ZEROS More consecutive zeros received than are permitted for the selected coding scheme. For AMI-encoded T-1 signals, 16 or more zeros are excessive. For B8ZS encoded serial data, 8 or more zeros are excessive.

EXCHANGE 1. Sometimes used to refer to a telephone switching center — a physical room or building. Outside North America, telephone central offices are called "Public Exchanges."

2. A geographic area in which there is a uniform set of charges for telephone service.

EXCHANGE ACCESS In the telephone networks, the provision of exchange services for the purpose of originating or terminating interexchange telecommunications. Such services are provided by facilities in an exchange area for the transmission, switching, or routing of interexchange telecommunications originating or terminating within the exchange area.

EXCHANGE AREA Geographic area in which telephone services and prices are the same. The concept of exchange is based on geography and regulation, not equipment. An exchange might have one or several central offices. Anyone in that exchange area could get service from any one of those central offices. It's good to ask which central offices could serve your home or office and take service from the most modern. There will be no difference in price between being served by a one-year old central office, or a 50-year old step-by-step central office.

EXCHANGE CARRIER. A Bellcore definition. A company that provides telecommunication within a franchised territory.

EXCHANGE CARRIERS ASSOCIATION An organization of long distance telephone companies with specific administrative duties relative to tariffs, access charges and payments. See EXCHANGE CARRIERS STANDARDS ASSOCIATION.

EXCHANGE CARRIERS STANDARDS ASSOCIATION ECSA. According to their literature ECSA is "the national problem-solving and standards-setting organization where local exchange carriers, interexchange carriers, manufacturers, vendors and users rationally resolve significant operating and technical issues such as network interconnection standards and 800 database trouble reporting guidelines. The Association was created in 1983. The major committees sponsored by ECSA are The Carrier Liaison Committee (to coordinate and resolve national issues related to provision of exchange access); the Telecommunications Industry Forum (TCIF) (to respond to the growing need for voluntary guidelines to facilitate the use of new technology that offers cost savings throughout the telecommunications industry — e.g. EDI, bar coding, automatic number identification); and the Information Industry Liaison Committee (IILC) (an inter industry forum for discussion and voluntary resolution of industry wide concerns about the provision of Open Network Architecture (ONA) services and related matters and Committee T1-Telecommunications (an accredited standards group under ANSI to develop technical standards and reports for US telecommunications networks. In October, 1993, The Exchange Carriers Standards Association changed its name to the Alliance for Telecommunications Industry Solutions (ATIS). It is based in Washington, D.C.

EXCHANGE FACILITIES Those facilities included within a local access and transport area.

EXCHANGE NETWORK FACILITIES FOR INTERSTATE ACCESS See ENFIA.

EXCHANGE, PRIVATE AUTOMATIC BRANCH (PABX) A private telephone exchange which transmits calls internally and to and from the public telephone network.

EXCHANGE SERVICE A name that BellSouth gives to its local phone services, which it also calls Plain Old Telephone Service (POTS).

EXCHANGE TERMINATION ET. In Integrated Services Digital Network (ISDN) nomenclature, ET refers to the central office link with the end user.

EXCLUDE A memory management command-line option that tells the memory manager in an MS-DOS machine not to use a certain segment of memory. For example, you may exclude upper memory locations D200 through D800 (hexadecimal) because your network adapter card uses that space. The reciprocal term — include — specifically directs the memory manager to use an area of memory.

EXCLUSION A PBX feature that prevents the attendant from silently monitoring a call once he/she has extended it.

EXCLUSIVE HOLD Only the telephone putting the call on hold can take it off. This feature assures that the call on hold will not be picked up by someone at another telephone who can then listen to your call.

EXCLUSIVE HOLD RECALL When a call is placed on "Exclusive Hold" and is not picked up after a predetermined amount of time, you will hear a beeping at that phone, which indicates the call is still on hold.

EXCLUSIVE OR PRIVATE UNIT A circuit card installed in each key telephone set sharing the same line or intercom path that causes the first caller on the line to lock out (exclude) all other stations from using or listening in, until the line is released (or privacy feature is defeated by the active caller).

EXECUNET An intercity switched telephone service introduced by MCI in 1975. Execunet was the first dial-up switched service introduced by a long distance phone company in competition with AT&T. At that time, all of AT&T's competitors, including MCI, were selling full-time private lines and shared private lines. The service was named by Carl Vorder-Bruegge, MCI's VP marketing at that time and introduced and made successful by Jerry Taylor, who was MCI's regional manager in Texas and is now one of the company's most senior executives. The service was the forerunner of what is today a $10 billion plus industry — the non-AT&T provided switched long distance business. MCI no longer uses the word Execunet to describe its switched long distance service. It's just plain long distance. Jerry Taylor started Execunet using a 104-port Action WATSBOX in Dallas, Texas. He deserves a place in the history books, not just a dictionary.

EXECUTABLE FILE A computer program that is ready to run. Application programs, such as spreadsheets and word processors, are examples of executable files. Such files in PCs running MS-DOS and Windows usually end with the BAT, COM or EXE extension.

EXECUTE To complete a task.

EXECUTION TIME The time needed to complete a task.

EXECUTIVE BARGE-IN See EXECUTIVE OVERRIDE.

EXECUTIVE BUSY OVERRIDE See EXECUTIVE OVERRIDE.

EXECUTIVE CAMP-ON A feature for use by executives or other privileged people. When they call a someone lowly, that low person hears a special distinctive tone or sees a special light or sees a special signal that their phone has been camped on by someone significant. These days many PBXs let you know who's calling — even though you're on the phone. So executive camp-on is not that useful.

EXECUTIVE OVERRIDE A feature of some telephone systems which permits certain users to intrude on conversations on other extensions. In some systems, executive barging-in will not be heard by the person outside the office, only the one inside the office. In some systems, such as the Mitel SX series with the Mitel Superset 4 phones, this feature activates the hands-free speakerphone of the called party, who is using his other line to speak on a normal phone conversation.

EXIT EVENT An event occurring in an ASC (AIN Switch Capabilities) that causes call processing to leave a PIC (Point in Call). Definition from Bellcore in reference to its concept of the Advanced Intelligent Network.

EXM Exit Message. The seventh ISUP message. It's a message sent in the backward direction from the access tandem to the end office indicating that call setup information has successfully proceeded to the adjacent network. See ISUP and COMMON CHANNEL SIGNALING.

EXOS Abbreviation for EXtension OutSide; a phone connected to a key system based in another building. The wiring belongs to the telephone company, even though the phone equipment may not. Unlike an OPX, the circuit between the two locations does not pass through a central office.

EXOSPHERE This region lies beyond an altitude of about 400km from the surface of the earth. The density is such that an air molecule moving directly outwards has an even chance of colliding with another molecule or escaping into space.

EXPANDED MEMORY MS-DOS running on the Intel 80286, 80386, 80486 and Pentium family of microprocessors can only address one megabyte at one time. Expanded memory is memory located between base memory (either 512K or 640K) and one megabyte. Expanded memory is reserved by MS-DOS for "housekeeping" tasks such as managing output to the screen. As programs got larger and more hungry for memory (640K was no longer enough), people started jealously eyeing the memory between 640K and 1024K (one megabyte). The first technique was a standard called LIM-EMS, named after the three companies which developed it — Lotus, Intel and Microsoft. Essentially LIM grabs 64K of the 640-1024 memory and uses it to swap pages of other memory in and out quickly. This fools DOS into thinking that it has actually more memory. LIM-EMS lets you work on bigger spreadsheets, and do other jobs faster.

There are many ways of using expanded memory, including special memory management application program or DOS 5.0 or higher. 80386, 80386SX, 80486 and Pentium computers can create expanded memory readily by using the EMS (expanded memory specification) driver provided with DOS, through Windows 3.xx or Windows 95, or through a memory manager such as Quarterdeck QEMM or Qualitas 386. To use expanded memory, a program must be EMS-aware or run under an environment such as Microsoft Windows. See also EXTENDED MEMORY, which is memory above 1MB.

EXPANDED SPECTRUM A cellular telephone term for having the full 832-channel analog cellular spectrum currently available to you, the user of the cellular phone.

EXPANDER That device in a transmission facility which expands the amplitude of received compressed signals to their approximate normal range. The receiving side of a compandor.

EXPANDOR See EXPANDER.

EXPANSION The switching of a number of input channels, such as telephone lines onto a larger number of output channels.

EXPANSION CARRIER An AT&T Merlin term. A carrier added to the control unit when the basic carrier cannot house all the modules needed. An expansion carrier houses a power supply module and up to six additional modules.

EXPANSION SLOTS In a computer there are card slots for adding accessories such as internal modems, extra drivers, hard disks, monitor adapters, hard disk drivers, etc. Most modern PBXs are actually cabinets with nothing but expansion slots inside. Into these slots we fit trunk cards, line cards, console cards, etc. Some phone systems have "universal" slots, meaning you can put any card in any slot. Some phone systems have dedicated expansion slots, meaning that they expect only a certain card in that slot. In the PC industry, many manufacturers make cards for IBM and IBM compatible slots. In the phone industry, nobody makes cards for expansion slots in anyone else's phone system. See also EISA and MCA.

EXPERT SYSTEM A very sophisticated computer program consisting of three parts. 1. A stock of rules or general statements, e.g. Some long distance phone calls are free. These rules are generally based on the collective wisdom of human "experts" who are interviewed. 2. A set of particular facts, e.g. Three companies provide the bulk of long distance service in the United States. 3. Most importantly, a "logical engine" which can apply facts to rules to reach all the conclusions that can be drawn from them — one of which might be "Three companies give away long distance phone calls." (Which would be wrong.) The idea of expert systems is to help people solve problems. For example, Compaq is trying to improve its customer service by installing automated assistants that work on the principle that reasoning is often just a matter of remembering the best precedent. The simplest expert systems, according to the Economist Magazine, assume that their rules and facts tell them everything there is to know. Any statement that cannot be deduced from the system's rules and facts is assumed to be false. This can lead machines to answer "YES" or "NO," when they should say "I don't know." Slowly we are beginning to find ways of dealing with the inflexibility of machines. One such gadget is a "truth maintenance machine" invented by Dr. Jon Doyle of MIT. As each fact is fed into the system, Dr. Doyle's program checks to see if it (or the deductions derived from it) contradict any of the facts or deductions already in the system. If there is a contradiction, the machine works backward along its chain of reasoning to find the source and dispose of that troublesome fact or deduction. So the system maintains one consistent set of beliefs.

EXPONENTIAL BACK-OFF DELAY The back-off algorithm used in IEEE 802.3 systems by which the delay before retransmission is increased as an exponential function of the number of attempts to transmit a specific frame.

EXPORT Imagine you have a software program, like a spreadsheet or a database. And you have information in that program. Let's say it's Microsoft Word or Lotus 123. And you want to get it into a different program, say to give it to a workmate who uses WordPerfect or Excel. You have to convert it from one format to another. From Word to WordPerfect or from Lotus to Excel. That process is typically called "exporting." And you'll typically see the word "EXPORT" as a choice on one of your menus. The opposite is called importing. See IMPORT.

EXPORT SCRIPT First read my definition of EXPORT. An export script is a series of specifications which control the export process. It contains the fields to be sent, which records to be sent, the name of file to send as well as the name of the import script (if there is one) located at the receiver's end which will control the merge. See EXPORT.

EXPORT SERVER A Windows NT term. In directory replication, a server from which a master set of directories is exported to specified servers or workstations (called import computers) in the same or other domains.

EXPRESS CALL COMPLETION Someone calls an information operator. "What is the name?" the operator answers. "Here is the number. Would you like me to get that number for you now? If so, please hit 1." Express Call Completion lets the operator complete the call for you while you're on line. Express Call Completion was begun in the September of 1990 by Pacific Bell using a Northern Telecom central office. Express Call Completion is part of Northern Telecom's Automated Directory Assistance Call Completion (ADACC) software and Traffic Operator Position Systems Multipurpose (TOPS MP).

EXPRESS ORDERWIRE A permanently connected voice circuit between selected stations for technical control purposes.

EXT See EXTENSION.

EXTEND A verb used by the phone industry to describe an operator transferring a call to a telephone extension. The word is used thus: The operator extended the call to Mr. Smith on extension 200. "Putting a call through" is a clearer way of saying "extending" a call. The word "extend" probably comes from the old days when the operator extended her arm to plug you in on her cordboard.

EXTENDED ADDRESSING In many bit-oriented protocols, extended addressing is a facility allowing larger addresses than normal to be used. In IBM's SNA, the addition of two high-order bits to the basic addressing scheme.

EXTENDED AREA SERVICE An option offered by local telephone companies where a subscriber can pay a higher rate and reach more areas as local calls (no long distance charges).

EXTENDED BINARY CODED DECIMAL INTERCHANGE CODE EBCDIC. (Pronounced Eb-Si-Dick.) An IBM standard of coding characters. It's an 8-bit code and can represent up to 256 characters. A ninth bit is used as a parity bit. See PARITY and EBCDIC.

EXTENDED BIOS DATA AREA In PCs, extended BIOS data area is 1KB of RAM located at 639KB. It is used to support extended BIOS functions including support for PS/2.

EXTENDED CALL MANAGEMENT A Northern Telecom term for a collection of features being added to its DMS Meridian central office Automatic Call Distribution (ACD) service. Using Switch-to-Computer Applications Interface (SCAI), ECM will work with user-provided computer equipment to integrate call processing, voice processing (recorded announcements, voice mail and voice response) and data processing. For example, ECM will allow an outboard computer device to coordinate the presentation of customer data on the ACD agent's computer screen with an incoming call. The D channel of an ISDN Basic Rate Interface (BRI) serves as the transport mechanism from the DMS-100 central office switch to an outboard computing device. Communication is peer-to-peer, meaning that neither the switch or the computer is in a "slave" relationship to the other. The application layer messaging — i.e. layer 7 messaging as defined by the Open Systems Interconnection (OSI) reference model — is in the Q.932 format and is designed to conform to the T1S1 SCAI message protocol.

462

EXTENDED CHARACTER SET The characters assigned to ASCII codes 128 through 255 on IBM and IBM-compatible microcomputers. These characters are not defined by the ASCII standard and are therefore not "standard." See EXTENDED GRAPHICS CHARACTER SET.

EXTENDED DIGITAL SUBSCRIBER LINE The ISDN EDSL combines 24 B-channels and one 64-Kb/s D-channel on a single line, ISDN primary rate interface.

EXTENDED DEFINITION TELEVISION EDTV. Television that includes improvements to the standard NTSC television system, which improvements are receiver-compatible with the NTSC standard, but modify the NTSC emission standards. Such improvements may include (a) a wider aspect ratio, (b) higher picture definition than distribution-quality definition but lower than HDTV, and/or (c)any of the improvements used in improved-definition television. When EDTV is transmitted in the 4:3 aspect ratio, it is referred to simply as "EDTV." When transmitted in a wider aspect ratio, it is referred to as "EDTV-Wide."

EXTENDED GRAPHICS CHARACTER SET The characters assigned to ASCII codes 128 through 255 on IBM and IBM-compatible microcomputers. These characters are not defined by the ASCII standard and are therefore not "standard." The original ASCII code used a seven bit one-or-zero code. There are two to the seventh power, or 128 possible combinations. The IBM PC uses a 16-bit CPU with an eight bit data bus and thus transmits data internally in eight big bytes. Instead of using the seven bit ASCII code, the PC uses the equivalent eight bit code, by simply making the left most digit, a zero. In seven bit code, an R is 1010010. In 8-bit, it's 01010010. The only difference between the first 128 characters and the second 128 characters is that in the second, the first bit is a 1.

EXTENDED KEY CODE The two digit code that represents pressing a key outside the typewriter portion of the keyboard, such as a function key, cursor-control key or combinations of CTRL (control) and ALT keys with another key. The first number is always 0 (zero) and is separated from the second number by a semicolon.

EXTENDED LAN A collection of local area networks connected by protocol independent devices such as bridges or routers.

EXTENDED MEMORY Memory beyond 1 megabyte in 80286, 80386, 80486 and Pentium computers. Windows uses extended memory to manage and run applications. Extended memory can be used for RAM disks, disk caches, or Microsoft Windows, but requires the processor to operate in a special mode (protected mode or virtual real mode). With a special driver, you can use extended memory to create expanded memory. Extended memory typically is not available to non-Windows applications or MS-DOS. See also EXPANDED MEMORY.

EXTENDED SUPERFRAME FORMAT ESF. A new T1 framing standard used in Wide Area Networks (WANs). With this format 24 frames — instead of 12 — are grouped together. In this grouping, the 8,000 bps frame is redefined as follows:

• 2,000 bps for framing and signaling to provide the functions generally defined in the D-4 format.

• 2,000 bps are CRC-6 (Cyclic Redundancy Check-code 6) to detect logic errors caused by line equipment, noise, lightning and other interference. Performance checking is done by both the carrier and the customer without causing any interference with the T-1 traffic.

• 4,000 bps are used as a data link. This link is to perform functions such as enhanced end-to-end diagnostics, networking reporting and control, channel or equipment switching, and/or optional functions or services. See also T-1 FRAMING and D-4 FRAMING.

EXTENDED SUPERFRAME MONITORING UNIT ESFMU. An MCI definition. Placed on customer data circuits to provide performance monitoring throughout MCI's Digital Data Network.

EXTENDED TELEPHONY LEVEL The lowest level of service in Windows Telephony Services is called Basic Telephony and provides a guaranteed set of functions that corresponds to "Plain Old Telephone Service" (POTS - only make calls and receive calls). The next service level is Supplementary Telephone Service providing advanced switch features such as hold, transfer, etc. All supplementary services are optional. Finally, there is the Extended Telephony level. This API level provides numerous and well-defined API extension mechanisms that enable application developers to access service provider-specific functions not directly defined by the Telephony API. See WINDOWS TELEPHONY SERVICES.

EXTENDED TEXT MODE Standard text mode is 80 columns wide. So-called extended text mode is 132 columns wide. This mode allows you to view more text on-screen when using such applications as Lotus 1-2-3.

EXTENSIBLE In strictest terms, the word means "capable of being extended." When Microsoft introduced its At Work operating system on June 9, 1993 it said that one of the operating system's key features was that it was "extensible." Microsoft's explanation: The software is designed to allow both manufacturers and customers to add new features. For example, local area network connectivity will be able to be added easily by installing an optional LAN hardware module and a software driver. Additional memory will be able to be added to the system, and the system will automatically make use of this memory. New image-processing software and communications protocols will be able to be added on the premises, and it will even be able to be done over the phone line, allowing manufacturers to create basic models that can be enhanced in many different ways to fit the needs of different user groups.

EXTENSION 1. An additional telephone connected to a line. Allows two or more locations to be served by the same telephone line or line group. May also refer to an intercom phone number in an office.

2. The optional second part of an PC computer filename. Extensions begin with a period and contain from one to three characters. Most application programs supply extensions for files they create. Checking a file's extension often tells you what the file does or contains. For example, most BASIC files use a filename extension of .BAS. Most backup files have an extension of .BAK. MS-DOS programs have .EXE or .COM. dBASE database files have the extension .DBF and .DBT. Paradox files have the extension .DB. Files of sounds have their own extensions. Here are the typical extensions on sound files of various computers:

Microsoft Windows — .wav Apple — .aif NeXT — .snd MIDI — .mid and .nni Sound Blaster — .voc

Here are the typical extensions on graphics formats:
.TIFF, .EPS, .CGM, .PCX, .DRW, .WMF, and .BMP

EXTENSION CORD A multi-conductor, male/female modular line cord generally used to permit greater separation between the Communications Outlet and the telephone equipment. Available in various lengths up to 25 feet. May be of tinsel or stranded wire construction.

EXTERNAL MEMORY Storage devices, such as magnetic disks, drums or tapes which are outside (externally attached) to the main telephone or computer system.

EXTERNAL MODEM A modem external to the computer, it sits in its own little box connected to a computer through the computer's serial port. Compare with an internal modem, which typically comes on one printed circuit card and is placed into one of the computer's expansion slots and thus connects to the computer through the computer's "backplane." Internal modems cost less because they don't need any external housing and separate power supply. But because they're mounted inside the computer, it's harder to see what they're doing. You can't see the various status lights, like OH (for Off-Hook) and CD (for Carrier Detect). They also take up valuable slots instead of a serial port.

EXTERNAL PHOTOEFFECT In fiber optics, an external photoeffect consists of photon-excited electrons that are emitted after overcoming the energy barrier at the surface of a photo-emissive surface.

EXTERNAL STORAGE See also EXTERNAL MEMORY.

EXTERNAL TIMING REFERENCE A timing reference obtained from a source external to the communications system such as one of the navigation systems. Many of which are referenced to Coordinated Universal Time (UTC).

EXTN Extension.

EXTREMELY HIGH FREQUENCY EHF. Frequencies from 30 GHz to 300 GHz.

EXTREMELY LOW FREQUENCY ELF. Frequencies from 30 Hz to 300 Hz.

EXTRINSIC JOINT LOSS For an optical fiber, that portion of a joint loss that is not intrinsic to the fibers, e.g., loss caused by end separation, angular misalignment, or lateral misalignment.

EXTRUSION Method of continuously forcing plastic, rubber or elastometer material through an orifice to apply insulation or jacketing over a conductor or cable core.

EYE PATTERN An oscilloscope display used to visually determine the quality of an equalized transmission line signal being received. So called because portions of the pattern appearing on the scope resemble the elliptical shape of the human eye.

EYE PHONE Several researchers are studying something they call "virtual reality." One version of it, a system developed by a company called VPL Research, Redwood City, CA, is based around three things: a three-dimensional glove worn on the head (called an Eye Phone), an electronic glove (the Data Glove) and a high-speed computer. The whole system cost $250,000 in the fall of 1990.

EYEBALL A viewing audience. "There are plenty of new eyeballs available in this time slot."

EZTV A software created by Apple which will enable consumers to order movies, go shopping and play games on their TV sets. The product is mostly on the drawing boards.

F LINK Fully Associated Link. A link used to connect two SS7 signaling points when there is a high community of interest between them and it is economical to link them. Also called associated signaling.

F PORT In Fiber Channel, refers to the port residing on the fabric side of the link, or the fabric port.

F TYPE CONNECTOR A low cost connector used by the TV industry to connect coaxial cable to equipment.

F2F Face to Face. When you actually meet those people you been corresponding electronically with.

FAB Factory that makes ("fabricates") IC chips.

FABRIC An Internet term. In Fabric Channel, refers to a non-blocking switch which interconnects all nodes to which it's attached.

FAC See FORCED AUTHORIZATION CODE.

FACEPLATE A cover that fits around the pushbuttons or rotary dial of a telephone. Hotels and motels put instructions on them. More businesses should also.

FACILITIES A stupid, imprecisely defined word that means anything and everything. To me it sounds like toilets. But it's not. It can mean the equipment and services which make up a telecom system. It can mean offices, factories, and/or building. It can be anywhere you choose to put telecom things. Oops, I nearly said telecom facilities. So "facilities" means practically anything you want it to mean so long as it covers a sufficiently broad variety of "things" which you haven't got a convenient name for. "Facilities" sounds better than things, especially if you want to sound pompous.

FACILITIES ADMINISTRATION AND CONTROL A PBX feature which allows you, the subscriber, to assign to your users features and privileges like authorization codes, restriction levels and calling privileges.

FACILITIES ASSURANCE REPORTS This feature allows a subscriber to get an audit trail of the referrals produced by the automatic circuit assurance feature of some PBXs. The audit trail will identify the trunk circuit, the time of referral, the nature of the problem and if a test was performed, the outcome of the test.

FACILITIES BASED CARRIER Long distance carriers which own call switching equipment and transmission lines regionally or nationally are called facilities based carriers. The major national facilities based carriers are AT&T, MCI and Sprint. Facilities based carriers other than AT&T along with resellers also are known as Other Common Carriers. The national facilities based long distance carriers have switching offices in all service areas of the country and provide originating service nationwide. Major facilities based carriers sell their services to business and residential users and other long distance companies which resell those services.

FACILITIES MANAGEMENT Also called Outsourcing, facilities management is having someone else run your computers or your telecommunications system. The concept is that you're a great bank and you should concentrate on being in the banking business. Your outside facilities manager should concentrate on running your computers or telecom systems. He can do it cheaper, allegedly. Ross Perot's Electronic Data Systems (EDS) probably started facilities management. Mr. Perot incorporated EDS on June 27, 1962. At that time he was a leading IBM salesman. See also OUTSOURCING.

FACILITIES RESTRICTION LEVEL Which types of calls a PBX user is entitled to make.

FACILITY A telephone industry term for a phone or data line. Sometimes (but rarely) used to describe equipment. See FACILITIES.

FACILITY GROUNDING SYSTEM The electrically interconnected system of conductors and conductive elements that provides multiple current paths to the earth electrode subsystem. The facility grounding system consists of the earth electrode subsystem, the lightning protection subsystem, the signal reference subsystem, and the fault protection subsystem. Faulty grounding causes more phone and computer problems than any other single factor.

FACILITY WORK ORDER An order to a phone company to rearrange things.

FACS 1. How they abbreviate the word facsimile in Bermuda. 2. Facilities Access Control Systems. A collection of dozens of interrelated computer applications developed by the former AT&T Bell Operating Companies which manage the local loops connecting customers to the Public Switched Telephone Network.

FACSIMILE EQUIPMENT FAX. Equipment which allows hard copy (written, typed or drawn material) to be sent through the switched telephone system and printed out elsewhere. Think of a fax machine as essentially two machines — one for transmitting and one for receiving. The sending fax machines typically consists of a scanner for converting material to be faxed into digital bits, a digital signal processor (a single chip specialized microprocessor) for reducing those bits (encoding white space into a formula and not an endless series of bits representing white), and a modem for converting the bits into an analog signal for transmission over analog dial-up phone lines. The receiving fax consists of a modem and a printer which converts the incoming bits into black and white images on paper. More modern and more expensive machines also have memory — such that if the machine runs out of paper, it will still continue to receive incoming faxes, storing those faxes into memory until someone fills the machine with paper and it prints the faxes out.

There are five internationally accepted specifications for facsimile equipment. Group 1, Group 2, Group 3, Group 3 Enhanced and Group 4. Only 1, 2, 3 and 3 Enhanced will work on "normal" analog dial-up phone lines. Group 4 is designed for digital lines running at 56/64 Kbps, e.g. ISDN lines. Among the analog line fax machines, Group 2 is faster than Group 1. Group 3 is faster than Group 2, etc. Virtually all machines sold today are Group 3, though an increasing percentage are Group 3 enhanced, which has speeded up Group 3's transmission speed from

9,600 bps to 14,400 bps and improved its error correction. Group 3 faxes send an 8-1/2 x 11 inch page over a normal phone line in about 20 seconds. How much time it actually takes depends on how much stuff is actually on the paper. Unlike older machines, Group 3 machines are "intelligent." They only transmit the information that's on the paper. They do not transmit white space, as earlier machines did. Group 3 fax machines are now available in "slimy" (i.e. chemically coated) paper and plain paper, the same paper your photocopy machines now uses.

When a fax machine calls a phone line, it emits a standard ITU-T-defined, "CNG tone" (calling tone) — 1100 Hz tone every three seconds. When the receiving fax machine hears this tone, it knows it's an incoming fax call and it can automatically connect. With this tone it is possible to insert a "fax switch," which would "listen" for an incoming fax call and switch it to a fax machine if it heard the CNG tones or to something else — like a phone or answering machine — if it didn't. It is not possible to do this with a modem. A calling modem does not issue any tones whatsoever. A modem works backwards — when the receiving modem answers the phone, it emits a tone.

Typically, a Group 3 machine can speak to a Group 2 and a Group 1 machine. A Group 2 can speak to a Group 1. Speaking down means slowing down. Fax machines are dropping in price. "Personal" fax machines are emerging. Most fax machines today at Group 3 or Group 3 enhanced.

A Group 4 standard has been promulgated by the ITU-T. Group 4 facsimile machines are 100% digital and directly attach to the B (bearer channel) of a digital ISDN line. They will transmit a sheet of 8 1/2 x 11 paper in under six seconds. The author of this dictionary has seen a working Group 4 fax machine. It's mighty impressive.

Some warnings on fax machines:

1. All analog Group 3 and enhanced Group 3 fax machines pose a security risk. Anyone can attach a normal audio cassette recorder to a phone line, record the incoming or outgoing fax "tones" of an analog fax machine. By playing back to another fax machine at a later time, you'll get a perfect reproduction of the fax. There are now fax encryption devices which make the fax transmission unintelligible to any machine other than the one it's intended for — i.e. the one that has a similar un-encryption device.

2. Some plain paper fax machines present a different security risk. Some (not all) use a carbon ribbon the width of their paper. As a result, if you want to read what came in, you simply read the carbon ribbon, which you open like a scroll, which the cleaning lady finds in the trash. These machines are increasingly less common, as plain paper fax machines acquire laser printing engines.

3. Most fax machines record all the digits dialed into them which were used to set up a fax call. If a fax machine is sitting behind a PBX (as many are these days) it will capture all the confidential authorization codes of all the company's employees. To get those codes all you need do is ask the machine to print out a report. There is no easy solution to this problem as at the time of writing this dictionary, except that some fax makers have told me they intend to obscure these numbers on their reports, at some stage. Some may, by the time you read this.

4. Slimy paper fades. How long it takes to fade depends on a bunch of factors — from what's sitting on top of the fax, to the temperature in the room, to whether it's

exposed to sunlight, etc. Recommendation: If you want to retain a slimy fax, make a photo copy of it the moment you get it and throw out the original.

5. Poor quality slimy fax paper can abrade the fax machine's drum and cause a costly repair. Don't buy cheap slimy fax paper.

6. Plain paper fax machines cost more to buy, but less to run. You can buy a second tray for some plain paper fax machines which will hold 8 1/2" wide x 14" long paper, which is useful for receiving faxes from outside the US where they use longer paper. This way you save a sheet of paper.

7. It makes sense to have banks of fax machines attached to phones which roll over — also called "hunt." It makes absolutely no sense to have multiple fax machines on separate phone lines that don't hunt, i.e. one for everybody in the office. Two fax machines in rotary can receive and transmit more than twice the number of faxes that two machines on separate, non-hunting phone lines can send and receive. "Personal" fax machines should be out. Banks of fax machines should be in. Egos, though, usually prevail over logic.

8. The paper feed mechanism on plain fax machines has a tendency to jam. Slimy paper fax machines don't jam because their paper typically comes in rolls. And roll paper doesn't jam. The feed mechanism is much simpler.

9. Plain paper fax machines, like laser printers (which many are) use supplies, like toner, which run out. When the supplies run out, such machines usually accept incoming faxes into memory — until that runs out. Then they just ring and ring and ring. Which means that incoming faxes don't get through and don't roll over to the next machine. There is no simple solution since the FCC (Federal Communications Commission) has ruled that fax machines must not return a busy signal to the central office if it runs out of supplies or paper. We have a separate machine that automatically busies out a line if it failed to answer on the fifth ring. But so far, the device is not commercially available. I don't know the answer to this problem except to make sure your fax machine is always stuffed with supplies. Especially check every Friday night. A final note: If your plain paper fax machine is missing supplies, but stuffed with incoming messages in memory, don't turn it off, since you'll lose the messages. Simply replace the supplies and pray your messages will emerge.

10. Some slimy fax paper rolls are coated on the inside of the paper. Others are coated on the outside. When you put one in a fax machine and images don't appear on the paper, then turn the roll over and feed it from underneath. In short, ignore what the instruction book says.

11. Fax modem switches only work when they're called automatically by a fax machine — not by a person using a fax machine manually and is waiting the sound of the distant fax prior to pushing the "Send" button. Make sure you warn your senders. It's remarkable how many people manually dial their faxes and thus penetrate fax modem switches.

11. Think about putting your fax machine on "fine." You'll transmit better quality faxes and may only cost yourself 10% more in transmission time. But that savings depends on the quality of the fax machine at the other end. If it's an older machine, it may cost you as much as double the transmission time. Here are the numbers: Standard is 203 x 98 dpi. Fine is 203 x 196 dpi. "Fine" faxes obviously look much better.

12. Printed circuit cards which slide into slots of PCs and allow you to transmit and receive faxes work well — when transmitting faxes. They work far less well when receiving faxes — largely because of the difficulty of reading faxes. Faxes conform to one type of digital encoding and PC screens conform to another. Moreover a PC screen is landscape (i.e. horizontal), while a fax message is portrait (i.e. vertical). Viewing vertical images on horizontal screens is difficult. Here is a comparison of how fax machines and how personal computer screens encode their images. Obviously, the more digits or pixels, the clearer the end picture. Notice that the encodings are completely dissimilar:

FAX ENCODING

Standard, Group III	203 x 98
Fine, Group III	203 x 196
Superfine, Group III	203 x 391
Standard, Group IV	400 x 400

PC SCREEN ENCODING

CGA	320 x 200
Enhanced CGA	640 x 400
EGA	640 x 350
Hercules	720 x 348
VGA	640 x 480
Super VGA	800 x 600
8514/A (also called XGA)	1,024 x 768

See also 1966, 1978, 1980, AT WORK, DEMODULATION, FACSIMILE CONVERTER, FACSIMILE RECORDER, FACSIMILE SIGNAL LEVEL, FACSIMILE SWITCH, FAX, FAX AT WORK, FAX BACK, FAX BOARD, FAX DATA MODEM, FAX DEMODULATION, FAX MAILBOX, FAX MODEM, FAX PUBLISHING, FAX SERVER, FAX SWITCH, FAXBIOS, GROUP 1, 2, 3, 3 BIS AND 4, PHASE A thru E, and WINDOWS TELEPHONY.

FACSIMILE CONVERTER A facsimile device that changes the type of modulation from frequency shift to amplitude and vice versa.

FACSIMILE RECORDER That part of the facsimile receiver that performs the final conversion of the facsimile picture signal to an image of the original subject copy on the record medium.

FACSIMILE SIGNAL LEVEL The facsimile signal power or voltage measured at any point in a facsimile system. It is used to establish the operating levels in a facsimile system, and may be expressed in decibels with respect to some standard value such as 1 milliwatt.

FACSIMILE SWITCH A new breed of "black box." Its purpose is to avoid having to lease a separate phone line for your facsimile machine, for your phone and for your modem. You buy this box, connect it to an incoming line, connect it to your fax machine, your phone and, possibly, your modem. When a call comes in, the fax switch answers the call, listens if the call coming in is from a fax machine (it can hear the fax machine's CNG calling tone) and switches the call to the fax machine, or switches the call to your modem if a computer is calling. It knows if a computer is calling because the calling computer will, when it hears the fax switch answer, send out some ASCII characters — e.g. 22. (You must put those numbers in your modem dialing stream.) And it knows if a person is calling because it hears neither a CNG tone from a fax machine nor touchtones from the dialing stream of a modem.

The above are the basics of how fax switches work. There are variations on this theme. Some fax switches work automatically. Some work by the incoming caller punching in digits. Some allow you to switch from fax machine to modem to phone and back again. And some fax switches will answer and connect to three modems and one fax or other combinations. The major problem with fax switches is that they typically send a DC ringing tone to whatever device they're trying to connect you (the incoming caller with). Sometimes some devices — for example, high-speed 9600 baud and higher modems — have difficulties responding to low power, DC ringing signals. And they just sit there not answering. Better to buy one that sends standard telephone company AC ringing signals. In short, before you buy a fax/modem/phone switch, test it on your favorite 9,600 or 14,400 bps modem. The more expensive switches tend to work better.

FACTORY REFURBISHED A term used in the secondary telecom equipment business. Equipment that has been returned to the factory and the factory has replaced plastic, repaired, upgraded boards, or otherwise reconditioned.

FADE A reduction in a received signal which is caused by reflecting, refraction or absorption. See also FADING.

FADE MARGIN The depth of fade, expressed in dB, that a microwave receiver can tolerate while still maintaining acceptable circuit quality.

FADING The reduction in signal intensity of one or all of the components of a radio signal.

FADS Force Administration Data System. A system which takes basic statistics on telephone traffic and gives hints as to how many operators should be employed to answer the incoming calls and when they should be present.

FAIL SAFE A specially designed system that continues working after a failure of some component or piece of the system. There are precious few, genuinely fail safe systems. To be genuinely fail safe, a system needs to be completed duplicated. It is prohibitively expensive for most commercial users to duplicate every part of their system. But you can duplicate selectively and bring yourself closer to "fail safe." The extent of the duplications you choose (and thus the cost of your telephone equipment and transmission system) depends on how important it is that your system function as close to 100% as possible. The idea is to identify those things most likely to break and to duplicate them. Power is clearly the first area to focus on. These days, the words "FAIL SAFE" are increasingly being replaced with "FAULT TOLERANT." Given the number of times your local, friendly airline has told you that its "computer is down," you can understand the reason for the wording change.

FAIR CONDITION A term used in the secondary telecom equipment business. One step up from "as is" condition. Equipment may have been tested; i.e., product is in working order but looks semi-awful.

FAIR MARKET VALUE See FMV.

FALLBACK RATE A modem speed that is lower than its normal (that is, maximum) speed of operation. May be used when communicating with a slower, compatible modem, or to help transmission over a line that is too noisy for full speed operation.

FALL.COM An early virus which made the characters on a screen fall to the bottom.

FALSE RINGING False ringing is a recording of a telephone ringing signal (two seconds on, four seconds off, which is played while a call is transferred or while a switching device listens for modem for facsimile CNG (calling) tones.

FALSING In telecom signaling, DTMF tones are created using specific combinations of frequencies to prevent the possibility of "falsing." Falsing is the condition where a DTMF detector incorrectly believes a DTMF is present when in fact it is actually a combination of voice, noise and/or music.

FAKE ROOT A subdirectory on the file server of a local area network that functions as a root directory, where you can safely assign rights to users. Fake roots only work with NetWare shells included with NetWare v2.2 and above. If you use older versions of the workstation shell, you will not be able to create fake roots.

FAN ANTENNA An aerial consisting of a number of wires radiating upwards from a common terminal to points on a supporting wire.

FANATIC Someone who's overly enthusiastic about something in which you have zero interest.

FAP Formats And Protocols. The set of rules that specifies the format, timing, sequencing and/or error checking for communication between clients and servers.

FAQ Either a Frequently Asked Question, or a list of frequently asked questions and their answers. Many Internet USENET news groups, and some non-USENET mailing lists, maintain FAQ lists (FAQs) so that participants won't spend lots of time answering the same set of questions.

FAR END CROSSTALK Crosstalk which travels along a circuit in the same direction as the signals in the circuit. The terminals of the disturbed channel at which the far-end crosstalk is present and the energized terminals of the disturbing channel are usually remote from each other.

FAR FIELD PATTERN Synonym for Far-Field Radiation Pattern.

FAR TALK In voice recognition, far talk is an arrangement where a microphone is more than four inches from the speaker's mouth. The opposite is CLOSE TALK, where the microphone is closer than four inches.

FARAD The practical unit of capacity. A capacity which retains a charge of one coulomb with a potential difference of one volt. See FARADAY and FARADAY CAGE.

FARADAY As a Faraday shield: refers to the protection a material or container provides to electronic devices to keep them from exposure to electrostatic fields. Named after M. Faraday, the English physicist.

FARADAY CAGE A structure designed to isolate a sensitive electronic system or device from outside interference, usually constructed of metal screens. Named for 19th century inventor Michael Faraday, whose name also gave us the FARAD, the unit of measuring capacitance.

FARMS OF MAINFRAMES Picture a hall full of large mainframe computers. Picture a hall full of American Airline mainframe computers, lined one after another. Now you have the concept of a farm of mainframes.

FAST BUSY A busy signal which sounds at twice the normal rate (120 interruptions/minute vs. 60/minute). A "fast busy" signal indicates all trunks are busy.

FAST ETHERNET A way to run Ethernet at 100 million bits per second, up tenfold from today's Ethernet, which runs at 10 Mbps. Fast Ethernet, running on two pairs of standard unshielded telephone copper wire, is positioned as an alternative to CDDI and FDDI, which is also delivering 100 Mbps on unshielded twisted pairs. We'll see.

FAST ETHERNET ALLIANCE A group of vendors who are writing the 100Base-X technical and wiring specifications, which would allow fast Ethernet (100 megabits a second) to run over Category 3, voice-grade unshielded twisted pair wiring.

FAST NETWORK An AT&T term for a network with low delay relative to the needs of the application.

FAST PACKET MULTIPLEXING Multiplexing is putting more than one "conversation" onto one circuit. You can do this in either of two ways — by splitting the channels sideways into subchannels of narrower frequency. This is called Frequency Division Multiplexing. Or you could split it by time. Like a railroad train. The first car carries "Conversation 1." The second carries "Conversation 2." And split them apart at the other end.

Fast packet multiplexing is a combination of three techniques — time division multiplexing, packetizing of voice and other analog signals and computer intelligence. Here are the main advantages fast packet multiplexing has over today's industry standard time division multiplexing:

1. Fast packet multiplexing doesn't blindly slot in "information" from devices if there's no information to send. Most other multiplexing techniques, including the most common — time division and frequency division — slot in capacity, whether the device is "talking" or not.

2. The fast packet multiplexer can start sending a packet before it has completely received the packet. This speed of movement is critical to voice, for example, which must move ultra-fast. Delays are devastating. (No one can afford to replace the phone instruments broken in anger.)

3. Fast packet multiplexing can interrupt the delivery of one packet in favor of sending another. It's OK to delay a packet of data by several milliseconds. It's not OK to delay a packet of voice or video.

FAST PACKET SWITCHING A recent wide area networking technology capable of transmitting data, digitized voice and digitized image information. It makes use of short, fixed length packets (or cells) that are all the same size. The underlying switching technology is based on the statistical multiplexing of data and voice in fixed length cells. Any of these packets could carry digital voice, data or digital image information. All the packets travel at Level Two of the OSI Model, and routing is performed on the basis of the Level Two addressing. Fast packet is claimed to be very effective way of make best use of available bandwidth. It is claimed to offer the benefits of conventional multiplexing techniques and circuit switching techniques because of the way it operates. It is one of the transmission technologies being developed for use with B-ISDN (Broadband ISDN). The switch used to route packets in a fast packet network is termed a fast packet switch. Also, fast packet technology can carry data transmissions that enter the network using frame relay. For particularly high speed networking, an implementation of fast packet switching known as ATM is being developed. See ATM and FAST PACKET MULTIPLEXING.

FAST SCAN RECEIVER A cellular term. A piece of equipment that scans all 1,300 channels in an entire cellular network. It is a quick way to determine channel usage and signal strength.

FAST SELECT In packet switched networks, a calling method which allows the user to send a limited amount of information along with a "call request packet" rather than after the packet. A more technical explanation: An optional user facility in the virtual call service of ITU-T X.25 protocol that allows the inclusion of user data in the call request/connected and clear indication packets. An essential feature of the ITU-T X.25 (1984) protocol.

FAST STAT MUX MICOM's advanced statistical multiplexer that uses data compression, priority echoplex handling and fast packet technology to improve throughput.

FAST SWITCHING CHANNEL A single channel on a GPS (Global Positioning System) which rapidly samples a number of satellite ranges. "Fast" means that the switching time is sufficiently fast (2 to 5 milliseconds) to recover the data message.

FAT File Allocation Table. The FAT is an integral of the MS-DOS operating system. It is like an index of a hard or floppy disk. It keeps track of where the various pieces of each file on a disk are stored. A hard disk's directory and file allocation tables are extremely important because they contain the address and mapping information the operating system needs to figure where to store and retrieve data. If any of the data storage blocks containing these tables is damaged, some or all of the data may be lost. For a much longer explanation, see MS-DOS. Novell's NetWare maintains duplicate copies of directory entries and file allocation tables on separate areas of the hard disk, thus reducing the chance of a catastrophic loss of data. See FAT FILE SYSTEM and VFAT.

FAT CLIENT Clients are devices and software that request information. Client is a fancy name for a PC on a local area network. It used to be called a workstation. Now it is the "client" of the server. Clients come in two varieties — Fat and Thin. Here's a definition of Fat Client, courtesy of Oracle Corporation, writing in early 1994: "Since the early 1980s, users have loaded their personal computers will more and more software and data. PCs often are connected to file servers that store information. With each loaded PC costing thousands of dollars, the fat client model has a high cost per machine. Example, a PC or a Macintosh. See also CLIENT, CLIENT SERVER, CLIENT SERVER MODEL, MAINFRAME SERVER, MEDIA SERVER and THIN CLIENT.

FAT FILE SYSTEM A file system based on a file allocation table, maintained by the operating system, to keep track of the status of various segments of disk space used for file storage. The 32-bit implementation in Windows 95 is called the Virtual File Allocation Table (VFAT). See FAT.

FATBITS A computer imaging term. Extreme magnification of individual pixels to allow easy pixel-by-pixel editing of images.

FATHERBOARD First there is the motherboard. That's the main circuit board of a computer system. The motherboard contains edge connectors or sockets so other PC (printed circuit) boards can be plugged into it. Those PC boards are called Fatherboards. Some fatherboards have pins on them into which you can plug smaller boards. Those boards are called Daughterboards. In a voice processing system, you might have a Fatherboard to do faxing. And you might have a range of Daughterboards, which allow you to connect different types of phone connections. Different boards exist for standard analog tip and ring, digital switched 56, t-1, etc.

FAU Fixed Access Unit. A fixed, wireless telephone placed in a user's home or business using cellular or PCS (Personal Communications Service). A new, lower powered, higher-frequency technology. The device provides local telephony service circumventing existing LEC (Local Exchange Carrier) transmission equipment using wired connections.

FAULT ISOLATION The process of determining where a network problem, or fault, is located.

FAULT MANAGEMENT Detects, isolates and corrects network faults. It is also one of five categories of network management defined by the ISO (International Standards Organization).

FAULT TOLERANT A method of making a computer or network system resistant to software errors and hardware problems. A fault tolerant LAN system tries to ensure that even in the event of a power failure, a disk crash or a major user error, data isn't lost and the system can keep running. Cabling systems can also be fault tolerant, using redundant wiring so that even if a cable is cut, the system can keep running. True fault tolerance is very difficult to achieve.

FAX Abbreviation for FACSIMILE. See FACSIMILE and FACSIMILE SWITCHES.

FAX AT WORK Fax At Work is a subset of Microsoft's office equipment architecture called At Work which it announced on June 9, 1993. Microsoft's idea is to put a set of software building blocks into both office machines and PC products, including:

Desktop and network-connected printers.

Digital monochrome and color copiers.

Telephones and voice messaging systems.

Fax machines and PC fax products.

Handheld systems.

Hybrid combinations of the above.

According to Microsoft, the Microsoft At Work architecture focuses on creating digital connections between machines (i.e. the ones above) to allow information to flow freely throughout the workplace. The Microsoft At Work software architecture consists of several technology components that serve as building blocks to enable these connections, including

Microsoft At Work operating system. A real-time, pre-emptive, multitasking operating system that is designed to specifically address the requirements of the office automation and communication industries. The new operating system supports Windows-compatible application programming interfaces (APIs) where appropriate for the device.

Microsoft At Work communications. Will provide the connectivity between Microsoft At Work-based devices and PCs. It will support the secure transmission of original digital documents, and it is compatible with the Windows Messaging API and the Windows Telephony API of the Windows Open Services Architecture (WOSA).

Microsoft At Work rendering. Will make the transmission of digital documents, with formatting and fonts intact, very fast and, consequently, cost-effective; will ensure that a document sent to any of these devices will produce high-quality output, referred to as "What You Print Is What You Fax Is What You Copy Is What You See."

Microsoft At Work graphical user interface. Will make all devices very easy to use and will make sophisticated features accessible; will provide useful feedback to users. Leveraging Microsoft's experience in the Windows user interface, Microsoft At Work-based products will use very simple graphical user interfaces designed for people who are not computer users.

Microsoft At Work desktop software for Windows-based PCs. Will provide Windows-based PC applications the ability to control, access and exchange information with any product based on Microsoft At Work. Desktop software is the one piece of the Microsoft At Work architecture that will reside on PCs.

Despite the dramatic growth in fax usage in recent years, the fax machine, according to Microsoft (and it's right) is still a fairly primitive communications tool. Difficulty using machine features, low-quality printing, lack of integration with the work environment and lack of security are all commonly identified problems. Microsoft At Work-based fax capabilities will address these deficiencies with a broad spectrum of fax solutions that will transform the fax from an independent tool to a powerful, integrated part of the modern communications process. Microsoft At Work-based fax products include the following:

Microsoft At Work-based departmental fax machines. A standalone multi functional machine (fax, print, scan, copy) will be able to be used by a single person or an entire department of people. In addition to being great standalone devices, they will be able to be integrated completely with PCs. They will also be shareable via direct network connection or via direct PC connection.

Microsoft At Work-based fax servers. High-volume, LAN-connected fax solutions will offer the ideal platform for automating wide area communication tasks, such as forms automation, billing and invoicing with suppliers, distribution of information to a field organization, etc. A host of new applications will be possible when users and developers can count on a widely deployed, secure, anywhere-to-anywhere messaging platform that will be provided by Microsoft At Work-based systems that are also integrated with Windows-based PCs.

Microsoft At Work-based PC faxes. Any user of Windows with an industry-standard fax board will benefit from rich document transmission through Microsoft At

Work desktop software that will become a standard part of the Windows operating system and other Microsoft At Work-based products and services.

● Microsoft At Work-based fax-enabled network. Public networks will be adding support for Microsoft At Work communications, allowing users to benefit from their high-volume broadcasting capabilities and the ability to access integrated, public mailboxes from any location.

Key benefits of Microsoft At Work-based faxes (as implemented in any of the above products or services) will include the following:

● Far Greater Ease of Use

While today's fax machines have dozens of advanced features, few are ever used. In fact, many users do not even know these features exist. The problem is that the small, cryptic display on today's fax machines makes these features inaccessible to users. To compound the problem, owners' manuals are rarely available when a problem occurs.

Microsoft At Work-based fax machines will use a graphical, touch-sensitive display to make every feature simple to use. Context-sensitive features will help guide users through tasks. For example, if a jam occurs, a picture showing users how to clear it will be displayed.

● Ability to Send Original-quality "Published" and Editable Documents

Today's fax machines send fuzzy pages that are often difficult to read. As a result, people either don't use a fax when the document has to look professional, or they send another "good copy" via courier. Today's machines also don't allow users to send editable documents, which would enable wide area joint authoring and the automation of many communication tasks.

Using Microsoft At Work rendering technology, a fax machine will become a remote publishing tool, allowing users to distribute final, laser-quality versions of documents directly from PC applications. Users will also be able to send editable versions of documents to reviewers and co-authors so that changes can be made directly without re-keying information, and then be returned to the author.

● Full Document Security

The most frequently faxed documents include contracts, internal correspondence and purchase orders. Despite the sensitive nature of these documents, anyone can walk by and read or pick up received faxes, and there's no guarantee that the document will even get to the proper recipient. Some fax machines advertise security features, but these machines are not really secure. Passwords are included in the message, but the encryption method is easy to break. Moreover, all of these methods require both sending and receiving machines to be from the same manufacturer, a rare occurrence in today's market.

Microsoft At Work-based faxes will have strong built-in security that will allow users to encrypt messages so that documents aren't read by others. It will also be able to ensure that documents are delivered to intended recipients and verify document contents as authentic. By implementing Microsoft At Work security in both Windows-based applications and in devices from a broad base of manufacturers, secure messaging could become as commonplace in the future as regular fax transmissions are today.

● Strong PC Connectivity

While the vast majority of all documents today are created on PCs, most users still print documents and manually feed them into fax machines. Users who choose to investigate PC fax alternatives find them unreliable and not well-integrated into their PC environment.

The Microsoft At Work-based fax is designed to fully integrate faxes with the rest of a PC's messaging environment by integrating this functionality into the operating system. Users will be able to send fax messages in the same way they send other messages, simply by selecting "Send" from their mail package or their favorite application. Received faxes will be automatically delivered into the user's mailbox - the same mailbox where e-mail and voice mail messages are received. They will be able to forward and reply to the message with a single button click.

● MIS Support

Today's fax machines are a nightmare for MIS professionals. They can't be centrally managed, so someone has to walk around to every machine to update fax numbers, change settings, collect activity reports and fix problems. Most machines don't support "default settings," so they can't set up machines to do things such as automatically send faxes when telephone rates are lowest. Users frequently can't enter accounting codes to track costs, and even when they can, the resulting reports can only be printed out, so the data must be manually entered into the accounting system. Finally, fax machines represent a network entirely distinct from the advanced data networks that they pay every month to maintain. MIS professionals should rightly wonder why they can't send all that "charged-per-minute" fax traffic over the data lines for which they pay a fixed monthly fee. Microsoft At Work-based fax machines are designed to let MIS manage fax services in the same way as other corporate communication resources. They will be centrally administrable so that any settings can be changed directly, and common resources such as address books will be able to be maintained and downloaded automatically. They are programmable so that faxes queued up after 4 p.m., for example, will be able to automatically be sent at discount rates, saving between 25 percent and 40 percent on toll charges. Activity reports will be able to automatically be sent in binary format to accounting, where they could be entered into accounting systems directly. They will automatically send trouble reports when problems occur. They will easily route traffic over existing corporate data networks, saving 95 percent of the transmission costs.

● Features to Reduce Fax Costs

Long-distance charges and the employee time required to send and receive faxes account for more than three-fourths of total fax costs, while the cost of the fax machine accounts for only 15 percent. Yet today's fax machines do little to address these costs. Moreover, the few features that manufacturers have added are virtually unused because they are so difficult to access. For example, while most mid- to higher-end machines offer the ability to delay fax transmissions until rates decrease, few people know how to use this feature today.

Microsoft At Work-based fax machines will have features to dramatically reduce fax costs. In addition to making cost-saving features easy to find and use, Microsoft At Work rendering will reduce file sizes and, as a result, transmission times. Digital cover sheets can decrease the cost of a typical four-page fax by up to 25 percent. Cost savings assumes that digitally transmitted header eliminates the majority of cover sheet data that is currently sent in bitmap form. . As noted above, simple access to discount transmissions can reduce toll charges by 25 percent to 40 percent and integration with corporate networks would reduce toll charges by as much as 95 percent.

FAX BACK You dial a computer using the handset of your fax machine. The distant computer answers. "What documents would you like? Here's a menu." You touchtone in 123. It says "Touch your Start button." You do. Seconds later your fax machine disgorges the document you wanted. Fax-back is the generic term for the process of ordering fax documents from remote machines. Fax-back uses a combination of fax and voice processing technology. Fax-back is also called fax on demand.

FAX BOARD A specialized synchronous modem for designed to transmit and receive facsimile documents. Many fax boards also allow for binary synchronous file transfer and V.22 bis communication. See also FAX SERVER.

FAX DATA MODEM See FAX MODEM.

FAX DEMODULATION A technique for taking a Group III fax signal and converting it back to its original 9.6 Kbps. It works like this: When a sheet of paper is inserted into a fax machine, the fax machine scans that paper into digital bits — a stream of 9600 bps. Then, for transmission over phone lines, that 9.6 Kbps is converted into an analog signal. But if you wish to transmit the fax signal over a digital line, then it makes sense to convert it back to its original 9.6 Kbps. That means you can put several fax transmissions on one 56 Kbps or 64 Kbps line — the capacity you'd normally need if you transmitted one voice conversation, or one erstwhile analog fax transmission. See FAX/DATA modem.

FAX MAILBOX Companies can send facsimiles of documents to be stored for later retrieval to a fax mailbox. Fax mailbox is like voice mail for faxes. Travelers can check their fax mailboxes and have the faxes sent to convenient locations, like a hotel front desk. You can do fax mailboxes with fax servers. You can also subscribe to a fax mailbox, as you can subscribe to a voice mailbox.

One company with a fax mailbox service is Bell Atlantic. Here's their explanation of their service, which they call FAX Mailbox. They say it gives you the freedom to leave the office and pick-up your faxes on the run. Wherever you need them, they're always as close as the nearest fax machine. With FAX Mailbox, you can control your faxes as though you were in the office. Every fax sent to you is kept strictly confidential in a private mailbox, instead of being left by the machine for anyone to see. You can access the faxes in your mailbox by calling from any touchtone phone and entering your personal code. Then you can review, store or delete faxes — or send them to any machine you choose. There's no need to be dependent on office support to receive and send faxes. Or have to delegate or postpone work because you're out of the office. You determine when and where you receive faxes, according to your schedule and itinerary.

FAX MODE The mode in which the fax modem is capable of sending and receiving files in a facsimile format. See FAX MODEM.

FAX MODEM A combination facsimile machine/modem. A device which lets you send documents from a computer to a fax machine. It comes in many shapes and sizes. It may come as a card which you slip into a vacant slot in your desktop PC (called an internal fax/modem). It may come as a PCMCIA card which you slip into your laptop. It may come as a small box which you connect by a cable to your computer's serial port. It may also come as a small self-contained package about the size of a cigarette package. The technology of "fax modems" is changing radically. Originally they contained dedicated fax/modem chipsets, i.e. microprocessors designed as fax modems and good for nothing else. Increasingly, fax modems are now coming with powerful, general purpose digital signal processors (DSPs), instead of dedicated fax modem chipsets. These DSP devices become fax modems when you load the appropriate software. When you load other software they can also become the equivalent of sound blaster cards, or become a Microsoft Sound System, etc.

There are big advantages to sending faxes from a fax modem, as compared to sending it from a fax machine. First, faxes sent are cleaner because they're not scanned but computer generated. Second, sending faxes directly from your computer is faster than printing the document, then sliding it in a fax machine, dialing and sending it. Third, a fax modem is typically cheaper than a fax machine. Fourth, because a fax modem uses computer software it may have some neat features, like the ability to send faxes when phone costs are low, like running the fax software in the background while you're doing something else.

There are two main disadvantages:

1. Viewing incoming faxes on your PC's screen is not easy. A PC screen is horizontal. Most faxes are vertical. It's also not easy to translate an incoming fax into the pixels on your computer screen. Here's why:

FAX ENCODING

Standard, Group III	203 x 98 pixels
Fine, Group III	203 x 196
Superfine, Group III	203 x 391
Standard, Group IV	400 x 400

PC SCREEN ENCODING

CGA	320 x 200 pixels
Enhanced CGA	640 x 400
EGA	640 x 350
Hercules	720 x 348
VGA	640 x 480
Super VGA	800 x 600
8514/A (also called XGA)	1,024 x 768

2. For these two reasons, you may still have to print your incoming faxes.

3. Keeping faxes on your hard disk is also pretty consuming of hard disk space. A typical one page fax can easily use between 40,000 and 50,000 bytes. Twenty pages and you've used up a megabyte. See also FAX DEMODULATION, FAX SERVER AND FAX SWITCH.

FAX ON DEMAND You dial a computer using the handset of your fax machine. The distant computer answers. "What documents would you like? Here's a menu." You touchtone in 123. It says "Touch your Start button." You do. Seconds later your fax machine disgorges the document you wanted. Fax on demand is one term for the process of ordering fax documents from remote machines. Fax on demand uses a combination of fax and voice processing technology. Fax on demand is also called fax-back. See FAX SERVER for a more complete explanation.

FAX PUBLISHING Fax publishing allows a caller to have electronically stored information automatically faxed to them via a touchtone telephone. By pressing touchtone keys, callers can have timely information, including product brochures, business forms and benefits information, automatically faxed to them anytime, anywhere. See also FAX SERVER.

FAX SERVER 1. A relatively high-powered computer which sits on a LAN and has one or more PC fax boards in its slots. The fax server receives incoming faxes over phone lines, stores them on its hard disk and, if it knows for whom the faxes are meant, it will alert that person over the LAN. If it doesn't know for whom the faxes are meant, it may send the faxes to a printer or alert a supervisor to manually check the incoming faxes and distribute them — electronically or on paper. The fax server also accepts from workstations on the LAN, stores them and gets them ready for sending out over phone lines. It might send the faxes immediately or wait until later, when phone calls are cheaper. 2. A fax server is also a specialized interactive voice response system which you call. When you call it, it answers, reads you a menu of options — including various documents it can send you. You choose which documents you want by touchtoning in numbers. Then you designate to which fax machine you want the documents sent. The fax machine you designate might be the one you're calling from (i.e. you dialed using your fax machine's handset).

There are two types of interactive voice response fax servers. One is a one-call machine. The caller calls from his own fax machine. When he's chosen his faxes and he's ready to receive a fax, he simply hits the "Start" button on his fax machine and his machine receives the chosen faxes. There is also a two-call machine. The caller will call from a phone and touchtone in the phone number of a fax machine he wants the fax of his desired documents sent. One-call IVR fax servers are the newer breed, harder to build than the older two-call machines. There are obvious advantages to both. The one call machine — in which the user pays the phone bill — will, I suspect, become the more popular type. See also FAX PUBLISHING and other FAX definitions.

FAX SWITCH A device which allows you to share one phone line with a fax machine, a phone and a modem. Here's how it works. A call comes in. The device answers the call. The switch listens for the distinctive CNG (Calling) tone which a calling fax machine emits (the "cry" of the fax machine). When it hears this sound, it switches the call to the fax machine. If it doesn't and hears nothing (or at least nothing it can recognize) it switches the call to the phone. If it hears some touchtones — e.g. 44, or *6 — it will switch the call to the modem (and therefore the attached computer) or whatever other device you've designated, including a modem-equipped cash register, etc. Some fax switches allow you to have a data conversation with one device (the cash register), then switch to another device (the second cash register) and another, etc. — all on the one conversation.

The advantage of a fax switch is that it saves having to buy several phone lines. Phone lines are expensive compared to fax switches. There are disadvantages to a fax switch — it typically must hear an incoming CNG tone to switch the call to the fax machine. This means if your friend wanting to send you a fax is dialing manually (i.e. not letting his fax machine do it), your fax switch may not ever send the call to your fax machine. Also you have to set up to dial those extra digits for your distant computer to "dial through" your fax switch. And finally, some fax switches don't send the "right" ringing signal to their attached devices. Some 9,600 baud and 14,400 baud modems, for example, are very sensitive and won't answer certain fax switches' ringing signals, especially if the fax switch's ringing signal is a DC square wave, not an AC sine wave. All this can be solved, however, with intelligence, checking and proper programming. I use a fax modem switch every day. It saves me money and is convenient. See CNG.

FAX WAITING SERVICE The name of a Bell Atlantic service. FAX WAITING Service is like Call Waiting for your fax machine. If your fax line is busy, a second incoming fax is electronically stored. When your machine is clear, FAX Waiting service sends it through. So customers, prospects and suppliers can get their faxes through on the first call — without the frustration of busy signals. And employees can use your fax machine without interrupting your important fax communications. In fact, FAX Waiting is the next best thing to a second fax machine. A great idea.

FAXBIOS The FaxBios Association is an organization of fax printed circuit card manufacturers who have formed an association in order to promulgate a standard applications programming interface (API) which they are calling FaxBios. Phone 801-225-1850; 2625 Alcatraz Avenue, Berkeley CA 94705.

FAXED The past tense of the new verb "to fax," as in "I faxed the document to him."

FB Framing bit.

FBT Fused Biconic Tape.

FBU Functional Business Unit. A fancy name for a group of workers inside a company. An FBU might be your sales department, your accounting department, etc.

FC 1.Fiber optic Connector (developed by NTT). 2. Frame Control. On Token Ring networks, this data supplies the frame type.

FC AND PC Face Contact and Point Contact. Designations for fiber optic connectors designed by Nippon Telegraph and Telephone which feature a movable anti-rotation key allowing good repeatable performance despite numerous matings.

FCB The abbreviation for File Control Block. FCBs are used by older MS-DOS application programs to create, open, delete, read, and write files. One FCB is set up for each file you open.

FCC Federal Communications Commission. See FEDERAL COMMUNICATIONS COMMISSION.

FCC REGISTRATION NUMBER A number assigned to specific telephone equipment registered with the FCC, as set forth in FCC docket 19528, part 68.

The presence of this number affixed to a device indicates that the FCC has approved it as being a compatible device for direct connection to telephone line facilities.

FCC TARIFF #9 The FCC tariff for private line services including Accunet T-1.5, DDS, Voice Grade circuits, and Accunet T45.

FCC TARIFF #11 AT&T's tariff file at the FCC for local private line services.

FCC TARIFF #12 AT&T's tariff filed at the FCC tariff for custom-designed integrated services. A special tariff that allows AT&T to develop custom network solutions, including allowing customers to install their networking multiplexers in AT&T central offices and letting AT&T manage the network.

FCC TARIFF #15 AT&T's FCC tariff filed at the FCC that allows AT&T to lower rates after all bids are placed to be competitive with other carriers.

FCFS A silly abbreviation for First Come First Served. See FIFO (First In, First Out).

FCN Abbreviation for Function. This button enables your cellular phone or fax machine or other telecom device to access special features, like switching from one cellular phone company to another. See also DUAL NAM.

FCOS Fully programmable classes of service that control user (Feature Class of Service) access to mailbox features, operations and options. Feature Classes of Service (FCOS) are entirely independent of Limits Classes of Service (LCOS).

FCS 1. Frame Check Sequence. In bit-oriented protocols, a 16-bit field that contains transmission error checking information, usually appended to the end of the frame. See FRAME CHECK SEQUENCE. 2. Federation of Communications Services. 3. An MCI term for Fraud Control System.

FDD Floppy Disk Drive.

FDDI Fiber Distributed Data Interface. FDDI is a 100 megabits per second fiber optic LAN. It is an ANSI standard. It uses a "counter-rotating" token ring topology. FDDI is ANSI X3T12 standard for a dual-ring LAN operating at 100 Mbps and using token passing; FDDI rings may use up to 200 km of optical fiber, or may employ twisted copper pairs for short hops. FDDI is compatible with the standards for the physical layer of the OSI model. An FDDI LAN is often known as a "backbone" LAN. It is used to join file servers together and to join LANs together. The theoretical limit of Ethernet, measured in 64 byte packets, is 14,800 packets per second (PPS). By comparison, Token Ring is 30,000 and FDDI is 170,000 pps. See FDDI TERMS and FDDI-II.

FDDI TERMS DAC, Dual Attachment Concentrator DAS Dual Attachment Station ECF, Echo Frames ESF, Extended Service Frames LER, Link Error Rate LLC, Logical Link Control MAC, Media Access Control MIC, Media Interface Connector NIF, Neighborhood Information Frame NSA, Next Station Addressing PDU, Protocol Data Unit PHY, Physical Protocol PMD, Physical Media Department PMF, Parameter Management Frames RAF, Resource Allocation Frames RDF Request Denied Frames SAC, Single Attachment Concentrator SAS, Single Attachment Station SDU, Service Data Unit SIF, Station Information Frames SMT, Station Management SRF, Status Report Frame THT, Token Holding Timer TRT, Token Rotation Timer TTRT Target Token Rotation Timer TVX Valid Transmission Timer UNA Upstream Neighbor Address

FDDI-II Fiber Distributed Data Interface-II is a recently standardized enhancement to FDDI. It still runs at 100 megabits per second on fiber or on twisted copper pairs, but in addition to transporting conventional packet data like other LANs, FDDI-II allows portions of the 100 Mbps bandwidth to carry low delay, constant bit rate, isochronous data like 64 Kbps telephone channels. This means the same LAN that carries computer packet data can carry live voice or live video calls. Some additional terms used with FDDI-II are: I-MAC which stands for Isochronous Media Access Control; P-MAC which stands for Packet Media Access Control; and WBC which stands for Wide Band Channel. See FDDI, FDDI TERMS, ISOCHRONOUS and ISOETHERNET.

FDM Frequency Division Multiplexing. A technique in which the available transmission bandwidth of a circuit is divided by frequency into narrower bands, each used for a separate voice or data transmission channel. This means you can carry many conversations on one circuit. The conversations are separated by "guard channels." At one point, FDM was the most used method of multiplexing long haul conversations when they were transmitted in analog microwave signals. No more. Fiber optic transmission (today's preferred method) uses TDM — Time Division Multiplexing.

FDMA Frequency Division Multiple Access. One of several technologies used to separate multiple transmissions over a finite frequency allocation. FDMA refers to the method of allocating a discrete amount of frequency bandwidth to each user to permit many simultaneous conversations. In cellular telephony, for example, each caller occupies approximately 25 kHz of frequency spectrum. The cellular telephone frequency band, allocated from 824 MHz to 849 MHz and 869 MHz, consists of 416 total channels, or frequency slots, available for conversations. Within each cell, approximately 48 channels are available for mobile users. Different channels are allocated for neighboring cell sites, allowing for re-use of frequencies with a minimum of interference. This technique of assigning individual frequency slots, and re-using these frequency slots throughout the system, is known as FDMA. See CDMA, TDMA.

FDS Frequency Division Switching. Seldom used for voice switching. Primarily used for radio and TV broadcasting.

FDX See FULL DUPLEX.

FE Extended Framing ("F sub E"). An old name for ESF, also known as Extended SuperFrame, a T-1 carrier framing format that provides a 64 Kbps clear channel, error checking, 16 state signaling and some other nice data transmission features.

FE D4 SUPERFRAME EXTENDED Another designation for AT&T's ESF (Extended Super Frame).

FEATHER An imaging term. An effect in which the edges of a pasted selection or paint tool fade progressively at the edges for a seamless blend with the background.

FEATURE BUTTONS Think of a feature button on a telephone as a collection of numbers stored in a bin. When you hit the button, the bin quickly disgorges all the numbers one after another. Feature buttons are fast ways of doing things. You have a feature button labelled "Conference." Hit the button, set up a conference call. Without a feature button, you'd probably have to hit the switch hook and some numbers on your touchtone pad. In computer terms, a feature button on a phone is the same as a macro — an easy way of doing something. On most phones with feature buttons, the feature buttons are "programmable." This means you can assign different features to different buttons, i.e. the ones you want. For example, I always assign "Last Number Redial," "Saved Number Redial" and "Conference Call" to the buttons of any phone I'm programming. Some phones have many feature buttons. Some don't.

FEATURE CARTRIDGE A replaceable software cartridge containing software features. The Feature Cartridge is inserted into the central cabinet, or Key Service Unit (if it's a key system). Several small phone systems (under 100 lines) use cartridges to upgrade their software. The manufacturers find cartridges are cheaper than equipping their phone systems with a floppy drive and the associated electronics.

FEATURE CODE This is a number that is used to activate a particular feature on a phone system.

FEATURE CREEP A term to show how features tend to get added to telecom equipment as time passes and new models appear. The term "feature creep" makes no judgments about whether the new features are actually useful. In book called "Startup; A Silicon Valley Adventure Story," Jerry Kaplan, the author, describes "Feature creep as "the irresistible temptation for engineers to load a product down with their favorite special features."

FEATURE GROUP A, B, C, D FGA, FGB, FGC, FGD, are four separate switching arrangements available from local exchange carrier (LEC) end central offices to interexchange (long distance) carriers. These switching arrangements allow the LEC's end-users to make toll calls via their favorite LEC. Feature groups are described in a tariff filed by the National Exchange Carrier Association with the FCC. The feature group used by each IX (IntereXchange) carrier together with any special access surcharge determines the service they can provide their customers and the carrier common line access fee they will pay to the local exchange carrier involved. The most common Feature Group now is D. See the next four definitions. See FEATURE GROUP A, FEATURE GROUP B, FEATURE GROUP C, FEATURE GROUP D

FEATURE GROUP A Offers access to the local exchange carrier's network through a subscriber-type line connection rather than a trunk. It is a continuation of the ENFIA arrangement used in the early days of OCCs, until equal access using an access tandem central office is available. Remember, without equal access the IX carrier had to require its customers to dial a local number to reach their long distance facilities, then dial an identification number, then dial long distance numbers of the called party desired. This service handicap, compared to AT&T's superior connections, qualifies the OCC for a discount off the FGA rate until access is equal. The IX carrier is billed by the LEC based upon actual monthly use rather than the ENFIA method of projected "minutes of use" rate.

FEATURE GROUP B Is similar to FGA, but provides a higher quality trunk line connection from end CO to the IX carrier's facilities, instead of the subscriber-type line. The IX customer can originate a call from anywhere within the LATA, while FGA requires customers to initiate the call from within the local exchange of the exchange carrier connecting to the IXC. FGB billings to the IX are on a flat usage basis, and a discount is applicable.

FEATURE GROUP C Is the traditional toll service arrangement offered by LECs to AT&T prior to breakup of the Bell System. Quality is superior, and the service includes automatic number identification of the calling party, answerback, and disconnection supervision, and the subscribers can use either a dial or touchtone pad. This FGC service is offered only to AT&T without a discount.

FEATURE GROUP D Is the class of service associated with equal access arrangements. All IX carriers (i.e. long distance phone companies) enjoy identical connections to the local exchange carrier. All customers dial the same number of digits, and can reach the predetermined IX of their choice by dialing 1 plus the telephone number being called. Eventually, all other feature groups convert to FGD and the IX is billed for actual measured use, without discount. In some cases an IX carrier may desire to maintain FGA or FGB arrangements, but the FGD equal access rates will apply.

FEATURE KEYS Same as FEATURE BUTTONS. A key is to a telephone man what a switch is to an electrical man.

FEATURE PHONE A generic name for a telephone that has extra features (often speed dial buttons) designed to simplify and speed making and receiving phone calls.

FEC Forward Error Correction. A technique used by a receiver for correcting errors incurred in transmission over a communications channel without requiring retransmission of any information by the transmitter. Typically involves a convolution of the transmitter using a common algorithm. See FORWARD ERROR CORRECTION.

FECN Forward Explicit Congestion Notification. This bit notifies the user that congestion-avoidance procedures should be initiated where applicable for traffic in the same direction as the received frame. It indicates that this frame, on this logical connection, has encountered congested resources.

FED Field Emission Display. A new way of making TV and computer screen displays. FED screens are flat and potentially cheap. Like conventional glass screens, they emit light. LCDs, by comparison, don't. A typical FED screen packs millions of tiny individual emitters between two ultra-thin glass layers. Each emitter fires electrons simultaneously across a minuscule vacuum gap onto a phosphor coating very much like a CRT's. See also FIELD EMISSION DISPLAYS.

FED-STD A system of standards numbered FED-STD-1001 to 1008 which set modulation specifications for data transmission.

FEDERAL COMMUNICATIONS COMMISSION The federal organization in Washington D.C. set up by the Communications Act of 1934. It has the authority to regulate all interstate (but not intrastate) communications originating in the United States. The FCC is run by a seven member board appointed by the President. Stripped of all the extensive regulatory and legal mumbo jumbo, the FCC does three things: 1. It sets the prices for interstate phone, data and video service. 2. It determines who can or cannot get into the business of providing telecommunications service or equipment in the United States. 3. It determines the electrical and physical standards for telecommunications equipment. The FCC's powers, although strong, are tempered (limited) by the Federal Courts. Anyone who disagrees with FCC rulings can appeal them to a Federal Court. The FCC's power and rulings are also affected by the Justice Department (The Justice Department changed the industry with Divestiture), Congress and The 50 state public service commissions.

FEDERAL INFORMATION PROCESSING STANDARDS FIPS. The identifier attached to standards developed to support the U.S. government computer standardization program. The FIPS effort is carried out by the U.S. Department of Commerce, Springfield, VA. See the next definition.

FEDERAL TELECOMMUNICATIONS STANDARDS COMMITTEE FTSC. A U.S. government agency established in 1973 to promote standardization of communications and network interfaces. FTSC standards are identified by the designator FED-STD. The FTSC's address is General Services Administration, Specification Service Administration, Bldg 197, Washington Navy Yard, Washington DC 20407.

FEDERAL TELECOMMUNICATIONS SYSTEM FTS. The private network used primarily by the civilian agencies of the federal government to call other government locations and to place calls to phones connected to the public network.

FEDERAL-STATE JOINT BOARD An organization with representatives from the FCC and the state public service commissions which tries to resolve Federal and State conflicts on telecommunications regulatory issues. Sometimes successfully and sometimes not successfully.

FEEDBACK The return of part of an output signal back to the input side of the device. Think of the high-pitched squeal you hear when someone brings a microphone too close to the loudspeaker. Not all feedback is as obvious or as irritating. Some feedback is good. See SIDETONE, which is what happens when you hear a little in the receiver of you're saying in the transmitter of a phone.

FEEDER CABLE A group of wires, usually 25-pair or multiples of 25-pair, that supports multiple phones in a single cable sheath. These cables may or may not be terminated with a connector on one or both ends. Feeder cable typically connects an intermediate distribution frame (IDF) to a main distribution frame (MDF). But the term "feeder cable" is also used in backbone wiring. And Bellcore defines the term slightly differently: A large pair-size loop cable emanating from a central office and usually placed in an underground conduit system with access available at periodically place manholes.

FEEDWARE Software designed to get demand for a product or a new market segment started. Feedware is typically a less-full featured piece of software than the software you're really trying to sell. Feedware typically costs very little. It may even be free. See also SEEDWARE.

FEEDHOLES Holes punched in paper or papertape which allow the paper or paper tape to be driven by sprocket wheels.

FEFO First Ended, First Out. A rule for dealing with things in a queue. For example, higher priority messages will be sent before lower priority messages.

FEMTOSECOND One-millionth of a billionth of a second. Femtoseconds are used in laser transmission and in other measures of very small happenings. It's 10 to the minus 15. There are as many femtoseconds in one second as there are seconds in thirty million years. There are 1,000,000,000,000,000 femtoseconds in one second. How small is a femotsecond? In a little more than a second, light can

MNP4 and LAP-M. The ITU-T title says "Error-correcting procedures for DCEs using Asynchronous-to-Synchronous Conversion". It also notes in the text that it applies only to full-duplex devices. The ITU-T modulation schemes with which V.42 may be used are V.22, V.22 bis, V.26 ter, and V.32, and V.32 bis. LAPM, based on HDLC, is the "primary" protocol, on which all future extensions will be based. The Alternative Protocol specified in Annex A of the Recommendation is for backward compatibility with the "installed base" of error-correcting modems. See V.42 bis.

V.42 bis DATA COMPRESSION ITU-T data compression standard. It compresses files "on the fly" at an average ratio of 3.5:1 and can yield file transfer speeds of up to 9,600 bps on a 2,400 bps modem, 38,400 bits per second with a 9,600 bps modem, 57,600 bps with a 14,400 bps V.32 bis modem, or 115,600 bit/s on a 28,800 bps modem. On-the-fly data compression only has value if you use it to transfer and receive material that is not already compressed. Compressing stuff a second time yields no significant improvement in speed (assuming your compression technique the first time around worked). So the decision to buy a V.42 bis modem depends on the material you're working with and your pocketbook. V.42 bis modems are more expensive.

V.42 bis was approved by the ITU-T because of its technical merits. Existing data compression methods (MNP 5 for example) only provided up to two-to-one compression. Also, V.42 bis provides for built-in "feedback" mechanisms, so that the modem can monitor its own compression performance. If the DTE starts send pre-compressed or otherwise uncompressible data, V.42 bis can automatically suspend its operation to avoid expansion of the data. It continues to monitor performance even when sending data "in the clear," and when a performance improvement can be gained by reactivating compression, it will do so automatically.

V.42 bis was selected because it would work with a wide variety of different implementations — different amounts of memory, different processor speeds, etc. Because of this, there WILL be differences between various manufacturer's products in terms of THROUGHPUT performance (although they will all properly compress and decompress, some will do it faster than others). If maximum throughput is important, you should check published benchmark tests to find the modem that provides the best performance.

This chart, courtesy Hayes, shows the speedup that's possible. It includes information on a modem called the Hayes Optima 288, which includes a proprietary (i.e. not compatible with anyone else) Hayes enhanced implementation of V.42 bis.

V.32	9,600 + data compression	=	38,400 bit/s
V.32 bis	14,400 + data compression	=	57,600 bit/s
V.34	28,800 + data compression	=	115,600 bit/s
Hayes Optima 288	28,800 + Hayes enhanced V.42 bis	=	230,400 bit/s

V.54 ITU-T standard for loop test devices in modems, DCEs (Data Communications Equipments) and DTEs (Data Terminal Equipment). Defines local and remote loopbacks. There are four basic tests — a local digital loopback test that is used to test the DTE's send and receive circuits; a local analog loopback test that is used to test the local modem's operation; a remote analog loopback test that is used to test the communication link to the remote modem; and a remote digital loopback test that is used to test the remote modem's operation. If a modem has V.54 capability (most V.32 and V.32 bis modems do), its manual should include documentation on performing the various tests. Version 7 of the Norton Utilities (from Symantec) also includes a local digital loopback test for your PC's COM ports, for which you will need the optional jumper plug offered with the software. Where a modem supports local digital loopback testing, it simulates the jumper plug and does not, therefore, need to be disconnected.

V.8bis New start-up sequence for multimedia modems.

V.ASVD Analog Simultaneous Voice and Data modem.

V.AVD Alternating voice and data. This is the same function as provided by VoiceView products.

V.DSVD Digital simultaneous voice and data.

V.GMUX The multiplexer for V.DSVD.

V.FAST V.FC. An interim modem standard to support speeds to 28,800 bits per second for uncompressed data transmission rates over regular dial up, voice-grade lines. V.FAST stands for Very Fast. V.Fast was a "standard" that only a few manufacturers of modems adopted. These manufacturers adopted V.Fast because they were impatient with the ITU's slowness. Eventually, however the ITU did adopt a new standard, called V.34. See V.34 and V.34bis.

V.FC Version Fast Class. It is an interim standard that was developed for use until the ITU-T ratified V.Fast, i.e. V.34, which is the speed that a V.34 modem communicates at — namely at 28,800 bits per second. V.FC was eventually obsoleted by V.34, which the ITU-T eventually adopted. See V.34.

VAB Value Added Business partner. A term which Hewlett-Packard uses for developers which write software for its computers. HP helps its VABs sell software. Clearly, by doing so, it helps sell more HP computers.

VAC Voice Activity Compression.

VACANT CODE An unassigned area code, central office or station code.

VACANT CODE INTERCEPT Routes all calls made to an unassigned "level" (first digit dialed) to the attendant, a busy signal, a "reorder" signal or to a recorded announcement.

VACANT NUMBER INTERCEPT Routes all calls of unassigned numbers to the attendant, a busy signal or a prerecorded announcement.

VACC Value Added Common Carrier. A common carrier that provides some network service other than simple end-to-end data transmission. Services include least-cost routing, accounting data, and delivery clarification.

VACUUM TUBES The first electronic computers, Eniac and Univac, built in the wartime secrecy of the 1940s, employed vacuum tubes. They have an average life span of about 20 hours, but with thousands of hot glowing tubes in a single machine, some computers shut down every seven to twelve minutes. Vacuum tubes imposed a limit on the size and power of planned next generations of computers. The second generation of computers, never used vacuum tubes. It used transistors, which were invented in 1947.

VAD Value Added Dealer. Another term for Value Added Reseller (VAR).

Essentially, VARs or VADs are companies who buy equipment from computer or telephone manufacturers, add some of their own software and possibly some peripheral hardware to it, then resell the whole computer or telephone system to end users, typically corporations.

VAIL, THEODORE N. Theodore N. Vail began his career with the Bell System as general manager of the Bell Telephone Company in 1878. He later became the first president of the American Telephone & Telegraph Company in 1885. He left AT&T two years later. After pursuing other interests for 20 years, he returned as president of AT&T in 1907, retiring in 1919 as chairman of the board. Vail believed in "One policy, one system, universal service." He regarded telephony as a natural monopoly. He saw the necessity for regulation and welcomed it.

VALIDATION 1. Generally, all long distance carriers, operator service providers and private pay phone companies will not put a call through unless they can "validate," the caller's telephone company calling card, home/business phone number or credit card. Until the advent of US West's Billing Validation Service and other similar databases in 1987, the companies who needed to validate their callers' billing requests had to turn back the caller or accept the call on faith. Validating a user's calling card is, simply, a Yes-No. If the card number is validated, it is Yes. Getting the validation involves a data call from the provider to the owner of the database. There are many ways of doing this, including a dedicated trunk and an port through an X.25 network. Here's an explanation from material put out by Harris, maker long distance switches, including the P2000V: "Validation processing starts with a check of the P2000V's own internal database of invalid 'billed to' numbers. This database contains numbers that the system administrator wishes to temporarily block. If a call's 'billed to' number does not appear in the database, the P2000V then queries the external validation service. The P2000V directly accesses external validation services via an X.25 modem connected to a leased line. The P2000V can also access Line Information Database (LIDB) through LIDB service bureau providers." 2. Tests to determine whether an implemented system fulfills its requirements. The checking of data for correctness or for compliance with applicable standards, rules, and conventions. The portion of the development of specialized security test and evaluation, procedures, tools, and equipment needed to establish acceptance for joint usage of an automated information system by one or more departments or agencies and their contractors.

VALIDITY CHECK Any check designed to insure the quality of transmission.

VALUE ADDED Refers to a voice or data network service that uses available transmission facilities and then adds some other service or services to increase the value of the transmission.

VALUE ADDED CARRIER VAC. A voice or data common carrier that adds special service features, usually computer related, to services purchased from other carriers and then sells the package of service and features.

VALUE ADDED COMMON CARRIER VACC. A common carrier that provides some network service other than simple end-to-end data transmission. Services include least-cost routing, accounting data, and delivery clarification.

VALUE ADDED NETWORK VAN. A data communications network in which some form of processing of a signal takes place, or information is added by the network. No one knows, however, exactly what a VAN is. The general idea is that a VAN buys "basic" transmission and sometimes switching services from local and long distance phone companies and adds something else — typically an interactive computer with a database, a computer and massive storage. In this way, the VAN adds value to basic communications services. Dial up stock market quoting services are VANs. Electronic mail providers are VANs. But VANs can also simply be basic X.25 packet switching networks which are open to the public. Such a network will use X.25 packet switching to provide error correction, redundancy, and other forms of network reliability. Private organizations (companies, universities, etc.) may set up their own value-added networks, or — as in the case of PDNs (Public Data Networks) — another fancy name for a VAN that offers its services to the public. The classic VAN is a packet-switched operation like Tymnet, GTE Telenet, MCI Mail or AT&T Mail.

VALUE ADDED RESELLER See VAR.

VALUE DRIVEN RE-ENGINEERING A fancy term for Re-Engineering, which is a term probably invented by Michael Hammer in the July-August, 1990 issue of Harvard Business Review. In that issue, he wrote "It is time to stop paving the cow-paths. Instead of embedding outdated processes in silicon and software, we should obliterate them and start over. We should 're-engineer' our business: use the power of modern information technology to radically redesign our business processes to achieve dramatic improvements in their performance." The term re-engineering now seems to me mean taking tasks presently running on mainframes and making them run on file servers running on LANs — Local Area Networks. The idea is to save money on hardware and make the information more freely available to more people. More intelligent companies also redesign their organization to use the now, more-freely available information. See RE-ENGINEERING.

VALUE ADDED SERVICE A communications facility using common carrier networks for transmission and providing extra data features with separate equipment. Store and forward message switching, terminal interfacing and host interfacing features are common extras. See also VALUE ADDED NETWORK.

VALUFLEX A New York Telephone service which lets you make and receive regular phone calls and 800-number calls from local areas on your normal business phone lines. There are big advantages here. You don't have to rent additional phone lines. You don't have to expand your existing phone system — or buy a new one (if getting extra lines means you'd grow out). And you can combine your incoming 800 lines with features you can get on business lines — like call forwarding, conferencing, etc. Have your 800 calls come into your office during the day. Have them call forwarded at night to your home. 800 Valuflex is aimed at smaller business.

VALVE The original British word for an electron tube.

VAMPIRE TAP In local area networking technology, a cable tap that penetrates through the outer shield to make connection to the inner conductor of a coax cable.

VAN See VALUE ADDED NETWORK.

VAN ALLEN BELTS Two layers of charged particles emitted from the sun that are trapped within the earth's magnetic influence. These are named after the discoverer, J. Van Allen. The inner layer exists from about 2,400 to 5,600 km altitude above the earth's surface and consists of secondary charged particles. The outer layer lies between about 13,000 and 19,000 kilometers and is thought to consist of the original particles released from the sun's surface.

VAPORWARE A semi-affectionate slang term for software which has been announced, perhaps even demonstrated, but not delivered to commercial customers. Hyperware is hardware which has been announced but has not yet been delivered. Slideware is hardware or software whose reason for existing (eventually) has been explained in 35-mm slides, foils, charts and/or PC presentation programs. Slideware is usually less real than vaporware or hyperware, though some people would argue with this. Allegedly the term vaporware cam as a result of the many delays in releasing Windows after Bill Gates of Microsoft announced it at the Fall, 1983 Comdex show in Las Vegas. See also HOOKEMWARE, HYPERWARE, MEATWARE, SLIDEWARE and SHOVELWARE.

VAR Value Added Reseller. Typically VARs are organizations that package standard products with software solutions for a specific industry. VARs include business partners ranging in size from providers of specialty turn-key solutions to larger system integrators.

VARI-A-BILL A 900 service of AT&T whereby the call's price varies depending on certain events — the caller punching out some tones on his phone, or a service technician coming on line, etc.

VARIABLE CALL FORWARDING An optional feature of AT&T's 800 IN-WATS service. It allows the subscriber to route calls to certain locations based on time of day or day of week.

VARIABLE FORMAT MESSAGE A message in which the page format of the output is controlled by format characters embedded in the message itself. The alternative is to have the format determined by prior agreement between the origin and the destination.

VARIABLE LENGTH BUFFER A buffer into which data may be entered at one rate and removed at another, without changing the data sequence. Most first-in, first-out (FIFO) storage devices serve this purpose in that the input rate may be variable while the output rate is constant or the output rate may be variable while the input rate is fixed. Various clocking and control systems are used to allow control of underflow or overflow conditions.

VARIABLE LENGTH RECORD A file in a database containing records not of uniform length and in which the distinctions between fields are made with commas, tabs or spaces. Records become uniform in length either because they are uniform to start with or they are "padded" with special characters.

VARIABLE QUANTIZING LEVEL VQL. A speech-encoding technique that quantizes and encodes an analog voice conversation for transmission at 32,000 bits per second.

VARIABLE RESISTOR A resistance element which may be varied to afford various values.

VARIABLE TERM PRICING PLAN VTPP. A rate plan developed by AT&T to replace two-tier pricing. VTPP generally provides for two, four, five or six year contracts, over which period the customer is promised stable prices for some — not all — of the equipment and/or tariffed services he uses. Generally, under VTPP, the customer does not end up owning any of the equipment. VTPP has now been replaced by more normal ways of doing commercial business — outright sale, leasing, etc.

VARIABLE TIMING PARAMETER Timing durations for features such as hold recall, camp-on recall, off-hook duration, and many other programmable telephone system services.

VARIOLOSSER A device with a variable level of attenuation which is controlled by an external signal. Often this signal is the level of the signal being attenuated, that is the higher the level of the signal the more it is attenuated.

VARTI Value Added Reseller Telephone Integrator. A term coined at Telecom Developers '92. It refers to the VARs and interconnects of the 90s that are combining telephony and personal computers to offer products that tie the telephone network to personal computer applications.

VAX A line of minicomputers made by Digital Equipment Corporation (DEC).

VAX MAILGATE FOR MCI MAIL An MCI product that enables users of DEC's ALL-IN-1 Integrated Office and Information System to communicate with others outside their internal network via MCI Mail.

VBI Vertical Blanking Interval. The vertical blanking interval is the portion of the television signal which carries no visual information and appears as a horizontal black bar between the pictures when a TV set needs vertical tuning. The VBI is used for carrying close-captioned signals for the hearing impaired. Digitized data can also be inserted into the VBI for transmission at rates greater than 100,000 bps. Information services such as stock market quotations and news offerings are now available via the VBI of a CATV signal. The data embedded in the VBI signal is retrieved from a standard cable or satellite receiver wall outlet by a receiver set, which connects to a RS-232 port on a microcomputer. Software packages then allow subscribers instant access to the information, which may be displayed in a number of formats.

VBNS Very high-speed Backbone Network Service. It's a service run by MCI for the National Science Foundation (NSF). It runs at speeds up to 155 megabits per second.

VBR Variable Bit Rate. A voice service over a an ATM switch. Voice conversations receive only as much bandwidth as they need, the remaining bandwidth is dynamically allocated to other services that may need it more at any given moment. Northern Telecom refers to this approach as "making bandwidth elastic." VBR also refers to networking processes such as LANs which generate messages in a random, bursty manner rather than continuously.

VC 1. Virtual Channel or Virtual Circuit — a communications path between two nodes identified by label rather than fixed physical path. 2. Virtual Circuit. In packet switching, network facilities that give the appearance to the user of an actual end-to-end circuit. A dynamically variable network connection where sequential user data packets may be routed differently during the course of a "virtual connection." Virtual circuits allow many users to share transmission facilities simultaneously. 3. An ATM term. Virtual channels, defined in the UNI 3.0 specification, are physical connections between end points that are not assigned dedicated bandwidth. Instead, bandwidth is allocated on demand by the network at a user's request. See UNI.

VCA See VOICE CONNECTING ARRANGEMENT.

VCC Virtual Channel Connection.

VCEP Video Compression/Expansion Processor chip.

VCI Virtual Channel Identifier. The address or label of a VC (a virtual circuit).

VCN Virtual Corporate Network. Stentor's name for a service it later changed to Advantage VNet. It's similar to MCI's VNet.

VCOS Visible Caching Operating System. VCOS is a realtime multitasking DSP operating system for the AT&T DSP3210 Digital Signal Processor. Visible Caching means the programmer caches the program and the data onchip, in contrast to logic caching where state machines (implemented in silicon) perform all caching.

VCPI An acronym for the Virtual Control Program Interface, a standard developed by Quarterdeck and Phar Lap Software for running multiple programs and controlling the Virtual-86 mode of 386 microprocessors. A program that's VCPI-compatible and can run in the protected mode under DOS without conflicting with other programs in the system.

VCR VideoCassette Recorder (or Player).

VDE Verband Deutscher Elektrotechniker. Federation of German Electrical Engineers similar in form to the IEEE.

VDI Video Device Interface. A software driver interface that improves video quality by increasing playback frame rates and enhancing motion smoothness and picture sharpness. VDI was developed by Intel and will be broadly licensed to the industry.

VDISK Virtual DISK. Part of the computer's Random Access Memory assigned to simulate a disk. VDISK is a feature of the MS-DOS operating system.

VDM Voice Data Multiplexer.

VDRV Variable Data Rate Video. In digital systems, the ability to vary the amount of data processed per frame to match image quality and transmission bandwidth requirements. DVI symmetrical and asymmetrical and asymmetrical systems can compress video at variable data rates.

VDS Vocabulary Development System

VDT 1. Video Display Terminal. A data terminal with a TV screen. Another name for computer monitor. VDT is the term you hear in Europe. 2. Video Dial Tone. The new concept of getting home entertainment, information and interactive services to residences over some form of new broadband network stretching into the nation's homes. Video Dial Tone is a term used by traditional telephone companies. They're the ones allegedly building this broadband network to provide "Video Dial Tone."

VDU Visual Display Unit.

VECTOR A quantity in the visual (video) telecommunications industry that describes the magnitude and direction of an object's movement — for example, a head moving to the right. See VECTOR IMAGES.

VECTOR GRAPHICS Images defined by sets of straight lines, defined by the locations of the end points.

VECTOR IMAGES Images based on lines drawn between specific coordinates. A vector image is based on the specific mathematics of lines. In contrast, a raster image is a bit-mapped (i.e. bit-drawn) image. A vector engineering image is more useful for engineering, since it can be changed easier than a bit-mapped image. A vector image can easily be converted to a raster image. But it's much more difficult to go from a raster image to a vector image. Some storage systems now store images as combination raster/vector.

VECTOR PROCESSOR Array Processor.

VELOCITY OF LIGHT The speed of light in a vacuum is 186,280 miles per second, or 299,792 kilometers per second. The speed of light is very important because today we can measure time more accurately than length. In effect, we define the meter as the time traveled by light in 0.000000003335640952 of a second as measured by the cesium clock.

VELOCITY OF PROPAGATION The speed at which a signal travels from a sender, through a transmission line and finally arrives at the receiver.

VELOCITY OF SOUND The velocity of sound varies with the medium carrying it. In air at 0 degrees centigrade, it's 331 meters per second. In glass at 20 degrees centigrade, its 5485 meters per second.

VELVEETA An Internet Usenet posting, often commercial in nature, excessively cross-posted to a large number of newsgroups. Similar to Spam, although that term is often used to describe an identical post that's been loaded onto lots of inappropriate newsgroups, one group at a time (rather than cross-posted). This definition courtesy Wired Magazine.

VENDOR CODE Software written by the same company that manufactured the computer system on which it is running (or not running...).

VENDOR ID A Plug and Play term. Vendor ID is the 32-bit vendor ID that indicates the manufacturer, specific model, and version of a device. It is this number which helps Plug and Play configure the PC to run the device.

VENDOR INDEPENDENT Hardware or software that will work with hardware and software manufactured by other vendors. The opposite of proprietary.

VENDOR INDEPENDENT MESSAGING GROUP A group of software and software companies who are trying to create non-proprietary, standard programming interfaces to help software and corporate developers write messaging and mail-enabled applications. Ultimately, end users should be able to work together more effectively and be able to exchange information from within desktop applications in a work group environment regardless of vendor platform. Members of the group include Apple, Borland, IBM, Lotus, Novell and WordPerfect.

VENUS-P A CCITT X.25 packet-switched network operated in Japan by Nippon Telephone and Telegraph (NTT) Co.

VERIFICATION A service of a phone company operator who dials into a busy or otherwise impossible-to-reach line and checks that line and reports on that check to the caller. Phone companies are beginning to charge for this service. As of writing, AT&T, for example, was charging 40 cents to verify the line was busy and 70 cents additional for the operator to interrupt the conversation and say another call was coming in.

VERIFICATION TRUNK A trunk to which an operator has access and which will switch through to a called line even if the line is busy.

VERIFIED OFF-HOOK In telephone systems, a service provided by a unit that is inserted on each of a transmission circuit for the purpose of verifying supervisory signals on the circuit. Off-hook service is a priority telephone service for key personnel, affording a connection from caller to receiver by the simple expedient of removing the phone from its cradle or hook.

VERIFIER A device that checks the correctness of transcribed data, usually by comparing with a second transcription of the same data or by comparing a retranscription with the original data.

VERONICA Very Easy Rodent Oriented Netwide Index to Computerized Archives. An Internet service that allows users to search Gopher systems for documents.

VERSIT Versit (201-327-2803) is a loose association between Apple, AT&T, IBM and Siemens Rolm. Its "vision"? To "enable diverse communication and computing devices, applications and services from competing vendors to interoperate in all environments. Communicate and collaborate with anyone, any time, anywhere.." The products include PDAs, notebooks, phones, servers and "collaboration products." One early thrust: standardize on call control within Novell/AT&T's Telephony Services. Background: Call control among PBXs "conforming" to Telephony Services is not standard. PBXs often do the same things differently. Example: Conference a call on one PBX, the PBX may put one call automatically on hold as the other is dialed. Another PBX may expect it to be done manually. The good news: IBM has agreed to pass all its CallPath call control standards over to Versit. Versit's members (including Novell coopted for this task) are now working on making Telephony Services call control more standard. Upshot: Developers won't have to test their "standard" telephony services software on each and every PBX. What works on one will work on the others. That's the goal. In late July 1995, Versit effectively merged all its activities into another association, called ECTF. (www.versit.com) Versit@cup.portal.com. See ECTF and PBX DRIVER PROFILES.

VERTICAL That part of a wiring grid which connects the host computer of Main Distribution Frame (MDF) to equipment located on other fields.

VERTICAL AND HORIZONTAL COORDINATES V & H Coordinates. For purposes of determining airline mileage between locations, vertical and horizontal coordinates have been established across the United States. These V&H coordinates are derived from geographic latitude and longitude coordinates. See V & H.

VERTICAL BLANKING INTERVAL The interval between television frames in which the picture is blanked to enable the trace (which "paints" the screen) to return to the upper left hand corner of the screen, from where the trace starts, once again, to paint a new screen. Several companies are eyeing the vertical blanking interval as a place to send digital data, including news and weather information. The vertical blanking interval was the basis of teletext, a 1970s technology that, with the help of a decoder, displays printed information on the TV screen.

Teletext has never caught on in the U.S. in part because the amount of data that could be transmitted comfortably was small.

VERTICAL REDUNDANCY CHECK VRC. A check or parity bit added to each character in a message such that the number of bits in each character, including the parity bit, is odd (odd parity), or even (even parity). See PARITY.

VERTICAL SERVICE Options that the customer can add to his basic service such as touchtone, conference calling, speed dialing, etc. No one can explain why it's called "vertical" service.

VERY HIGH FREQUENCY VHF. Frequencies from 30 MHz to 300 MHz.

VERY LARGE SCALE INTEGRATION VLSI. Semiconductor chip with several thousand active elements or logic gates — the equivalent of several thousand transistors on a single chip. VLSI is the technique for making the micro chip, the so-called "computer on a chip."

VERY LOW FREQUENCY VLF. Frequencies from 3 KHz to 300 KHz.

VESA Video Electronics Standards Association, San Jose, CA. Along with eight leading video board manufacturers, NEC Home Electronics founded VESA in the late 1980s. The association's main goal is to standardize the electrical, timing, and programming issues surrounding 800 x 600 pixel resolution video displays, commonly known as Super VGA. VESA has also issued a standard called "local bus," a new high-speed bus for the PC designed to move video between the CPU and the screen a lot faster than the conventional AT bus.

VESTIGIAL SIDEBAND TRANSMISSION VSB. A modified double-sideband transmission in which one sideband, the carrier, and only a portion of the other sideband are transmitted.

VF Voice Frequency.

VFAST More commonly spelled V.FAST. A future modem standard in the early stages of development, expected to be released in the early part of 1994. If approved by the ITU-T, it would raise modem speeds to about 19,200 bps.

VFAT Virtual File Allocation Table. A fat file system is a file system based on a file allocation table, maintained by the operating system, to keep track of the status of various segments of disk space used for file storage. The 32-bit implementation in Windows 95 is called the Virtual File Allocation Table (VFAT). An extension of the FAT file system in DOS and Windows 3.xx, VFAT supports long filenames while retaining some compatibility with FAT volumes. See also FAT.

VFDN Voice Frequency Directory Number. A Northern Telecom term.

VFTG Voice Frequency TeleGraph.

VG Voice Grade.

VGA Variable Graphics Array. A graphics standard developed by IBM for the IBM PC. VGA allows the PC's screen to generate any of four levels of resolution — with one of the sharpest being 640 horizontal picture elements, known as pels or pixels, by 480 pels vertically with 16 colors. VGA is superior to earlier graphics standards, such as CGA and EGA. VGA is barely adequate for CAD-CAE. See MONITOR for all the numbers on pixels in various screens. VGA was the graphics standard introduced for IBM PS/2 line and quickly adopted by PC compatibles;

supports analog monitors with a 31.5 Hz horizontal scan rate.

VGPL Voice Grade Private Line.

VHD Very High Density. Techniques of recording 20 megabytes and more on a 3 1/2" magnetic disk.

VHF Very High Frequency. The portion of the electromagnetic spectrum with frequencies between 30 and 300 MHz.

VHI Virtual Host Interface.

VHS Video Home System using half-inch tape introduced by Matsushita/JVC in 1975 and now the most popular form of video tape. There is also a VHS at 3/4". It's often used inside ad agencies for previewing work in progress. Industrial video tape — the stuff the TV stations use — is one inch. And it shows a much better quality picture than half-inch VHS.

VIA NET LOSS VNL. A planning factor used in allocating the attenuation losses of trunks in a transmission network. A specified value for this loss is selected to obtain a satisfactory balance between loss and talker echo performance. The lowest loss in dB at which it is desirable to operate a trunk facility considering limitations of echo, crosstalk, noise and signing.

VIBRATORY PLOW A plow that rips open the ground by vibrating a plow share.

VIDCAP Microsoft's Video For Windows program to capture video input to RAM or hard disk memory.

VIDEO CAPTURE Video Capture means converting a video signal into a format that can be saved onto a hard disk or optical storage device and manipulated with graphics software. This is accomplished with a device internal in a computer called a "frame grabber" or video capture board. Images thus captured are digitized, and can be dropped into a document or database record and may be transmitted locally on a LAN or long distance over a WAN. See VIDEO CAPTURE BOARD.

VIDEO CAPTURE BOARD To capture a single frame of motion video successfully, you need a board inside your PC that can capture the two fields comprising a single video frame. The best source of single frame video images is a laser disk player which can pause and display a perfect frame of video without noise or jitter. Video cameras or camcorders aimed at a static, non-moving image also work well. VCR, which produces a jittery image when the tape is paused, are the poorest source. See also FRAME GRABBER.

VIDEO CODEC The device that converts an analog video signal into digital code.

VIDEO COMPRESSION A method of transmitting analog television signals over a narrow digital channel by processing the signal digitally. You can compress an analog TV signal into one T-1 signal of 1.544 megabits per second. More advanced compression techniques will enable video signals to be compressed into fewer bits per second. One increasingly common method allows a full-color reasonably full-motion video to be compressed into two 56 Kbps channels.

VIDEO CONFERENCE See VIDEOCONFERENCE.

VIDEO DIAL TONE Video dial tone in telco-speak means the phone company, in competition with the cable TV business, provides video to houses and offices. It does not affect the content of that video signal in any way. Thus the term video dial tone, which is like voice dial tone, whose content the phone company also does not affect or change in any way, shape or form. The definition contributed by Stephen Butera, staff director, technical training, New England Telephone.

This is Northern Telecom's explanation of video dial tone: "Recent advances in communications and computer technology, such as fiber optic cables, digital switching and hyperspeed computing, make it possible to transmit extraordinary volumes of interactive electronic information in digital form through telephone networks. Consumers may soon be able to access an intriguing array of multimedia electronic entertainment and information services from the comfort of their homes via a gateway service called Video Dial Tone, which is part of what multimedia is all about. Multimedia means interactive full-motion video, sound, text and graphics all available on your TV, computer terminal or advanced intelligent telecomputer. There may soon be a proliferation of so-called 'intelligent phones' that will transform the touchtone telephone into a versatile home computer. By means of simple pushbutton commands, customers will be able to:

  Select entertainment on demand (movies, music, video).

  Order groceries or other services or products.

  Record customized news and sports programming.

● Enroll and participate in education programs from the convenience of their living rooms.

  Find up-to-minute medical, legal and encyclopedic information.

  Pay bills and manage finances.

  Make airline, rental car and hotel reservations.

  Buy sports and entertainment tickets."

See also VIDEO ON DEMAND and VIDEO SERVER.

VIDEO DRIVER A piece of software which translate instructions from the software you are running into thousands of colored dots, or pixels, that appear on your video monitor. A video driver is also called a display Driver. Symptoms of a video driver giving trouble can range from colors that don't look right, to horizontal flashing lines to simply a black screen. In the Macintosh world, Apple rigidly defined video drivers. Windows, in contrast, is a free-for-all. Windows 3.1 defined the lowest common denominator of displays — namely 16 colors at 640 x 480 pixels. But most multimedia programs and many games won't run with only 16 colors. They require at least 256 colors.

VIDEO ELECTRONICS STANDARDS ASSOCIATION See VESA.

VIDEO FOR WINDOWS An extension to Microsoft's Windows operating environment. It includes a set of low-end software tools for the playback, capture and editing of video. It includes three different codecs: Intel's Indeo, Microsoft Video 1 an a RLE codec. It also includes a CD-ROM with hundreds of sample video clips. The product offers "scalable performance." It automatically adapts the size and frame rate of a video image to the computer hardware available. See INDEO VIDEO.

VIDEO MAIL Electronic mail that includes moving or still images.

VIDEO ON DEMAND VOD. Punch some buttons. Order up Gone With the Wind to start playing at your house at 8:26 P.M. on Channel 35. Bingo, you have video on demand. It's a great concept with two major problems: The equipment to provide the service is complex and expensive. Second, there's little consumer research on whether consumers are prepared to pay the high price that will be necessary. Still, it's a neat idea. See NVOD and VIDEO SERVER.

VIDEO WALL Multi-screen video system where a large number of video monitors (typically 16 monitors arrayed in a 4 x 4 matrix) or back projection modules together produce one very large image or combinations of images. Video walls come with their own software, which lets you program the video effects you want. Typically, you can feed a video wall everything from VGA computer output to moving TV (NTSC) signals. Video walls are used for exhibitions and trade shows. They're not cheap. But, when programmed properly, they ARE spectacular.

VIDEO SERVER A device that could store hundreds, if not thousands of movies, ready for watching by subscribers at their individual whim. A video server could be jukebox like device that would stack several hundred movies. Or it could be a powerful, large computer with several large hard disks and/or optical disk drives. The device would be used in conjunction with the local telephone companies' service called video dial tone — providing movies over normal phone lines to their subscribers or it could be used with the CATV industry's Video On Demand service.

VIDEO SIGNAL Transmission of moving frames or pictures of information requiring frequencies of 1 to 6 Megahertz. A commercial quality full-color, full-motion TV signal requires 6 MHz.

VIDEO TELECONFERENCING Also called Videoconferencing. The real-time, and usually two-way, transmission of digitized video images between two or more locations. Transmitted images may be freeze-frame (where television screen is repainted every few seconds to every 20 seconds) or full motion. Bandwidth requirements for two-way videoconferencing range from 6 MHz for analog, full-motion, full-color, commercial grade TV to two 56 Kbps lines for digitally-encoded reasonably full motion, full color, to 384 Kbps for even better video transmission to 1,544 Mbit/s for very good quality, full-color, full motion TV. See also VIDEO-CONFERENCING.

VIDEO WINDOWS A Bellcore invention which is basically a large, high capacity video conferencing device. Bellcore's Video Windows are connected by two optical links, each carrying 45 million bits of information per second. Though impressive, Bellcore's Video Windows is not considered "high definition" TV. For that to happen, you'd probably need 100 to 150 million bits being transmitted in both directions each second.

VIDEOCONFERENCE Videoconference is to communicate with others using video and audio software and hardware to see and hear each other. Audio can be provided through specialized videoconferencing equipment, through the telephone, or through the computer. Videoconferencing has traditionally been done with dedicated video equipment. But, increasingly personal computers communicating over switched digital lines are being used for videoconferencing. See also VIDEOCONFERENCING.

VIDEOCONFERENCING Video and audio communication between two or more people via a videocodec (coder/decoder) at either end and linked by digital circuits. Formerly needing at least T-1 speeds (1.54 megabits per second), systems are now available offering acceptable quality for general use at 128 Kbit/s and reasonable 7 KHz audio. Factors influencing the growth of videoconferencing are improved compression technology, reduced cost through VLSI chip technology, lower-cost switched digital networks — particularly T-1, fractional T-1, and ISDN — and the emergence of standards. See VIDEOCONFERENCING STANDARDS.

VIDEOCONFERENCING STANDARDS ITU-T H.261 was the standards watershed. Announced in November 1990, it relates to the decoding process used when decompressing videoconferencing pictures, providing a uniform process for codecs to read the incoming signals. Originally defined by Compression Labs Inc. Other important standards are H.221: communications framing; H.230 control and indication signals and H.242d: call setup and disconnect. Encryption, still-frame graphics coding and data transmission standards are still being developed.

VIDEOPHONE 2500 In January, 1992 AT&T introduced a product called VIDEOPHONE 2500, which transmitted moving (albeit slowly-moving) color pictures over normal analog phone lines. The phone carried a price tag $1,500 a piece. It was not compatible with one MCI later introduced, made for it by GEC-Marconi of England and costing only $750 retail. Videophone 2500 relies on video compression from Compression Labs, Inc. of San Jose, CA. According to the New York Times, the phone took two years, about $10 million and 30 full-time people at AT&T to develop. The January 3, 1993 New York Times carried a quote from John F. Hanley, group VP for AT&T consumer products division, "We could make an AT&T phone talk to an MCI phone. It would be in both of our interests."

VIDEOTEX Two-way interactive electronic data transmission or home information retrieval system using the telephone network. Videotex has not been successful because of its (erstwhile) need for expensive, proprietary (i.e. dedicated) equipment and lack of variety in information offered. There are various forms of videotex. The "classic" European version of interactive videotext typically works at 75 baud going out from the terminal and 1200 baud coming in from the central office. Some American versions ape the European system. Some have 1200 baud both ways. In interactive videotext, you can do everything from sending serious electronic mail to your business suppliers to holding raunchy conversations with perverts in distant cities. As long as you pay your bills, no European PTT seems to care about what you transmit or receive. In France, videotex is called Minitel. And it's a success because the French phone company funds it.

VIDICON CAMERA An image sensing device that uses an electron gun to scan a photosensitive target on which a scene is imaged.

VIEW 1. In satellite communications, the ability of a satellite to "see" a satellite earthstation, aimed sufficiently above the horizon and clear of other obstructions so that it is within a free line of sight. A pair of satellite earthstations has a satellite in "mutual" view when both enjoy unobstructed line-of-sight contact with the satellite simultaneously. 2. An alternative way of looking at the data in one or more database tables. A view is usually created as a subset of columns from one or more tables.

VIEWCALL A module of Active Voice's TeLANophy that allows users to manage incoming calls on screen via Microsoft Windows. For instance, they can ask callers to hold, route callers to another extension, or play customized per-record-ed greeting that ask callers to leave a message. Active Voice is in Seattle, WA. See also ViewFax and ViewMail.

VIEWFAX A module of Active Voice's TeLANopy that allows users to receive and preview their faxes on their personal desktop computer. Each fax document is stored electronically until the receiver wants to see it on screen or send it to a printer. Active Voice is in Seattle, WA. See also ViewFax and ViewMail.

VIEWMAIL A module of Active Voice's TeLANopy which allows users to see all voice, and e-mail message on the desktop PC, allowing users to retrieve them in any desired order. Active Voice is in Seattle, WA. See also ViewCall and ViewFax.

VIEWDATA An information retrieval system that uses a remote database acces-sible through the public telephone network. Video display of the data is on a mon-itor or television receiver. Another name for Videotex, the original English (UK) name for it. See VIDEOTEX.

VIM Vendor Independent Messaging. A new E-mail protocol developed by Lotus, Apple, Novell and Borland to provide a common layer where dissimilar messag-ing programs can share data and back-end services. A group called the Vendor Independent Messaging Group will is intent on developing an open, industry-stan-dard interface that will allow e-mail features to be built into a variety of software products. See also MAPI, which is the E-mail protocol developed by Microsoft.

VINES VIrtual NEtwork System. A network operating system developed and mar-keted by Banyan Systems, Westboro, MA. Vines is based on Unix system V. This network operating system provides transparent communication across heteroge-neous networks and is more expansive, although attracting far fewer users, than Novell's NetWare. VINES is based on the UNIX operating system.

VIPER A deadly computer virus.

VIRTUAL In the telephone industry, "Virtual" is something that pretends to be something it isn't, but can be made to appear to be that thing. A virtual private line is effectively a dial up phone line with an auto-dialer on it. To the user, it appears to be a private line. (But the phone company can re-sell that capacity when it's not in use.) The concept of "virtual" is to give the telephone company an excuse to lower the price to the end user. See VIRTUAL NETWORK.

VIRTUAL 8086 MODE Virtual 8086 mode allows the Intel 80386 and beyond microprocessors to emulate multiple real mode processors and still switch to and from protected modem. The processor can load and execute real mode applica-tions (in virtual 8086 mode), then switch to protected mode and load and execute another application that requires access to the full extended memory available. The microprocessor, together with a control program like Microsoft Windows 3.x or OS/2 assumes the responsibility of protecting applications from one another. See REAL MODE and PROTECTED MODE.

VIRTUAL BANDING 1. In WATS services, virtual banding is the ability of trunks to carry traffic to all WATS bands, with billing based on the end points of the call instead of the band over which the traffic went. 2. MCI's definition: Allows customers of MCI's, PRISM, Hotel WATS, and University WATS to call nationwide while only paying for the distance to the actual area. For example, if a customer calls to a Band 1 area, Band 1 pricing is used. Similarly, if a call is placed to a Band 4 area, Band 4 pricing is used.

VIRTUAL BYPASS Virtual bypass is a way smaller users can fill the unused portion of local T-1 dedicated loops going from a user site to a local office of a long distance company, called a POP (Point of Presence).

VIRTUAL CALL CAPABILITY Provides setup and clearing on a per call basis. Each call placed appears to have a dedicated connection for the duration of the call.

VIRTUAL CELL A call, established over a network, that uses the capabilities of either a real or virtual circuit by sharing all or any part of the resources of the circuit for the duration of the call.

VIRTUAL CALL CAPABILITY A data communications packet network service feature in which a call setup procedure and a call-clearing procedure will determine a period of communication between two DTEs. This service requires end-to-end transfer control of packets within a network. Data may be delivered to the network before the call setup has been completed but it will not be delivered to the destination address if the call setup is not successful. The user's data are delivered from the network in the same order in which they are received by the network. See also VIRTUAL CIRCUIT.

VIRTUAL CIRCUIT A communications link — voice or data — that appears to the user to be a dedicated point-to-point circuit. Virtual circuits are generally set up on a per-call basis and disconnected when the call is ended. The concept of a virtual circuit was first used in data communications with packet switching. A packetized data call may send packets over different physical paths through a network to its destination, but is considered to have a single virtual circuit. Virtual circuits have become more common in ultra-high speed applications, like frame relay or SMDS. There the connection might be permanently connected like a LAN. When the user wants to transmit he simply transmits. There's no dialing in the conventional sense, just the addition of an address field on the information being transmitted. A virtual circuit is referred to as a logical, rather than physical path for a call. A virtual voice circuit is anything from as simple as a phone with an auto dialer in it to a high-speed link in which voice calls are digitized and send on the equivalent of a ultra high-speed, wide-area equivalent of a local area network. There are two basic reasons people buy virtual circuits. They're cheaper and faster. See PERMANENT VIRTUAL CIRCUIT.

VIRTUAL CIRCUIT CAPABILITY A network service feature providing a user with a virtual circuit. This feature is not necessarily limited to packet mode transmission. e.g., an analog signal may be converted at its network node to a digital form, which may then be routed over the network via any available route. See VIRTUAL CIRCUIT.

VIRTUAL CO-LOCATION There are several definitions of this evolving. First: Someone other than the local phone company (called an interconnector) can designate his choice of transmission equipment to be located within a local exchange carrier's central office and dedicated to its use. The interconnector would have the right to remotely monitor and control the equipment, but the local exchange carrier would install, maintain, and repair it. Second; And this is a more restricted definition. Connection is done from sites near telephone central offices, but not within them.

VIRTUAL COMPUTING A new term for software that shapes computing hardware into hardware that never was. Virtual computing uses FPGAs — Field Programmable Gate Arrays. See FPGAs.

VIRTUAL CONNECTION A logical connection that is made to a virtual circuit.

VIRTUAL DEVICE A device that software can refer to but that doesn't physically exist.

VIRTUAL DISK A portion of RAM (Random Access Memory) assigned to simulate a disk drive. Also called a ram disk. See RAM DISK.

VIRTUAL FAX A device consisting of a personal computer and an image scanner that can duplicate the functions of a facsimile machine.

VIRTUAL FILE ALLOCATION TABLE VFAT. A fat file systems is a file system based on a file allocation table, maintained by the operating system, to keep track of the status of various segments of disk space used for file storage. The 32-bit implementation in Windows 95 is called the Virtual File Allocation Table (VFAT). See FAT.

VIRTUAL HARD DRIVE MEMORY FACTOR The available space on a hard drive partition that Windows can address as physical memory.

VIRTUAL LAN A logical grouping of users regardless of their physical locations on the network. Racal-Datacom defines a virtual LAN as "a LAN extended beyond its geographical limit and flexibly configured to add or remove locations." LANs are typically extended beyond their geographical limits (i.e. several thousand feet within a building or campus) by using telephone company facilities, like T-1, T-3, Sonet, etc.

VIRTUAL MACHINE FACILITY VM/370. An IBM system control program, essentially an operating system that controls the concurrent execution of multiple virtual machines on a single System/370 mainframe.

VIRTUAL MACHINE VM. Software that mimics the performance of a hardware device. For Intel 80386 and higher processors, a virtual machine is protected memory space that is created through the processor's hardware capabilities.

VIRTUAL MEMORY 1. In computer systems, the memory as it appears to the operating programs running in the CPU. Virtual memory is typically the addition of RAM memory and swapfile memory — portion of a hard disk devoted solely to swapfile memory. 2. The term used with Apple Macintoshes to connote the ability to use disk swap files as RAM. This requires the Macintosh to be running System 7 and PMMU. 3. The space on your hard disk that various versions of Windows (including Windows for Workgroups and NT) use as if it were actually memory. Windows NT does this through the use of swap files. The benefit of using virtual memory is that you can run more applications at one time than your system's physical memory would otherwise allow. The drawbacks are the disk space required for the virtual-memory swap file and the decreased execution speed when swapping to the hard disk is required.

VIRTUAL MEMORY MANAGER Virtual Memory Manager is a software-only approach to Expanded Memory. These work almost identically to the EMS emulators, except that they use your hard disk rather than extended memory as the storage medium for blocks of memory copied out of your program. As you can imagine, this is painfully s-l-o-w. Use this approach only as a last resort.

VIRTUAL NETWORK A network that is programmed, not hard-wired, to meet a customer's specifications. Created on as-needed basis. Also called Software Defined Network by AT&T. See SOFTWARE DEFINED NETWORK and VIRTUAL PRIVATE NETWORK.

VIRTUAL PRINTER MEMORY In a PostScript printer, virtual printer memory is a part of memory that stores font information. The memory in PostScript printers is divided into banded memory and virtual memory. Banded memory contains graphics and page-layout information needed to print your documents. Virtual memory contains any font information that is sent to your printer either when you print a document or when you download fonts.

VIRTUAL PRINTER TECHNOLOGY VPT. Virtual Printer Technology is the enterprise network printer architecture developed by Dataproducts Corporation that enables a printer to become an intelligent node in a networked computing environment and provide printing services to other network nodes through a Client/Server type relationship.

VIRTUAL PRIVATE NETWORK VPN. A carrier-provided service in which the public switched network provides capabilities similar to those of private lines, such as conditioning, error testing, and higher speed, full-duplex, four wire transmission with a line quality adequate for data. A virtual private network eliminates or partly eliminates the need for fixed point-to-point private line because it provides on demand dial up circuits or bandwidths that can be dynamically allocated. AT&T, a major provider of virtually private networks, defines them as the equivalent of a private network designed logically within a public network,thus achieving the economy of scale of a public network while offering the user control of the simulated private network. Virtual private network resources are occupied only while information is transiting the network.

VIRTUAL PRIVATE NETWORK SERVICE An MCI software-defined network service with multiple locations that customers can access through the use of customized dialing plans.

VIRTUAL REALITY VR. The publisher of Virtual Reality Report says, "Virtual reality is a way of enabling people to participate directly in real-time, 3-D environments generated by computers." Virtual reality involves the user's immersion in and interaction with a graphic screen/s. Using 3-D goggles and sensor-laden gloves, people "enter" computer-generated environments and interact with the images displayed there. Says Business Week, "Imagine the difference between viewing fish swimming in an aquarium and donning scuba gear to swim around them. That's the sensory leap between regular computer graphics and virtual reality. There are three kinds of VR (Virtual Reality) immersion. First, the toe in the water experience of beginners who stand outside the imaginary world and communicate by computer with characters inside it. next, wading up to the hips, are the "through the window" users, who use a "flying mouse" to project themselves into the virtual, or artificial, world. Then there are the hold-the-nose plungers: "first persona interaction within the computer-generated world via the use of head-mounted stereoscopic display, gloves, bodysuits and audio systems providing binaural sound. The trick with virtual reality is not only to simulate another world but to interact with it — pouring in data affecting its plots, changing its characters and introducing real-world unpredictability into this "mirror world." Once virtual reality was called artificial reality. But artificial means "fake," while virtual means "almost." The father of virtual reality is Joran Lanier. A term close to virtual reality is telepresence. See TELEPRESENCE.

VIRTUAL ROUTE Virtual circuit in IBM's SNA. See SYSTEMS NETWORK ARCHITECTURE.

VIRTUAL ROUTE PACING CONTROL SNA congestion control at the path control level. See SYSTEMS NETWORK ARCHITECTURE.

VIRTUAL STORAGE Storage space that may be viewed as addressable main storage to a computer user, but is actually auxiliary storage (usually peripheral mass storage) mapped into real addresses. The amount of virtual storage is limited by the addressing scheme of the computer.

VIRTUAL TELECOMMUNICATION ACCESS METHOD VTAM (Pronounced "Vee-Tam.") A program component in an IBM computer which handles some of the communications processing tasks for an application program. VTAM also provides resource sharing, a technique for efficiently using a network to reduce transmission costs.

VIRTUAL TERMINAL VT. A universal terminal. The ISO virtual terminal (VT) protocol is designed to describe the operation of a so-called universal terminal so any terminal can talk with any host computer.

VIRTUAL TERMINAL PROTOCOL VTP. An International Standards Organization (ISO) standard for virtual terminal service.

VIRTUAL TRIBUTARY VT. 1. A structure designed for transport and switching of sub-DS3 payloads. 2. A unit of sub-Sonet bandwidth that can be combined, or concatenated, for transmission through the network; VT1.5 equals 1.544 Mbps; VT2 equals 2.048 Mbps; VT3 equals 3 Mbps; VT6 equals 6 Mbps.

VIRTUALIZATION The process of implementing a network based on virtual Network segments.

VIRUS A software program capable of replicating itself and usually capable of wreaking great harm on the system.

VISIBLE LIGHT Electromagnetic radiation visible to the human eye at wavelengths of 400-700 nm.

VISION ONE Vision One "is a strategy for evolution of telecommunications developed by Siemens AG, Siemens companies worldwide and GPT. Vision One comprises all the innovative, homogeneous and compatible network elements required for the high performance universal network of the future." This from an advertisement Siemens ran in conjunction with Telecom '91 in Geneva Switzerland.

VISIT Northern Telecom's name for its desktop multimedia conferencing system. There's Visit Voice, Visit FastCall and Visit Messenger. See below.

VISIT FASTCALL A low-cost PC-based call center from Northern Telecom. Allegedly, Visit Fastcall will go as low as one agent.

VISIT VIDEO A desktop video conferencing system from Northern Telecom.

VISTA A videotext service offered in Canada.

VISTIUM A desktop videoconferencing device which AT&T introduced and then withdrew from the market towards the end of 1995.

VISUAL BASIC A version of the programming language BASIC written by Microsoft Corporation for Windows. The new program promises to make it much easier for businesses to develop customized Windows applications. Some programmers are calling the software a major breakthrough in ease of programming. When I wrote this, Microsoft had sold over one million copies of Visual Basic.

VISUAL DISPLAY UNIT VDU. Another term for a computer monitor. VDU is preferred in Europe.

VISUAL SOLUTIONS A family of AT&T products which do videoconferencing, first announced on March 23, 1993.

VISUAL VOICE MESSAGING A term created by Microsoft as part of its At Work announcement in June of 1993. There'll be At Work-based visual voice messaging servers sitting on a LAN. Messages for PC users on the LAN will be able to be displayed in a list, much like electronic mail, including the caller's name or number, the time he or she called and the length of the call. This information would let the user browse all messages and select the order for listening to the messages. Administrative options, such as creating a new greeting, will be accessed with a single button. Operations that are difficult today, such as forwarding a voice message to multiple people, will be dramatically simplified, according to Microsoft. One will simply select the recipients from the phone book and broadcast the message. Using visual voice messaging, users will be able to bypass today's inconsistent, time consuming and confusing audio menus and access their voice messages with the push of a button or the click of a mouse on a Windows type icon. Messages will be able to be retrieved in any order and even delivered to a single mailbox along with other messages such as e-mail and faxes. These visual voice messaging servers will, according to Microsoft, provide applications beyond basic voice messaging, such as supporting voice annotation of PC documents or reading electronic mail over the phone to a traveler.

VISUALIZATION A combination of computerized graphics and imaging technology that provides high-resolution, video-like results on the workstation or personal computer's screen.

VISUALLY IMPAIRED ATTENDANT SERVICE Visually impaired attendant service capability is achieved by augmenting the normal visual signals provided on a standard attendant position with special tactile devices and/or audible signals which enable a visually impaired person to operate the position.

VITA VFEA International Trade Association. A widely supported industry trade group in Scottsdale, AZ. VITA is chartered to promote the growth and technical excellence of the VME bus and Futurebus based microcomputer board market. VITA is chartered to submit standards for ANSI registration. See VME.

VITREOUS SILICA Glass consisting of almost pure silicon dioxide.

VIVID Newbridge Networks' brand name for some ATM equipment it sells.

VL A new PC bus from VESA — the Video Electronics Standards Association.

The VL bus is up to 20 times as fast as an ISA bus, the most common PC bus and the one common to the original PC, the PC XT and the PC AT and clones. See ISA and MICROCHANNEL.

VLC Variable length coding.

VLF Very Low Frequency. That portion of the electromagnetic spectrum having continuous frequencies ranging from about 3 Hz to 30 kHz.

VLR Visitors' Location Register. A wireless telecommunications term. A local database to an MSC (Mobile services Switching Center) for registering visiting mobile station users. This information is retained as long as the user resides in the geographical area of the visited MSC. The VLR obtains information from the HLR of the user. See MSC.

VLSI Very Large Scale Integration. The art of putting hundreds of thousands of transistors onto a single quarter-inch square integrated circuit. Compare with LSI and ULSI.

VM Voice Mail, Voice Messaging or Virtual memory. See VIRTUAL STORAGE and VOICE MAIL.

VME Acronym for "VersaModule-Europe". A one through 21 slot, mechanical and electrical bus standard originally developed by the Munich, Germany division of Motorola in the late 70s. VME uses most of the bus structure from then current Motorola's VersaBus board standard along with the newly developed DIN 41612 standard pin-in-socket connector for enhanced reliability. After years of work, VME was finally adopted by the ANSI/IEEE in 1987 (as ANSI/IEEE-1014). VME is known in Europe as the IEC 821 bus. This makes it an open standard. The VME backplane runs at 80 Mbytes per second. It is the most common bus on big open computers (i.e. ones larger than the PC). As of writing, there were over 300 vendors offering more than 3,000 off-the-shelf VME products. The IEEE standard is soon to lapse and be replaced by an extended VME64 specification, now in ANSI ballot being conducted by VITA.

VME64 An enhanced VME bus standard which includes multiplexed address and data cycles with 40 and 64 bit address modes and 64 bit data transfer modes allowing up to 80 MB/s transfer speed. This standard is under the ANSI ballot process conducted by VITA. See VME.

VME64 EXTENSIONS A VITA draft standard that provides extra functionality to VME64 including 5 row J1/P1 and J2/P2 connectors that support live insertion on both 3U and 6U VME boards. Other features: 3.3V power, more grounds, ETL (slew rate) drivers, geographic addressing (slot ID) as well as support for parity, a serial diagnostic bus, JTAG test support and lots of user I/O. Some mechanical features: locking extractors, RFI gasketing, and ESD chassis discharge strips. See VME.

VMEC VOICE MESSAGING EDUCATIONAL COMMITTEE An organization formed by voice messaging manufacturers and service providers to promote a better understanding of voice mail and its business benefits, and to help business implement voice mail systems in ways that meet the needs of callers and mailbox owners alike. See VME.

VMI Voice Messaging Interface.

VMF Validation Message Fraud

VMR Violation Monitoring and Removal. The process of removing a violations which are detected, so that violations do not propagate beyond the maintenance span.

VMS Virtual Memory System

VMS OSI TRANSPORT SERVICES VOTS. A Digital Equipment Corp. software product that modifies Digital's DECnet transport layer to conform to the International Standards Organization (ISO) Transport Protocol Class Four (TP4).

VMUF Voice Messaging User Interface Forum. A standards body formed by voice messaging end users, service providers and manufacturers to define a minimum set of common human interface specifications for voice messaging systems.

VMX Voice Message Exchange. One day in 1979, Gordon Matthews came back from lunch and noticed that he had received the usual half dozen messages that had been randomly taken down semi-correctly by a harried receptionist. Already a noted inventor, Matthews saw an opportunity to build an adjunct device to the company PBX which would these messages to be recorded by the caller without an intermediary and would allow the recipient to store these messages, forward them to others or to directly reply to them if they were generated from another internal extension. He called this device the Voice Message Exchange, and the company later became VMX, which later got bought by Octel.

VNET Virtual private NETwork. An MCI term for a service it offers to customers who want to join geographically dispersed switches (typically PBXs). Instead of private lines joining the PBX, Vnet uses fast switched lines.

VNL Via Net Loss. A loss objective for trunks, the value of which has been selected to obtain a satisfactory balance between two data terminals for the duration of the call.

VO Verification Office.

VOCABULARY DEVELOPMENT Development of specific word sets to be used for speaker independent recognition applications.

VOD Video On Demand. A one stage it was considered a gigantic potential money maker for the phone companies who were real intersted in getting into this market. Now it doesn't seem so hot. See NVOD and VIDEO ON DEMAND.

VODAS Voice Operated Device Anti-Sing. A device used to prevent the overall voice frequency singing of a two-way telephone circuit by ensuring that transmission can occur in only one direction at any given instant.

VOCODER An early type of voice coder, consisting of a speech analyzer and a speech synthesizer. The analyzer circuitry converts analog speech waveforms into digital signals. The synthesizer converts the digital signals into artificial speech sounds. For COMSEC purposes, a vocoder may be used in conjunction with a key generator and a modulator-demodulator device to transmit digitally encrypted speech signals over normal narrowband voice communication channels. These devices are used to reduce the bandwidth requirements for transmitting digitized speech signals. There are analog vocoders that move incoming signals from one portion of the spectrum to another portion.

VOGAD Voice-Operated Gain Adjusting Device. A voice-operated compressor circuit that is designed to provide a near-constant level of output signal from a range of input amplitudes. Such a circuit has a fast attack time with a relatively slow release time to avoid excess volume compression at the system output.

VOICE ACTIVATED DIALING A feature that permits you to dial a number by calling that number out to your cellular phone, instead of punching it in yourself. See VOICE ACTIVATED VIDEO.

VOICE ACTIVATED VIDEO A microphone/camera that is activated in response to voice. Imagine you're watching a videoconference going on in four locations. You can hear what everyone is saying. What you need is to be able to see the person who is speaking the loudest, and therefore, presumably the principal speaker — the person whose attention everyone should be focused on. In voice activated video, the videoconferencing system senses who's speaking the loudest and throws that person's face up on everyone's screen.

VOICE ACTIVITY COMPRESSION VAC. A method of conserving transmission capacity by not transmitting pauses in speech.

VOICE APPLICATIONS PROGRAM System software providing the necessary logic to carry out the functions requested by telephone system users. It is responsible for actual call processing, making the various voice connections and providing user features, such as Call Forwarding, Speed Dialing, Conference, etc.

VOICE BOARD Also called a voice card or speech card. A Voice Board is an IBM PC- or AT-compatible expansion card which can perform voice processing functions. A voice board has several important characteristics: It has a computer bus connection. It has a telephone line interface. It typically has a voice bus connection. And it supports one of several operating systems, e.g. MS-DOS, UNIX. At a minimum, a voice board will usually include support for going on and off-hook (answering, initiating and terminating a call); notification of call termination (hang-up detection); sending flash hook; and dialing digits (touchtone and rotary). See VOICE BUS and VRU.

VOICE BODY PART An X.400 term. A body part sent or forwarded from an originator to a recipient which conveys voice encoded data and related information. The related information consists of parameters which are used to assist in the processing of voice data. These parameters include information detailing the duration of the voice data, the voice encoding algorithm used to encode the voice data, and supplementary information.

VOICE BULLETIN BOARDS These are voice mailboxes which contain prerecorded information that can be updated as frequently as the provider of the mailboxes desires and can be accessed by the public 24 hours a day. Voice bulletin boards can be used by city or county departments which receive a large number of calls asking for routine information, e.g., summer programs for kids as listed by a parks and recreation department; jobs currently open in the city as listed by the personnel departments; etc.

VOICE BUS Picture an open PC. Peer down into it. At the bottom of the PC, you'll see a printed circuit board containing chips and empty connectors. That board is called the motherboard. Fatherboards are inserted into the connectors on the motherboard. These fatherboards do things on the PC — like pump out video to your screen or material to your printer or your local area network. The mother-board controls which device does what WHEN by sending signals along the moth-erboard's data bus — basically a circuit that connects all the various fatherboards through their connectors. That data bus was not designed for voice. For voice you need another bus. Several voice processing manufacturers have addressed that need by creating a voice bus at the top of their PC-based voice processing cards. They have tiny pins sticking out of their cards. You attach a ribbon cable from one set of pins on one voice processing card to the next set on the adjacent card and then the next. There are several voice bus "standards." Two come from Dialogic. One is called AEB, Analog Expansion Bus. And one is called PEB, PC Expansion Bus (a digital version). One comes from a consortium of companies and is called MVIP. There are many advantages to having a voice bus. It gives you enormous flexibility to mix and match voice processing boards, like voice recognition, voice synthesis, switching, voice storage, etc. You can build really powerful voice pro-cessing systems inside today's fast '386 and '486 PCs with the great variety of voice processing now available. For more information on this exciting field, read TELECONNECT Magazine. 212-691-8215. See MVIP.

VOICE CALLING One manufacturer describes this as allowing a phone user to have calls automatically answered and connected to his phone's loudspeaker. Not a common definition. A Northern Telecom Norstar definition: This feature allows a voice announcement to be made, or a conversation to begin, through the speak-er of another telephone in the system.

VOICE CIRCUIT A circuit able to carry one telephone conversation or its equiva-lent, i.e. the typical analog telephone channel coming into your house or office. It's the standard subunit in which telecommunication capacity is counted. It has a band-width between 300 Hz and 3000 Hz. The U.S. analog equivalent is 3 KHz. The dig-ital equivalent is 56 Kbps in North American and 64 Kbps in Europe. This is not suf-ficient for high fidelity voice transmission. You'd probably need at least 10,000 Hz. But it's sufficient to recognize and understand the person on the other end.

VOICE COIL The element in a dynamic microphone which vibrates when sound waves strike it. The coil of wire in a loudspeaker through which audio frequency current is sent to produce vibrations of the cone and reproduction of sound.

VOICE COMPRESSION Refers to the process of electronically modifying a 64 Kbps PCM voice channel to obtain a channel of 32 Kbps or less for the purpose of increased efficiency in transmission.

VOICE CONNECTING ARRANGEMENT VCA. A device that, once upon a time, was necessary for connecting your own phone system to the nation's switched telephone network. Most phones now meet FCC (and other) safety stan-dards, so VCAs are no longer necessary. Most phone systems (as opposed to phones) do have internal protection circuitry, as shown by the "F" (for fully pro-tected) in their FCC registration number.

VOICE COUPLER An interface arrangement once provided by the telephone company to permit direct electrical connection of customer-provided voice termi-nal equipment to the national telephone network. No longer needed because of the FCC's Registration Program.

VOICE DATA An SCSA definition. Encoded audio data.

VOICE DIALING The ability to tell your phone to dial by talking to it. Say, "Call Police" and it will automatically dial the police. This feature has enormous benefits for handicapped people. It will have greater benefits for normal people when the technology of voice recognition improves.

VOICE DIGITIZATION The conversion of an analog voice signal into binary (digital) bits for storage or transmission.

VOICE DTMF FORMS APPLICATIONS This Voice DTMF (DUAL TONE MULTIPLE FREQUENCY) application allows a use of a voice mail system to take specific information from its customers 24 hours a day. By prompting callers to respond by speaking or pressing the keys of their touchtone phones, a city department, for example, could plan service calls, building inspections or send out appropriate forms.

VOICE FRAME See VOICE FRAME.

VOICE FREQUENCY VF. An audio frequency in the range essential for transmission of speech. Typically from about 300 Hz to 3000 Hz. See VOICE FREQUENCIES.

VOICE FREQUENCIES VF. Those frequencies lying within that part of the audio range that is employed for the transmission of speech. In telephony, the usable voice frequency band ranges from a nominal 300 Hz to 3400 Hz. In telephony, the bandwidth allocated for a single voice frequency transmission channel is usually 4 KHz, including guard bands.

VOICE FREQUENCY TELEGRAPH SYSTEM A telegraph system permitting use of up to 20 channels on a single voice circuit by frequency division multiplexing.

VOICE GRADE A communications channel which can transmit and receive voice conversation in the range of 300 Hertz to 3000 Hertz.

VOICE HOGGING See VOICE SWITCHED.

VOICE MAIL Voice Mail allows you to receive, edit and forward messages to one or more voice mailboxes in your company or in your universe of friends. With voice mail, employees can have their own private mailboxes. Here's an explanation of how it works: You call a number. A machine answers. "Sorry. I'm not in. Leave me a message and I'll call you back." It could be a $50 answering machine. Or it could be a $200,000 voice mail "system." The primary purpose is the same — to leave someone a message. After that, the differences become profound. a voice mail system lets you handle a voice message as you would a paper message. You can copy it, store it, send it to one or many people, with or without your own comments. When voice mail helps business, it has enormous benefits. When it's abused — such as when people "hide" behind it and never return their messages — it's useless. Some people hate voice mail. Some people love it. It's clearly here to stay.

In the fall of 1991, the Wall Street Journal carried a story negative on voice mail. Les Lesniak, Rolm's Senior VP Marketing disagreed. His reply published in the Journal is one of the finest explanations of voice mail's virtues:

● The writer's observations ignore the way today's voice communication technology is making communication between people easier and more convenient, and is elevating the level of service savvy companies provide their customers.

Manufacturers use it to take orders after hours and on weekends. Financial services companies use it to provide account information to customers on a 24-hour basis. Colleges use it to register students. A retail executive uses it to broadcast messages to her staff. And a lawyer uses it to respond to calls when traveling.

Voice messaging keeps calls confidential, simplifies decision making, saves time and money, eliminates inaccurate messages and "telephone tag," allows people to use their time more productively. In short, it keeps communication crisp, clear and constant. The writer's line of thinking would demand that people remain at their desk 24 hours a day. If they don't, the phone goes unanswered, a receptionist answers the phone and takes a message, or an answering machine records the message and cuts off the caller at will. None of these scenarios is ideal.

To be successful, voice mail technology must be understood by users and supported by top management, And it must meet the needs of the customer. Training for all employees must be mandatory and the system must be administered and managed properly. 'Must answer' lines and greetings that are changed daily are only two ideas that make voice mail not just helpful, but essential to customer service and an enhanced company image.

Contrary to the writer's view, voice mail contributes to effective business communication and is far superior to an unanswered phone call, a misplaced message or an answering machine."

here are some statistics which add weight to voice mail's logic:

75% of all business calls are not completed on the first attempt.

This can easily waste $50 to $150 per employee per month in toll charges.

Half of the calls are for one-way transfers of information.

Two thirds of all-phone calls are less important than the work they interrupt.

The average length of a voice mail message is 43 seconds. The average long distance call is 3.4 minutes. Voice mail is 80% faster.

Here are the standard benefits of voice mail:

1. No more "telephone tag." Voice mail improves communications. It lets people communicate in non-real time.

2. Shorter calls. When you leave messages on voice mail, your calls are invariably shorter. You get right to the point. Live communications encourage "chit chat" - wasting time and money.

3. No more time zone/business hour dilemma. No more waiting till noon (or rising at 6 A.M.) to call bi-coastally or across continents.

4. Reduce labor costs, Instead of answering phones and taking messages, employees are free to do more vital tasks.

5. Fewer callbacks. In some cases, as many as 50%.

6. Improved message content. Voice mail is much more accurate and private than pink slips. Messages are in your own voice, with all the original intonations and inflections.

7. Less paging and shorter holding times.

8. Less peakload traffic.

9. 24-hour availability.

10. Better customer service.

11. Voice mail allows work groups to stay in contact - morning, noon and night.

12. Voice mail reduces unwanted interruptions.

See Also VOICE MAIL JAIL and VOICE MAIL SYSTEM.

VOICE MAIL JAIL What happens when you reach a voice mail message and you try and reach a human by punching "0" (zero) and you get transferred to another voice mail box and you try again by punching "0" or some other number you're told to punch...and you never reach a human. You're stuck forever inside the bowels of a voice mail machine, being instructed to go from one box to another, never reaching a real human. You're in voice mail jail.

VOICE MAIL SYSTEM A device to record, store and retrieve voice messages. There are two types of voice mail devices — those which are "stand alone" and those which profess some integration with the user's phone system. A stand alone voice mail is not dissimilar to a collection of single person answering machines, with several added features. You can instruct the machines (voice mail boxes) to forward messages among themselves. You can organize to allocate your friends and business acquaintances their own mail boxes so they can dial, leave messages, pick up messages from you, pass messages to you, etc. You can also edit messages, add comments and deliver messages to a mailbox at a pre-arranged time. Messages can be tagged "urgent" or "non-urgent" or stored for future listening. The range of voice mail options varies among manufacturers.

An integrated voice mail system includes two additional features. First, it will tell you if you have any messages. It does this by lighting a light on your phone and/or putting a message on your phone's alphanumeric display. Second, if your phone rings for a certain number of rings (you set the number), the phone will transfer your caller automatically to your voice mail box, which will answer the phone, deliver a little "I am away" message and then receive and record the caller's message.

There are other levels of integration. You might have a phone which has "soft" buttons and an alphanumeric display. That display might label your phone's soft buttons like those on a cassette recorder — forward, reverse, slow, fast, stop, etc. so you can go through your messages any way you like. Telenova has such a phone. It's very impressive.

There are pros and cons to voice mail systems. Some employees will hide behind them, forwarding calls from their customers into voice mail boxes and never returning them. Some employees will make good use of them. They dial in for their messages, research what the customer wants and return the voice mail calls quickly. Many voice mail systems are being combined with automated attendants. Many are being combined with interactive voice processing systems, including sophisticated tie-ins to mainframe databases. Some people hate voice mail systems. Others love them. It all depends on how the system is used, managed and sold. See also VOICE MAIL, AUDIOTEX, AUTOMATED ATTENDANTS, INFORMATION CENTER MAILBOXES, ENHANCED CALL PROCESSING and VOICE PROCESSING.

VOICE MESSAGE SERVICE A leased service typically over dial up phone lines which provides the ability for a phone user to access a voice mail system and leave a message for a particular phone user. See VOICE MAIL SYSTEM.

VOICE MESSAGE EXCHANGE See VMX.

VOICE MESSAGING Recording, storing, playing and distributing phone messages. Essentially voice messaging takes the benefits of voice mail (such as bulk messaging) beyond the immediate office to almost any phone destination you select. Voice messaging is often done through service bureaus. New York Telephone has an interesting way of looking at voice messaging. NYTel sees it as four distinct areas: 1. Voice Mail, where messages can be retrieved and played back at any time from a user's "voice mailbox"; 2. Call Answering, which routes calls made to a busy/no answer extension into a voice mailbox; 3. Call Processing, which lets callers route themselves among voice mailboxes via their touchtone phones; and 4. Information Mailbox, which stores general recorded information for callers to hear.

VOICE MODEM A new type of modem which handles both voice and data over standard analog phone lines. A voice modem is the classic computer telephony device, since it applies intelligence to the making and receiving of normal analog phone calls. Such voice modem might be a full-duplex speakerphone and an answering machine / voice mail device. Such modem might be able to detect incoming and outgoing touchtone and other signals, such as Caller ID. Such modem might also include music on hold, pager dialing, bong and SIT tone detect, line break detect, local phone on / off detect, extension off hook detect, remote ring back detection and VoiceView. The thrust towards voice modems is coming from chip manufacturers, including Sierra Semiconductor, Rockwell and Cirrus Logic. Some standards bodies are working on voice modems. Two standards are emerging — IS-101 and PN-3131.

VOICE OPERATED RELAY (VOX) CIRCUIT A voice-operated relay circuit that permits the equivalent of push-to-talk operation of a transmitter by the operator.

VOICE OVER TIE/communications name for a totally wonderful feature on a phone system — namely that while you are speaking to someone on the phone, your operator can talk to you "over" the conversation you're having. What happens is that you hear your operator in your telephone's handset receiver, but the person you're speaking with can't. You can reply to the operator (telling him/her you'll be one minute, please call back, etc.) by hitting a DND/MIC (Do Not Disturb/Microphone) button on your phone. Voice Over has major benefits. It saves on long distance calls you don't have to return. It closes deals that can't wait. And it gives customers immediate answers. In short, it improves corporate efficiency and customer satisfaction.

VOICE PAGING ACCESS Gives attendants and phone users the ability to dial loudspeaker paging equipment throughout the building. An unbelievably useful feature, if your people are prone to wander.

VOICE PRINT A voice recognition term. A voice print is a speech template used to "train" systems, in particular voice patterns. When a system is operating, the user's speech is compared to the stored voice prints. If they match, the system recognizes the word and executes the command.

VOICE PROCESSING Think of voice processing as a voice computer. Where a computer has a keyboard for entering information, a voice processing system recognizes touchtones from remote telephones. It may also recognize spoken words. Where a computer has a screen for showing results, a voice processing system uses a digitized synthesized voice to "read" the screen to the distant caller.

Whatever a computer can do, a voice processing system can too, from looking up train timetables to moving calls around a business (auto attendant) to taking messages (voice mail). The only limitation on a voice processing system is that you can't present as many alternatives on a phone as you can on a screen. The caller's brain simply can't remember more than a few. With voice processing, you have to present the menus in smaller chunks.

Voice processing is the broad term made up of two narrower terms — call processing and content processing. Call processing consists of physically moving the call around. Think of call processing as switching. Content consists of actually doing something to the call's content, like digitizing it and storing it on a hard disk, or editing it, or recognizing it (voice recognition) or some purpose (e.g. using it as input into a computer program.) See VOICE BOARD, VOICE RESPONSE UNIT and VOICE SERVER.

VOICE RECOGNITION The ability of a machine to recognize your particular voice. This contrasts with speech recognition, which is different. Speech recognition is the ability of a machine to understand human speech — yours and most everyone else's. Voice recognition needs training. Speech recognition doesn't. See SPEAKER DEPENDENT and SPEAKER INDEPENDENT VOICE RECOGNITION.

VOICE RESPONSE UNIT VRU. Think of a Voice Response Unit (also called Interactive Voice Response Unit) as a voice computer. Where a computer has a keyboard for entering information, an IVR uses remote touchtone telephones. Where a computer has a screen for showing the results, an IVR uses a digitized synthesized voice to "read" the screen to the distant caller. An IVR can do whatever a computer can, from looking up train timetables to moving calls around an automatic call distributor (ACD). The only limitation on an IVR is that you can't present as many alternatives on a phone as you can on a screen. The caller's brain simply won't remember more than a few. With IVR, you have to present the menus in smaller chunks. See IVR and VOICE BOARD.

VOICE RING Multiple Digital Intertie Buses connected in series to all nodes. Provides extra channels for voice data transmission when direct link (DI) channels are busy.

VOICE SERVER A PC sitting on a LAN (Local Area Network) and containing voice files which are accessible by the PCs on the LAN. Such voice files may be transmitted on the LAN or over phone lines under the control of the PCs on the LAN. A voice server might contain voice mail. It might contain voice annotated electronic mail. Its primary function is to store voice in such a way that it's accessible easily. Voice servers are typically faster, have more disk capacity and more backup provisions than normal PCs. According to a letter I received in early May, 1993 from the lawyers for a company called Digital Sound Corporation, that company owns federal trademark registration number 1,324,258 for the mark Voiceserver, spelled as one word, not two.

VOICESPAN VoiceSpan is a new class of modem technology that combines existing modem technology with the ability to simultaneous transfer voice (without digitizing the voice).

This general technology has been termed analog simultaneous voice and data (ASVD) to contrast it from digital simultaneous voice and data (DSVD) where the voice is first digitized and then multiplexed with the data. Currently V.asvd is based on technology similar to V.32bis (maximum data rate 14,400 bit/s) but the technology allows the possibility of expansion to include V.34 like capabilities (maximum data rate 33,600 bit/s).

The advantages of ASVD verses DSVD are likely to include better sound quality, rapid ability to detect pauses in voice and send the highest data rate, simpler technology and reduced voice delay between speakers. The disadvantages are likely to be a lower data rate when voice is present and the possibility of less flexibility compared to the all digital approach (DSVD).

Currently two different Recommendations: V.8 and V.25 are used to define what happens when a telephone call is started in fax or data mode. These Recommendations are responsible for the initial sounds (`beeps and squawks'), you hear when your modem connects to a remote modem. However these Recommendations do not easily allow a modem to connect after a voice telephone conversation has started. Most conferencing calls would likely begin with a voice conversation and then switch to data and/or video conferencing. So there is considerable interest in defining a new way to accomplish this. Although some ITU members believe that just making some changes to V.8 would accomplish the same as V.8bis, more simply.

In the market Radish Communications Inc. has established a protocol to accomplish the start- up of data communications during a call as part of an alternating voice and data system called VoiceView(TM). Radish proposed to SG 14 the use of the VoiceView start-up sequence for V.8bis. Unfortunately, while no insurmountable technical problems were identified with the VoiceView approach, the standards committees could not agreed to make V.8bis compatible with the VoiceView start up. The proposed draft V.8bis created at this meeting of SG 14 is independent (the two start-up mechanisms will not confuse each other) of the VoiceView proposal. Therefore manufacturers can make equipment that supports both the VoiceView start-up and the proposed draft V.8bis if they wish.

The bigest remaining problem to SG 14 members is compatibility. Whenever a new sequence of `beeps and squawks' is created all the different types of fax machines, modems, voice response systems, DTMF detectors, etc. currently installed on and in the telephone networks worldwide need to be tested to make sure that the new signals do not cause any serious compatibility problems. The current draft of V.8bis just hasn't been tested yet. This makes the members of SG 14 uncomfortable about its compatibility.

As a result of this concern the US, United Kingdom and France all expressed reservations about Study Group 14 supporting the current draft of V.8bis. This will result in a delay in the approval of V.8bis until at least March 1996. Such a delay is in favor of Radish and the VoiceView partners. The delay allows them to develop an installed base of alternative voice and data VoiceView users. However the likely approval of V.8bis in March 1996 means that the simultaneous voice and data applications will use V.8bis as their start-up sequence. And over the long term markets usually move away from the proprietary solutions to the ITU standard, e.g. MNP4 to V.42, MNP5 to V.42bis, V.FC to V.34.

Two different start-up sequences, three if you count V.8, for different appplications is not the best solution. But it appears that it will work. And the output of standards work is often the best that can be agreed, not the best that can be conceived.

VSE A British Term. Voice Services Equipment, a generic term for voice response unit, interactive voice response, voice processing unit and so on.

VSELP Vector Sum Exited Linear Prediction. A speech coding technique used in U.S. and proposed Japanese DMR standards. Second generation European DMR will probably use some version of VSELP.

VOICE STORE AND FORWARD Voice mail. A PBX service that allows voice messages to be stored digitally in secondary storage and retrieved remotely by dialing access and identification codes. See VOICE MAIL SYSTEM.

VOICE SWITCHED A device which responds to voice. When the device hears a voice, it turns on and transmits it, muting the receive side. The most common voice-switched device is the desk speakerphone. With voice switching, it's easy to hog a circuit. Just keep making a noise. Watch out for voice hogging. If you're calling someone and waiting for them by listening in on your speakerphone, mute your speakerphone. This way you'll hear them when they answer.

VOICE SWITCHING Equipment used in voice and video conferences. The equipment is activated by sounds of sufficient amplitude; hopefully speech, but also loud noises. Fast switching activates microphones so that only one conference participant can speak at a time. See also VOICE ACTIVATED VIDEO.

VOICE TERMINAL A pretentious AT&T term for a TELEPHONE.

VOICE VERIFICATION The process of verifying one's claimed identity through analyzing voice patterns.

VOICEBAND A transmission service with a bandwidth considered suitable for transmission of audio signals. The frequency range generally is 300 or 500 hertz to 3,000 or 3,400 hertz — the frequency range the common analog home phone service is made at.

VOICEFRAME VoiceFrame is Harris Digital Telephone Systems' name for their open application platform for voice and call processing. According to Harris, VoiceFrame allows businesses to create a comprehensive set of applications that link computers, telephone networks and the telephone. Examples of applications that use the VoiceFrame platform include

● touchtone driven transaction processing such as telebanking

● operator services

● dvanced paging systems

● intelligent call routing via host computer database inquiries

● other call center applications.

VoiceFrame serves as a communications controller whose primary responsibility is the disposition of inbound and outbound call traffic under computer control. VoiceFrame has these abilities

● It interprets call signaling information and translates it into protocols for host computer use.

● It accepts commands from the host and interprets them to switch, route and complete calls.

● It provides host computer access to private and public network services, such as DNIS, DID, SMSI, ANI, 950, 900 and 800 services.

● It allows the host computer to perform those tasks for which it is best suited — real-time call routing decision making, database look up, complex calculations and detailed billing.

VOICEMUX 100 Trademark for MICOM's combined TDM and APV products.

VOICEVIEW The family name for the concept and the product line from Radish Communications, Boulder, CO. VoiceView describes the protocol, the transaction, and the platform. Essentially, VoiceView is technology for switching between voice, data, fax and binary image transmission on the same conversation on a standard 3 Khz analog phone line — the one you have in your home. Three types of information transfer modes are available: Modem Data Mode, Fax Data Mode and VoiceView Data Mode. Imagine that you're talking to your travel agent and want to fly from Newark to Chicago. Your travel agent starts reading off the eight different flights. You begin to scribble down the information as she reads through them as quickly as they come up on her screen. As you struggle to get the information down, she says, "Do you have VoiceView?" You purchased a modem with VoiceView capability a month ago and loaded on the software just in case, so you say, "Yes!" She says, "Great! I'll just transfer the information on my screen to your PC screen and it will save both of us a lot of time and hassles — it will only take about 3 to 10 seconds (depending on the amount of information on the screen), and then we can begin talking again. Here it comes!" At your end you experience being put on hold briefly. You hear a faint chirp at the beginning of the transmit time and another a few seconds later. You can then begin talking again with the information you need right in front of you. In the same way, you can also send and receive faxes and binary files.

VoiceView is the protocol that allows all of this to happen. The VoiceView technology must be embedded in a separate box and/or modem through which the conversation and your various communications devices — PCs, fax machine, modem — etc. are connected. To use VoiceView, you must either own a ViewBridge, made by Radish, or a VoiceView certified modem. VoiceView software will be included with the hardware. Microsoft has released a dynamic link library on the Microsoft Developers Network that will help application developers more easily take advantage of VoiceView from Microsoft Windows, with which it is compatible, since VoiceView is simply implemented as a set of AT-command set extensions. The VoiceView software in Windows95 and other Windows products will allow for the transfer and receipt of the VoiceView file. It will not allow for the viewing of the file. For that, you will need extra software. Here are some typical VoiceView applications:

● Collaborative computing. Spreadsheets and documents are easily exchanged, discussed and modified.

● Call Centers can be VoiceView enabled, for example, letting agents send complex flight times, availabilities and itineraries to customers — while the agent is on the phone, or while the customer is in the queue.

● Mixed messaging systems with VoiceView combine the retrieval of voice messages, faxes and electronic mail with one standard phone call.

● Transactions, such as sales orders, processed or confirmed using both visual and audible interchange.

● Hardware and software support is simplified with VoiceView. During a single phone call, the support person can capture diagnostic files, can send diagrams showing how to fix things, etc. troubleshoot and install fixes.

● Other apps include business card exchange and remote presentations where both audio and visual materials are sent via VoiceView. See also VOICEVIEW AGENT, VOICEVIEW BRIDGE, VOICEVIEW PEER and VOICEVIEW SET.

VOICEVIEW AGENT VoiceView Agent, also known as Agent Software, is the original software developed by Radish to launch the VoiceView Protocol. It enables the ViewBridge or VoiceView enabled modems to send PC screens, files, graphics, or bit-maps to other VoiceView compatible users. This includes the VoiceView Formatting Toolkit and is available from Radish. See VOICEVIEW.

VOICEVIEW BRIDGE VoiceView Bridge, also known as a Viewbridge, is a device originally developed to allow a provider to send to or exchange information with another VoiceView-equipped PC user, VRU, IVR database or computer. Used in conjunction with VoiceView Peer software to receive or send data and is required at both endpoints. The Viewbridge attaches to the PC via an RS-232 interface. It connects directly to an analog telephone line and has a modular jack for connecting to the telephone. The ViewBridge can also emulate a ViewSet. See VOICEVIEW.

VOICEVIEW PEER Also known as Peer software, the software that allows a caller equipped with a PC and a Viewbridge to send and receive VoiceView messages. This software has now largely been superseded by Windows DLLs from Microsoft. See VOICEVIEW.

VOICEVIEW SET Also known as a Viewset. A display unit used by callers to receive visual information during VoiceView phone conversation. The Viewset connects directly to an analog telephone line and has a modular jack for connecting to your telephone. See VOICEVIEW.

VOLATILE STORAGE Computer storage that is erased when power is turned off. RAM is volatile storage.

VOLSER An MCI term used to denote a volume of calls. Based on the words "Volume Serial." The term "Volser" can be applied to the manual collection of calls from a switch on a switch tape or through call data transmitted via NEMAS.

VOLT The unit of measurement of electromotive force. Voltage is always expressed as the potential difference in available energy between two points. One volt is the force required to produce a current of one ampere through a resistance or impedance of one ohm.

VOLT METER An instrument for measuring voltages, resistance and current.

VOLTAGE Electricity is a essentially a flow of electrons. They're pushed into a gadget — toaster, computer, phone — on one wire and they sucked out on the other wire. For this movement of electrons to occur there must be "pressure," just as there must be pressure in the flow of water. The pressure under which a flow of electrons moves through a gadget is called the electric voltage. Voltage doesn't indicate anything about quantity, just the pressure. The amount of electricity moving through a wire is called its current and is measured in amps. You figure the power in an electron flow (i.e. in electricity) by multiplying the flow's current by the voltage under which it flows.

VOLTAGE DROP The voltage differential across a component or conductor due to current flow through the resistance or impedance of the component or conductor.

VOLTAGE RATING The highest voltage that may be continuously applied to a conductor in conformance with standards or specifications.

VOLTAGE SPIKE An extremely high voltage increase on an electrical circuit that lasts only a fraction of a second, but can damage sensitive electronic equipment like telephone systems or can cause it to act "funny." If your phone system starts acting "funny," one "cure" is to shut it off, count to ten, and then turn it on again. This sometimes clears the problem.

VOLTAGE STANDING WAVE RATIO VSWR. The ratio of the maximum effective voltage to the minimum effective voltage measured along the length of mis-matched radio frequency transmission line.

VOLTMETER A device for measuring the difference of potential in volts.

VOLUME 1. A volume is a partition or collection of partitions that have been formatted for use by a computer system. A Windows NT volume can be assigned a drive letter and used to organize directories and files. In NetWare a volume is a physical amount of hard disk storage space. Its size is specified during installation. NetWare v2.2 volumes, for example, are limited to 255MB and one hard disk, but one hard disk can contain several volumes. A NetWare volume is the highest level in the NetWare directory structure (on the same level as a DOS root directory). A NetWare file server supports up to 32 volumes. NetWare volumes can be subdivided into directories by network supervisors or by users who have been assigned the appropriate rights. 2. Under ISO 9660, a single CD-Rom disc.

VOLUME LABEL A name you can assign to a floppy or hard disk in MS-DOS. The name can be up to 11 characters in length. You can assign a label when you format a disk or, at a later time, using the LABEL command.

VOLUME SERIAL NUMBER A number assigned to a disk by MS-DOS. The FORMAT command creates the serial number on a disk.

VOLUME UNIT VU. The unit of measurement for electrical speech power in communications work. VUs are measured in decibels above 1 milliwatt. The measuring device is called a VU meter.

VOM Abbreviation for VOLT-OHM-MILLIAMETER, probably the most common form of electronic test equipment. It measures voltage, resistance and current, and may have either a digital or analog meter readout. Some VOMs have other test functions such as audible continuity signals and special tests for semiconductors.

VOMIT COMET A plane used to simulate zero-G for astronaut flight training. Trainers often get motion sickness inside.

VOTE ACK Also known as Mass ACK; in Usenet, the posting of the e-mail address of each person that voted for or against a newsgroup proposal.

VOTING RECEIVERS A group of mobile base phone receivers operating on the same frequency as a control unit to pick the best signal from among them.

VOTS VMS OSI Transport Services. A Digital Equipment Corp. software product that modifies Digital's DECnet transport layer to conform to the International Standards Organization (ISO) Transport Protocol Class Four (TP4).

VOX Voice Operated eXchange. Your voice starts it. When you stop speaking, it stops. Tape recorders use it to figure when to start recording and when to stop. There are pros and cons to VOX. With VOX you often miss the beginning of the conversation. And the tape goes on for 3 or 4 seconds after you've stopped talking. Also if ambient noise is high, VOX might mistake it for speaking and turn the recorder on and keep it running. Cellular phones also use VOX to save battery. A cellular phone without VOX is continuously transmitting a carrier back to the cell cite the entire time your call is in progress. The VOX operation used in smaller phones allows the phone to transmit only when you're actually talking. This reduces battery drain and enables handheld phones to operate longer on a smaller battery.

VOYCALL An early key system manufacturer, which made a combination 1A2 handsfree intercom telephone system. It was wood grained, inlaid into black plastic. An impressive phone system. Sadly, no more.

VP Virtual Path. A collection of VCs (Virtual Channels) all traveling between common points.

VPI Virtual Path Identifier. The address of a Virtual Path. Combined with the VPI, defines a virtual circuit through an ATM network.

VPI/VCI Virtual Path Identifier/Virtual Channel Identifier. Combined, these fields identify a connection on an ATM network.

VPDN Virtual Private Data Network. A private data communications network built on public switching and transport facilities rather than dedicated leased facilities such as T1s.

VPDS Virtual Private Data Services. MCI's equivalent of Vnet for data.

VPN Virtual Private Network. Virtual Private Network is a software-defined network offering the appearance, functionality and usefulness of a dedicated private network, at a price savings. Here's how it works: Your company buys a bunch of leased lines from your offices to the nearest local offices of your chosen long distance carrier. You're in your New York offices. You want to dial your offices in Chicago. You pick up the phone, dial perhaps seven digits. The phone rings in Chicago. What's happened is that your local PBX has recognized that call as belonging to your VPN. So it shunts the calls over the dedicated local loop to your long distance carrier. Your carrier then checks your dialed number, perhaps changing it with the aid of a database look up table, and completes the call over the carrier's own switched telephone facilities (fiber optic, microwave, copper, etc.). These are the same facilities which you and I use when we dial 1 and the long distance number (assuming we're equal accessed to that carrier).

There are several differences between a VPN and normal dial service:

1. VPN's price per minute is cheaper, often a lot cheaper.

2. You dial fewer digits with VPN. Sometimes you can get right to the distant desk, without going through the operator at the distant end.

3. You have to pay for the dedicated phone lines at the various ends of the VPN which have those dedicated phone lines. But they're often T-1, and thus not expensive on a per voice circuit basis.

4. You have to commit to use VPN for much longer than you do with normal dial up service — which is typically month-to-month.

VPN 56 Sprint's Switched 56 Kbps service, supports advanced voice, data and image network communication tools including Group IV Fax, high resolution image transfer, file transfer, videoconferencing and switched data service via access to SprintNet, a large public data network.

VPOTS Very Plain Old Telephone Service. No automated switching.

VPU Virtual Physical Unit.

VQL Variable Quantizing Level. Speech-encoding technique that quantizes and encodes an analog voice conversation for transmission, nominally at 32 Kbps.

VR 1. Voice Recognition. See VOICE RECOGNITION. 2. Virtual Reality. See VIRTUAL REALITY.

VRAM Video RAM. Memory used to buffer an image and transfer it onto the display. It is a form of DRAM specially suited for video. VRAM differs from common DRAM in that it has two data paths — a technique known as dual porting — rather than the single path of traditional RAM; thus, it can move data in and out simultaneously. Two devices can access it at once. The CRT controller, which converts bits and bytes in video memory to pixels on the screen, and the CPU, which manipulates the contents of video memory, can access VRAM simultaneously. In video boards fitted with the less expensive DRAM, performance suffers somewhat because the CRT controller and the CPU must takes turns getting to the video buffer held in VRAM. See also DRAM and WRAM.

VRC Vertical Redundancy Check.

VREPAIR A Novell NetWare program somewhat analogous to MS-DOS's CHKD-SK program. VREPAIR fixes FAT (File Allocation Table) and DIR (Directory) Tables. It's a most useful program. Highly recommended.

VRML Virtual Reality Modeling Language. A language for writing 3D HTML applications. VRML, according to PC Magazine, is an open standard for 3-D imaging on the World-Wide Web that paves the way for virtual reality on the Internet. The way VRML code describes a 3-D scene is analogous to four points describing a square, or a center point and radius describing a sphere. VRML viewers, similar to HTML Web browsers, interpret VRML data downloaded from the Web and render it on your computer. This allows the bulk of the processing to be performed locally and drastically reduces the volume of information that must be transmitted from the Web — a key consideration if rendering is to be performed in real time.

VROOMM Virtual Runtime object oriented Memory Manager. VROOMMM is Borland's proprietary technology designed to save memory by reducing commands to compact objects. Because of VROOMM Quattro Pro has had three fully-featured releases without compromising spreadsheet capacity or performance on current machines — even if it's an 8088-based PC with 512K or RAM. How does

VROOOMM make more memory available for your spreadsheet data? According to Borland, most spreadsheet programs work with only a small number of large overlays, loading one or another into memory depending on the operations being performed. In contrast, VROOMM moves hundreds of small program modules, which are in effect code objects in and out of memory as necessary. Individual areas of Quattro Pro use different code objects, so it's possible to have very large spreadsheets in memory while significantly increasing functionality. Quattro Pro's graphics subsystem also take advantage of VROOMM by storing the graphics you, the user, create in available EMS.

VRPRS Virtual Route Pacing Response in SNA.

VRU See VOICE BOARD and VOICE RESPONSE UNIT.

VRU CONNECT SIGNALING A Rockwell ACD definition. When the incoming call is answered by a VRU, a caller typically inputs information via a DTMF key-pad. This user-defined information can now be "whispered" as an audio announcement by the VRU to a service representative. After the VRU has conveyed the caller's information to the agent, the VRU drops out and the call is transferred to the agent. The most notable benefits are 1) enabling agents to better anticipate and consequently address the needs of callers, 2) eliminating the need for agents to request information already gathered by the VRU, 3) presenting a better organized and professional appearance to callers, and 4) expediting the transaction process.

V-SERIES RECOMMENDATIONS Sets of telecommunications protocols and interfaces defined by ITU-T Recommendations.

VS See VIRTUAL STORAGE.

VS&F Voice Store and Forward. Voice is digitally encoded, sent to large storage devices and later forwarded to the recipient. See VOICE MAIL.

VSAT Very Small Aperture Terminal. A relatively small satellite antenna, typically 1.5 to 3.0 meters in diameter, used for transmitting and receiving one channel of data communications. You see VSATs on top of retail stores which use them for transmitting the day's receipts and receiving instructions for sales, etc.

VSB Vestigial SideBand. A form of AM modulation that compresses required bandwidth.

VSCBX A Rolm PBX called a Very Small Computerized Branch EXchange.

VSE Virtual Storage Extended.

VSS Voice Server System.

VSWR Voltage Standing Wave Ratio. The ratio of the maximum effective voltage to the minimum effective voltage measured along the length of mis-matched radio frequency transmission line.

VT Virtual Tributary. A structure designed for transport and switching of sub-DS3 payloads. VT1.5 equals 1.544 Mbps; VT2 equals 2.048 Mbps; VT3 equals 3 Mbps; VT6 equals 6 Mbps. These are measures of speed in Sonet. See SONET.

VT100 A terminal-emulation system. Supported by many communications program, it is the most common one in use on the Internet. VT102 is a newer version.

VTAM Virtual Telecommunications Access Method. A program component in an

IBM computer which handles some of the communications processing tasks for an application program. In an IBM 370 or compatible, VTAM is a method to give users at remote terminals access to applications in the main computer. VTAM resides in the host. It performs addressing and path control functions in an SNA network that allows a terminal or an application to communicate with and transfer data to another application along some sort of transmission medium. VTAM also provides resource sharing, a technique for efficiently using a network to reduce transmission costs. See SYSTEMS NETWORK ARCHITECTURE.

VTP Virtual Terminal Protocol. An International Standards Organization (ISO) standard for virtual terminal service.

VTTH Video To The Home. The general ability to provide interactive multimedia services to people in their homes.

VU METER VU is the unit of measurement for electrical speech power in communications work. VUs are measured in decibels above 1 milliwatt. The measuring device is called a VU meter.

VUI First came the CLI (Command-Line Interface). Then came the GUI (Graphical User Interface). Get ready for the VUI: the Video User Interface. Actually, you don't need to get ready for it any time soon, but you might start wondering how to use it.

VW-1 A test used by Underwriters Laboratories to classify wires and cables by their resistance to burning. (Formerly designated as FR-1.)

W 1. Abbreviation for WATT.

2 The Hayes AT Command Set describes a standard language for sending commands to asynchronous modems. One of the commands is "W." If you embed a W in your dialing string, i.e. 212-691-8215-W-10045, the modem will dial 212-691-8215 and wait until it hears dial tone. When it hears dial tone, it will dial out 10045. That is the standard Hayes command set interpretation of W. There is another. When using some of the communications software products from Crosstalk (now a subsidiary of DCA) you can place a [W] in your dialing string. If you do, your modem will dial the number until it encounters a [W]. It will then wait until you hit any button on your keyboard. The purpose of W commands is to allow you to dial through private networks (your own), through public networks (MCI, Sprint, etc.), through fax/modem/telephone switches and through any other device or network.

W-DCS Wideband Digital Cross-connect System. W-DCS is an electronic digital cross-connect system capable of cross-connecting signals below the DS3 rate.

W3 An abbreviation for the Internet's World Wide Web. See WORLD WIDE WEB.

W3C World Wide Web Consortium based in Cambridge, MA. An organization of commercial firms who are trying to drive standards into the Internet. In some ways, its ambitions are not that different to the IETF, the Internet Engineering Task Force, except that its members are commercial firms. The IETF's members are volunteers and tend to come from academia. Its Web site is www.w3.org/hypertext/WWW/Consortium.

WACK Wait before transmitting positive ACKnowledgement. In Bisynch, this DLE sequence is sent by a receiving station to indicate it is temporarily not ready to receive.

WAFER A thin disk of a purified crystalline semiconductor, typically silicon, that is cut into chips after processing. Typically, a wafer is about one fiftieth of an inch thick and four or five inches in diameter.

WAFER FABS Wafer fabs are a slang term for ultraclean factories that fabricate chips on silicon wafers.

WAIS Wide-Area Information Servers. A very powerful system for looking up information in databases (or libraries) across the Internet. WAIS allows you to perform a keyword search. WAIS is like an index, whereas Gopher, which is sometimes used as a complement to WAIS, is like a table of contents.

WAIT ON BUSY An English term for the American term "Camp On" or "Call Waiting." A service allowing the subscriber to make a call to a busy phone line, wait until the call is over, then be connected automatically.

WAIT STATE A period of time when the processor does nothing; it simply waits. A wait state is used to synchronize circuitry or devices operating at different speeds. Wait states are introduced into computers to compensate for the fact that the central microprocessor might be faster than the memory chips next to it. For example, wait states used in memory access slow down the CPU so that all components seem to be running at the same speed. A wait state is a "missed beat" in the cycle of information to and from the CPU that is necessary for a memory transaction to be completed.

WALK TIME The time required to transfer permission to poll from one station to another.

WALKAWAYS People who walk from coin phones though they owe it extra money. You can tell a phone that has just been visited by walkaway: It's typically ringing. And when you answer it, the operator will ask you to deposit some additional coins.

WALKIE-TALKIE Hand-held radio transmitter and receiver. Like the police carry. Probably the best named device in telecom. You walkie, you talkie.

WALL OUTLET A phone outlet positioned at shoulder height to accept a wall telephone set. The typical installation includes a special modular jack containing two mounting bosses that insert into key-hole slots in the base of the telephone set. Electrical connection is made by a short cord or a lug element that is integral to the telephone set base.

WALL PHONE A phone that is mounted on the wall. Where else would a wall phone be mounted? Some new phones — especially some key systems — come so you can use them on the desk or mount them on a wall, without extra hardware. Some desk phones cannot be mounted on a wall. This is a disadvantage when you run out of space on your desk, as you will with all the computers and workstations you'll be putting there.

WALL THICKNESS A term expressing the thickness of a layer of applied insulation or jacket.

WALLPAPER The area of your Windows desktop on your PC behind and around your windows and icons. The color and pattern you put on it through the desktop manager is called wallpaper.

WAN Wide Area Network. Uses common carrier-provided lines that cover an extended geographical area. Contrast with LAN. This network uses links provided by local telephone companies and usually connects disperse sites. See WIDE AREA NETWORK.

WANDER Long-term random variations of the significant instants of a digital signal from their ideal position in time. Wander variations are usually considered to be those that occur over a period greater than 1 second. See also WANGNET. As I wrote this, WANG had just filed for Chapter 11 protection under US Bankruptcy laws. For more, see CHAPTER 11.

WANG Wang's name for its telephony link is STEP, which stands for Speech and Telephony Environment for Programmers.

WANGNET Wang Laboratories' proprietary broadband LANs. Used as the brand name for Wang's LAN products.

WAR ROOM Also called a "solutions room." This is an enclosed area with a large table used for decision- or strategy-making.

WARBLE TONE A tone changing in frequency at a slow enough rate to give the effect of warbling. A warble tone is the sound of an electronic ringer, according to many people.

WARC World Administrative Radio Conference. Sets international frequencies. Just before Telecom '87, WARC allocated important new frequencies for satellite-based land mobile (satellite to truck, etc.) and radio determination navigation services (electronic maps for your car). WARC is part of the 154-member International Telecommunication Union. ITU-T is part of the ITU. See ITU-T.

WARM START Restarting or resetting a computer without turning it off (also called "soft boot"); press Ctrl + Alt + Del on an IBM or IBM compatible.

WARRANTY Span of time that equipment will be repaired or replaced due to failure. Usually does not include reimbursement of engineer's fees required for replacement. May not include equipment failure due to abuse or destruction by either intentional or unintentional means. Lightning, floods, and other Acts of God are not covered under warranty.

WATCH COMMANDS Watch Commands are found in programming. They allow you to "watch" the value of selected application variables while the application is executing (e.g., see the last-entered touchtone digits from a caller).

WATCHING TIMER A circuit used in ETHERNET transceivers to ensure that transmission frames are never longer than the specified maximum length.

WATER PIPE GROUND A water pipe to which connection is made for the ground.

WATS Wide Area Telecommunications Service. Basically, a discounted toll service provided by all long distance and local phone companies. AT&T started WATS but forgot to trademark the name, so now every supplier uses it as a generic name. There are two types of WATS services — in and out WATS, i.e. those WATS lines that allow you to dial out and those on which you receive incoming calls (the typical 800 line service). You subscribe to in- and out-WATS services separately. In the old days you needed separate in and out lines to handle the in and out WATS services. But these days you can choose to have in- and out-WATS on the same line. This is not particularly brilliant traffic engineering, since you can't receive an incoming 800 call if you're making an outgoing call. But I do know someone who has an 800 line on his cellular phone!

Many users inside companies think their company's WATS lines (and thus their WATS calls) are free, so they speak longer. This can kill the idea of buying WATS lines to save money. In the old days, interstate WATS was charged at effectively a flat rate and thus, there was some reason to believe that marginal WATS calls were 'free.' These days EVERY WATS call costs money. EVERY one! Without exception. See 800 SERVICE and PLANT TEST NUMBER.

WATT The unit of electricity consumption and representing the product of amperage and voltage. the power requirement of a device is listed in watts, you can convert to amps by dividing the wattage by the voltage (e.g., 1,200 watts divided by 120 volts, equal 10 amps). See OHM's LAW. Don't confuse WATTS (the measure of electricity) with WATS, which stands for Wide Area Telecommunications Service. See WATS.

WAVE AUDIO Also called "waveform audio," is a digital representation of actual sound waves. Wave audio "samples" the sound waveforms at regular intervals. The three standard sampling frequencies are 11.025 KHz, 22.05 Khz, and 44.1 KHz. Higher sampling frequencies yield higher fidelity sound.

WAVE LENGTH The distance between peaks of an electromagnetic (or other) wave. The distance traveled by a wave during one complete cycle. See also WAVELENGTH.

WAVEFORM The characteristic shape of a signal usually shown as a plot of amplitude over a period of time.

WAVEFORM EDITOR A word processor for sound. You record something. Then you "play" it back on your PC's screen. Your PC screen now looks like an oscilloscope. Then you use this wave form editor to edit (i.e. change, replace. amplify, echo, fade in or out, cut out noise, cut/paste from other files, or generally muck with) the sound. A wave form editor is used in voice processing.

WAVEGUIDE A conducting or dielectric structure able to support and propagate one or more modes. More specifically, a waveguide is a hollow, finely-engineered metallic tube used to transmit microwave radio signals from the microwave antenna to the radio and vice versa. Waveguides comes in various shapes — rectangular, elliptical or circular. They are very sensitive and should be handled very gently. Waveguides may contain a solid or gaseous dielectric material. In optical, a waveguide used as a long transmission line consists of a solid dielectric filament (optical fiber), usually circular. In integrated optical circuits an optical waveguide may consist of a thin dielectric film.

WAVEGUIDE SCATTERING Scattering (other than material scattering) that is attributable to variations of geometry and refractive index profile of an optical fiber.

WAVELENGTH The length of a wave measured from any point on one wave, to the corresponding point on the next wave, such as from crest to crest. In other words, a wavelength is the distance an electromagnetic wave travels in the time it takes to oscillate through a complete cycle. There is a direct proportion between the wavelength of a radio signal and its frequency.

WAVELENGTH DIVISION MULTIPLEXING WDM. A way of increasing the capacity of an optical fiber by simultaneously operating at more than one wavelength. With WDM you can multiplex signals by transmitting them at different wavelengths through the same fiber. Wavelength division multiplexing works similar to frequency division multiplexing. In optical fiber communications, WDW is any technique by which two or more optical signals having different wavelengths may be simultaneously transmitted in the same direction over one strand of fiber, and then be separated by wavelength at the distant end.

WAY OPERATED CIRCUIT A circuit shared by three or more phones on a party line basis. One of the phones usually operates as the control point.

WAY STATION One of the phones, other than the central controller, on a way operated circuit. See WAY OPERATED CIRCUIT.

WBC Wide Band Channel. An FDDI-II term. See FDDI II.

WCV See Weighted Call Value.

WDM Wavelength Division Multiplexing. A technique in fiber-optic transmission for using different light wavelengths to send data parallel-by-bit (one discrete wavelength per bit), serial-by-character. One multimode fiber can act as an 8-bit parallel bus.

WDMA Wavelength-Division Multiple Access: a technique which is used to provide multiple channels on different wavelengths on the same fiber-optic cable.

WEATHER TRUNK GROUP A trunk group used to provide customers with weather information.

WEATHERMASTER METHOD A distribution method where the unused wall space inside heating and cooling units beneath windows is used for satellite location. Cables are fed from a riser or other serving closet to the location through baseboards, conduit, or underfloor system.

WEB An abbreviation for the Internet's World Wide Web. See WORLD WIDE WEB and INTERNET.

WEB ART A definition for the artwork that you are beginning to see proliferating the Internet, especially on home pages.

WEB BROWSER Clients software which navigates a web of interconnected documents on the World Wide Web. A Web Browser is software which allows a computer user (like you and me) to "surf" the Internet. It lets us move easily from one World Wide Web site to another. Every time we alight on a Web Page, our Web Browser moves a copy of documents on the Web to your computer. A Web Browser uses HTTP — the HyperText Transfer Protocol. Invisible to the user of a Web Browser, HTTP is the actual protocol used by the Web Server and the Client Browser to communicate over the Internet. The most famous Web Browser is currently Netscape. Many online commercial services such as AOL, CompuServe, Microsoft, Prodigy, etc. distribute Web Browsers to surf their "intranet" as well as the "internet." See INTERNET, MOSAIC, NETSCAPE and SURF.

WEB SERVICE PROVIDER A vendor who provides customers with Web Pages on the vendor's computer/s. Frequently, a Web Service Provider will provide additional services such as design help and usage statistics. Often they will just provide the computer space and leave the rest to you. A Web Service Provider may or may not also be an Internet Service Provider.

WEB SITE Any machine on the Internet that is running a Web Server to respond to requests from remote Web Browsers is a Web Site. In more common usage it refers to individual sets of Web Pages that can be visited with Web Browsers. It is also spelled as one word, namely WEBSITE. See also INTERNET.

WEBMASTER An Internet term. The Webmaster is the administrator responsible for the management and often design of a company's World Wide Web site.

WEBSITE See WEB SITE.

WECO Western Electric COmpany. The company is now called AT&T Technologies. It is the equipment manufacturing arm of AT&T. No one knows why this company changed its name, since Western Electric had a wonderful reputation and is remembered with great fondness. It has an excellent reputation for high quality products and is still used as a brand name on some AT&T Technologies' products.

WEIGHTED AVERAGE A call center term. A method of averaging several numbers in which some numbers are increased before averaging because they have more significance relative to the other numbers.

WEIGHTED CALL VALUE WCV. The average handling time of a call transaction. ACD vendors count this differently. Typically, a combination of the talk time and the after-call work or wrap-up time.

WESTAR Family of communications satellites owned and operated by Western Union.

WESTERN UNION INTERNATIONAL WUI. Acquired by MCI in 1982 to establish MCI in the International Telex and communications market. WUI is now part of MCI International.

WESTNET One of the National Science Foundation funded regional TCP/IP networks that covers the states of Arizona, Colorado, New Mexico, Utah, and Wyoming.

WET CIRCUIT A circuit carrying direct current.

WET LOOP POWERING Defined as local power (non-Span provided) with use of copper pairs (power is looped at the last repeater).

WET T-1 A T-1 line with a telephony company powered interface.

WETTING AGENT A chemical which reduces surface tension in a liquid, motivating the liquid to spread more evenly on a surface.

WFWG Windows For Workgroups. See WINDOWS.

WG An abbreviation for workstation, i.e. a computer on a desktop that isn't a server.

WHEATSTONE BRIDGE An instrument for measuring resistances.

WHETSTONES How well does a computer work? Let's test it. The Whetstone benchmark program, developed in 1976, was designed to simulate arithmetic intensive programs used in scientific computing. It is applicable in CAD and other engineering areas where floating-point and trigonometric calculations are heavily used. The Whetstone program is completely CPU-bound and performs no I/O or system calls. The speed at which a system performs floating point operations is measured in units of Whetstones per second or floating point operations per second (flops). Whetstone I tests 32-bit, and Whetstone II tests 64-bit operations. See also DHRYSTONES.

WHISPER TECHNOLOGY A call comes into a call center. The voice response unit prompts the caller to the enter their account number. When the call is transferred to the agent, the VRU "whispers" the account number to the agent, who then manually types it into his computer. This technology is now obsolete, since VRUs can now transfer their account number directly into the agent's database and have the look up done automatically. And the call is transferred simultaneously.

WHITE BOARD See Whiteboard below.

WHITE FACSIMILE TRANSMISSION In an amplitude-modulated facsimile system, that form of transmission in which the maximum transmitted power corresponds to the minimum density of the subject copy. In a frequency-modulated system, that form of transmission in which the lowest transmitted frequency corresponds to the minimum density of the subject copy.

WHITE LINE SKIP A facsimile transmission technique used to speed up the transmission time by bypassing redundant areas such as white space. (Also known as skip scan.)

WHITE NOISE A signal whose energy is uniformly distributed among all frequencies within a band of interest. Seldom occurring in nature, white noise is a useful tool for theoretical research. White noise is also used less scientifically to simply mean background noise. When the first digital PBXs came out, their intercom circuits were so "clean," they spooked users out who were used to some noise on the line. And some PBX manufacturers added a little "white noise" to their PBXs.

WHITE PAGES 1. In many countries, including the U.S., Canada and Australia, the phone company publishes two types of telephone directories. One called the "White Pages" lists all the subscribers in alphabetical order. The other, called the Yellow Pages, lists businesses by industry. On the Internet, the White Pages are the lists of Internet users that are accessible through the Internet.

WHITE SIGNAL In facsimile, the signal resulting from the scanning of a minimum-density area of the subject copy.

WHITEBOARD a device which lets you share images, text and data simultaneously as you speak on the phone with someone else. That someone might be in the next office. Or that someone might be 3,000 miles away. The transport mechanism might be a local area network or an analog phone line running a special modem designed for whiteboarding or it might be an ISDN digital line running special PC software and hardware. The concept of whiteboarding is new; there are no standards. As a result to do whiteboarding successfully, you typically need the same equipment (hardware and software) on either end. Whiteboarding has the potential to be one of the most successful "multimedia" applications around.

WHO-ARE-YOU CODE WRU. A control character which operates the answerback unit in a terminal (typically a telex terminal) for identification of sending and receiving stations in a network.

WHOIS An Internet program which allows users to query a database of people and other Internet entities, such as domains, network, and hosts. The information for people shows a person's company name, address, phone number and electronic mail address.

WHOLE PERSON PARADIGM This is one of the more fascinating telecom concepts in a while. General Magic created it as some sort of psychological basis for the product/s it is producing. Here's General Magic's definition:

A psychological or behavior model of needs that all people experience. This paradigm is the design center for General Magic's personal intelligent communication products and services. It consists of three elements. 1. Remember - managing your internal agenda, such as things to do and people to see. 2. Communicate - maintaining relationships with your friends, family, and associates. 3. Know - getting information about the world.

WHOLS A name look up service on the Internet.

WIDE AREA NETWORK WAN. An data network typically extending a LAN (local area network) outside the building, over telephone common carrier lines to link to other LANs in remote buildings in possibly remote cities. A WAN typically uses common-carrier lines. A LAN doesn't. WANs typically run over leased phone lines — from one analog phone line to T1 (1.544 Mbps). The jump between a local area network and a WAN is made through a device called a bridge or a router. Bridges operate independently of the protocol employed. They will work, according to Jeff Weiss, of Cryptall Communications, with all present and expected future communications packages. Routers are specific to the protocol being employed. New routing software is needed for each new protocol or protocol deviation. See BRIDGE, ROUTER, CORPORATE NETWORK and DIGITAL HIERARCHY.

WIDE AREA TELEPHONE SERVICE See WATS and 800 SERVICE.

WIDE CHARACTERS 16-bit characters. See UNICODE.

WIDE FREQUENCY TOLERANT POWER PLANT PBX power facilities are provided that will operate from AC energy sources which are not as closely regulated as commercial AC power. The wide tolerant plant will tolerate average frequency deviations of up to plus or minus 3 Hz or voltage variations of -15% to +10% as long as both of the conditions do not occur simultaneously. This feature permits operation with customer provided emergency power generating equipment.

WIDEBAND Refers to a channel wider in bandwidth than a voice-grade channel.

WIDEBAND CHANNEL Any channel wider in bandwidth that a single voice-grade channel. That's the more modern definition. An older definition is a communication channel of a bandwidth equivalent to twelve or more analog voice-grade channels.

WIDEBAND MODEM A modem whose modulated output signal can have an essential frequency spectrum that is broader than that which can be wholly contained within a voice channel with a nominal 4-kHz bandwidth. A modem whose bandwidth capability is greater than that of a narrow band modem.

WIDEBAND PACKET TRANSPORT Transmission of addressed, digitized message fragments (packets) interleaved among the addressed fragments of other messages at a rate high enough to support general purpose telecommunications services.

WIDEBAND SWITCH Switch capable of handling channels wider in bandwidth than voice-grade lines. Radio and TV switches are examples of wideband switches.

WILDCARDS Special characters you use to represent one or more characters in an MS-DOS filename. An asterisk (*) represents several characters and a question mark (?) represents a single character. For example, the command ERASE *.BAK would erase all the files with the suffix "BAK." The command ERASE *.?A? would erase all the files with "A" as the middle letter in a three-letter suffix.

WILDFIRE The all-hearing, all-doing computer telephony slave from a company called Wildfire Communications, Lexington MA. The product uses very sophisticated voice recognition software so that its "master" (i.e. the user) can get Wildfire to take messages, find him, connect his calls, transfer his calls and act as a super intelligent on-line, computerized, 24-hour a day, never resting, all obedient secretary. A real breakthrough product, first introduced in the fall of 1994. And one deserving of its own definition in this illustrious dictionary.

WILL A name Motorola uses for its Wireless Local Loop (WiLL) product, which was developed to serve the basic telephony needs of people in urban and difficult to reach rural areas. Cellular based, WiLL technology is intended to provide fixed telephony services in areas with little or no existing wireline telephone service or as a supplement to the existing wireline service. It uses very few cellular transmit/receivers — often just one at the end of the landline.

The WiLL system provides three major benefits to the telecom operator looking to expand their service area: more rapid deployment of telephone service; lower cost alternative to copper wire installation, and increased flexibility in system implementation and design. A WiLL system can be operational in weeks, compared to the huge amounts of time it would take to lay and install copper wire from an end office to each of the subscriber points in a typical local loop. Although WiLL is cellular-based, the system does not require a cellular switch. This makes the WiLL system a lower cost alternative to using "typical" cellular systems for fixed telephony applications because the total system outlay costs as well as associated backhaul and maintenance costs are reduced.

WiLL has three elements: the WiLL System Controller (WiSC), a Digital Loop Concentrator (DLC), and a Motorola cellular base station. It interfaces directly to the central office switch via 2-wire analog subscriber loops.

WILLFUL INTERCEPT The act of intercepting messages intended for a station experiencing a line or equipment malfunction.

WIMP INTERFACE Stands for Windows, Icons, Menus and a Pointing device. A derogatory reference to GUI. Some people think WIMP is on the way out. See also GRAPHICAL USER INTERFACE.

WIN Wireless In-building Network. WIN is a technology from Motorola which uses microwaves to replace local area network cabling.

WIN32 API A 32-bit application programming interface for both Windows 95 and Windows NT. It updates earlier versions of the Windows API with sophisticated operating system capabilities, security, and API routines for displaying text-based applications in a window.

WIN95 See WINDOWS 95.

WINCH A machine for pulling cable into conduit (in the street or in the building) or duct liner. A winch has a rotating drum that winds up the pulling line.

WINCHESTER DISK A sealed hard disk. The Winchester magnetic storage device was pioneered by IBM for use in its 3030 disk system. It was called Winchester because "Winchester" was IBM's code name for the secret research project that led to its invention. A Winchester hard disk drive consists of several "platters" of metal stacked on top of each other. Each of the platter surfaces is coated with magnetic material and is "read" and "written" to by "heads" which float across (but don't touch) the surface. The whole system works roughly like the old-style Wurlitzer jukebox. There are several advantages to a Winchester disk system:

1. It can store, read and write enormous quantities of information. Some

Winchesters have a capacity of over 100 megabits; 2. You can access information on a Winchester faster than on most computer storage medium (RAM and ROM are obviously faster); and 3. Winchesters are reliable and relatively inexpensive. There are also disadvantages: 1. They are very sensitive to rough handling (they hate being moved); 2. They are very sensitive to the organization of their directory track (lose that and you're in big trouble); and 3. When Winchesters "crash" (i.e. the heads touch the surface of the rotating platters), you can lose an enormous amount of precious data — possibly millions of bytes of data.

WINDING Coils of wire usually found in transformers and used to boost inductance.

WINDOW 1. A band of wavelengths at which an optical fiber is sufficiently transparent for practical use in communications applications.

2. A flow-control mechanism in data communications, the size of which is equal to the number of frames, packets or messages that can be sent from a transmitter to a receiver before any reverse acknowledgment is required. It's called a pacing group in IBM's SNA.

3. A box on the CRT (cathode ray tube) of your personal computer or terminal. A software program is running inside the box. It's possible with new "windows" software to run several programs simultaneously, each accessible and visible through the "window" on your CRT.

4. A technique of displaying information on a screen in which the viewer sees what appears to be several sheets of paper much as they would appear on a desktop. The viewer can shift and shuffle the sheets on the screen. Windowing can show two files simultaneously. For example, in one window you might have a letter you're writing to someone and in another window, you might have a boilerplate letter from which you can take a paragraph or two and drop it in your present letter. Being able to see the two letters on the screen makes writing the new letter easier.

WINDOW CONTROL A credit or token scheme in which a limited number of messages or calls are allowed into the system.

WINDOW SIZE The minimum number of data packets that can be transmitted without additional authorization from the receiver.

WINDOW TREATMENT You take the world's most beautiful window and you screw it up with expensive stuff you affix around it. Paula Friesen invented the term.

WINDOWING A technique of running several programs simultaneously — each in running a separate window. For example, in one window you might run a word processing program. In another, you might be calculating a spreadsheet. In a third, you might be picking up your electronic mail.

WINDOWS A Microsoft operating system that hides the cryptic DOS system of typed commands behind a graphical facade (also called a Graphical User Interface, GUI). Windows let you issue commands (i.e. run programs and complete tasks within programs) by pointing (with or without a mouse) at symbols or menu items and clicking, or hitting "Enter." Most Windows programs have the same "look and feel" to them. So issuing commands becomes almost intuitive. The idea is that "use one Windows program, you can use them all." Sort of. The latest versions of Windows were 3.1 and 3.11 (also called Windows for Workgroups). These versions contained two big improvements over 3.0 — namely OLE (Object Linking and Embedding) and DLL (Dynamic Link Library). Windows 3.1 and 3.11 is now about to be obsoleted by a new version, called Windows 95. See DLL, OLE, WINDOWS 95, WINDOWS FOR WORKGROUPS, WINDOWS NT and WINDOWS TELEPHONY.

WINDOWS 95 Windows 95 is a new operating system from Microsoft which first shipped on August 24, 1995. The August, 1995 issue of our Computer Telephony Magazine said the following about Windows 95:

Win95 is the first Windows operating system designed for communications. It does for modems and phones (of all sorts — from single line analog to proprietary ISDN phones) what Windows did for printing — insulate the suffering user from the idiocies of device drivers. Win95 does wonders for fax, for sending color pictures of the kids to Grandma and for making the world one gigantic personal local area network. And, for the first time ever, an operating system is treating voice as it should be treated — another media stream no different, no more complex than printing a pretty document.

Computer Telephony (voice, fax, e-mail) is a major focus of Windows 95. It will have a revolutionary impact on computer telephony's desktop interface and CT-enabling hardware, from simple off-the-shelf SOHO apps built on inexpensive multimedia modems to full-blown unified-messaging systems humming on the LAN. One of the key improvements of Win95 over Windows 3.xx is the replacement of the latter's monolithic communications driver (COMM.DRV) with a far more flexible communications architecture that splits communication tasks into three primary areas: Win32 communications APIs and TAPI; the universal modem driver; and comm port drivers.

VCOMM is the new communications device driver. It protect-modes services and lets Windows apps and drivers use ports and modems. To conserve system resources, comm drivers are loaded into memory only when in use by an app. VCOMM also uses new Plug and Play services in Windows 95 to help configure and install comm devices. The Win32 communications APIs provide an interface for using modems and comm devices in a device-independent fashion. Applications call the Win32 APIs to configure modems and perform data I/O through them. Through TAPI, meantime, apps can control modems or other telephony devices.

The universal modem driver (Unimodem) is a layer that provides services for data and fax modems and voice so that users and app developers don't have to learn or maintain difficult modem AT commands to dial, answer and configure modems. Rather, Unimodem does these tasks automatically by using mini-drivers written by modem vendors. Unimodem is both a VCOMM device driver and a TAPI service provider. Other service providers (like those supporting things such as an ISDN adapter, a proprietary PBX phone or an AT-command modem) can also be used with TAPI. Port drivers are specifically responsible for communicating with I/O ports, which are accessed through the VCOMM driver. Port drivers provide a layered approach to device communications.

For example, Win95 provides a port driver to communicate with serial communications and parallel ports, and other vendors can provide port drivers to communicate with their own hardware adapters, such as multiport voice and fax cards. With the port driver model in Win95, it's not necessary for vendors to replace the communications subsystem as they did in Windows 3.xx, whose COMM.DRV forced people to completely replace the comm driver if something new was needed by a hardware device. The Win95 driver means we no longer have to be "hard wired" to a 16550 UART. Previous versions of Windows assumed this type of port hardware. This means new ports like USB (Universal Serial Bus) can be slipped in with full apps compatibility.

Besides this strong attempt at "virtualizing" many of the communications hardware interface problems that plagued Windows developers in the past, Win95 also strengthens itself considerably by acknowledging voice as a data type, filtered into its Plug and Play world of communication device compatibility via the Windows Telephony API (TAPI). TAPI-aware apps, for example, no longer need to provide their own modem support list because interaction with a modem is now centralized by the OS. All comm services provided with Win95 use these services. (The analogy is printing under Windows 3.xx.)

TAPI provides a standard way for communications apps to control telephony functions for data, fax and voice calls. It manages all signaling between a computer and phone network, including basic functions such as dialing, answering and hanging up a call. It also includes supplementary call-handling things such as hold, transfer, conference and call park that are often found in PBXs, Centrex, ISDN and other phone systems. In general, TAPI services arbitrate requests from apps to share comm ports and devices. Win32-based apps can use TAPI to make outgoing calls while others are waiting for incoming calls. Of course, only one call can be performed at a time, but users no longer have to close apps that are using the comm port.

TAPI does not need local hardware. It can also use drivers that work on a LAN, which support multiple systems today (e.g. Genesys, Dialogic's CT Connect, Northern Telecom's Tmap, etc.) Microsoft is making the client side ubiquitous and is planning on dropping the server side in (i.e. Windows NT Server) shortly.

MODEMING: Win95 lets you install and configure a modem once to work for all communications apps, just as you do for a printer. Benefits: Centralized modem and COMM port configuration through the "modems" option in the control panel for all comm apps created for Windows 95; Support for hundreds of modems, including automating the detection of them (again, just like Windows did with printers); Modem connections and configuration using point-and-click options rather than annoying AT commands.

The Windows OS includes three tools here: 1. HyperTerminal. This lets you connect two computers through a modem and TAPI for transferring files. It also automatically detects data bits, stop bits and parity. 2. Phone Dialer. This lets you use your computer to dial numbers for voice calls. It includes a phone dialpad, user-programmable speed dials and a call log. 3. Microsoft File Transfer. This lets you send and receive files while talking on the phone. This works with VoiceView-enabled modems.

E-MAILING: Also in Win95 is its included Microsoft Exchange client capability. Exchange is a messaging app that retrieves messages into one inbox from many kinds of messaging service providers, including, Microsoft Mail, The Microsoft Network and Microsoft Fax. With Microsoft Exchange client, you can: send or receive e-mail in a Win95 workgroup; include files and objects created in other apps as part of messages; use multiple fonts, font sizes, colors and text alignments in messages (via an included OLE-compatible text editor); create a personal address book or use books from multiple service providers; and create folders for storing related messages, files and other items.

According to Microsoft, Exchange client will work with any electronic mail system or unified messaging app that has a MAPI service provider, which architects very similar to the TAPI schematic. The MAPI service provider specifies all the connections and addressing settings needed to talk with a mail server on one end and with the Exchange client on the other.

MAPI is a set of API functions and OLE interface that lets messaging clients, such as Microsoft Exchange, interact with various message service providers, such as Microsoft Mail, Microsoft Exchange Server, Microsoft Fax and various computer telephony servers running under Windows NT server. Overall, MAPI helps Exchange manage stored messages and defines the purpose and content of messages — with the objective that most end users will never know or care about it.

FAXING: As part of Windows 95, Microsoft included a new technology called Microsoft Fax. With this embedded Group 3-compatible software, users with modems and running Microsoft Fax can exchange faxes and editable files (pictures, binary files, *.EXE software, etc.) as easily as printing a document or sending an electronic mail message. To use it, you must install Microsoft Exchange. Microsoft integrated the two as a messaging application programming interface (MAPI) service provider. All faxes sent to Microsoft Fax are received in the Exchange universal inbox. You can send a fax by composing a Microsoft Exchange message or by using the Send option on the File menu of a MAPI-compatible application (such as Microsoft Excel or Microsoft Word). In addition, Microsoft Fax includes a fax printer driver so that users can "print to fax" from within any Windows-based application.

Key features: 1. Delivery By Address Type. The MAPI service provider architecture lets you mix different types of recipients in the same message. For example, it's possible to send a message simultaneously to destination addresses in Microsoft Mail, CompuServe, Internet, normal fax and Microsoft Fax as long as profiles for these destinations have been defined within Microsoft Exchange. A recipient's fax address can be selected from the Microsoft Exchange Personal Address Book or the fax can be addressed by using an address that you use just once, such as [fax:555-1212].

1. Binary File Transfer (BFT). Microsoft Fax supports Microsoft At Work BFT, which makes it possible to attach an editable document to a Microsoft Exchange mail message. These editable documents can be sent to users of Windows 95, Windows for Workgroups 3.11, and other Microsoft FAX BFT enabled platforms.

2. Security. Microsoft Fax lets you securely exchange confidential documents by using public key encryption or digital signatures. Any security specified by user is applied before the message is passed to the modem or connected fax device.

3. Network Fax Service. You can install a fax device in one computer and share it with other users within a workgroup. Individual computers can have their own fax devices installed and still use the shared fax device.

4. Microsoft Fax Viewer. The Microsoft Fax Viewer displays outgoing fax messages that have been queued to a local fax modem or to a Microsoft Fax network fax that are queued for transmission. You can also browse multipage faxes in thumbnail or full-page views.

5. Connecting to Fax Information Services. Microsoft Fax can connect to fax-on-demand systems by using a built-in, poll-retrieve feature that allows you to retrieve rendered faxes or editable documents from a fax information service.

6. "Best Available" Fax Format. When you make a fax connection in Windows 95, Microsoft Fax queries and exchanges its fax capabilities with the recipient. This exchange of capabilities determines whether the recipient is a traditional Group 3 fax machine, which can only receive rendered faxes, or if the recipient has Microsoft Fax capabilities, and can receive editable files. Windows 95, Windows for Workgroups 3.11 and Microsoft At Work fax platforms are all capable of receiving binary files and traditional faxes. Perks:

If the receiving fax device supports Microsoft Fax capabilities and an editable document is attached to a Microsoft Exchange message, then the file is transferred in its native format. If the receiving fax device is a traditional Group 3 fax machine, then Microsoft fax converts the document to the most compressed type of fax supported by the machine (MH, MR or MMR compression type) and transmits the image by using the best available communications protocol supported by the mutual connection (that is, V.17, V.29 or V.27). If Microsoft Fax sends a noneditable fax to another Microsoft Fax user, then the fax is transmitted by using the Microsoft At Work rendered fax format. This special format is much more compressed, on average, than Group 3 MMR. Therefore, the exchange of noneditable faxes between Microsoft Fax users is always faster than between Group 3 fax machines.

Overall, you can send faxes either by using the mail client or the Microsoft Fax printer driver. In each case, the message is sent to the Microsoft Fax service provider by using MAPI. If you sent the message from a mail client, it might contain text, embedded OLE formats and attachment to the mail message. MAPI allows messages to be preprocessed based on the transport protocol used to send them. The transport protocol chooses the correct modem connection, uses TAPI to create a dial string and sends the message into a fax form to be printed by a fax machine. The rendered format is attached to the original message as a message property and is deleted either when the message is sent or when the transport protocol tries to send the message but determines it cannot.

If the message does not have to be rendered, the message is converted from its original binary format to a line image (also called a linearized form), and then it is compressed. After the message is submitted, the transport protocol determines what type of recipient the message is intended for through TAPI subkey values.

See also DIAL STRING, MICROSOFT FAX and WINDOWS TELEPHONY for fuller explanations.

WINDOWS APPLICATION A term used in this document as a shorthand term to refer to an application that is designed to run with Windows and does not run without Windows. All Windows applications follow similar conventions for arrangement of menus, style of dialog boxes, and keyboard and mouse use.

WINDOWS CHARACTER SET The character set used in Windows and

Windows applications. Most TrueType fonts have a set of about 220 characters.

WINDOWS FOR WORKGROUPS Windows for Workgroup is a local area networked version of Microsoft Windows operating system version 3.1 that offers integrated file sharing, electronic mail (Microsoft Mail) and workgroup scheduling (Schedule+), thus bringing the graphical user interface to the workgroup. Windows For Workgroups also has Network DDE, which allows users to create compound documents that share data across network. Most importantly, Windows for Workgroups 3.11 lets you do 32-bit disk access and 32-bit file access.

WINDOWS INTERNET NAME SERVICE WINS. A name resolution service that resolves Windows networking computer names to IP addresses in a routed environment. A WINS server, which is a Windows NT Server computer, handles name registrations, queries, and releases.

WINDOWS METAFILE WMF. A method of encoding files. Other methods include EPS, PCX and TIFF.

WINDOWS NT Windows New Technology is a 32-bit operating system from Microsoft, designed to replace Windows and MS-DOS. As an operating system, Windows NT is targeted at the top 10% "power" users who need the power of a big, powerful operating system. Other less demanding souls will continue to run Windows and Windows for Workgroups and MS-DOS and possibly access Windows NT through a local area network to a server running Windows NT AS. Windows NT require a minimum of 12 megabytes of RAM and 100 megs of free hard disk space. Here are the main advantages of Windows NT, as explained by Microsoft:

• Interoperability. Windows NT delivers support for open computing benefits through its protected subsystem architecture. Windows NT was also designed to be protocol independent. As such it will interoperate with all leading network systems, regardless of the native protocol of the system.

• Portability. Windows NT was designed to be portable across a variety of hardware systems. The Hardware Abstraction Layer (HAL) limits and isolates the amount of code necessary to port Windows NT to a new platform. Windows NT will run on processors other than those made by Intel. MS-DOS, for example, doesn't.

• Scalability. Windows NT scales to work on both single and multi processor computer systems. This scalability gives users the flexibility to implement their own solutions, today or over time, on machines that meet the performance needs of sophisticated client server solutions.

• System Management. Windows NT supports SubNetwork Access Protocol (SNMP) and NetView network management standards.

• Published Interfaces. The interfaces to the Windows NT operating system are fully documented and published. Software developers are free to add functionality to the system based on their interface definitions.

• Support of Industry Standards. These include POSIX.1, OSF DCE, TCP/IP and WOSA, which is Microsoft's Windows Open Services Architecture. WOSA is a standard set of interfaces to connect a variety of applications with a range of back-end devices and services, such as messaging, telephony, databases, etc.

Windows Telephony is part of WOSA. See WINDOWS NT ADVANCED SERVER.

WINDOWS NT FILE SYSTEM NTFS. An advanced file system designed for use specifically with the Windows NT operating system. NTFS supports file system recovery and extremely large storage media. It also supports object-oriented applications by treating all files as object with user-defined and system-defined attributes.

WINDOWS NT SERVER Windows NT Server is a specialized (and larger) version of the Windows NT operating system, which is designed to run a server on a local area network. To run it effectively, you'll need a server with at least 150 megabytes of free space on a hard disk, 20 megs of RAM and a high speed processor. Here are words from Microsoft which give a good idea of what it's meant to do. (Ignore the obvious epithets.)

"The Windows NT Server is designed to be a dedicated server in a client server environment. With its power, scalability, enhanced fault tolerance and standards-based openness, the Windows NT Server will make an excellent applications server on Novell NetWare, Banyan VINES and Microsoft Networks, providing a platform for sophisticated business solutions such as financial, accounting and vertical applications. As an application server, it provides a powerful platform for the following:

"Database servers, such as Microsoft SQL Server and ORACLE Server, on top of which customers can build retail, banking, insurance and similar solutions "Communications servers such as the Microsoft SNA Server "Mail servers such as Microsoft Mail

"For network management, the Windows NT Server also provides customers with centralized security and server management, along with graphical tools to manage multiple systems, and gives users a single log on for the enterprise.

"A superset of the Windows NT operating system, Windows NT Server provides additional reliability by supporting advanced fault tolerance including RAID 5. It also delivers Macintosh connectivity and the Remote Access Service — providing network and client server connections to telecommuters, traveling executives and remote system managers over phone lines, X.25 and ISDN networks."

WINDOWS OPEN SERVICES ARCHITECTURE See WOSA.

WINDOWS TELEPHONY Introduced in the spring of 1993 jointly by Microsoft and Intel, Windows Telephony is a piece of software called a Windows Telephony DLL AND two standards. The first standard is the Service Provider Interface (SPI). If a hardware manufacturer's product honors that SPI, that product can happily talk to the Windows Telephony DLL. The second standard is called the Application Programming Interface and it is directed at software developers who write applications programs. If those developers' programs adhere to the API, they can take advantage of the Windows Telephony DLL to drive whatever telephony devices or services adhere to the SPI. The Windows Telephony API is affectionately called TAPI. DLL stands for Dynamic Link Library. It is a Windows feature that allows executable code modules to be loaded on demand and linked at run time.

Windows Telephony should bring about an explosion of shrink-wrapped Windows based telephone software applications — from simple personal rolodexes to power dialers, to customized phone systems for banks and for bakers. It should also bring about an explosion of new telephony hardware devices — from telephones that look more like PCs than phones, to PCs that are phones, to blackbox telephony devices that hook to laptops and transform hotel phones.

Windows Telephony effectively removes earlier overwhelming barriers to creating PC-driven telephony applications, namely the wide enormity of telephony "network" services — from the many telephone company interfaces (POTS to T-1), to the many more proprietary interfaces behind dozens of proprietary PBXs, key systems and hybrid phone systems.

The goal is to bundle the Windows Telephony DLL in the next major release of Windows, sometime in 1994. It will also be included in Windows NT and Windows NT Server. Although the Windows NT code may be different, the API and SPI interfaces will be the same, thus causing no re-write of software code or necessitating redesign of telephony hardware.

The original work on the Windows Telephony DLL was done by Herman D'Hooge, a senior software architect with Intel's Architecture Development Lab in Hillsboro, Oregon. The final effort is a result of joint development effort with Microsoft, where the team was headed by Charles Fitzgerald. It also includes input from 40-odd companies — including virtually all major telecom switch vendors and several major telephony developers.

The goal of joint Microsoft/Intel Windows Telephony is to get rid of the bottleneck to bringing the power of the PC to telephony. Intel and Microsoft believe that the bottleneck exists because of two factors:

First, it has been incredibly difficult to interface to the variety of telecom switches in existence today. For example, no manufacturer's switch will talk to another's manufacturer's proprietary phone.

Second, it has been incredibly redundant and time consuming for software to talk to the various switches. The big analogy is word processing in the old days. In those days, each word processing software company could easily spend 99% of his R&D budget writing drivers to get his program to work with yet another new printer. That is no longer necessary under Windows. Windows takes care of interfacing the printers. All you have to do, as a developer is to make sure you conform to Windows specs.

According to Microsoft, Windows Telephony products will include ones, such as those including:

• Visual interface to telephone features.

• Personal communication management. With a graphical user interface, people can have their PCs handle incoming telephone calls, automatically controlling which calls reach them. For example, people will be able to ensure that they receive important calls by requesting that certain calls be forwarded automatically to locations at which they expect to be working.

• Telephone network access. A personal information management can be used not only to look up phone numbers, but also to actually place calls to those numbers.

• Integrated messaging. People will be able to check their messages — electronic mail, fax mail and voice mail — from a single place, namely their telephony empowered PC. Also voice mail messages can be accessed randomly, which is far more efficient than the serial access provided on most telephone based voice mail-mail systems.

• Integrated meetings. Here's Microsoft's explanation: "One of the most attractive capabilities of the computer is that it can store, communicate and present information that spans the entire spectrum of media — text, data, graphics, voice and video in any combination. By itself, the telephone can communicate and present voice information only. By combining the functions of the computer and the telephone, people in geographically separate locations can participate in interactive meetings and share visual as well as audio information. That means they can hold meetings over the telephone network that are nearly as rich in information content as in-person meetings."

The Windows Telephony Software Development Toolkit is available from several sources:

• CompuServe. Either GO MSL (Microsoft Software Library) and search for the keyword "S14400," or GO WINNEXT (the Windows Extensions Forum) and download the file TAP110.ZAP from Library 3.

• Internet. Use anonymous FTP to ftp.microsoft.com(198.105.323.1) and look in the directory "/devtools/tapi" for the file TAP110.ZIP.

• Microsoft Download Service BBS. Dial 1-206-936-6735, log in, and look for the file TAPISDK.EXE.

• Microsoft Windows Development Platform Level II CD-ROM. This set of four CD-ROMs contains all Microsoft SDKs, DDKs and operating systems. This quarterly offering for developers accompanies the MSDN Level 1 Development Library, which contains all documentation for the development platform (but no code). Call 1-800-759-5474 or 1-402-691-0173.

Private questions or feedback about Windows Telephony can be sent via Internet to "telephon@microsoft.com or via fax to Windows Telephony Coordinator at 1-206-936-7329.

See AT WORK, FAX AT WORK, TELEPHONY SERVICES, WINDOWS TELEPHONY SERVICES, WINDOWS TOOLKITS and WOSA.

WINDOWS TELEPHONY SERVICES

Here is Microsoft's definition: "The Windows Telephony services are provided as a WOSA (Windows Open Services Architecture) component. It consists of both an application programming interface (API) used by applications and a service provider interface (SPI) implemented by service providers.

The focus of the API is to provide "personal telephony" to the Windows platform. Telephony services break down into Simple Telephony services and Full Telephony services. Simple Telephony allows telephony-enabled applications to be easily created from within these applications without these apps needing to become aware of the details of the Full Telephony services. Word processors, spreadsheets, data bases, personal information managers can easily be extended to take advantage of this.

Complete call control is only possible through the use of the Full Telephony services. Applications access the Full Telephony API services using a first-party call control model. This means that the application controls telephone calls as if it is an endpoint of the call. The application can make calls, be notified about inbound calls, answer inbound calls, invoke switch features such as hold, transfer, conference, pickup, park, etc., detect and generate DTMF for signaling with remote equipment. An app can also use the API to monitor call-related activities occurring in the system.

The fact the API presents a first-party call control model does not restrict its use to only first-party telephony environments. The Windows Telephony API can be meaningfully used for third-party call control.

The API provides an abstraction of telephony services that is independent of the underlying telephone network and the configuration used to connect the PC to the switch and phone set. The API provides independent abstractions of the PC connections to the switch or network and the phone set. The connection may be realized in a variety of arrangements including pure client based wired or wireless connections, or client/server configurations using some sort of local area network.

The Telephony API by itself is not concerned with providing access to the information exchanged over a call. Rather, the call control provided by the API is orthogonal to the information stream management. The Telephony API can work in conjunction with other Windows services such as the Windows multimedia wave audio, MCI, or fax APIs to provide access to the information on a call. This guarantees maximum interoperability with existing audio or fax applications.

The Telephony API defines three levels of service. The lowest level of service is called Basic Telephony and provides a guaranteed set of functions that corresponds to "Plain Old Telephone Service" (POTS - only make calls and receive calls). The next service level is Supplementary Telephone Service providing advanced switch features such as hold, transfer, etc. All supplementary services are optional. Finally, there is the Extended Telephony level. This API level provides numerous and well-defined API extension mechanisms that enable application developers to access service provider-specific functions not directly defined by the Telephony API.

WINDOWS TOOLKITS Windows toolkits are libraries of code that implement the graphical user interface objects that every software application uses. The toolkits save time by eliminating the need for software developers to re-implement the same code repeatedly for each application. Toolkits also have the benefit of consistent user interface implementation across all applications that use the toolkit. See also WINDOWS.

WINK A signal sent between two telecommunications devices as part of a handshaking protocol. It is a momentary interruption in SF (Single Frequency) tone, indicating that the distant central office is ready to receive the digits that have just been dialed. In telephone switching systems, a single supervisory pulse. On a digital connection such as a T-1 circuit, a wink is signaled by a brief change in the A and B signaling bits. On an analog line, a wink is signaled by a change in polarity (electrical + and -) on the line.

WINK OPERATION A timed off-hook signal normally of 140 milliseconds, which indicates the availability of an incoming register for receiving digital information from the calling office. A control system for phone systems using address signaling.

WINK PULSING Recurring pulses of a type where the off-pulse is very short with respect to the on-pulse, e.g., on key telephone instruments, the hold position (condition) of a line is often indicated by wink pulsing the associated lamp at 120 impulses per minute, 94 percent make, 6 percent break (470 ms on, 30 ms off).

WINK RELEASE On most modern central offices when the person or device at the other end hangs up, your local central office will send you a single frequency tone. That tone is called wink release. Such a tone can be used to alert a data device that the device at the other end has hung up. (Remember it can't tell by just listening — like you and me.) When a data device hears a wink release, it usually takes it as a signal to hang up also.

WINK SIGNAL A short interruption of current to a busy lamp causing it to flicker. Indicates there is a line on hold.

WINK START Short duration off hook signal. See WINK OPERATION.

WINS Windows Internet Name Service. A name resolution service that resolves Windows networking computer names to IP addresses in a routed environment. A WINS server, which is a Windows NT Server computer, handles name registrations, queries, and releases.

WINSOCK 2 Winsock 2 is a network programming interface at the transport level in the ISO reference model. It is being defined by an open, industry wide workgroup, called the Winsock Forum. Microsoft currently includes a Winsock 1.1 interface in all versions of ITS operating systems from Windows 3.11 onward, and has committed to supply version 2 of Winsock (when its definition has been finalized) as well. Virtually all vendors of TCP/IP protocol stacks supply a Winsock 1.1 programming interface for their stacks, and a large number of TCP/IP applications are written to the Winsock 1.1 standard. The Winsock 2 API maintains backwards compatibility with Winsock 1.1 which is based on the familiar Berkeley "sockets" paradigm for establishing connections and sending and receiving data over those connections. Winsock version 2 significantly extends the interface by providing applications with transport independence across a wide range of communication transports such as TCP/IP, NetBEUI or SPX/IPX local area networks, analog and digital telephone networks, wirEless networks such as cellular and CDPD, and ATM. In addition, Winsock 2 will include mechanisms for applications to negotiate quality of service with a network, thus improving its use for multimedia applications. Stack vendors who wish to make their transport protocols accessible via Winsock 2 need only implement the Winsock 2 service provider interface (SPI), which is itself very socket-like. The Winsock Forum's stated objective is to finalize the Winsock 2 specifications during the second quarter of '95, and have the needed SDKs available (for both 16 and 32 bit operating environments) during the 2nd half of 95. Key Contacts: Martin Hall, Stardust Technologies, 408-438-6643 (Leader of the Winsock Forum) Dave Treadwell, Microsoft, davidtr@microsoft.com Dan Ohlemacher, Intel Architecture Labs, 503-264-5914 dan_ohlemacher@ccm.jf.intel.com

As regards the current status on defining version 2, draft copies of the proposed API and SPI specs are available via anon ftp:

ftp://aurora.intel.com/pub/winsock2/gen_api_ext /* API spec */

ftp://aurora.intel.com/pub/winsock2/oper_framework /* SPI spec */

A series of email reflectors are established and are the primary means of conducting forum business. To get information on these, send an email to majordomo@mailbag.intel.com Leave the subject blank, and put the following in the body: lists help. You will be mailed the names of all the mailing lists and instructions on how to subscribe.

Several Web pages also exist:

http://sunsite.unc.edu:80/winsock/

http://www.microsoft.com/pages/developer/winsock/

http://www.stardust.com/

WIRE CENTER The location where the telephone company terminates subscriber outside cable plant (i.e. their local lines) with the necessary testing facilities to maintain them. Usually the same location as a class 5 central office. A wire center might have one or several class 5 central offices, also called public exchanges or simply switches. A customer could get telephone service from one, several or all of these switches without paying extra. They would all be his local switch.

WIRE CENTER SERVING AREA That area of an exchange served by a single wire center.

WIRE CONCENTRATOR A conduit; a pipe within which a large number of individual wires are routed through.

WIRE PAIR Two separate conductors traveling the same route, serving as a communications channel.

WIRE PRINTER A matrix printer which uses a set of wire hammers to strike the page through a carbon ribbon, generating the matrix characters.

WIRE RUNNING TOOLS Tools that help you run wire in and around a building. The most common form of wire running tools that help you fish wire through hollow drywalls.

WIRE SPEED The rate at which bits are transmitted over a cable. Ethernet's wire speed is 10 Mbps. Wire speed is not transmission speed. That depends on many factors, including how many devices are transmitting simultaneously on the same cable. See MULTIPLEX.

WIRE STRIPPER A tool which takes the insulation off a wire without hurting the inside metal conductor.

WIRE TAP The attaching to a phone line of a piece of equipment whose job is to record all conversations on that phone line. Wire taps are illegal. Law enforcement agencies use them, but must receive authorization from a court to apply the tap. Such authorizations are given if the law enforcement agency argues that applying the tap will prevent crime or help bring a suspected criminal to justice. Wire taps are not authorized lightly. See also TRAP and TRACE.

WIRE TELEPHONY The transmission of speech over wires.

WIRED FOR CAPACITY The wired-for capacity represents the upper limit of capacity for a particular configuration. To bring to a phone system to its "wired for capacity," all that's necessary is to fill the empty slots in the system's metal shelving (its cage) with the appropriate printed circuit boards. "Wired-for Capacity" is a marginally useful term, giving little indication of the type of printed circuit boards

— trunk, line, special electronic line, special circuit, etc. — that can be installed. And many PBXs allow only their printed circuit boards to go into assigned slots. Your PBX cabinet might, for example, have plenty of empty space for extra printed circuit boards, but it may not have any more space for boards which service electronic phones. Thus, it is effectively maxed out.

WIRED LOGIC A required logic function implemented in hardware, not software.

WIRELESS Without wires. An English and Australian word for radio and, now in the U.S., a phone system that operates locally without wires. Cellular is wireless in the strictest sense of the term. But "wireless" has come to mean wire-less systems that work within a building. See WIRELESS ACCESS CONTROLLER.

WIRELESS ACCESS CONTROLLER The first component in an in-building wireless phone systems is the wireless access controller. It does many things. It provides access to the host network, be it a host PBX or the public switched telephone network (including Centrex). The access controller also manages the picocellular infrastructure of the wireless system through connections to the radio base stations. In the case of a Northern Telecom wireless business systems, base stations are connected to the controller via 144-kilobit-per-second (kbit/s) digital links that offer 2B+D interface connectivity. This digital connectivity (two 64-kbit/s channels for voice and data, and one 16-kbit/s channel for signaling information) provides the high-speed signaling capability needed by the controller to offer advanced business services and to manage mobility across several base stations. These digital links also make it possible to enhance radio system capacity by having the controller synchronize all base stations.

The controller software structures are designed so that untethered personal directory numbers and physical ports (specific interface circuits wired to a particular location) are dynamically associated at every call and at every hand-off to another base station. This dynamic assignment makes it possible for the same personal or group directory number to be used for a variety of wireless and wireline terminals, irrespective of location. The controller also handles user registration, roaming, and hand-off.

Roaming which is the capability to redirect incoming calls to the appropriate base station, is accomplished through a combination of radio protocols, system software, and databases. The databases make it possible to locate portable terminals, through various broadcasting or polling schemes, without incurring excessive search delays.

Hand-off, on the other hand, is the capability needed in order to cope with the fact that a user will continuously move from one location, and hence one cell, to another, while communicating. As this happens, the link must be maintained in a manner transparent to the end user, always maintaining communications with the strongest base station signal in the neighborhood of the portable terminal. The controller monitors the radio signal strength of the portable and, when the signal weakens, switches it to a base station with a stronger signal. It then switches the communications link from the former base station to the new one and signals the terminal to begin radio communication on the new channel. Interference could be caused, for example, by other portable terminals in the same cell or an adjacent cell, or by external influences, such as nearby traffic or people moving partitions in an office. In such cases, the base station redirects the call rapidly to a less noisy channel in the same cell or an adjacent cell.

WIRELESS LANS The conventional local area network (LAN) uses wires or optical fiber as a common carrier medium. However, other possibilities exist. Low microwave frequencies (lower than about 10 GHz) can provide data rates as high 10 Mbit/s. Millimetric waves at around 60 GHz could support several 10 Mbit/s channels, while infra-red beams could support even greater data throughputs. The area covered by such a scheme would be restricted by the low allowable power radiation. The data rates of such systems tend to be restricted by walls, by interference and by mulitpath propagation problems that arise due to reflections within the building. Because of the wide bandwidth available, channeling can easily be provided by using spread spectrum methods and code division multiple access (CDMA), a technique that significantly improves the system security.

WIRELESS MESSAGING Technology allowing the exchange of electronic messages without plugging into a wired land-based phone line. Two wireless messaging types are available: one-way, based on existing radio paging channels; and two-way, based on either radio-packet technology or cellular technology. Some people include in-room infra-red links in the term "wireless messaging." Some of the PDAs use wireless links.

WIRELESS PACKET SWITCHING Unlike existing cellular networks, wireless packet-switched networks are designed specifically for data communications. Packet switching breaks messages into packets and sends these packets individually over the network. Here's how a message is sent over the RAM Mobile Data Wireless Networks, one of the packet radio networks in operation today:

1) After you've written a message and turned on your modem, you enter a send command in your e-mail software.

2) The modem breaks your message into packets. A typical packet has a message space for as much as 512 bytes (about 100 words). Longer messages are divided into 512 byte sections.

3) The modem then sends each packet separately over the RAM packet radio network. Each packet includes the sender's and receiver's addresses.

4) The network routes the message to the recipient.

5) The recipient's packet radio modem reassembles the individual packets into a single message.

6) Your recipient can then read the message.

A packet radio network, typically uses a hierarchical architecture to route messages. At the lowest level, base stations exchange wireless messages with nearby mobile computers. Base stations can route messages to other users who are within its service area, or the local switch to read recipients who are in other areas, on LANs, or on public e-mail services. The local switch can either route the message to a different base station or to a regional switch. Users of these packet radio networks can typically send messages anywhere in the network — regardless of the physical distance — for the same rate per message.

WIRELESS SERVICE PROVIDER WASP. A carrier authorized to provide wireless communications exchange services (for example, cellular carriers and paging services carriers).

WIRELESS SWITCHING CENTER WSC. A switching system used to terminate wireless stations for purposes of interconnection to each other and to trunks interfacing with the Public Switched Telephone Network (PSTN) and other networks.

WIRELINE Another name for a telephone company that uses cables, not radio. See WIRELINE CELLULAR CARRIER.

WIRELINE CELLULAR CARRIER Also called the Block B carrier. Under the FCC's initial cellular licensing procedures, the Block B carrier is the local telephone company. The FCC reserved one of the two systems in every market for the local telephone — or wireline company. Wireline or Block B systems operate on the frequencies 869 to 894 Megahertz. See NON-WIRELINE CELLULAR COMPANY.

WIRETAPPING To listen in clandestinely to someone else's conversation. Other than scrambling, there is no known method to protect your telephone call against wiretapping, no matter what equipment you buy from companies advertising their wares nationally. Wiretapping can be accomplished without physical connection to a phone line, though technically this would be called "bugging." For all intents and purposes you should consider your telephone conversations as public and treat your conversations as such.

WIRING CLOSET Termination point for customer premises wiring, offering access to service personnel. Generally serves a specific area, with cross-connected multiple wiring closets.

WIRING CONCENTRATOR A wiring concentrator is an FDDI node that provides additional attachment points for stations that are not attached directly to the dual ring, or for other concentrators in a tree structure. The concentrator is the focal point of Digital's Dual Ring of Trees topology.

WIRING DENSITY Refers to the number of wires that may be terminated on a connecting block in a given area. A high density block may terminate twice as many wires as a low density block, while a low density block may provide better wire management since fewer wires are being dressed into and out of the connecting block.

WIRING GRID The overall architecture of building wiring.

WITTING In on a secret.

WITS Wireless Interface Telephone System.

WIZOP A Chief Sysop (System Operator). See SYSOP.

WLAN Wireless Local Area Network. A LAN without wires. There are major benefits, the biggest being the ability to move items on the LAN around fast, easily and cheaply.

WOO WOO TONE A tone on a phone line indicating the number is unavailable. Also the words to a neat Jeffrey Osborne song, as in "Will you woo woo with me?"

WORD A collection of bits the computer recognizes as a basic information unit and uses in its operation. Usually defined by the number of bits contained in it, e.g. 8, 16 or 32 bits. Using DOS, the IBM PC (and compatibles) defines a word as eight bits. Here's another explanation: A group of characters capable of being processed simultaneously in the processor and treated by computer circuits as an entity.

WORD LENGTH The number of bits in a data character without parity, start or stop bits.

WORDS PER MINUTE WPM. The speed of printing, typing or communications. 100 WPM is 600 characters per minute (six characters per average word) or 10 characters per second. In ASCII, asynchronous transmission at this rate is also 100 or 110 bits per second, depending on the number of stop bits.

WORK LOCATION WIRING SUBSYSTEM The part of a premises distribution system that includes the equipment and extension cords from the information outlet to the terminal device connection.

WORK ORDER A term used in the secondary telecom equipment business. Internal document used by a remarketer specifying: 1. Work to be performed; 2. Machine or item on which work is to be performed; 3. Required completion date; 4. Cost of work; 5. Customer purchase order number and/or other pertinent billing information. This document is used internally to: 1. Implement required work; 2. Monitor progress; and 3. Issue final billing. A work order is implemented once a written request has been received authorizing the work to be performed.

WORD SPOTTING In speech recognition over the phone, word spotting means looking for a particular phrase or word in spoken text and ignoring everything else. For example, if the word to spot was "brown," then it wouldn't matter if you said "I want the brown one," or "how about something in brown?" In short, word spotting is the process whereby specific words are recognized under specific speaking conditions (i.e. natural, unconstrained speech). It can also refer to the ability to ignore extraneous sounds during continuous word recognition.

WORK STATION In this dictionary I spell it as one word WORKSTATION. See WORKSTATION.

WORKFLOW The way work moves around an organization. It follows a path. That path is called workflow. Here's a more technical way of defining workflow: The automation of standard procedures (e.g. records management in personnel operations) by imposing a set of sequential rules on the procedure. Each task, when finished, automatically initiates the next logical step in the process until the entire procedure is completed.

WORKFLOW MANAGEMENT The electronic management of work processes such as forms processing (e.g. for insurance policy acceptances, college admissions, etc.) or project management using a computer network and electronic messaging as the foundation. See WORKFLOW.

WORKFORCE MANAGEMENT According to Jim Gordon of TCS in Nashville, Call center workforce management is the art and science of having the right number of people...agents...at the right times, in their seats, to answer an accurately forecasted volume of incoming calls at the service level you desire.

WORKGROUP A fancy new word for a department, except that the members of the workgroup may belong to different departments. The idea is that members of the workgroup work with themselves, so they'd be perfect candidates to buy electronic mail packages that could send messages between themselves and other software packages that would allow them to share their collective wisdoms and schedule their meeting times. Typically members of the workgroup would be on the same local area network and share the same telephone system. See WORKGROUP TELEPHONY.

WORKGROUP COMPUTING An approach to the supply of computer services whereby access to computer power and information is organized on a workgroup by workgroup basis. Such systems normally consist of computers of varying capabilities connected to a local area network. See WORKGROUP.

WORKGROUP MANAGER An assistant network supervisor with rights to create and delete bindery objects (such as users, groups, or print queues) and to manage user accounts. A Workgroup Manager has supervisory privileges over a part of the bindery. When several groups share a file server, Workgroup Managers can provide autonomous control over their own users and data.

WORKGROUP TELEPHONY See TELEPHONY WORKGROUPS.

WORKLOAD A call center term. The total duration of all calls in a given period (half hour or quarter hour), not counting any time spent in queue. This figure is equal to the number of calls times the average handle time per call.

WORKSTATION In the telecom industry, a workstation is a computer and a telephone on a desk and both attached to a telecom outlet on the wall. The computer industry tends to refer to workstations as high-speed personal computers, such as Sun workstations, which are used for high-powered processing tasks like CAD/CAM, engineering, etc. A common PC — like the one you find on my desk — is not usually considered a workstation. The term workstation is vague.

WORLD NUMBERING ZONE One of eight geographic areas used to assign a unique telephone address to each telephone subscriber.

WORLD WIDE WEB Also called WEB or W3. The World Wide Web is the universe of accessible information available on many computers spread through the world and attached to that gigantic computer network called the Internet. The Web has a body of software, a set of protocols and a set of defined conventions for getting at the information on the Web. The Web uses hypertext and multimedia techniques to make the web easy for anyone to roam, browse and contribute to. The Web makes publishing information (i.e. making that information public) as easy as creating a "home page" and posting it on a server somewhere in the Internet. Pick up any Web access software (e.g. Netscape), connect yourself to the Internet (through one of many dial-up, for-money, Internet access providers or one of the many free terminals in Universities) and you can discover an amazing diversity of information on the Web. From weather to stock reports to information on how to build nuclear bombs to the best tennis tips, it can be posted on the Web for all to read. See HOME PAGE, HTML and INTERNET.

WORLD ZONE 1 The area of the World Numbering Plan which is identified with the single-digit country code "1" and includes the territories of the United States and Canada, and the following Caribbean countries: Antigua, Bahamas, Barbados, Bermuda, British Virgin Islands, Cayman Islands, Domenican Republic, Granada, Jamaica, Montserrat, Puerto Rico, St. Kitts, St. Lucia, St. Vincent, Virgin Islands.

WORLDWIDEWEB WWW. An easy but powerful global information system, based on a combination of information retrieval and hypertext techniques.

WORM 1. Write Once, Read Many times. Refers to the new type of optical disks (similar to compact discs) which can be written to only once, but read many times. In other words, once the data is written, it cannot be erased. WORM disks typically hold around 600 megabytes. See also ERASABLE OPTICAL DRIVE.

2. A computer program which replicates itself. The Internet worm was perhaps the most famous; it successfully (and accidentally) duplicated itself on many of the systems across the Internet.

WORN Write Once, Read Never (A joke).

WORST HOUR OF THE YEAR That hour of the year during which the median noise over any radio path is at a maximum. This hour is considered to coincide with the hour during which the greatest transmission loss occurs.

WOSA Windows Open Services Architecture. According to Microsoft, WOSA provides a single system level interface for connecting front-end applications with back-end services. Windows Telephony, announced in May 1993, is part of WOSA. According to Microsoft, application developers and users needn't worry about conversing with numerous services, each with its own protocols and interfaces, because making these connections is the business of the operating system, not of individual applications. WOSA provides an extensible framework in which Windows based applications can seamlessly access information and network resources in a distributed computing environment. WOSA accomplishes this feat by making a common set of APIs available to all applications. WOSA's idea is to act like two diplomats speaking through an interpreter. A front-end application and back-end service needn't speak each other's languages to communicate as long as they both know how to talk to the WOSA interface (e.g. Windows Telephony). As a result, WOSA allows application developers, MIS managers, and vendors of back-end services to mix and match applications and services to build enterprise solutions that shield programmers and users from the underlying complexity of the system.

This is how WOSA works: WOSA defines an abstraction layer to heterogeneous computing resources through the WOSA set of APIs. Initially, this set of APIs will include support for services such as database access, messaging (MAPI), file sharing, and printing. Because this set of APIs is extensible, new services and their corresponding APIs can be added as needed.

WOSA uses a Windows dynamic-link library (DLL) that allows software components to be linked at run time. In this way, applications are able to connect to services dynamically. An application needs to know only the definition of the interface, not its implementation. WOSA defines a system level DLL to provide common procedures that service providers would otherwise have to implement. In addition, the system DLL can support functions that operate across multiple service implementations. Applications call system APIs to access services that have been standardized in the system. The code that supports the system APIs routes those calls to the appropriate service provider and provides procedures and functions that are used in common by all providers.

The primary benefit of WOSA is its ability to provide users of Windows with relatively seamlessly connections to enterprise computing environments. Other WOSA benefits, according to Microsoft include:

* Easy upgrade paths. * Protection of software investment. * More cost-effective software solutions. * Flexible integration of multiple-vendor components. * Short development cycle for solutions. * Extensibility to include future services and implementations.

See also ODBC, MAPI, and TAPI.

WPM See WORDS PER MINUTE.

WRAM Windows Random Access Memory. Similar to VRAM, but with added logic to accelerate common video functions such as bit-block transfers and pattern fills. See also VRAM.

WRAP 1. In data communications, to place your diagnostic and test equipment around parts of a network so you can monitor their use (i.e. do network diagnostics on them). You are, in essence, wrapping your products around theirs.

2. To make a connection between a flexible wire and a hard tag by tightly wrapping the cable around the tag. There are automatic wire wrapping tools available for this job.

3. Redundancy measure in IBM Token Ring LANS. Trunk cabling used in Token Ring TCUs contains two data paths: a main and backup normally unused). If the trunk cable is faulty, the physical disconnection of the connector at the TCU causes the signal from the main path to wrap around on to the backup path, thus maintaining the loop. The term wrap is now used on FDDI networks. If a failure occurs on one of the FDDI rings, the stations on each side of the failure reconfigure. The two rings then are combined into a single ring topology that allows all functioning stations to remain interconnected.

WRAP-UP Between-call work state that an ACD agent enters after releasing a caller. It's the time necessary to complete the transaction that just occurred on the phone. In wrap-up, the agent's ACD phone is removed from the hunting sequence. After wrap-up is completed, it is returned to the hunting sequence and is ready to take the next call.

WRAP-UP DATA Ad hoc data gathered by an agent in the ACD system following a call.

WRAP-UP TIME A call center term. The time an employee spends completing a transaction after the call has been disconnected. Sometimes it's a few seconds. Sometimes it can be minutes. Depends on what the caller wants.

WRAPPING In token-ring networks, the process of bypassing cable faults without changing the logical order of the ring by using relays and additional wire circuits.

WRITE To record information on a storage device, usually disk or tape.

WRITE HEAD A magnetic head capable of writing only. You find write heads on everything from tape recorders to computers.

WRITE PROTECT Using various hardware and software techniques to prohibit the computer from recording (writing) on storage medium, like a floppy or hard disk. You can write protect a 5 1/4 diskette by simply covering the little notch with a small metal tag. The idea of "Write Protect" is to stop someone (including yourself) from changing your precious data or program. You can't write protect a hard disk easily. The easiest way to stop someone changing a file is to use the program ATTRIB.EXE. See ATTRIBUTES.

WRITE PROTECTION A scheme for protecting a diskette from accidental erasure. 5 1/4" diskettes have a notch which must be uncovered to allow data on the diskette to be modified. 3 1/2" diskettes have small window with a plastic tab which must be slid into place to cover the window to allow data on the diskette to be modified. See WRITE PROTECT and ATTRIBUTES.

WRITE PROTECTION LABEL A removable label, the presence or absence of which on a diskette prevents writing on the diskette.

WRT With respect to.

WSC Wireless Switching Center. A switching center designed for wireless communications services, typically fixed wireless services including data and voice.

WTAC World Telecommunications Advisory Council. WTAC is comprised of telecommunications leaders from the private and public sectors and from every region of the world. WTAC gives advice to the ITU — the International Telecommunications Union. The WTAC held its first meeting in Geneva, Switzerland, in April, 1992. In February 1993, it published a small booklet called "Telecommunications Visions of the Future."

WTNG WaiTiNG.

WWW World Wide Web; a hypertext-based system for finding and accessing resources on the Internet network. See WORLD WIDE WEB and INTERNET.

WYPIWYF Acronym for "What You Print Is What You Fax," also "The Way You Print Is the Way You Fax." Coined by Intel to describe its one-step pop-up menu that makes sending faxes from the PC as easy as sending a document to a printer.

WYSIWYG (pron. Whiz-i-wig) What You See Is What You Get. A word processing term meaning what you see on your computer screen is what you will see printed on paper. The exact typeface, the correct size, the right layout, etc. Some word processors do WYSIWYG. Others don't. You usually need a screen with graphics to get the full effect.

WZ1 World Zone One. The part of the earth covered by what used to be called The North American Numbering Plan. It includes the U.S., Canada, Alaska, Hawaii, and the Caribbean islands, but does not include Mexico or Cuba.

X An abbreviation for the word "cross," as in crossbar. 5XB would be the abbreviation for a No. 5 Crossbar.

X BAND 7 GHz and 8 GHz. Used by military satellites.

X RECOMMENDATIONS The ITU-T documents that describe data communication network standards. Well-known ones include: X.25 Packet Switching standard, X.400 Message Handling System, and X.500 Directory Services.

X SERIES Recommendations drawn up by the ITU-T to establish communications interfaces for users' Data Terminal Equipment (DTE) and Data Circuit Terminating Equipment (DCE). They govern the attachment of data terminals to public data networks (PDNs) and the Public Switched Telephone Network (PSTN). In short, a set of rules for interfacing terminals to networks.

X WINDOWS X Windows is officially called X Window, or the X Window System, or X.

It is used primarily with UNIX systems, but not exclusively. X was originally designed to be an industry-standard network windowing system, and because UNIX is widely used, X has become the windowing standard for UNIX.

X-10 PROTOCOL A protocol found in home automation. You can use X-10 to control conforming black boxes and devices. The protocol is a command signal that rides on the AC 60 cycle sine power curve. The signal is a series of 120 kHz pulses sent on the "zero crossing" of each cycle. The signal is in a binary fashion, transmitting the letter code, unit code and command for a device. All receivers monitor the power line waiting for a command to respond. The limit of number of unique codes available is 256. This is derived by having 16 letter codes and 16 unit codes, hence 16x16=256 "addresses." More than one device can share an address. If you decide that every time you select "A1" on, you want all the front lights to come on, then you can place all the receivers to the same address. The system is easy to use and very flexible.

X-AXIS Horizontal axis on a graph or chart.

X-BASE A term used to describe any database application capable of generating custom programs with dBASE-compatible code.

X-OFF/X-ON A flow control protocol for asynchronous serial transmission. Flow control is a method of adjusting information flow. For example, in transmitting between a computer and a printer, the computer sends the information to be printed at 9600 baud. That's several times faster than the printer can print. The printer, however, has a small memory. The computer dumps to the memory, called a buffer, at 9600 baud. When it fills up, the printer signals the computer that it is full and please stop sending. When the buffer is ready to receive again, the printer (which also has a small computer in it) sends a signal to the desktop computer (the one doing the printing) to please start sending again. X-OFF means turn the transmitter off (xmit in Ham radio terms). It is the ASCII character Control-S. X-ON means turn the transmitter on. It is the ASCII character Control-Q. You can use these characters with many microcomputer functions. For example, if you do DIR in MS-DOS and you want to stop the fast rush of files, then type Control-S.

X-DIMENSION OF RECORDED SPOT In facsimile, the center-to-center distance between two recorded spots measured in the direction of the recorded line. This term applies to facsimile equipment that responds to a constant density in the subject copy by yielding a succession of discrete recorded spots.

X-DIMENSION OF SCANNING SPOT In facsimile, the center-to-center distance between two scanning spots measured in the direction of the scanning line on the subject copy. The numerical value of this term will depend upon the type of system used.

X-OPEN An international consortium of computer vendors working to create an internationally supported vendor-independent Common Applications Environment based on industry standards.

X-SERIES RECOMMENDATIONS Set of data telecommunications protocols and interfaces defined by the ITU-T.

X-WINDOWS The UNIX equivalent of Windows. What Windows is to MS-DOS, X-Windows is to Unix. A network-based windowing system that provides a program interface for graphic window displays. X-Windows permits graphics produced on one networked station to be displayed on another. Almost all UNIX graphical interfaces, including Motif and OpenLook, are based on X-Windows. X-Windows is a networked window system developed and specified by the MIT X Consortium. Members of the X Consortium include IBM, DEC, Hewlett-Packard and Sun Microsystems. Sun Microsystems has been contracted by the MIT X Consortium to implement PEX (PHIGS Extensions to X), which will be the standard networking protocol for sending PHIGS (Programmers Hierarchical Graphics System) graphics commands through X-Windows. Some people spell it X-Windows and some spell it X Windows.

X-Y A specific variety of electromechanical switch. Does the same things as a Stronger step-by-step switch but in a horizontal plane. It's so called because it's a two motion switch with horizontal and vertical movements. The first pulse sends the switch horizontally to the right place, then the next pulse sends it vertically up to the right place and so on, until it has switched the call through. One of the most reliable switches ever produced. Unfortunately, it's slow, space-consuming and unable to be programmed with many new customer pleasing features.

X.1 A ITU-T specification that defines classes of service in a packet-switched network, such as virtual-circuit, datagram, and fast-packet services.

X.110 International routing principles and routing plan for PDNs.

X.121 International Numbering Plan for public data networks. X.121 defines the numbering system used by data devices operating in the packet mode. X.121 is used by ITU-T X.25 packet-switched networks and has been proposed by several computer vendors as the future universal addressing scheme.

X.121 ADDRESS A standard O/R (Originator/Recipient) attribute that allows Telex terminals to be identified in the context of store-and forward communications.

X.130 Call setup and clear down times for international connection to synchronous PDNs.

X.132 Grade of service over international connections to PDNs.

X.150 DTE and DCE test loops in public data networks.

X.2 International user services and facilities over public switched telephone networks.

X.20 Asynchronous communications interface definitions between data terminal equipment (DTE) and data circuit terminating equipment (DCE) for start-stop transmission services on public switched telephone networks.

X.20 bis Used on public data networks of data terminal equipment (DTE) that is designed for interfacing to asynchronous duplex V-series modems.

X.200 A series of CCITT (International Telegraph and Telephone Consultative Committee) recommendations that defines the type of service offered by specific layers in the OSI (Open Systems Interconnection) Model, and defines the protocol to be used at those layers. CCITT is now the ITU.

X.21 Interface between data terminal equipment (DTE) and data circuit-equipment (DCE) for synchronous operation on public switched telephone networks.

X.21 bis Used on public switched telephone networks of data terminal equipment (DTE) that is designed for interfacing to synchronous V-series modems.

X.21 TSS Specification for Layer 1 interface used in the X.25 packet-switching protocol and in certain types of circuit-switched data transmissions.

X.224 A ITU-T standard associated with the transport layer of the Open Systems Interconnect (OSI) architecture used in networks employing circuit-switched techniques.

X.225 A ITU-T standard associated with the session layer of the Open Systems Interconnect (OSI) architecture used in networks employing circuit-switched techniques.

X.226 A ITU-T standard associated with the Open Systems Interconnect (OSI) architecture that defines specific presentation layer services used with circuit-switched network services.

X.24 List of definitions for interchange circuits between data terminal equipment (DTE) and data circuit terminating equipment (DCE) on public switched telephone networks.

X.25 From its beginning as an international standards recommendation from ITU-T, the term X.25 has come to represent a common reference point by which mainframe computers, word processors, mini-computers, VDUs, microcomputers and a wide variety of specialized terminal equipment from many manufacturers can be made to work together over a type of data communications network called a packet switched network. On a packet switched data network (private or public), the data to be transmitted is cut up into blocks. Each block has a header with the network address of the sender and that of the destination. As the block enters the network, the number of bits in the block are put through some mathematical functions (an algorithm) to produce a check sum.

The check sum is attached as a "trailer" to the packet as it enters the network. Packets may travel different routes through the network. But, ultimately, the packets are routed by the network to the node where the destination computer or terminal is located. At the destination, the packet is disassembled. The bits are put through the same algorithm, and if the digits computed are the same as the ones attached as the trailer, there are no detected errors. An ACK, or acknowledgement, is then sent to the transmitting end. If the check sum does not match, a NAK, or Negative Acknowledgement is sent back, and the packet is retransmitted. In this manner, high speed, low error rate information can be transmitted around the country using shared telecommunications circuits on public or private data networks.

X.25 is the protocol providing devices with direct connection to a packet switched network. These devices are typically larger computers, mainframes, minicomputers, etc. Word processors, personal computers, workstations, dumb terminals, etc. do not support the X.25 packet switching protocols unless they are connected to the network via PADs -- Packet Assembler/Disassemblers. A PAD converts between the protocol used by the smaller device and the X.25 protocol. This conversion is performed on both outgoing (from the network) and incoming data (to the network), so the transmission looks transparent to the terminal. (See TRANSPARENT.) There's a very good book on X.25 called X.25 Explained, Protocols for packet switching networks by R. J. Deasington of IBM. It is available from Telecom Library on 1-800-LIBRARY, or 1-212-691-8215.

X.25 NETWORK Any network that implements the internationally accepted ITU-T standard governing the operation of packet-switching networks. The X.25 standard describes a switched communications service where call setup times are relatively fast. The standard also defines how data streams are to be assembled into packets, controlled, routed, and protected as they cross the network.

X.28 DTE/DCE interface for start-stop-mode data terminal equipment accessing the packet assembly/disassembly facility (PAD) in a public switched telephone networks situated in the same country.

X.29 Procedures for the exchange of control information (handshaking) and user data between a packet assembly/disassembly facility (PAD) and a packet mode DTE or another PAD.

X.3 ITU-T recommendation describing the operation of a Packet Assembly/Disassembly (PAD) device or facility in a public data network. X.3 defines a set of 18 parameters that regulate basic functions performed by a PAD to control an asynchronous terminal. The setting of these parameters governs such characteristics as terminal speed, terminal display, flow control, break handling and data forwarding conditions, and so on.

X.30 Support of X.20 bis, X.21 and X.21 bis DTEs by an ISDN.

X.31 Support of packet mode DTEs by an ISDN.

X.32 Interface between Data Terminal Equipment (DTE) and Data Circuit Terminating Equipment (DCE) operating in a packet mode and accessing a packet switched public data network via a public switched telephone network or a circuit switched public data network. X.32 describes the functional and procedural aspects of the DTE/DCE interface for DTEs accessing a packet switched public data network via a public switched network.

X.38 ITU-T recommendation for the access of Group 3 facsimile equipment to the Facsimile Packet Assembly/Disassembly (FPAD) facility in public data networks situated in the same country.

X.39 ITU-T recommendation for the exchange of control information and user data between a Facsimile Packet Assembly/Disassembly (FPAD) facility and a packet mode Data Terminal Equipment (DTE) or another pad, for international networking.

X.3T9.3 The ANSI committee responsible for the creation and perpetuation of Fiber Channel standards.

X.3T9.5 The ANSI committee responsible for the creation and perpetuation of FDDI Standards.

X.4 International Alphabet No.5 for character oriented data.

X.400 X.400 is an international standard which enables disparate electronic mail systems to exchange messages. Although each e-mail system may operate internally with its own, proprietary set of protocols, the X.400 protocol acts as a translating software making communication between the electronic mail systems possible. The result is that users can now reach beyond people on their same e-mail system to the universe of users of interconnected systems. One problem with e-mail sent between X.400 networks is that the sender's name is not sent. (I kid you not.) This was one element of the protocol the committees forgot! If your message crosses an X.400 network, remember to sign your name. The X.400 standard itself is an overview which is broken down under subsequent numbers:

X.402 Overall Architecture

X.403 Conformance testing

X.407 Abstract service definition conventions

X.408 Encoded information type conversion rules

X.411 Message transfer system

X.413 Message store

X.419 Protocol specifications

X.420 Interpersonal messaging system. An IPM format specification using the X.400 transfer protocol. In addition to text, it also allows CAD/CAM, graphics, Fax, and other electronic information.

X.435 An EDI (Electronic Data Interchange) format specification based on the X.400 transfer protocol. It can also allow for CAD/CAM, graphics, Fax, and other electronic information to accompany an EDI interchange.

X.440 A VM (Voice Messaging) format specification, using the X.400 transfer protocol. In addition to voice, it can also contain CAD/CAM, graphics, fax, and other electronic information.

X.445 The X.445 standard, or APS (Asynchronous Protocol Specification), lets X.400 clients and servers exchange all types of digital data over public telephone networks rather than over X.25 leased lines, which are required today. Among those backing the spec are Intel, AT&T, Microsoft Corp., Lotus and Isocor. X445 is an extension of the X.400 standard. X.400 provides an option to other messaging backbones such as System Network Architectural Distribution Services and SMTP. It supports multimedia data traffic including text, binary files, E-mail, voice images, and sound.

In its December 19, 1994 issue, PC Week said that the X.445 standard, which earlier this month gained final approval from the International Telecommunications Union, should ease messaging dramatically by allowing users to exchange X.400 data traffic over standard telephone networks.

X.50 Fundamental parameters of multiplexing scheme for the international interface between synchronous data networks.

X.500 The ITU-T international standard designation for a directory standard that permits applications such as electronic mail to access information which can either be central or distributed. The X.500 standard for directory services provides the means to consolidate e-mail directory information through central servers situated at strategic points throughout the network. These X.500 servers then exchange directory information so each server can keep all its local mail directory information current. With X.500, any e-mail user, whether on OpenVMS, Macintosh, DOS, or UNIX workstations, can be listed in a central directory that can be accessed using an X.500-compatible user agent.

X.51 Fundamental parameters of multiplexing scheme for the international interface between synchronous data networks using 10-bit envelop structure.

X.51 bis Fundamental parameters of a 48Kbit/s transmission scheme for the international interface between synchronous data networks using a 10-bit envelope structure.

X.58 Fundamental parameters of multiplexing scheme for the international interface between synchronous data networks using a 10-bit envelope structure.

X.60 Common channel signaling for circuit switched data applications.

X.61 Signaling system no. 7 -- data user part.

X.70 Terminal and transit control signaling for asynchronous services on international circuits between anisochronous data networks.

X.71 Decentralized terminal and transit control signaling on international circuits between synchronous data networks.

X.75 An international standard for linking X.25 packet switched networks. X.75 defines the connection between public networks, i.e. for a gateway between X.25 networks. See X.25.

X.80 Interworking of inter-exchange signals for circuit switched data services.

X.92 Hypothetical reference connections for synchronous PDNs in a packet switched network.

X.95 ITU-T specification dealing with a number of internal packet-switched network parameters such as packet size limitations and service restrictions.

X.96 Call progress signals in PDNs.

X/OPEN A group of computer manufacturers that promotes the development of portable applications based on UNIX. They publish a document called the X/Open Portability Guide.

X12 ANSI (American national Standards Institute) standard that is the dominant EDI (Electronic Data Interchange) standard in the U.S. today; designed to support cross-industry exchange of business transactions. Standard specifies the vocabulary (dictionary) and format for electronic business transactions.

X3.15 Bit sequencing of ASCII in serial-by-bit data transmission.

X3.16 Character structure and character parity sense for serial-by-data communications in ASCII.

X3.36 Synchronous high speed data signaling rates between data terminal equipment and data circuit terminating equipment.

X3.41 Code extension techniques for use with 7-bit coded character set of ASCII.

X3.44 Determination of the performance of data communications systems.

X3.79 Determination of performance of data communications systems that use bit oriented control procedures.

X3.92 Data encryption algorithm.

X.WINDOWS A networked GUI developed at the Massachusetts Institute of Technology (MIT) as part of Project Athena. Based on a client/server architecture it displays information from multiple networked hosts on a single workstation.

XA-SMDS Exchange Access SMDS. An access service provided by a local exchange carrier to an interexchange carrier. It enables the delivery of a customer's data over local and long distance SMDS networks.

XAPIA X.400 Application Program Interface Association. Microsoft has a new concept. It's called an Enterprise Messaging Server (EMS). The idea is to allow users to transparently access the messaging engine from within desktop applications to route messages, share files, or retrieve reference data. According to Microsoft, corporate developers will be able to add capabilities using Visual Basic and access EMS by writing either to the X.400 Application Program Interface Association's (XAPIA's) Common Mail Calls (CMC) or to Microsoft's Messaging API (MAPI). (ftp:/nemo.ncsl.nist.gov/pub/olw/dssig/xapla/) See MAPI.

XBAR Crossbar.

XC Cross connect.

XDP Ron Stadler of Panasonic dreamed this one up. It stands for eXtra Device Port. It's an analog RJ-11 equipped port on the back of a Panasonic digital telephone, which is driven by Panasonic's Digital Super Hybrid switch. The XDP is an extension line completely separate to your digital voice line. You can be speaking on the phone while receiving or sending a fax or while sending or receiving data. Or plug a cordless phone or answering machine into the XTP.

XENIX Microsoft trade name for a 16-bit microcomputer operating system derived from AT&T Bell Labs' UNIX.

XEROGRAPHIC RECORDING Recording by action of a light spot on an electrically charged photoconductive insulating surface where the latent image is developed with a resinous powder.

XEROX NETWORK SERVICES XNS. A multilayer protocol system developed by Xerox and adopted, at least in part, by Novell and other vendors. XNS is one of the many distributed-file-system protocols that allow network stations to use other computers files and peripherals as if they were local. XNS is used by some companies on Ethernet LANs. In local area networking technology, special communications protocol used between networks. XNS/ITP functions at the 3rd and 4th layer of the Open Systems Interconnection (OSI) model. Similar to transmission control protocol/internet protocol (TCP/IP).

XFR TransFeR.

XGA eXtended Graphics Array. A new IBM level of video graphics which has a screen resolution of 1,024 dots horizontally by 768 vertically, yielding 786,432 possible bits of information on one screen, more than two and a half times what is possible with VGA. See also MONITOR.

XID FRAME A High-Level Data Link Control (HDLC) transmission frame used to transfer operational parameters between two or more stations.

XIP eXecute-In-Place. Refers to specification for directly executing code from a PCMCIA Card without first having to load it into system memory.

XIWT Cross-Industry Working Team. About 28 companies (and growing) whose work centers on the Clinton-Gore administration's document "National Information Infrastructure -- Agenda for Action." The document spells out policy initiatives required to achieve the benefits of widespread, convenient and affordable access to existing and future information resources. In short, the Information SuperHighway.

XJACK A registered trademark of modem manufacturer, MegaHertz, for one of the most innovative ideas in PCMCIA modems. XJACK is the world's tiniest female RJ-11. It's about a quarter of an inch wide and the most convenient way of attaching your laptop's modem to the phone network.

XMA eXtended Memory specificAtion. Interface that lets DOS programs cooperatively use extended memory in 80286 and higher computers. One such driver is Microsoft's HIMEM.SYS, which manages extended memory and HMA (high memory area), a 64k block just above 1Mb.

XMIT Transmit.

XMODEM Also called "Christiansen Protocol". An error-correcting file transfer, data transmission protocol created by Ward Christiansen of Chicago for transmitting files between PCs. A file might be anything -- a letter, an article, a sales call report, a Lotus 1-2-3 spreadsheet. The XMODEM protocol sends information in 128 bytes blocks of data. Some sums (check sums) are done on each block and the result is sent along with the block. If the result does not check out at the other end, the computer at the other end sends a request (a NAK -- Negative AcKnowledgement) to re-transmit that block once again. If the block checks out, the computer sends an ACK -- an Acknowledgement. In this way, relatively error-free transmission can be accomplished.

XMODEM was first used by computer hobbyists and then by business users of PCs. If you're buying a telecommunications software program for your PC -- IBM, Radio Shack, Compaq, Apple, etc. -- it's a good idea to buy a program with XMODEM. It's among the most common data communications protocols. But it's not the fastest, just the most common. AT&T Mail supports XMODEM protocol. So does TELECONNECT Magazine's own E-mail InfoBoard system (212-989-4675). MCI Mail does not support XMODEM protocol. We don't know why. There are many variations of XMODEM including XMODEM 1K (which uses blocks of 1,025 bytes), MODEM7, YMODEM, Y-MODEM-G and ZMODEM. Most common communications software packages only support (i.e. will handle) the original version of XMODEM (checksum) and the newer CRC variation. A study in Byte Magazine (March, 1989) showed ZMODEM to be a far more efficient file transfer protocol than XMODEM, YMODEM, or W/XMODEM. The author now tends to use ZMODEM more commonly. It is supported by most on-line services, such as CompuServe, etc. See also DATA COMPRESSION PROTOCOLS, ERROR CONTROLS PROTOCOLS, FILE TRANSFER PROTOCOL, YMODEM and ZMODEM.

XMODEM-1K Xmodem-1K is an error-correcting file transfer, data transmission protocol for transmitting files between PCs. It is essentially Xmodem CRC with 1K (1024 byte) packets. On some systems and bulletin boards it may also be referred to as Ymodem.

XMODEM-CRC Cyclic Redundancy Checking is added to XMODEM frames for increased reliability of errors detection. See XMODEM.

XMP X/Open Management Protocol; an API and software interface specified in the Open Software Foundation's Distributed Management Environment.

XMS An acronym for eXtended Memory Specification. To run this standard, your system must have 350K of extended memory. XMS creates the HMA (High Memory Area), then governs access to and the allocation of the remainder of extended memory.

XNMS Trademark for MICOM's IBM PC-based packet data network (PDN) network management system software products.

XNS Xerox Network System. The lan architecture developed at the Xerox Palo Alto Research Center (Parc). It is a five-layer architecture of protocols and was the foundation of the OSI seven-layer model. It has been adopted in part by Novell and other vendors. XNS is one of the many distributed-file-system protocols that allow network stations to use other computers files and peripherals as if they were local. XNS is used by some companies on Ethernet LANs.

XO Crystal Oscillator.

XON/XOFF XON/XOFF are standard ASCII control characters used to tell an intelligent device to stop or resume transmitting data. In most systems typing -S sends the XOFF character, i.e. to stop transmitting. Some devices understand <Ctrl>-Q as XON, i.e. start transmitting again. Others interpret the pressing of any key after -S as XON.

XOPEN A group of computer manufacturers that promotes the development of portable applications based on UNIX. They publish a document called the X/Open Portability Guide. X/OPEN is the correct spelling.

XPAD An eXternal Packet Assembler/Disassembler.

XPC A set of protocols developed by British Telecom Tymnet to allow asynchronous terminals to connect to an X.25 packet-switched network.

XRB Transmit Reference Burst.

XT Abbreviation for crosstalk.

XTEL API The Sun Solaris Teleservices Application Programming Interface. See TELESERVICES for a long explanation.

XTELS The Sun Solaris Teleservices protocol. The XTELS protocol is essentially the XTEL provider protocol with extensions to support multiple clients and multiple XTEL providers. See TELESERVICES for a long explanation.

XTELTOOL A window-based tool used to configure providers in the Sun Solaris Teleservices platform. Basically a graphical user interface. See TELESERVICES for a long explanation.

XTEND EXTEND Telecommunications Integration Platform, a series of network software utilities and calls that allow a PBX to be integrated and directed by workstations on a local area network. XTEND is an offering of XTEND Communications, Inc. New York City.

XWINDOWS See X-WINDOWS.

Y-DIMENSION OF RECORDED SPOT In facsimile, the center-to-center distance between two recorded spots measured perpendicular to the recorded line.

Y-DIMENSION OF SCANNING SPOT In facsimile, the center-to-center distance between two scanning spots measured perpendicular to the scanning line on the subject copy. The numerical value of this term will depend upon the type of system used.

Y/C A two channel video channel. One is for color (chrominance) and the other for black and white (luminance).

YAGI ANTENNA A type of directional antenna.

YAHOO Huge directory of all kinds of places on the Web. hyyp://akebono.stanford.edu/yahoo/

YELLOW ALARM A T-1 alarm signal sent back toward the source of a failed transmit circuit in a DS-1 2-way transmission path. A yellow sends 0's (zeros) in bit two of all time slots. See also T-1.

YELLOW CABLE A coaxial cable used in 10Base-5 networks. It is also referred to as "Thick" coax. This was the first cable used on many early LANs.

YELLOW PAGES A directory of telephone numbers classified by type of business. It was printed on yellow paper throughout most of the twentieth century until it was obsoleted in the late 1990s by dial up yellow page directories operated by voice processing systems and in the early 21st century by electronic directories delivered on disposable laser disks. As a concession to history, the laser disks are now painted bright yellow. Actually, yellow pages remain one of the phone companies' most lucrative sources of revenues. Advertising rates are not cheap. There is now competition. There are many "Yellow Pages" directories, since AT&T never trademarked the term "Yellow Pages." Some "yellow page" directories are better value than others. And some are more legitimate than others. Some actually never get printed or, if they are printed, are not printed in great quantity and are not distributed as widely as their sales literature implies. Many businesses have been suckered into paying money for listings and advertisements in directories that never appeared. This fictitious directory scam also has happened with "telex" and "fax" directories. This "scam" is fraud by mail and is heavily stomped upon by the US Postal Service. As a result, many fake directories (especially the telex ones) are "published" abroad.

YES A program which Novell created to certify products — hardware and software — that work with its products. It's a rigorous program. It takes significant work to be "Yes" certified by Novell. Novell has Yes programs for NetWare and UnixWare. It's Novell's equivalent of the Good Housekeeping Seal of Approval.

YMMV Your Mileage May Vary. A response usually given when the answer is not precise and depends on the user's own circumstances. YMMV is an acronym used in electronic mail on the Internet to save words or to be hip, or whatever.

YMODEM A faster transfer variation of XMODEM. In YMODEM, XMODEM's 128-byte block grew to YMODEM's 1024 bytes (1 kilobyte). YMODEM combines the 1K block and the 128-byte block modems into the same protocols. YMODEM, or 1K as it is known, became the thrifty way to send files (i.e. it saved on phone time). Enhancements were added, such as auto-fallback to 128-byte blocks if too many errors were encountered (because of bad phone lines, etc.) See XMODEM for a much larger explanation of file transfer using X, Y and ZMODEM protocols.

YMODEM-G Ymodem-g is a variant of Ymodem. It is designed to be used with modems that support error control. This protocol does not provide software error correction or recovery, but expects the modem to provide it. It is a streaming protocol that sends and receives 1K packets in a continuous stream until told to stop. It does not wait for positive acknowledgement after each block is sent, but rather sends blocks in rapid succession. If any block is unsuccessfully transferred, the entire transfer is canceled. See also ZMODEM, which we prefer.

YURT A Mongolian circular shed. Some companies are making Yurt-like sheds for installation in the back yards of telecommuters — especially those telecommuters who don't have enough room inside for a home office.

YUV A color encoding scheme for natural pictures in which luminance and chrominance are separate. The human eye is less sensitive to color variations than to intensity variations. YUV allows the encoding of luminance (Y) information at full bandwidth and chrominance (UV) information at half bandwidth.

YUV9 The color encoding scheme used in Indeo Video Technology. The YUV9 format stores information in 4x4 pixel blocks. Sixteen bytes of luminance are stored for every one byte of chrominance. For example, a 640x480 image will have 307,200 bytes of luminance and 19,200 bytes of chrominance.

Z Abbreviation for Zulu time. See GREENWICH MEAN TIME.

ZAP To eradicate all or part of a program or database, sometimes by lightning, sometimes intentionally.

ZBTSI Zero Byte Time Slot Interchange. A technique used with the T carrier extended superframe format (ESF) in which an area in the ESF frame carries information about the location of all-zero bytes (eight consecutive "O"s) within the data stream.

ZEN A Japanese sect of Buddhism that stresses attaining enlightenment through intuition rather than by studying scripture.

ZENER DIODE A particular type of semiconductor which acts as a normal rectifier until the voltage applied to it reaches a certain point. At this point — at the zener voltage or the avalanche voltage — the zener diode becomes conducting.

ZERO BEAT RECEPTION Also called "homodyne" reception. A method of reception using a radio frequency current of the proper magnitude and phase relation so that the voltage impressed on the detector will be of the same nature as that of the wave. An old radio term.

ZERO BIT The high-order bit in a byte or a word.

ZERO BYTE TIME SLOT INTERCHANGE ZBTSI. A method of coding in which a variable address code is exchanged for any zero octet. The address information describes where, in the serial bit stream, zero octets originally occurred. It is a five-step process where data enters a buffer, zero octets are identified and removed, the nonzero bytes move to fill in the gaps, the first gap is identified, and a transparent flag bit is set in front of the message to indicate that one or more bytes originally contained zeros. See ZBTSI.

ZERO CODE SUPPRESSION The insertion of a "one" bit to prevent the transmission of eight or more consecutive "zero" bits. Used primarily with digital T1 and related telephone-company facilities which require a minimum "ones density" keep the individual sub channels of a multiplexed, high-speed facility active. Several different schemes are currently employed to accomplish this. Proposals for a standard are being evaluated by the ITU-T. See also ZERO SUPPRESSION.

ZERO FILL See ZEROFILL.

ZERO FREQUENCY The frequency (wavelength) at which the attenuation of the lightguide is at a minimum.

ZERO POWER MODEM A modem that takes its power from the phone line and therefore needs no battery or external power. Such modems are often limited in their speed and capabilities.

ZERO SLOT LAN A Local Area Network (LAN) that uses a PC's serial port to transmit and receive data. It doesn't require a network interface card to be installed in a slot in the PC, thus the name "zero-slot" LAN. RS-232 LANs usually use standard RS-232 or phone cable to link PCs. Software does the rest of the work. Due to the slow speed of serial communications on a PC, RS-232 LANs are usually restricted to speeds of around 19.2K bits per second. What they lose in speed, however, they make up in low price.

ZERO STUFFING Get a cup of coffee right now. Synchronous data transmission is done by sending what IBM and AT&T call Frames, and what everyone else calls Packets. A frame starts off by sending a bit pattern of 01111110 (notice the six 1's in a row). Synchronous transmission is for sending a bit stream, which means that the bits may (but probably do not) have any relation to the transmission of characters. This is especially true when sending digitized voice. As the bits pass to the receiver, they go through a shift register. When the flag signifying the end of a frame goes by, the last 16 bits in the shift register are the check digits.

The receiver computes the check digits based on the data bits that have gone by. As the sender sent the data, it computed the check digit, sent it after the end of the frame, and then sent the flag. If the receiver computes the same check digit that the sender sent, then one can be reasonably assured the data came through without error. But that's not what I came to talk to you about. I came to talk about Zero Stuffing. The problem is that somewhere in the bit stream, there is the possibility of there being six 1 bits in a row. To the receiving computer, six 1's means a flag. Therefore the sending computer, if it "sees" six 1 bits, will send five 1 bits, and stuff a zero in the bit stream.

In fact, if it sees even five 1 bits, it will stuff a zero anyway, so there will be no ambiguity. The rule is, "If there are five ones in a row and it is NOT the end of a frame, stuff a zero into the bit stream." This way the receiver will know that this is in no way the end of the frame yet. Now if the receiver sees six 1's in a row, it knows without a doubt that it IS at the end of a frame, and should proceed with the error checking.

ZERO SUPPRESSION The elimination of nonsignificant zeros from a numeral. Zero suppression is the replacement of leading zeros in a number with blanks so that when the number appears, the leading zeros are gone. The data becomes more readable. For example, the number 00023 would be displayed on the monitor or printed as 23.

ZERO TEST LEVEL POINT A level point used as a reference in determining loss in circuits. Analogous to using sea level when defining altitude. Written as 0 TLP.

ZERO TRANSMISSION LEVEL POINT ZTLP. In telephony, a reference point for measuring the signal power gain and losses of telecommunications circuit, at which a zero dBm signal level is applied.

ZERO TRANSMISSION LEVEL REFERENCE POINT A point in a circuit to which all relative transmission levels are referenced. The transmission level at the transmitting switchboard is frequently taken as the zero transmission level reference point.

ZERO USAGE CUSTOMER An MCI definition. An MCI customer who has not placed a call over the network, even though he/she is an active customer. Sometimes used interchangeably, but incorrectly, with the term "no usage customer."

ZEROFILL 1. To fill unused storage locations with the character "O."

2. Here's definition from GammaLink, a fax board maker: A traditional fax device is mechanical. It must reset its printer and advance the pages as it prints each scan line it receives. If the receiving machine's printing capability is slower than the transmitting machine's data sending capability, the transmitting machine adds "fill bits" (also called Zero Fill) to pad out the span of send time, giving the slower machine the additional time it needs to reset prior to receiving the next scan line.

ZIF Zero Insertion Force. Intel makes a bunch of math co-processor chips which are used with their 80XXX range of microprocessors. ZIF is a special device which is typically soldered to the motherboard. You place an 80387 chip on this device, move the handle down, it grabs the chip and pulls the chip down, seating it electrically. When you want to remove the chip, you simply lift the handle and up the chip comes. The device was invented by Intel because so many people were apparently breaking the legs on their math co-processor chips each time they removed them. Apparently the problem was most prevalent in the computer rental business.

ZINC SPARK GAP A spark gap having zinc as the electrode.

ZIP CODE The specific five-digit code assigned to each post office to facilitate mail delivery. The Postal Service is beginning to use nine-digit zip codes. The additional four digits will determine the precise letter carrier routing from the post office into the street. Some post offices now optically read zip codes. Allegedly this speeds up delivery.

ZIP TONE Short burst of dial tone to an ACD agent headset indicating a call is being connected to the agent console.

ZMODEM ZMODEM is an error-correcting file transfer, data transmission protocol for transmitting files between PCs. A file might be anything — a letter, an article, a sales call report, a Lotus 1-2-3 spreadsheet. Always use ZMODEM if you can. It's the best and fastest data transmission protocol to use. This is not my sole advice. Virtually every writer in data communications recommends it. Here's an explanation, beginning with XMODEM, an older, more common and less efficient protocol.

Both XMODEM and YMODEM transmit, then receive, then transmit. The handshake (ACK or NAK) happens when the sender isn't sending. ZMODEM adds full duplex-transmission to the transfer protocol. ZMODEM does not depend on any ACK signals from the host computer. It keeps sending unless it receives a NAK, at which time it falls back to the failed block and starts to retransmit at that point. ZMODEM was written by Chuck Forsberg. According to PC Magazine (April 30, 1991) ZMODEM is the first choice of most bulletin boards. ZMODEM, according to PC Magazine, features relatively low overhead and significant reliability and speed. ZMODEM dynamically adjusts it packet size depending on line conditions and uses a very reliable 32-bit CRC error check. It has a unique file recovery feature. Let's say ZMODEM aborts a transfer because of a bad line (or whatever), it can start up again from the point it aborted the transfer. Other file transfer protocols have to start all over again. ZMODEM's ability to continue is a major benefit. ZMODEM in some communications program is a little more automated than other protocols. For example, ZMODEM will start itself when the other end gives a signal — thus saving a keystroke or two and speeding things up. See FILE TRANSFER PROTOCOL, XMODEM and YMODEM.

ZONE 1. A telephony definition: One of a series of specified areas, beyond the base rate area of an exchange. Service is furnished in zones at rates in addition to base rates.

2. A LAN definition. Part of a local area network, typically defined by a router. A router will let you get into one part of someone else's network. They define what you are able to get access to. You might get to that router by an external telecommunications circuit — dial up, ISDN, Switched 56, T-1 etc.

ZONE BITS 1. One or two leftmost bits in a commonly used system of six bits for each character.

2. Any bit in a group of bit positions that are used to indicate a specific class of items, i.e., numbers, letters, commands.

ZONE METHOD A ceiling distribution method in which ceiling space is divided into sections or zones. Cables are then run to the center of each zone to serve the information outlets nearby. See also CEILING DISTRIBUTION SYSTEMS.

ZONE OF SILENCE Skip zone.

ZONE PAGING Ability to page a specific department or area in or out of a building. "Page John in the Accounting Department." Zone paging is useful for finding people who wander, as most of us do.

ZULU TIME Coordinated Universal Time.

ZZF Zentralamt fur Zulassungen im Fernmeldewessen (Approval Authority — Germany).

Centronics Parallel Interface

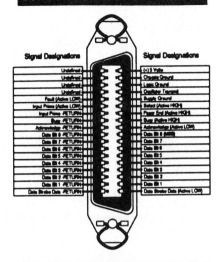

Signal Designations		Signal Designations
Undefined		(+) 5 Volts
Undefined		Chassis Ground
Undefined		Logic Ground
Undefined		Oscillator Transmit
Fault (Active LOW)		Supply Ground
Input Prime (Active LOW)		Select (Active HIGH)
Input Prime /RETURN		Paper End (Active HIGH)
Busy /RETURN		Busy (Active HIGH)
Acknowledge /RETURN		Acknowledge (Active LOW)
Data Bit 8 /RETURN		Data Bit 8 (MSB)
Data Bit 7 /RETURN		Data Bit 7
Data Bit 6 /RETURN		Data Bit 6
Data Bit 5 /RETURN		Data Bit 5
Data Bit 4 /RETURN		Data Bit 4
Data Bit 3 /RETURN		Data Bit 3
Data Bit 2 /RETURN		Data Bit 2
Data Bit 1 /RETURN		Data Bit 1
Data Strobe Data /RETURN		Data Strobe Data (Active LOW)

RS-449 Interface

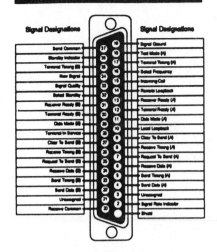

Signal Designations		Signal Designations
Send Common	37 / 19	Signal Ground
Standby Indicator	36 / 18	Test Mode (A)
Terminal Timing (B)	35 / 17	Terminal Timing (A)
New Signal	34 / 16	Select Frequency
Signal Quality	33 / 15	Incoming Call
Select Standby	32 / 14	Remote Loopback
Receive Ready (B)	31 / 13	Receiver Ready (A)
Terminal Ready (B)	30 / 12	Terminal Ready (A)
Data Mode (B)	29 / 11	Data Mode (A)
Terminal In Service	28 / 10	Local Loopback
Clear To Send (B)	27 / 9	Clear To Send (A)
Receive Timing (B)	26 / 8	Receive Timing (A)
Request To Send (B)	25 / 7	Request To Send (A)
Receive Data (B)	24 / 6	Receive Data (A)
Send Timing (B)	23 / 5	Send Timing (A)
Send Data (B)	22 / 4	Send Data (A)
Unassigned	21 / 3	Unassigned
Receive Common	20 / 2	Signal Rate Indicator
	1	Shield

RS-232 Interface

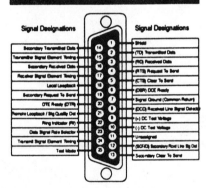

Signal Designations		Signal Designations
Secondary Transmitted Data	14 / 1	(Shield)
Transmitter Signal Element Timing	15 / 2	(TD) Transmitted Data
Secondary Received Data	16 / 3	(RD) Received Data
Receiver Signal Element Timing	17 / 4	(RTS) Request To Send
Local Loopback	18 / 5	(CTS) Clear To Send
Secondary Request To Send	19 / 6	(DSR) DCE Ready
DTE Ready (DTR)	20 / 7	Signal Ground (Common Return)
Remote Loopback / Sig Quality Det	21 / 8	(DCD) Received Line Signal Detector
Ring Indicator (RI)	22 / 9	(+) DC Test Voltage
Data Signal Rate Selector	23 / 10	(-) DC Test Voltage
Transmit Signal Element Timing	24 / 11	Unassigned
Test Mode	25 / 12	(SCF/CI) Secondary Rcvd Line Sig Det
	13	Secondary Clear To Send

IEEE 488 Interface

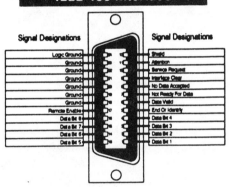

Signal Designations		Signal Designations
Logic Ground		Shield
Ground		Attention
Ground		Service Request
Ground		Interface Clear
Ground		No Data Accepted
Ground		Not Ready For Data
Ground		Data Valid
Remote Enable		End Or Identify
Data Bit 8		Data Bit 4
Data Bit 7		Data Bit 3
Data Bit 6		Data Bit 2
Data Bit 5		Data Bit 1

IBM PC Color Monitor Interface

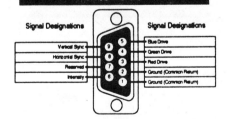

Signal Designations		Signal Designations
Vertical Sync	9 / 5	Blue Drive
Horizontal Sync	8 / 4	Green Drive
Reserved	7 / 3	Red Drive
Intensity	6 / 2	Ground (Common Return)
	1	Ground (Common Return)

IBM PC Monochrome Monitor Interface

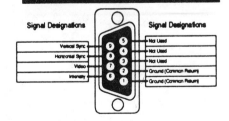

Signal Designations		Signal Designations
Vertical Sync	9 / 5	Not Used
Horizontal Sync	8 / 4	Not Used
Video	7 / 3	Not Used
Intensity	6 / 2	Ground (Common Return)
	1	Ground (Common Return)

IBM PS/2 Keyboard Interface

RESERVED 6   5 CLOCK
+5 VOLTS 4   3 GROUND
RESERVED 2   1 DATA

IBM PC Keyboard Interface

KEYBOARD RESET 3   1 KEYBOARD CLOCK
+5 VOLTS 5   4 GROUND

KEYBOARD DATA 2

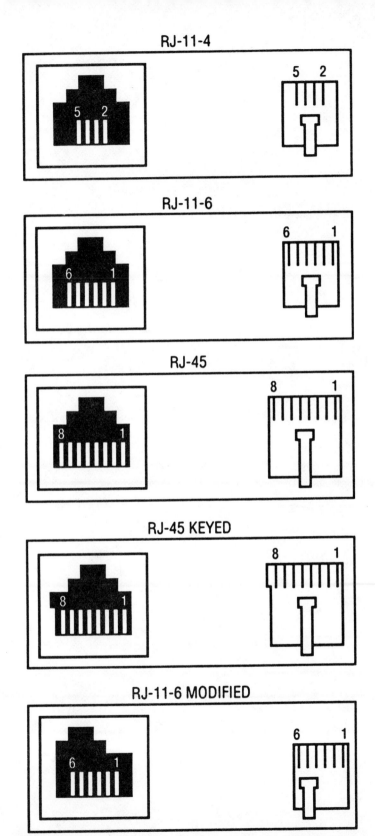

PUBLISHED BY FLATIRON PUBLISHING

Flatiron Publishing publishes books and magazines and organizes trade conferences on computer telephony, telecommunications, networking and voice processing. It also distributes the books of other publishers, making it the "central source" for all the above materials. Call or write for you FREE catalog.

236 Killer Voice Processing Applications
ATM Users' Guide
Client Server Computer Telephony
Complete Traffic Engineering Handbook
Customer Service Over the Phone
Frames, Packets and Cells in Broadband Networking
The Guide to Frame Relay
The Guide to SONET
The Guide to T-1 Networking
Local & Long Distance Telephone Billing Practices
Moore's Imaging Dictionary
The MVIP Book
Newton's Telecom Dictionary
PC-Based Voice Processing
SCSA
Speech Recognition
Telephony for Computer Professionals
VideoConferencing: The Whole Picture

Quantity Purchases

If you wish to purchase this book, or any others, in quantity, please contact:

Christine Kern, Manager
Flatiron Publishing, Inc.
12 West 21 Street
New York, NY 10010
212-691-8215 or 1-800-LIBRARY
facsimile orders: 212-691-1191

Flatiron Publishing, Inc.
12 West 21 Street
New York, NY 10010
212-691-8215 1-800-LIBRARY